Contributors

ETIENNE-EMILE BAULIEU

T. H. CLAUS

IRA D. GOLDFINE

JUDITH JUSKEVICH

WALTER LOVENBERG

E. MILGROM

RODRIGUE MORTEL

RICHARD J. PIETRAS

S. J. PILKIS

HOWARD RASMUSSEN

PAUL ROBEL

CLARA M. SZEGO

JOLINDA A. TRAUGH

DAVID WAISMAN

Biochemical Actions of Hormones

Edited by GERALD LITWACK

Fels Research Institute and Department of Biochemistry
Temple University School of Medicine
Philadelphia, Pennsylvania

VOLUME VIII

ACADEMIC PRESS 1981
A Subsidiary of Harcourt Brace Jovanovich, Publishers

New York   London   Toronto   Sydney   San Francisco

ACADEMIC PRESS, INC.
111 Fifth Avenue, New York, New York 10003

United Kingdom Edition published by
ACADEMIC PRESS, INC. (LONDON) LTD.
24/28 Oval Road, London NW1 7DX

Library of Congress Cataloging in Publication Data
Main entry under title:

Biochemical actions of hormones.

Includes bibliographies.
1. Hormones——Collected works. I. Litwack,
Gerald, ed. II. Axelrod, Julius, Date. [DNLM:
1. Hormones. 2. Physiology. WK102 B615]
QP571.B56   574.19'27   70–107567
ISBN 0–12–452808–2 (v. 8)

PRINTED IN THE UNITED STATES OF AMERICA

81 82 83 84   9 8 7 6 5 4 3 2 1

Contents

1. The Messenger Function of Calcium in Endocrine Systems

Howard Rasmussen and David Waisman

2. Neuronal Regulation of Blood Pressure

Judith Juskevich and Walter Lovenberg

3. Regulation of Protein Synthesis by Prosphorylation
Jolinda A. Traugh

4. Hormonal Control of Hepatic Gluconeogenesis
T. H. Claus and S. J. Pilkis

5. Effects of Insulin on Intracellular Functions
Ira D. Goldfine

6. Membrane Recognition and Effector Sites in Steroid Hormone Action
Clara M. Szego and Richard J. Pietras

7.   Activation of Steroid–Receptor Complexes

E. Milgrom

8.   Estradiol and Progesterone Receptors in Human Endometrium

Paul Robel, Rodrigue Mortel, and Etienne-Emile Baulieu

List of Contributors

Numbers in parentheses indicate the pages on which authors' contributions begin.

Etienne-Emile Baulieu (493), Unité de Recherches sur le Metabolisme Moléculaire et la Physio-Pathologie des Stéroides de l'Institut National de la Santé et de la Recherche Médicale, M 33 INSERM, and ER 125 CNRS, 94270 Bicêtre, France

T. H. Claus (209), Department of Physiology, Vanderbilt University School of Medicine, Nashville, Tennessee 37232

Ira D. Goldfine (273), Cell Biology Laboratory, Mount Zion Hospital and Medical Center, San Francisco, California 94120

Judith Juskevich (117), Section on Biochemical Pharmacology, Hypertension-Endocrine Branch, National Heart, Lung and Blood Institute, National Institutes of Health, Bethesda, Maryland 20205

Walter Lovenberg (117), Section on Biochemical Pharmacology, Hypertension-Endocrine Branch, National Heart, Lung and Blood Institute, National Institutes of Health, Bethesda, Maryland 20205

E. Milgrom (465), Groupe de Recherches sur la Biochimie Endocrinienne et la Reproduction, INSERM U. 135, Faculté de Médecine, Paris-sud, 94270 Bicêtre, France

Rodrigue Mortel[1] (493), Unité de Recherches sur le Metabolisme Moléculaire et la Physio-Pathologie des Stéroides de l'Institut

---

[1] Present address: Department of Obstetrics and Gynecology, Division of Gynecologic Oncology, M. S. Hershey Medical Center, The Pennsylvania State University, Hershey, Pennsylvania 17033.

National de la Santé et de la Recherche Médicale, M 33 INSERM, and ER 125 CNRS, 94270 Bicêtre, France

Richard J. Pietras (307), Department of Biology, The Molecular Biology Institute, and the Jonsson Comprehensive Cancer Center, University of California, Los Angeles, Los Angeles, California 90024

S. J. Pilkis (209), Department of Physiology, Vanderbilt University School of Medicine, Nashville, Tennessee 37232

Howard Rasmussen (1), Departments of Cell Biology and Internal Medicine, Yale University School of Medicine, New Haven, Connecticut 06510

Paul Robel (493), Unité de Recherches sur le Metabolisme Moléculaire et la Physio-Pathologie des Stéroides de l'Institut National de la Santé et de la Recherche Médicale, M 33 INSERM, and ER 125 CNRS, 94270 Bicêtre, France

Clara M. Szego (307), Department of Biology, The Molecular Biology Institute, and the Jonsson Comprehensive Cancer Center, University of California, Los Angeles, Los Angeles, California 90024

Jolinda A. Traugh (167), Department of Biochemistry, University of California, Riverside, California 92521

David Waisman (1), Departments of Cell Biology and Internal Medicine, Yale University School of Medicine, New Haven, Connecticut 06510

Preface

In this volume the subject of the messenger functions of calcium in hormonal systems is updated by Howard Rasmussen and David Waisman. Other general reviews are on subjects which have not appeared previously. These include neuronal regulation of blood pressure by Judith Juskevich and Walter Lovenberg, regulation of protein synthesis by phosphorylation by Jolinda Traugh, and hormonal control of hepatic gluconeogenesis by T. Claus and S. J. Pilkis. Ira Goldfine reviews the effects of insulin in intracellular functions. The subject of steroidal hormones is covered in part by Clara Szego and Richard Pietras in an extensive discussion of membrane recognition and effector sites in steroid hormone action. Edwin Milgrom reports on activation of steroid–receptor complexes, a relatively new subject. Finally, E. E. Baulieu and colleagues survey estradiol and progesterone receptors in the human endometrium which opens, for the first time in this series, the area of regulatory events in the female reproductive cycle. It can be expected that future contributions will include other aspects of this subject.

The continued cooperation of Academic Press in making this publication possible is appreciated.

GERALD LITWACK

xi

CHAPTER 1

The Messenger Function of Calcium in Endocrine Systems

Howard Rasmussen and David Waisman

I. INTRODUCTION

Just over 30 years ago, physiologists adduced the first concrete evidence that in addition to influencing plasma membrane excitability, calcium ion might also serve to couple the excitatory event at the plasma membrane to the eventual response of the cell, e.g., muscle contraction. In the first 15 years after this discovery, the major focus of investigative attention was confined to studies dealing with the various aspects of this coupling function of calcium ion in excitable tissues. However, in the past 15 years increasing attention has been devoted to the coupling or messenger role of calcium ion in stimulus–response coupling in various endocrine systems. The purpose of the present chapter is to summarize briefly the historical development of ideas concerning the role of calcium as a coupling factor in endocrine systems as a prelude to considering certain of these systems in detail as a means of delineating the present state of our knowledge.

Although there is some evidence that steroid and sterol hormones influence cellular calcium exchange and thus may regulate cell function, in part by altering the calcium ion concentration of one or more cellular compartments, this evidence will not be considered. We will confine our attention to those hormones and extracellular messengers which alter cell function by interacting largely, if not exclusively, with specific receptors on the plasma membrane of the cell, altering thereby the function of one or more membrane transducing elements which generate one or several intracellular messengers which serve to couple the initial membrane–receptor interaction to cellular response. We will include all such systems under the generic term of stimulus–response coupling even though this term usually has a more restricted usage being applied usually to stimulus–response coupling in excitable tissues. However, we feel this use is valid because a point that will be emphasized is that calcium is a nearly universal factor involved in coupling stimulus to response in both excitable and nonexcitable tissues. A second major point to be emphasized is that this coupling or messenger function of calcium ion, in nearly all cells, is related to and interdependent with a similar messenger function of cAMP. This means that an understanding of the role calcium ion plays in regulating cell function can not be achieved without understanding the role of cAMP. The converse is equally true.

It should also be noted that the present discussion will be largely confined to the role of calcium ion (and cAMP) as a messenger in activating processes in the cytosolic compartment of the cell. This choice is due to the fact that most intensively studied systems exemplify this particular messenger function of calcium. However, there is evidence that changes in the calcium ion content of the mitochondrial matrix space may lead to specific changes in the activity of enzymatic processes within this subcellular compartment (Rasmussen and Bikle, 1975). Because this evidence is sparse, and there is of necessity a limitation to the scope of this review, this aspect of the messenger function of calcium will not be considered.

II. HISTORICAL PERSPECTIVE

In 1947 Heilbrunn and Wiercinski showed that calcium ion was the only physiological substance that, when microinjected into a living muscle cell, could induce localized constrictions at the site of injection. At nearly the same time, it was shown that "skinned" muscle fibers could be induced to contract following application of external calcium ion (Natori, 1954). Within 5 years considerable evidence was accumulated in support of the concept that calcium ion played a critical role in excitation–contraction coupling, a term introduced by Sandow (1952). In the following decade, the role of the sarcoplasmic reticulum in this calcium coupling function was elucidated (see Weber and Murray, 1973), and in 1966, Ebashi and co-workers identified the first calcium receptor protein, troponin C (Ebashi *et al.*, 1969). In this same decade, Katz and Miledi (1967) demonstrated the absolute requirement for calcium in the electrically stimulated release of acetylcholine from nerve endings. Similarly, and nearly simultaneously, Douglas and Rubin (1961) showed that calcium ion was an essential coupling factor in the acetylcholine-induced increase in catecholamine secretion from the adrenal medulla, and coined the term stimulus–secretion coupling to characterize the process under study.

These findings had little immediate impact in the field of research devoted to an analysis of the mechanisms by which hormones act. The reasons for this lack of impact were at least three in number. In physiological studies of stimulus–response coupling, a distinction had been made between excitable (nerve and muscle) and nonexcitable tissues (liver, kidney, etc.). The focus of attention in studies of excitable tissues was upon the most dramatic characteristic of these tissues, the generation and propagation of an action potential. Thus, the questions related to how ionic messages generated at the cell surface produced a cellular response such as contraction or secretion. The discovery of the central role of calcium ion in coupling stimulus to response lent a certain symmetry to the organization of the coupling mechanisms in these tissues: both the initial and final signals were ionic in nature (Fig. 1).

In contrast, the focus of research upon peptide and amine hormone action centered upon biochemical mechanisms. These chemical messengers were considered mediators of a chemcial as opposed to an ionic messenger system. Because of the success of the concept of one enxyme-one trace substance in defining the mechanisms by which water-soluble vitamins control metabolism, a prevalent theory of hormone action was that these trace substances also acted by serving as cofactors of key enzymatic reaction (Hechter, 1955).

It was in testing this theory in the case of the epinephrine-induced increase in hepatic phosphorylase system, that led Sutherland and Rall (1958) to the discovery of cAMP. This discovery changed the field of hormone research irrevocably. It also preserved the seeming symmetry of extracellular chemical messengers giving rise to intracellular chemical messengers (Fig. 1). Hence two separate systems, appeared to be involved in the control of cell function. The first, utilized by excitable tissues, involved ionic signals upon the cell surface generating ionic signals within the cell and thereby initiating response. The second, utilized by so-called nonexcitable tissues, involved chemical messengers acting upon the cell surface to generate a second chemical message within the cell which was responsible for the initiation of cell response (Fig. 1).

The subsequent discovery that cAMP seemed to produce its effects by controlling a single class of intracellular enzymes, protein kinases (Kuo and Greengard, 1969), seemed further evidence for a distinction between the calcium messenger system which controlled muscle function by nonenzymatic means, and the cAMP system which regulated cell activity by altering the activity of this specific class of enzymes.

From the outset, there was evidence that this distinction might not hold. As the tissue distribution of the components of the cAMP messenger system were elucidated, it became apparent that these components were present in excitable tissues (Robinson *et al.*, 1971). Conversely, an ill-defined role of calcium in stimulus–response coupling in so-called nonexcitable tissues became increasingly evident. Equally important was the discovery that phosphorylase *b* kinase was a calcium-sensitive cAMP-insensitive protein kinase, and that calcium ion as well as cAMP regulated the phosphorylase cascade of enzymes in skeletal (Heilmeyer *et al.*, 1970) and cardiac muscle (Namm and Mayer, 1968). In 1968 we (Rasmussen and Tenenhouse, 1968) called attention to the fact that in many if not all tissues elements of both control systems seemed to exist, and we raised the

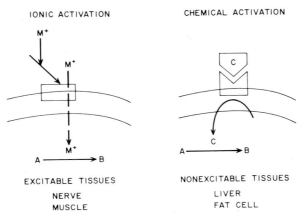

IONIC ACTIVATION   CHEMICAL ACTIVATION

EXCITABLE TISSUES   NONEXCITABLE TISSUES

NERVE   LIVER

MUSCLE   FAT CELL

Fig. 1. The prevalent theories of stimulus–response coupling in excitable (left) and nonexcitable tissues (right) held in the 1960s. There appeared to be a certain symmetry in each type of system with extracellular ionic signals giving rise to intracellular ionic signals in excitable tissues, and extracellular chemical signals giving rise to intracellular chemical signals in nonexcitable tissues.

possibility that these two systems interacted in coupling stimulus to response in certain cells.

This thesis was more fully developed in 1970 (Rasmussen, 1970), at which time it was proposed that in many tissues calcium ion and cAMP served related and interdependent coupling or messenger functions in endocrine as well as nonendocrine systems. Nevertheless, this thesis was not universally accepted. The paramount role of cAMP in hormonally controlled responses continued to be emphasized in spite of mounting evidence for the existence of a dual messenger system. In large part, this emphasis was a natural consequence of the fact that the molecular aspects of the cAMP messenger system could be explored in detail because all the elements in this system—the cAMP generator (adenylate cyclase); the cAMP sink (phosphodiesterase); and the cAMP receptor and response element (cAMP-dependent protein kinase)—could be isolated, characterized, and manipulated in subcellular as well as cellular systems. In contrast, aside from troponin C, a calcium receptor protein confined to skeletal muscle, the comparable elements in the calcium messenger system were largely undefined. However, within the past 5 years great advances have been made in our understanding of cellular calcium metabolism and calcium receptor proteins. With these advances has come a more balanced understanding of the interrelated roles of the calcium and cAMP messenger systems in mediating stimulus response coupling in endocrine systems.

A key discovery was that made by Cheung (1970) and by Kakukuchi and Yamazaki (1970) independently. They found that brain phosphodiesterase (the enzyme responsible for the hydrolysis of cAMP) required calcium for its activity. This finding was important in two respects. It was the first evidence at the molecular level of an interrelationship between cellular calcium and cAMP metabolism, and it led to the eventual isolation of a second calcium receptor protein, calmodulin. This protein has been found to be universally present in animal tissues of all phyla, and to mediate the effect of calcium ion upon a variety of cellular processes in addition to activating phosphodiesterase (Wang, 1976). In addition, it has been shown to be related structurally to troponin C and other calcium receptor proteins (Kretsinger, 1976; Wang, 1976). This means that a structurally similar, but functionally distinct, class of calcium receptor proteins have been identified and characterized. Their identification has opened the way to a detailed exploration of their function in subcellular and cellular systems.

The purpose of the present review is to consider the evidence that Ca^{2+} serves as a general messenger in hormone action, to illustrate some of the mechanisms by which the calcium signal is generated and terminated; to describe the molecular mechanisms by which Ca^{2+} exerts its regulatory function; and to emphasize the intimate nature of the interrelationships between the Ca^{2+} and cAMP messenger systems.

The review is selective rather than comprehensive emphasizing in detail the properties of certain systems and totally ignoring those of others. In particular, the role of calcium as a coupling factor in the response of the liver and adrenal glands are discussed in detail because historically these are the first two systems in which the second messenger model of cyclic AMP action were elucidated. The interested reader is referred to a number of recent reviews on various aspects of cellular calcium metabolism and the messenger function of calcium (Baker, 1973; Borle, 1973; Blaustein, 1974; Berridge, 1977; Rasmussen and Goodman, 1977; Fain, 1978).

III. CELLULAR CALCIUM METABOLISM

One of the major problems in defining the messenger function of calcium relates to the fact that the pool of calcium, which may contribute to the stimulus-induced increase in the cytosolic calcium ion concentration, varies from one responsive cell to the next. This may be the extracellular pool, the endoplasmic or sarcoplasmic reticulum pool, the pool within the mitochondrial matrix spaces, the pool bound to the plasma membrane, or in some cases a combination of these pools. This situation contrasts with that seen in the cAMP–messenger system in which, to the best of our present knowledge, the only source of this messenger is the adenylate cyclase confined to the plasma membrane of the cell. Thus, as a prerequisite to the study of the messenger function of calcium, it is necessary to know as much as possible about the cellular metabolism of calcium and its control. Although our knowledge in this sphere is still incomplete, significant advances have been made in the past 10–15 years by the application of a variety of techniques ranging from the calcium transport characteristics of isolated subcellular systems, e.g., microsomes and mitochondria, to the study of the kinetics of the change in calcium ion content of the cytosol of the barnacle muscle or squid axon using intracellularly injected calcium ion indicators. Since, the emphasis in this review is upon the messenger function of calcium and not on cellular calcium metabolism, no attempt will be made to review all of this work. Rather, the broad outlines of cellular calcium metabolism will be presented solely as the basis for the ensuing discussion of calcium's messenger role. The reader is referred to several recent reviews for more detailed information (Baker, 1973; Borle, 1973; Blaustein, 1974; Carafoli and Crompton, 1978; Brinley, 1978; Scarpa, 1979).

A. Cytosolic Calcium

From the point of view of the informational role of calcium ion in cell function, the critically important compartment is the free calcium ion concentration in the cell cytosol. This is normally in the range of 0.05 to 0.5 μM in resting cells. Yet the total cytosolic calcium content is in the range of 70 to 300 μM. This means that most of the cytosolic calcium is bound. In a sense, this system is the first and most primitive mechanism for maintaining a low concentration of calcium ion in the cytosol. However, its buffering capacity is limited so that other mechanisms supplement it. These other mechanisms are necessary because the calcium ion content of the extracellular fluids is in the range of 1000 to 2500 μM: a 10,000-fold difference in calcium ion concentration between the extracellular and cytosolic fluids. In addition, there are significant pools of calcium in the endoplasmic reticulum (CaR), the mitochondria (CaM), and in some cells in secretory vesicles (CaV) (Fig. 2).

The exchangeability of the latter pool is a point of continuing debate, however much of the calcium contained in the mitochondria and the endoplasmic reticulum is rapidly exchangeable. In either organelle if its calcium were ionized the concentrations within the organelle would be in the millimolar range. As it is, a significant percentage of the calcium in

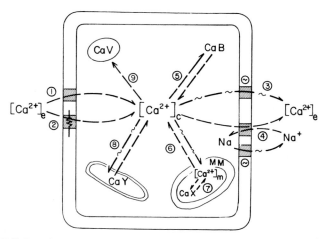

FIG. 2. Cellular calcium metabolism. The pool of central importance to the informational role of calcium is the ionic pool in the cell cytosol $[Ca^{2+}]_c$. This is maintained in part by (5) a cytosolic buffering system (CaB), and by pump lead systems across the plasma (1–4), mitochondrial (MM) (6), and endoplasmic reticular membranes (8). Two pathways exist whereby calcium enters the cell (1) by the Na^+ channel and (2) by a specific voltage-dependent (or independent) calcium channel. The energy-dependent efflux out of the calcium out of the cell also occurs by two processes: (3) via a specific ATP-dependent calcium pump and (4) via Na^+/Ca^{2+} exchange. Normally the extracellular calcium ion concentration $[Ca^{2+}]_e$ is nearly 10,000-fold greater than $[CA^{2+}]_c$. Calcium exchange across the mitochondrial membrane (MM) also takes place by a pump–leak system (6). Total intramitochondrial calcium consists of complexed (CaX) and free $[Ca^{2+}]$ in calcium. The bulk is complexed. Calcium exchange across the endoplasmic reticulum also takes place by a pump–leak system (8).

each organelle is nonionic. Our best estimates of the free or ionic calcium in these two subcellular compartments are in the range of 10^{-5} to 10^{-4} M: 100 to 1000 times greater than that in the cytosol. To maintain this calcium gradient both organelles possess calcium pumps oriented so as to pump calcium out of the cytosol into the respective subcellular pool. Likewise, a leak of calcium back into the cytosolic pool from these compartments occurs. The activities of these pump–leak systems in the three membranes determine the steady-state level of ionized calcium in the cell cytosol.

B. EVENTS AT THE PLASMA MEMBRANE

The calcium concentration difference between cytosol and extracellular fluid is maintained by two features of the plasma membrane. Under resting conditions its calcium permeability is quite low, and there are two active energy-dependent mechanisms for extruding calcium from cell interior to the extracellular space. The first of these is a specific Ca^{2+}/Mg^{2+} ATPase or calcium pump which has been most thoroughly studied in the human red cell (Schatzmann and Vincenzi, 1969). The concentration of calcium that is required to cause a half-maximal rate of pump activity is in the range of 1 μM. The pump is activated by the calcium receptor protein, calmodulin (Hinds *et al.*, 1978). The second is a Na^{+}/Ca^{2+} exchange mechanism which depends upon the fact that there is an asymmetric distribution of Na^{+} across the plasma membrane with a high Na^{+} outside and a low Na^{+} inside (Baker, 1973; Blaustein, 1974). This Na^{+} gradient is the driving force for the energy dependent efflux of calcium from the cell. The concentration of internal calcium required for half-maximal activation is in the range of 0.7 to 1.0 μM. This exchange is also dependent on the internal ATP concentration (Brinley, 1978).

The relative importance of these two energy-dependent mechanisms for regulating calcium efflux are not known for most cells. However, the Na^{+}/Ca^{2+} exchange system has been found in nerve axons, at presynaptic termini, and in the renal tubule cell. There are indications that it exists in many other cells. Conversely, the Ca^{2+}/Mg^{2+} ATPase has been found in red cell, nerve, kidney, and enterocytes but probably is more widely distributed. The only estimate of the relative importance of these two mechanisms in the same tissue has been made by Baker (1978) from studies of calcium fluxes in the squid axon. Under basal condition each pathway contributes upwards of 50% of the total calcium efflux. Their relative contributions in an activated cell has not been reported.

If an influx of calcium across the cell membrane serves to couple excitation to response, then a significant change in calcium influx must occur following cell activation. At least three separate mechanisms have been identified by which an increase in calcium entry occurs in response to cell activation. The first, seen in excitable tissues, is an early entry of Ca^{2+} concurrent with the onset of the action potential (Baker, 1973, 1978). This calcium entry is blocked by the same agents that block Na^{+} entry, it has the same time course as Na^{+} entry indicating that calcium is entering via the Na^{+} channel. The second, seen in a variety of tissues including nerve, smooth muscle, cardiac muscle, pancreatic islets, and chromaffin cells is a voltage-dependent calcium channel which is relatively specific for calcium ion, and is blocked by certain heavy metals and by Verapramil (Baker, 1978). The third is nonvoltage-dependent calcium entry after hormone–receptor interaction in mammalian and fly salivary gland, liver cells, mast cells, and probably a variety of other tissues (Borle, 1973).

The question of greatest importance is whether the voltage-dependent channel in tissues like the nerve axon, and the voltage-independent channel in the mast cell are similar differing only in terms of the membrane events which cause their opening. In the one case a change in membrane potential; in the other a consequence of extracellular chemical signal–receptor interaction. At present the answer to this question is not known.

C. Events in the Endoplasmic Reticulum

One of the most completely characterized calcium pump systems is that found in the sarcoplasmic reticulum of mammalian skeletal muscle. The active uptake of calcium is stoichiometrically linked to the hydrolysis of ATP. For each mole of ATP hydrolyzed two atoms of Ca^{2+} are transferred across the membrane. The transfer of calcium is associated with a phosphorylation and dephosphorylation of an aspartic acid residue in the protein (Martonosi *et al.*, 1978).

The fate of the calcium once it enters the membrane space is not completely established. However, the ATPase can establish a calcium gradient of approximately 10^3. Thus, if the external (cytosolic) calcium is 10^{-7}, the internal calcium ion concentration is 10^{-4}. However, *in situ* the total content is in the millimolar range. It appears that most of this calcium is bound in some readily releasable form. Two possibilities are (1) that it is complexed with phosphate, and (2) it is bound to the internal surface of the membrane. In this latter regard, a specific acid protein with a high capacity (43 mol of Ca^{2+} per MW of 46,000) but relatively low affinity (K_d of $8 \times 10^{-4} M$), has been shown to be an extrinsic membrane protein existing on the inner surface of the microsomal membrane. It represents approximately 7% of the total protein of skeletal muscle sarcoplasmic reticulum. This could account for approproximately 90 nmol of calcium per mg of vesicle protein which is probably sufficient to bind all the calcium accumulated by the SR.

The K_m for calcium accumulation has been found to vary in various preparations of isolated SR from 0.1 to 1.0 μM. The value of the intact SR is probably closer to the lower value.

Although not as completely studied microsomal preparations from cardiac (Fabiato and Fabiato, 1978) and smooth muscle also accumulate calcium by a similar ATP-dependent process. The maximal rates observed in these preparations are an order of magnitude lower than those measured in skeletal muscle preparations. Of considerable interest is the fact that these rates can be enhanced by either cAMP-dependent, or calcium-dependent (calmodulin regulated) protein kinases. These enzymes catalzye the phosphorylation of a specific membrane protein, phospholamban, and this phosphorylation leads to an increase in calcium transport and ATPase activity (Katz *et al.*, 1975).

Similar ATP-dependent calcium uptake systems have been described for the endoplasmic reticulum of liver, fibroblasts, kidney, brain, salivary gland, and platelets (Moore and Pastan, 1978). Most of these preparations are impure. Nonetheless, their maximal capacities for calcium accumulation are considerably lower than vesicles from skeletal muscle (liver—nmol/mg protein; skeletal muscle—1800 nmol/mg protein). Also, the K_m values have ranged from 4 to 100 μM in contrast to 0.1–1.0 μM in skeletal muscle. Some of these differences are probably attributable to technical problems so it is not yet possible to determine whether the K_m for calcium of this membrane pump system actually varies so widely from tissue to tissue.

The calcium uptake in liver microsomes is also stimulated by cAMP (Waltenbaugh and Friedmann, 1978). Hence, one apparently widespread and common effect of cAMP upon cellular calcium metabolism is that of stimulating the microsomal uptake of calcium.

If the sarcoplasmic reticulum is to serve as the source of calcium in excitation–response coupling, then a mechanism for the rapid release of its stored calcium must exist. In spite of considerable experimental effort, the mechanism responsible for release from the sarcoplasmic reticulum of muscle is still not completely defined. Two major mechanisms have been proposed (1) calcium-dependent calcium release; and (2) depolarization-induced release of calcium. Present evidence strongly favors the view that in skeletal muscle, depolarization is the primary mechanism inducing calcium release (Stephenson and Podolsky, 1978). However, in skinned muscle fibers Stephenson and Podolsky (1978) have shown that the chloride-induced depolarization of SR is calcium dependent. This raises the possibility that the primary signal is a depolarization leading to an initial release of calcium which then, in turn, causes a further release. These authors suggest that depolarization not only induces calcium release but also inhibits its ATP-dependent uptake. The combination of these changes leads to an amplification of the initial depolarizing signal.

In the case of cardiac muscle, Fabiato and Fabiato (1978) have presented convincing evidence that small physiologically appropriate amounts of free calcium ion cause the release of calcium stored in the SR. They argue that in this muscle the major mechanism regulating release of stored calcium is this calcium-dependent calcium release. In this view, the initial or "trigger" calcium needed to stimulate SR release is that calcium that enters the cell across the sarcolemma (plasma membrane) during the plateau of the action potential.

Nothing is yet known about the mechanisms by which calcium may be released from the endoplasmic reticulum in other cell types such as secretory cells, presynaptic nerve termini, or liver cells. It seems likely that calcium exchange between cytosol and endoplasmic reticulum may be of importance in exictation–response coupling in some, if not many, of these cells.

D. Events in the Mitochondria

Mitochondria isolated from nearly any mammalian tissue, and from tissue of lower forms when studied in isolation are able to accumulate large quantities of calcium from the medium (Carafoli and Crompton, 1978; Scarpa, 1979). Accumulation is energy-dependent, and may be driven either by substrate oxidation or ATP hydrolysis. In either case, the primary driving force for calcium entry is the electrical component (ΔE) of the gradient generated either by substrate oxidation or ATP hydrolysis.

$$\Delta \bar{u}_{H^+} = \Delta E - 60\ \Delta pH$$

In this view calcium is driven electrophoretically into the matrix space via a calcium uniport. If this takes place in the absence of a permeant anion then respiration and calcium uptake soon cease because the mitochondrial matrix space becomes alkaline. Addition of permeant anion (those that can donate H^+ within the matrix space) leads to an uptake of the anion, the generation of protons within the matrix space

$$HA + Ca \cdot X \rightleftharpoons H^+ + CaA$$

and release of calcium from the inner surface of the inner membrane. These anions stimulate calcium uptake. Under physiological conditions the major anion is phosphate which upon entering the matrix space interacts with calcium to form a nonionic calcium–phosphate complex which is osmotically inactive. Because of its formation, extremely large quantities of calcium can be taken up by isolated mitochondria. Up to 3 μmol/mg of mitochondrial protein can be accumulated. Given that 1 mg of mitochondrial protein is equivalent to approximately 1 μl of mitochondrial volume, this would give an internal calcium ion concentration in the molar range. However, the calcium content of freshly isolated rat liver mitochondria is in the range of 15 to 20 nmol/mg protein. Even so, this represents a calcium ion concentration in the 20 mM range if it were all ionized. Although the exact calcium ion concentration in the mitochondrial matrix space is not known, estimates range from 10^{-6} to 10^{-4} M which means that the bulk of the calcium in the mitochondrial matrix space is in some nonionic form. Nonetheless, a significant percentage (20–60) is rapidly exchangeable with extramitochondrial pools.

Considerable controversy surrounds the question of the K_m of the mitochondrial transport system. Most recent results place the value at 2–10

μM. However, the recent elegant experiments of Nicholls (1978b) have clarified considerably the calcium buffering function of rat liver mitochondria, and demonstrate that these organelles are capable of buffering cytosolic calcium. He showed that mitochondria incubated in the presence of an external calcium buffer (NTA) are able to maintain an extracellular pCa of 6.1 (free calcium = 0.8 μM). If the extramitochondrial calcium ion concentration falls below this value then the mitochondria release calcium, if it rises above this value the mitochondria take it up. As long as phosphate or a permeant weak anion is present the pCa changes very little even though the intramitochondrial content of total calcium increases. The uptake takes place through a uniport the activity of which is a linear function of pCa_o^{2+}.

Under the conditions where the ΔE is above 130 mU, the rate of calcium efflux is constant, but the rate of influx varies as a direct logarithmic function of the extramitochondrial calcium concentration. The efflux rate is 5 nmol/minute/ng protein, and this rate of influx is achieved when the extramitochondrial calcium reaches 0.8 μM (pCa_o^{2+} = 6.1). At this pCa_o^{2+} there is a continual recycling of calcium. The energy dissipated by this cycling is 2 nmol O_2/minute/mg protein which is a small percentage of the oxygen consumed by mitochondria.

As pointed out by Nicholls, a fine control of pCa_o^{2+} could be obtained by regulating the activity of the efflux pathway. A doubling of efflux rate would lead to a fall of 0.12 in pCa^{2+}; i.e., a rise in free Ca^{2+} from 0.8 to 1.1 μM. A 10-fold rise would lead to a pCa_o^{2+} in the range of 5.6 or a free calcium ion concentration of approximately 4 μM.

E. Plasma vs. Mitochondrial Membrane as Regulator of Cytosolic Calcium

Based on studies of the kinetics of calcium exchange in intact kidney cells, Borle (1973) has proposed that mitochondria play a major role in regulating cellular calcium metabolism. On the other hand, Rink and Baker (1975) and Brinley (1978) analyzing data obtained from the study of calcium uptake into stimulated squid axon, and from an analysis of calcium content and exchange in extruded axoplasm have concluded that under most physiological circumstances the mitochondria play a minor role in cellular calcium homeostasis.

In considering these different conclusions, it is important to point out that the requirements for a messenger function in the two tissues are quite different. In nerve, a sudden calcium influx is the signal for neurotransmitter release. In this situation the calcium signal must be brief with both a rapid rise and fall. Furthermore, the major calcium response element is situated just beneath the plasma membrane, hence a rise of calcium ion concentration in this restricted cellular domain is probably sufficient to activate neurotransmitter release. This means the domain in which a change in calcium ion concentration takes place is restricted in both time and space. In contrast, in a cell like the kidney or liver, a change in hormone status leads to a sustained change in metabolic response, and the response elements are throughout the cytoplasmic compartment. Under these circumstances the domain of calcium is extended both spacially and temporally. This must require a different organization of the mechanisms regulating cellular calcium metabolism. It is also evident that in the case of the squid axon mitochondria are sparse hence the ratio of surface area of the mitochondrial membrane to that of the plasma membrane is quite low, i.e., the plasma membrane may account for as much as 40–50% of the total calcium-transporting membrane surface. In contrast, it is estimated that in the liver, the surface area of the plasma membrane is only one-fifth of the area of the inner mitochondrial membrane. However, even in the nerve endings where mitochondria represent over 6% of the total volume, the temporal and spacial domains are severely restricted.

The problem is that different experimental approaches to this problem have been used in the case of nervous and nonnervous tissues so comparable data using the same techniques have not been obtained in these different tissues. However, if one reviews the data from various authors (Baker, 1978; Blaustein *et al.*, 1978; Borle and Uchikawa, 1978; Foden and Randle, 1978; Claret-Berthon *et al.*, 1977) concerning cellular calcium pools, and their rates of exchange, it seems likely that both groups are correct. In the squid axon under physiological circumstances the major determinants of the calcium ion content of the cell cytosol is the pump–leak system for calcium across the plasma membrane, and the cytosolic buffering system. In contrast, in liver, kidney or enterocyte, the mitochondrial pump–leak system also plays a major role.

F. cAMP AND MITOCHONDRIAL CALCIUM EXCHANGE

A question that arises concerns the role of mitochondria in the response of many cells to extracellular stimuli. For example, kidney and liver each respond to a peptide hormone, parathyroid hormone and glucagon, respectively, both hormones activate adenylate cyclase and both cause an efflux of calcium from the cell. Similarly, the hormone 5HT stimulates cAMP production and calcium efflux in the fly salivary gland. Since, in all three tissues the efflux of calcium is also promoted by exogenous cAMP, the presumption is that it is this nucleotide which mediates the hormonally induced release of calcium. Furthermore, there is indirect evidence that in all three tissues cAMP causes the mobilization of calcium from the mitochondrial pool. Furthermore, Borle and Uchikawa (1978) showed that addition of either PTH or cAMP to isolated kidney cells leads to marked increase in the rate of calcium efflux from both mitochondrial and cytosolic pool.

There are several interesting points about the Borle and Uchikawa data. First, in the kidney cell a significant fraction of the total calcium (60–80%) in the resting cell is in a "cytosolic" pool. Second, after hormone or cAMP addition there is an increase in calcium exchange across the mitochondrial membrane and an increase in the exchangeable pool within the mitochondria. These data indicate that cAMP influences mitochondrial calcium exchange. One can envision at least four possible ways cAMP might act (1) the effect of cAMP is mediated at the plasma membrane; (2) cAMP influences the calcium binding properties of a ligand in the cytosol; (3) cAMP influences calcium exchange across the mitochondrial membrane; or (4) cAMP alters the distribution of calcium between an ionic and nonionic compartment within the mitochondrial matrix space.

Definitive evidence in support of any one of these four possibilities is not presently available. However, this question can now be re-explored using the approach to the study of mitochondrial transport physiology developed by Nicholls. At present it appears that in many cells in which a rise in cytosolic calcium ion content is a signal to increase their activity, in order for this signal to be maintained there must be an increased influx of calcium into the cell. Second, it is not apparent that simply mobilizing calcium from the mitochondrial compartment will alter the calcium ion content of the cell cytosol. The key cellular calcium compartment that must be more fully characterized is the nonionic cytosolic pool. It is possible that cAMP acts by altering the buffering capacity or buffer dissociation constants in this pool, and thereby functions to couple excitation to response in polar as well as nonpolar cells. Finally, in all cells it has become clear that the mitochondria serve to limit the rise in cytosolic calcium ion content by serving as a sink for calcium that enters the cell. The mitochondrial calcium uptake system determines the upper limits of the calcium ion control range. Whether in hormonally responsive cells such as the kidney the mitochondria play a direct role in coupling by releasing calcium in response to cAMP remains an unresolved question but the present evidence strongly favor the view that directly or indirectly it does so.

Any discussion of the role of those factors coupling excitation to possible release of mitochondrial or intracellular calcium would be incomplete without a discussion of the possible role of sodium ion. This is particularly relevant to the calcium-coupling function in the secretory response of the exocrine pancreas. Two points about this system are worth noting. First, calcium derived largely from an intracellular pool is the factor coupling excitation to response (Petersen and Iwatsuki, 1978). Second, the mobilization of calcium from this pool is not brought about by a change in the cAMP content of the cell. The nature of this pool, whether mitochondrial or microsomal, is not known. Several possibilities exist. If it were microsomal then some type of coupling between the changes in ionic currents of the plasma membrane and a depolarization of the endoplasmic reticulum could lead to a release of calcium, i.e., in analogy with the situation in muscle.

However, in these cells the addition of veratridine leads to an increase in Na^+ permeability which in turn enhances secretion. Based upon the observation that Na^+ stimulates Ca^{2+} efflux from mitochondria in certain tissues (Carafoli and Crompton, 1978), these data have been taken as evidence that the mitochondrial pool is the one involved. This interpretation has to be questioned because Blaustein *et al.* (1978) showed that the uptake of calcium by the presumed microsomal system in the synaptosomes was also Na^+ sensitive. Therefore, the effect of Na^+ might equally well be to increase release from the microsomal as from the mitochondrial pool. Nevertheless, Carafoli and Crompton (1978) and Nicholls (1978a) have shown that in certain types of mitochondria (heart, pancreatic exocrine cells, but not liver) a small rise in Na^+ concentration increases the efflux rate of calcium considerably. At present it is not possible to decide whether the change in the intracellular Na^+ concentration after cell stimulation in a cell such as cardiac muscle is sufficient to alter calcium efflux from mitochondria.

G. The Control Range of Calcium

Based on the foregoing discussion, it is possible to present the concept that there is a very narrow range of calcium ion concentration in the cell cytosol over which this ion functions in information transfer (Rasmussen and Gustin, 1978). One way to place limits on this range is that of plotting the activities of the various membrane pumps as a function of pCa^{2+} (Fig. 3). This plot shows that the concentration range over which cytosolic calcium ion operates is from 0.1 to 5 μM. It is likely that only under extreme circumstances does the concentration rise above this value.

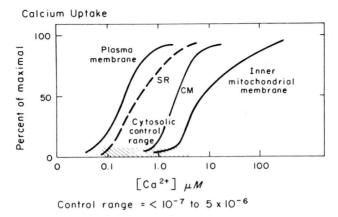

FIG. 3. A plot of the relative rates of calcium uptake by the plasma membrane, the sarco-plasmic reticulum (SR), and the mitochondrial membrane as a function of the log concentration of calcium ion. Also shown is the binding of calcium to calmodulin (CM) as a function of calcium ion concentration. The shaded area represents the range of calcium ion concentrations which are involved in the informational role of calcium in the cell cytosol.

Under most circumstances the range is from 0.4 to 4 μM, i.e., no more than a 10-fold change in concentration. In keeping with this supposition is the fact that a plot of known calcium-activated processes as a function of the calcium ion concentration shows that they all fall within this range. Furthermore, all go from essentially inactive to fully active over a 10-fold change in calcium ion concentration. From these data one could predict that a concentration of no more than 0.5–1.0 μM is achieved in most cells when activated under physiological circumstances.

IV. STIMULUS–RESPONSE COUPLING

A. INTRODUCTION

Considered as information transfer systems, the membrane transducing systems can be characterized as having at least seven steps (1) recognition; (2) transduction; (3) transmission; (4) reception; (5) modulation; (6) response; and (7) termination (Rasmussen and Clayberger, 1979).

This fashion of analyzing stimulus–response coupling is useful both from the philosophic and practical point of view. Philosophically, it focuses attention on the fact that the intracellular messengers are informational molecules. Practically it is a convenient way to analyze the general properties of these control systems.

Although generally given a more restricted definition by physiologists, the term stimulus–response coupling is employed in the present discussion to include chemical as well as electrical stimuli, and metabolic as well as contractile and secretory responses. The rationale for this broader use of this term is our conviction that calcium ions and cAMP form a nearly universal bimodal system for coupling stimulus to response in nearly all cell types.

B. RECOGNITION

At present the nicotinic type of acetylcholine receptor is the only one coupled to the calcium signaling system that has been isolated and characterized (Barrantes *et al.*, 1975; Chang, 1974; Changeux *et al.*, 1970, 1971, 1976; Dugrud and Raftery, 1973; Eldefrawi *et al.*, 1971; Fambrough and Hartzell, 1972; Hazelbauer and Changeux, 1974; Karlin, 1974; Meunier *et al.*, 1974; Michaelson and Raftery, 1974; Patrick and Lindstrom, 1973; Reed *et al.*, 1975; Barrantes, 1979. Some work has been done on isolating α-adrenergic receptors, but little work on other systems. A major difficulty in this field relates to the fact that not all "specific" binding sites on the cell surface are receptors in the sense that they are coupled to a transducing system, hence it is necessary to relate specific binding to a meaningful intramembranous transduction. This is easy in the case of the cAMP signaling system wherein the properties of the receptor and cyclase can be studied in isolated plasma membrane fragments. To date, no one has developed a method for studying the receptors in the calcium messenger system in isolation. Hence, practically nothing is known about the details of coupling between receptor and change in calcium flux in those systems where a direct coupling is thought to exist, e.g., the fly salivary gland, the mammalian salivary gland, etc.

The problem is complicated by the fact that there appears to be no universal relationship between receptor type and transducing event. Again, by way of contrast, as far as is presently known, beta receptors for catecholamines regulate cell function by being coupled to adenylate cyclase and thus always serve as a component of the cAMP messenger system (Robison *et al.*, 1971; Roth, 1973; Rodbell *et al.*, 1975; Helmreich, 1977; Ross and Gilman, 1980). In contrast, α-adrenergic receptors are sometimes coupled to the calcium messenger system and sometimes they are not (Ahlquist, 1959). For example, in the mammalian parotid

In terms of our concept of information transfer, it is therefore most useful to discuss these two features, transmission and termination, together since they are the point and counter-point of message transfer. Although the ensuing discussion will consider these characteristics of the calcium messenger system, many of the same conditions must apply to the cAMP messenger system. Of critical importance in both systems are the following facts (1) there are separate mechanisms for the generation and termination of the respective messages; (2) in large part the generating and terminating systems are spatially separated; and (3) there are multiple mechanisms for terminating the signal. Hence, the temporal and spatial domain of the message within the cell is restricted. These facts mean that the geometric distribution of the terminating systems as well as their concentration play an important role in determining the message domain. Hence, regulation of the terminating as well as the generating systems must be of critical importance in determining message domain.

An instructive manner in which to consider the questions of transmission and termination is to contrast the situation in three types of cellular responses (1) antigen-induced histamine release; (2) glucose-induced insulin release; and (3) serotonin-induced fluid secretion in the fly salivary gland. The first two exemplify cases in which the response takes place in a nonpolar cell with the difference between the two being a difference in the temporal domain: histamine release is a brief response; insulin release is sustained as long as the glucose concentration is kept high. The third is a situation in which there is a sustained response in a polar cell hence both the spatial and temporal domains are extended.

The interaction of antigen with a specific IgE receptor on the surface of the mast cell leads to an abrupt but brief release of histamine after which the cell is refractory to further antigen addition (Cochrane and Douglas, 1975; Douglas and Veda, 1973; Foreman and Mongar, 1975; Kanno *et al.*, 1973; Foreman *et al.*, 1973; Lichtenstein *et al.*, 1973). The primary messenger initiating the secretory response is an influx of calcium. This triggers secretion by as yet to be defined mechanism. As noted above, the domain of calcium is restricted spatially and temporally. The mechanisms of termination are not completely known but presumably involve uptake by intracellular organelles, intracellular buffering, and active calcium extrusion. In addition, the IgE-mediated calcium gating response is rapidly terminated so a major temporal restraint in the system is the transitory nature of the generated signal. The mechanism of this prompt shutting off of the signal generator is not known. What is known is that it can be modulated. Addition of the phosphotidylserine prolongs the calcium signal. Addition of agents which cause an increase in [cAMP] abort the calcium signal. It is not yet known whether cAMP plays a role in terminating the IgE–antigen response, or is merely a modulator of that response.

In any case, this system exemplifies a transitory response in a nonpolar cell in which both the temporal and spacial domains of the signal are restricted. As such, the major site for regulatory events is at the plasma membrane. Intracellular systems capable of binding and/or accumulating calcium may play a subsidiary role in restricting the domains of calcium.

The stimulation of insulin release by an increase in plasma glucose also involves the regulation of secretion in a nonpolar cell (see discussion below). However, in this case a sustained response is observed. Hence, the temporal domain of the calcium signal is extended. The basic signal for insulin release also appears to be an entry of calcium into the cell across the plasma membrane (Malaisse *et al.*, 1979d). Extension of the temporal domain of the response is determined by the fact that regenerative calcium-dependent action potentials (influxes of calcium ions) take place in this membrane (Matthews, 1975). The sequence of events appear to be the following: a glucose-dependent decrease in K^+ efflux from the cell leads to a depolarization of the membrane. This depolarization activates a voltage-dependent calcium channel leading to an influx of calcium. The consequent rise in calcium ion concentration in the subsurface domain of the cell cytosol induces insulin secretion by an unknown mechanism and also activates a K^+ channel in the membrane. The subsequent efflux of K^+ leads to a repolarization of the membrane and eventually to another cycle of depolarization, calcium gating, etc. Here again part of the termination signal is to cyclically decrease the flux of calcium through the calcium channel. However, with sustained stimulation of the cell by glucose, there is a significant net accumulation of calcium by the cell indicating that intracellular binding and/or sequestration is also a part of the termination response.

In this system agents known to alter the cAMP content of the cell alter the response to glucose. Agents inducing an increase in the cAMP content of these cells cause a given glucose signal to induce a greater response. Agents producing a fall in the cAMP content of these cells blunt the response to glucose. Changes in [cAMP] appear to act in two ways. First, they alter the properties of the plasma membrane so the magnitude of the initial calcium signal is greater the greater the [cAMP] concentration. Second, they influence the intracellular distribution of calcium presumably by altering the rates of calcium exchange across the mitochondrial and/or microsomal membranes. By these means they extend the spatial domain of calcium within the cell and thereby amplify the calcium signal leading to an increase in the magnitude of the final response. It is also possible the cAMP alters the sensitivity of the final response element to calcium. If so, this effect would be operationally similar to extending the domain of calcium.

This system represents one in which the domains of calcium are extended by controlling events both at the plasma membrane and at one or more intracellular membranes. Control of intracellular calcium distribution serves to extend the domain of calcium but does not serve as the primary source of calcium for cell activation.

In contrast, the situation in the fly salivary gland cell requires the involvement of both types of control to achieve sustained response due to the fact that this cell is polar. All available data indicate that 5HT acts upon the basal and lateral membranes of this cell to stimulate both adenylate cyclase and the influx of calcium ion inducing thereby a rise in the concentration of both within the cell (Berridge, 1977; Rasmussen and Goodman, 1977). Likewise, all available data indicate that a major response element for messengers is the luminal membrane of the cell: calcium increase, Cl^- permeability, and cAMP the activity of a K^+ pump. Given the fact that these cells are rich in mitochondria, the question arises as to how the calcium message generated at the baso-lateral membranes is transmitted from these membranes to its response element the luminal membrane. The answer appears to be that the increase in [cAMP] serves to alter the ability of the mitochondria to accumulate calcium hence the domain of the calcium signal is extended sufficiently in the spatial domain to account for response. Furthermore, as long as secretion is sustained it seems likely that the cytosolic calcium ion content remains high. As soon as 5HT is removed, response ends so there is no long-term memory of a transitory rise in the $[Ca^{2+}]$ of the cytosol. The point to be made is that in polar cells, the one end (and sides) of the cell is often the site of signal generation and the other the site of cellular response. In such cases, transmission of the signal involves, of necessity, regulation of the termination systems within the cell.

E. Reception

Once the signal is transmitted into the cell cytosol the next step in the information transfer process is the reception of the signal. Specific receptor proteins for cAMP, cGMP, and calcium have been identified. To date only one cAMP receptor protein has been found, but at least eight intracellular calcium receptor proteins are known. These are tropinin C, leotonin, parvalbumin, calmodulin, regulatory and essential myosin light chains, binding protein, and the intestinal calcium binding protein.

In the case of calcium ion, a major target for this messenger appears to be the plasma membrane of the cell and it is possible that specific receptor molecules for this ion are lipids as well as protein.

1. Lipid Binding Sites

The cytosolic face of the plasmalemma is known to interact with and bind Ca^{2+}. The sites of interaction of Ca^{2+} with the membrane are poorly defined, it is believed that Ca^{2+} binding by the membrane is accomplished by protein and by negatively charged phospholipids. The red blood cell membrane contains about 25 μmol/liter of cell Ca^{2+}, 34% of the Ca^{2+} binding is due to lipid headgroups and 66% to protein (Sato and Fujii, 1974). Szász *et al.* (1977) have classified Ca^{2+} binding by the membrane as tight and loose on the basis of the ease of removal of Ca^{2+} from the membrane. They have suggested that the probable candidates for tight Ca^{2+} binding are membrane proteins and loose Ca^{2+} binding are the membrane lipids.

The possible involvement of lipid Ca^{2+} binding in cellular activation has been discussed by Szász *et al.* (1977). They have reported that propranolol selectively displaces Ca^{2+} from the membrane lipids. The resulting increase in cytosolic Ca^{2+} concentration is thought to trigger a rapid and Ca^{2+}-dependent efflux of K^+. The efflux of K^+ occurs at a faster rate than the transport of the counter ion Cl^-, causing membrane hyperpolarization. It is proposed that the membrane hyperpolarization is responsible for increasing Ca^{2+} influx by opening the Ca^{2+} channels.

2. Calcium Receptor Proteins

The subject of calcium binding proteins has been reviewed recently by Kretsinger (1976, 1979) and will not be extensively considered. A summary of their major characteristics is given in Table I. Only those most relevant to the question at hand will be discussed. These include principally calmodulin and troponin C. These are two closely related proteins that appear to have arisen by gene duplication from a common ancestor. At present the only known function of troponin C is that of coupling stimulus to response in skeletal and cardiac muscle. On the other hand, calmodulin has been found to be involved in the regulation of a variety of calcium-mediated processes (Table II).

a. Evolutionary Interrelationships. The amino acid sequence of the carp cytosolic Ca^{2+} binding protein, parvalbumin has been examined by Kretsinger and Nockolds (1973). These investigations reported that the amino acid sequence of this protein was unusual in that it contained three regions of homologous sequence repeats, each of these repeating sequences was about 33 residues long. X-ray crystalographic analysis of the

TABLE I

Ca²⁺ RECEPTOR PROTEINS

Protein	Molecular weight	Number of EF domins	Number of Ca²⁺ bind-ing sites	Type of Ca²⁺ binding site	Apparent Ca²⁺ binding K_{diss} (μM)[a]	Physiological function	Reference
Parvalbumin	12,000	2	2	(Ca²⁺–Mg²⁺) site	8.0	Unknown	Potter et al. (1977)
Troponin C							
(a) Skeletal	18,000	4	4	(2) Ca²⁺ sites (2)(Ca²⁺–Mg²⁺)	20 2	Regulation of actomyosin ATPase	Potter et al. (1977)
(b) Cardiac	18,000	4	3	(1) Ca²⁺ site (2)(Ca²⁺–Mg²⁺)	200 3.6		
Calmodulin	16,700	4	4	Ca²⁺ sites	(2) 2–6 μM (2) 10–18 μM	General Ca²⁺ receptor	Wang and Waisman (1979)
Myosin light chains							
(a) regulatory light chain	19,000	4	1	(Ca²⁺–Mg²⁺)	2mM[b]	Regulation of actomyosin ATPase	Weeds et al. (1977) Kuwayama and Yagi (1979)
(b) Essential light chain	17,000–21,000	4	0	—	—		
Intestinal Ca²⁺ binding protein							
(a) Small form	12,500	2	2	(Ca²⁺–Mg²⁺)	0.1–1.0	Intestinal Ca²⁺ transport and storage (?)	Wasserman and Feher (1977)
(b) Large form	27,000	4	4	(Ca²⁺–Mg²⁺)	2 μM		

[a] K_{diss} of (Ca²⁺–Mg²⁺) sites is reported in the presence of millimolar Mg²⁺.

[b] When the RLC is associated with myosin the affinity of Ca²⁺ binding increases 100-fold.

TABLE II

PROPERTIES OF CALMODULIN REGULATED RESPONSE ELEMENTS

Enzyme	Tissue	Molecular weight	Apparent K_m (Ca^{2+})	Reference
Myosin light chain kinase	Gizzard	105,000	3 μM	Dabrowska et al. (1978)
	Skeletal Muscle	90,000	—	Wang and Waisman (1979)
	Platelet	105,000	—	Hathaway and Adelstein (1979)
Phosphorylase b kinase	Skeletal muscle	1.26×10^6	3 μM 0.5 μM (activated)	Brostrom et al. (1971)
Calmodulin-stimulated protein kinase	Liver	1.3×10^6	0.3 μM	Sakai et al. (1979)
	Syaptosomes	—	0.3 μM	Schulman and Greengard (1978)
Guanylate cyclase	Tetrahymena pyriformis	—	8 μM	Nago et al. (1979)
Tubulin	Brain	110,000	1 μM	Nishida et al. (1979)
NAD kinase	Plant	—	0.25 μM	Anderson and Cormier (1978)
Modulator binding protein I	Brain	85,000	—	Sharma et al. (1979)
Modulator binding protein II	Brain	70,000	—	Sharma et al. (1978)
Plasmalemma Ca^{2+} pump	Red blood cell	125,000	0.8 μM*	Niggli et al. (1979) *Waisman et al. (1980)
Adenylate cyclase	Brain	—	2.5 μM (activation) 200 μM (inhibition)	Brostrom et al. (1978)
Phosphodiesterase	Heart	155,000	2.3 μM	Ho et al. (1977)

conformation of parvalbumin (Moews and Kretsinger, 1975) suggested that the internal sequence repeats are the sites of a Ca^{2+} binding pocket of β antiparallel conformation by two regions of a helix (Fig. 4). Moews and Kretsinger (1975) have termed this Ca^{2+} binding, repeated sequence the "EF" region. As illustrated in Fig. 4 helix E, Ca^{2+} binding loop EF, and helix F represent the basic structural and homologous domain. Each EF region contains about 33 residues, 12 of which comprise the EF of Ca^{2+} binding loop. Overall parvalbumin contains six regions of α helix designated A through F. Of the nonhelical loops between A and B, C and D, and E and F only the loops between C and D and E and F have retained the ability to bind Ca^{2+}.

An examination of the amino acid sequence of troponin C (Collins *et al.*, 1973), essential myosin light chains of rabbit skeletal muscle (Weeds and McLachlan, 1974; Tufty and Kretsinger, 1975), regulatory myosin light chains of rabbit skeletal muscle (Mutsuda *et al.*, 1977), intestinal calcium binding protein (Hofman *et al.*, 1977), and calmodulin (Vanaman *et al.*, 1977) has revealed that these proteins also contain homologous internal sequence repeats. Furthermore, these repeat se-

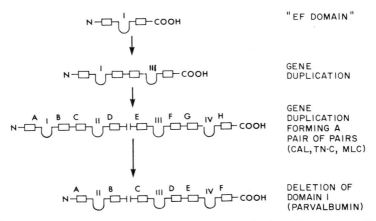

Fig. 4. Hypothetical ancestry and structural features of calmodulin, troponin C, parvalbumin, and myosin light chains. Kretsinger (1972) and Kretsinger and Nockolds (1973) first reported the internal sequence repeats of parvalbumin suggested gene triplication of a primitive Ca^{2+} binding domain referred to as an "EF hand." Analysis of the sequence data of troponin C, protein modulator, ICBP, and myosin light chains have also demonstrated the existence of homologous internal repeat sequences of the EF region. Several investigators (Collins *et al.*, 1973; Collins, 1976; Vanaman *et al.*, 1977; Kretsinger, 1979) have suggested that these homologous proteins are related to a common ancestral protein which arose from successive gene duplications of a 33 residue "EF" ancestor to form a protein of four "EF" regions. Analysis of the homology of the internal repeat sequences has suggested that calmodulin is most closely related to the ancestral protein. (From Waisman, 1979.)

quences are similar to the repeat sequences of parvalbumin. It, therefore, appears that the parvalbumin, troponin C, calmodulin, essential and regulatory myosin light chains, and the intestinal Ca^{2+} binding protein comprise a family of homologous, "EF" containing proteins. The "EF" domain represents the basic structural and homologous building block of this family of proteins.

Table I summarizes the general characteristics of the members of the family of homologous Ca^{2+} binding proteins. All are low molecular weight protein which contain 2, 3, or 4 EF regions. In some cases (e.g., essential and regulatory myosin light chains and cardiac troponin C), the number of "EF" domains do not correlate with the number of Ca^{2+} binding sites. This could represent a legitimate loss of Ca^{2+} binding by certain "EF" regions or it is possible that Ca^{2+} binding by these regions occurs under different experimental conditions. Also of interest is the specificity of the Ca^{2+} binding sites. These sites have been classified as either Ca^{2+} binding sites (Ca binding unaffected by millimolar concentrations of Mg^{2+}) or (Ca^{2+}–Mg^{2+}) sites (Ca^{2+} binding is competitive with Mg^{2+}). The affinity of binding of Mg^{2+} by the (Ca^{2+}–Mg^{2+}) sites is generally three orders of magnitude lower than the affinity of Ca^{2+} binding to these sites. The physiological significance of (Ca^{2+}–Mg^{2+}) vs. Ca^{2+} sites is at present unknown.

Attempts have been made to delineate the ancestral interrelationships of the family of homologous proteins. Kretsinger (1972) first suggested that parvalbumin evolved by gene triplication of a primitive ancestral protein which contained only one EF domain. Later Collins (1976) suggested that parvalbumin and troponin C were derived from a common ancestral protein containing one EF region which underwent two successive gene duplications and fusions to produce an ancestral protein containing four Ca^{2+} binding sites. The deletion of one of these sites from the four EF containing precursor produced parvalbumin. However, an examination of the individual domains of troponin C and calmodulin has revealed that regions two and four are more closely related to one another than they are to regions one and three (Vanaman *et al.*, 1977). This result is inconsistent with previous theories of Kretsinger (1972) or Collins (1976). In view of this observation Vanaman *et al.* (1977) and Kretsinger (1979) have suggested that existence of an ancestral odd-even pair, the subsequent duplication (domain I→I and III; domain II→II and IV) would produce a pair of pairs. Gene fusion would complete the procedure and produce the 4 EF domain containing ancestor.

Kretsinger (1979) has examined the extent of internal homology of the EF containing proteins and concluded that the level of internal homology is greatest within calmodulin. This suggests that calmodulin is more closely related to the ancestral protein than the other EF domain containing proteins. Of the other EF containing proteins troponin C has been shown to be the most closely related to calmodulin (Vanaman *et al.*, 1977). Since alignment of the amino acid sequence of troponin C and calmodulin to show maximum homology introduces a three residue gap in the sequence of calmodulin, Vanaman *et al.* (1977) have suggested that calmodulin arose by duplication of a smaller two EF domain containing precursor than troponin C. Therefore, it would appear that troponin C did not evolve from a calmodulin precursor, but that calmodulin and troponin, therefore, represent separate evolutionary lines. Barker *et al.* (1977) have constructed an evolutionary tree of the EF domain containing superfamily. The authors suggest that the evolutionary tree can be divided into two main branches and that the myosin light chains have evolved from the calmodulin branch of the tree while parvalbumin and the intestinal Ca^{2+} binding protein have evolved from the troponin branch of the tree. The trunk of the tree before this branching is thought to consist of the 4 EF containing ancestral protein.

b. Troponin C.   It is generally argued that a change in cytosolic free Ca^{2+} concentration from $< 0.1 \mu M$ in resting muscle to $10 \mu M$ in contracting muscle is the major event initiating muscle contraction. The molecular mechanisms by which Ca^{2+} regulates muscle contraction has been shown to involve two spatially distinct Ca^{2+} binding proteins; located on the thin filaments is troponin C (TN-C) and located on the thick filament is the myosin regulatory light chain (RLC).

Muscle contraction is believed to be a consequence of the interaction of actin with the globular heads of myosin (for an excellent review, see Perry, 1979). The regulatory systems of muscle are designed to prevent actin–myosin interaction in the presence of low cytosolic Ca^{2+}. Under these conditions the muscle is at rest and contraction does not occur. The rise in cytosolic Ca^{2+} concentration which occurs upon muscle stimulation allows the interaction of Ca^{2+} with the regulatory proteins either directly or indirectly resulting in conformational changes in the proteins. In this new Ca^{2+}-induced conformation the regulatory proteins can no longer inhibit actin–myosin interaction and as a result muscle contraction occurs.

The regulation of muscle contraction has been examined in a variety of animals and has been shown to involve two different mechanisms; thin filament regulation involving direct interaction of Ca^{2+} with TN-C or thick filament regulation involving either direct interaction of Ca^{2+} with the myosin RLC or by indirect interaction, i.e., Ca^{2+}-dependent phosphorylation of RLC.

In vertebrate cardiac and skeletal muscle the thin filaments are composed of actin, tropomyosin, and troponin. Troponin is composed of three subunits, troponin-T, the subunit responsible for anchoring troponin to tropomyosin, troponin-I, the component responsible for stearic inhibition of actin–myosin interaction, and troponin C, the Ca^{2+} binding subunit. It is currently believed that Ca^{2+} dependent conformational change in troponin C results in the movement of troponin-I and tropomyosin such that sites on the actin molecules are exposed and actin–myosin interaction can occur. It is, therefore, the binding of Ca^{2+} by troponin C that is the event initiating muscle contraction.

Troponin C contains two sites and two (Ca^{2+}–Mg^{2+}) sites (Table I). The report by Potter and Gergely (1975) that the Ca^{2+} dependence of the myofibrillar ATPase is insensitive to Mg^{2+} has suggested that only the Ca^{2+} sites of troponin C are involved in the regulation of myofibrillar ATPase. To this end, Potter *et al.* (1977) have demonstrated that the Ca^{2+}-dependent conformational changes (monitored by circular dichroism) in troponin C are biphasic with $K_{Ca^{2+}}$ of 0.27 μM and 33 μM representing Ca^{2+} binding to the (Ca^{2+}–Mg^{2+}) and Ca^{2+} sites respectively. Of the total Ca^{2+} induced conformation change 35% of the change is due to Ca^{2+} binding to the Ca^{2+} sites.

TN-C has also been implicated in the Ca^{2+}-dependent activation of phosphodiesterase (Dedman *et al.*, 1977a), although 600-fold more TN-C is required to produce an activation similar to that produced by calmodulin. Recently several laboratories have suggested the presence of TN-C-like proteins in the cytosol of a variety of tissues including bovine adrenal medulla (Kuo and Coffee, 1976), chick embryo brain (Fine *et al.*, 1975), smooth muscle (Head *et al.*, 1977), platelets (McGowan *et al.*, 1976), and several vertebrate brains (Vanaman *et al.*, 1975). These observations might suggest a regulatory role for TN-C in the cytosol. However, detailed analysis of the cytosolic and particular fractions of a variety of tissues (Drabikowski *et al.*, 1977; Grand *et al.*, 1979) has clearly demonstrated that soluble TN-C is in fact calmodulin. In these studies calmodulin was discovered in the soluble and particulate fractions of all tissues tested, while TN-C was found only in the particulate fraction of skeletal and cardiac muscle. The inability to demonstrate the existence of soluble TN-C has made the observation of Dedman *et al.* (1977a) of questionable physiological significance.

   c. Calmodulin.   Of all the Ca^{2+} receptors calmodulin has received the most intensive study (for a recent review, see Wang and Waisman, 1979). Calmodulin has been shown to exist in a variety of tissues within an organism (Smoake *et al.*, 1974) as well as in many different organisms including many plants and probably all animals (Waisman *et al.*, 1975; Charbonneau and Cormier, 1979; Waisman, 1979). Because of the widespread phylogenetic distribution and impressive number of enzymes and proteins shown to interact with calmodulin, it has been suggested that calmodulin represents a fundamental Ca^{2+} receptor in plants and animals (Waisman *et al.*, 1975).

Since the structural and functional properties of calmodulin are reasonably well understood a brief review of these properties will provide a molecular model of the physical and chemical basis of Ca^{2+} reception by this protein.

Calmodulin (Table III) is an asymmetrical (f/f_o 1.3) low molecular weight protein (18,000) which is highly acidic [pI (pH) 4.1]. Amino acid compositional analysis of the protein has demonstrated that it contains about 30% acidic residues (Glx + Asx), 45% nonpolar residues, and 55% polar residues. The amino acid composition is unusual in that the protein has a high content of Asx and Glx residues, an absence of tryptophan and cysteine, and a high Phe/Tyr ratio. The absence of tryptophan and high Phe/Tyr ratio is responsible for the low ultraviolet absorption (ξ275–279 1 2.0) and the unusual absorption spectrum (Fig. 5) of the protein. The spectrum is unusual in that while most proteins have absorption maximum at 280 nm calmodulin exhibits considerable vibrational structure in the region of 250–280 nm, with absorption peaks at 253, 259, 265, and 276. The acidic nature of the molecule is due to the high content of Glx and Asx residues, of these residues only 30% are represented by Gln and Asn (Liu and Cheung, 1976; Walsh and Stevens, 1977). Amino acid analysis of calmodulin has also revealed the presence of 1 mol of the unusual amino acid ξ-*N*-trimethyllysine (Watterson *et al.*, 1976; Vanaman *et al.*, 1977; Miyake and Kakiuchi, 1978; Jackson *et al.*, 1977). Lastly, it has been shown from sequence analysis that calmodulin contains an acetylated N terminus residue (Ac-Ala, Vanaman *et al.*, 1977).

Amino acid sequence analysis of the bovine brain and rat testes calmodulin has suggested that these proteins are virtually identical (Vanaman *et al.*, 1977; Dedman *et al.*, 1978). The calmodulins of bovine heart, bovine brain, and human erythrocyte are indistinguishable by tryptic peptide mapping (Stevens *et al.*, 1976; Jarrett and Kyte, 1979). Despite these findings discrepencies exist in the literature regarding the number and classes of Ca^{2+} binding sites on calmodulin and their relative affinities and capacities. These discrepancies could represent variation in the ionic strength of buffers as well as trace contamination of Ca^{2+} in buffers, different methods of Ca^{2+}, and protein determination and denaturation of calmodulin during the study. Generally it has been reported that calmodulin binds 4 mol Ca^{2+}/mol protein with micromolar dissociation constants when assayed at high ionic strength (> 40 mm). Concentrations of Mg^{2+} as high as 3 m*M* have no effect on Ca^{2+} binding. Different

TABLE III

Physical, Chemical Ca^{2+} Binding Properties of Various Calmodulins

Parameter	Bovine heart	Rat testes	Bovine brain	Porcine brain	Bovine adrenal medulla	Earthworm
			Source			
Molecular weight	19,000	18,000	15,000	16,500	16,000	18,000
Sedimentation constant						
$S^\circ_{20,w}$	2.0	1.9	1.85	—	1.9	1.95
f/f_o	1.3	1.34	1.2	—	—	1.3
pI (pH)	4.1	3.9	4.3	—	4.3	4.0
E275–278, 1% 1 cm	1.9	2.1	1.0	1.5	3	3.2
% Acidic residues (Glx + Asx)	34	33	33	36		34
Number of Ca^{2+} binding sites						
High affinity	1	4	3 (2)[a]	2.	—	2
Low affinity	2–3	0	1 (2)	2	2	—
Dissociation constants of Ca^{2+} binding (μM)						
High affinity	2.9	2.4	3.5 (1.1)	4	—	6
Low affinity	11.9	—	18 (8.6)	12	20	—
α Helical content						
+ Ca^{2+}	—	54	57	50	40	—
− Ca^{2+}	—	45	39	30 = 35	20	—
Reference	Teo et al. (1973)	Dedman et al. (1977b)	Lin et al. (1974); Lcu and Cheung (1976)	Klee	Kuo and Coffee (1976)	Waisman et al. (1978)

[a] Values according to Watterson and Vanaman (1976).

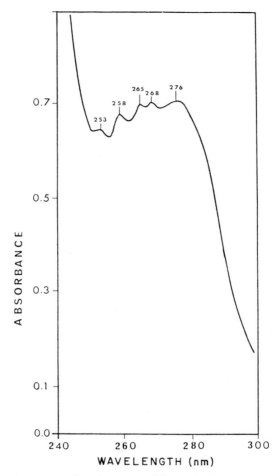

Fɪɢ. 5. Absorption spectra of earthworm modulator. Earthworm modulator at a protein concentration of 1.89 mg/ml in a pH 7.5 buffer containing 40 mM Tris/HCl, 1 mM MgAc$_2$, and 50 μM CaCl$_2$ was used. (From Waisman, 1979.)

classes of binding sites appear to be present but there is no cooperativity in the binding of Ca^{2+} to these sites. At low ionic strength cation binding properties become more complicated and competition between Ca^{2+} and Mg^{2+} for the binding sites may occur (Wolff *et al.*, 1977).

It appears that the structural and functional properties of calmodulin have been conserved phylogenetically. Although tryptic peptide analysis of the earthworm calmodulin has shown that it is not identical to the bovine brain protein (Waisman *et al.*, 1978a) there is a remarkable similarity between this protein and the mammalian calmodulin (Table III). Waisman (1979) has used the technique of polyacrylamide disk gel electrophoresis as a measure of the physical chemical properties of crude extract calmodulin from a variety of plants and animals. The demonstration of similar relative mobilities of calmodulin activity in these extractions suggested phylogenetic conservation of calmodulin structure. Functionally, earthworm calmodulin has been shown to be equally as effective in the activation of bovine brain phosphodiesterase as is bovine brain calmodulin; both proteins have similar specific activities and both require about 2 μM Ca^{2+} to half-maximally activate the bovine enzyme. These results suggest that calmodulin is a highly conserved ubiquitous protein. Presumably the remarkable conservation of structural and functional properties is due to the fundamental function of this protein as a Ca^{2+} receptor.

Detailed analysis of the Ca^{2+} binding sites of calmodulin by X-ray diffraction has not been achieved due to technical difficulties in the production of calmodulin crystals. However, from amino acid sequence data and because of the homology shared by calmodulin and parvalbumin a Ca^{2+} binding protein of known 3D structure, Kretsinger (1979) has made several suggestions concerning the structure of calmodulin.

1. The amino acid sequence can be divided into four homologous domains each of which contains a potential Ca^{2+} binding site (Fig. 6, I–IV).

2. Each domain is about 33 residues long and consists of a Ca^{2+} binding loop of β-antiparallel conformation consisting of about 12 amino acids which is flanked by two regions of α helix. As will be discussed in detail in the following section the internal repeat domain has also been

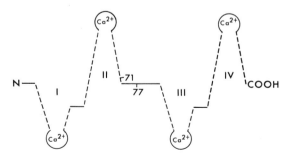

Fig. 6. Structure of calmodulin. Dashed lines represent regions of α helix. The basic homologous internal repeat domain or "EF" hand is indicated, domain I, residues 8–40, domain II 44–76, domain III 81–113, and domain IV 117–148 (Kretsinger, 1979). The residues lysine 75 and 77 and methionine 71, 72, and 76 are suggested to respresent the possible site of interaction with phosphodiesterase. (From Drabikowski *et al.*, 1977.)

referred to as the EF domain and forms the common building block of the homologous Ca^{2+} binding proteins.

3. The Ca^{2+} ions are liganded to oxygen atoms donated by six specifically located amino acids in the Ca^{2+} binding loop, at least four of which are acidic.

4. Apolar residues located in specific regions of the α helix contribute to a hydropholic core which serves to stabilize the structure.

The secondary structure of calmodulin has been examined by several techniques including CD and ORD. The molecule consists of approximately 40% α helix, 18% β pleated sheet, and 42% random coil in the presence of Ca^{2+} (Klee, 1977). The changes in calmodulin secondary structure due to Ca^{2+} binding have been reported by several investigators. While discrepancies appear to exist as to the content of α helix in the secondary structure of the molecule there is general consensus that Ca^{2+} binding increases the content of α helix (Table III). In addition to changes in α helix content due to Ca^{2+} binding, calmodulin has been reported to show enhanced resistance to proteolytic inactivation (Ho *et al.*, 1975; Liu and Cheung, 1976), and a decrease in Stokes radius (Kuo and Coffee, 1976) when bound to calcium. Therefore, the conformation change in calmodulin due to Ca^{2+} binding can be characterized as a transformation from a less ordered structure to one that is more ordered, symmetrical compact and stable.

Since calmodulin contains multiple Ca^{2+} binding sites the question has been raised as to whether or not all four Ca^{2+} binding sites need to be filled before the Ca^{2+}-dependent conformation change can occur. Klee (1977) has demonstrated that the binding of 2 mol of Ca^{2+} to the high-affinity sites ($K_{diss} = 4\ \mu M$, Table III) is sufficient for the bulk of the conformational change in the molecule. This result suggests that the binding of only 2 mol of Ca^{2+} is required for enzyme activation. Dedman *et al.* (1977b) have examined the dependency on Ca^{2+} concentration of Ca^{2+} binding, conformational change, and enzyme activation. They reported that 95% of the α helical change occurred before threshold enzyme activation; the maximum enzyme activation by calmodulin corresponded to the binding of about 2 mol Ca^{2+}/mol calmodulin.

Chemical modification studies of calmodulin have been carried out to identify specific amino acid residues at the site of interaction between calmodulin and the calmodulin-regulated enzyme. To date, this type of analysis has been performed only on cyclic nucleotide phosphodiesterase. The correlation between modification of a residue and loss of calmodulin activity could be interpreted to mean involvement of that residue in Ca^{2+} binding, the Ca^{2+}-dependent conformational change, or at the site of interaction between calmodulin and phosphodiesterase. Walsh and Stevens (1977) have shown that carboxylation of histidine, nitration, acetylation, or iodination of both tyrosines, and modification of the arginine residues have little effect on calmodulin activity. On the other hand, modification of some of the methione, lysine, and carboxyl groups produce varying degrees of inactivation of the protein. In particular, modification of Met 71, 72, 76, and possible 109 result in loss of calmodulin activity, however, the modified protein appears to retain its ability to bind Ca^{2+} albeit at lower affinity. Furthermore, the Ca^{2+}-dependent conformation of the modified protein is identical with the unmodified protein (Walsh *et al.*, 1978). Based on these observations Walsh *et al.* (1978) have suggested that these residues are a portion of the site of interaction between calmodulin and phosphodiesterase. Walsh and Stevens (1977) have also reported that agents which modify lysine 75 and 77 result in a 50% loss of calmodulin activity. Interestingly, agents that do not alter the charge properties of these residues do not result in loss of calmodulin activity. Accordingly, Walsh and Stevens (1977) have implicated the positive charge of the lysine residues as an important factor in enzyme activity. Figure 6 presents a diagramatic view of the location of the methione and lysine residues which may be involved at the site of interaction. It would appear from the chemical modification studies that the site of interaction between calmodulin and phosphodiesterase is located between the second and third domains.

Walsh *et al.* (1977) have tested the activity of five peptide fragments obtained from tryptic digestion of calmodulin. Among the peptides, fragments 1–106 and 18–148 had the highest activity, about 0.5 and 0.190 of the native calmodulin. This result suggests that the whole protein may contribute to the active site.

d. Myosin Regulatory Light Chain.   Fast skeletal muscle myosin is composed of two heavy chains (MW 200,000) and two pairs of light chains (MW 20,000) (Table I). One class of light chain can be selectively removed from the myosin without loss of myosin ATPase activity and are referred to as the regulatory light chains (RLC). The other class, which are called the essential light chains (ELC), appear to be essential for myosin ATPase activity and cannot be removed without loss of enzymatic function. The presence of homologous RLC and ELC have been documented in the myosins of a variety of animals as well as in the myosin of nonmuscle contractile systems.

In vertebrate smooth muscle and scallop adductor muscle it has been demonstrated that the RLC are responsible for the Ca^{2+}-linked regulation of muscle contraction. This type of regulation is referred to as thick filament regulation. It is thought to occur by two distinct mechanisms. In the scallop adductor muscle, direct binding of Ca^{2+} by the RLC is thought to represent the signal for the onset of muscle contraction (Lehman *et al.*, 1972) while in vertebrate smooth muscle it is the phosphorylation of the RLC that is responsible for turning on muscle contraction. The phosphorylation of the RLC is catalyzed by a myosin light chain kinase which is regulated by Ca^{2+} and calmodulin (Dabrowska *et al.*, 1978). Recently Sherry *et al.* (1978) have demonstrated that once the RLC is phosphorylated, muscle contraction remains turned on in the absence of Ca^{2+}, dephosphorylation of RLC by the myosin light chain phosphatase is required to turn muscle contractions off, a process (dephosphorylation) which is insensitive to Ca^{2+}. Therefore, smooth muscle appears to be regulated by the cyclic phosphorylation and dephosphorylation of the RLC.

The Ca^{2+}-dependent phosphorylation of RLC has been demonstrated in a variety of myosins including rabbit fast skeletal (Yagi *et al.*, 1978; Waisman *et al.*, 1978b), chicken gizzard (Sobieszek, 1977), pig arterial (Barron *et al.*, 1979), porcine cardiac, and rabbit white skeletal (Holroyde *et al.*, 1979), and in several nonmuscle myosins such as platelets and alveolar macrophages (Hathaway and Adelstein, 1979) and hamster kidney (Verna *et al.*, 1979).

In skeletal and cardiac muscles the Ca^{2+}-dependent phosphorylation of RLC is not believed to be directly involved in the regulation of muscle contraction. Bárány *et al.* (1979) have shown a reversible phosphorylation–dephosphorylation of RLC of frog skeletal muscle during the contraction and relaxation cycles. They have proposed that RLC phosphorylation in this muscle may serve to facilitate actin–myosin interaction by effecting the orientation of the myosin head away from the myosin backbone and toward the actin molecule.

The RLC is thought to account for the Ca^{2+} binding properties of myosin: 2 mol Ca^{2+}/mol myosin are bound with affinities K_{Ca} 40 μM (0.3 mM Mg^{2+}). The binding of Ca^{2+} by myosin is sensitive to Mg^{2+} concentration. However, under physiological conditions 0.7 mol calcium/mol myosin may be bound (Holroyde *et al.*, 1979). The binding of Ca^{2+} by myosin has been shown to induce conformational changes in the molecule (Morimoto and Harrington, 1974). Furthermore, phosphorylation of the RLC is not suspected to affect the affinity of Ca^{2+} binding (Kuwayama and Yagi, 1979; Holroyde *et al.*, 1979).

From the above discussion it should be apparent that in cardiac and skeletal muscle Ca^{2+} binding and phosphorylation of the RLC occur physiologically, however, the contribution of these properties to a regulatory mechanism is not understood. In smooth muscle phosphorylation of the RLC is the event turning on muscle contraction. Of widespread significance is the growing body of evidence that RLC phosphory-lation regulates the myosin of nonmuscle cells. It is, therefore, possible that RLC phosphorylation may play a role in the regulation of nonmuscle contractile systems.

  e. Myosin Essential Light Chain. The essential light chains (ELC) of myosins cannot be phosphorylated nor do they bind Ca^{2+}. Their function remains largely unknown. Wagner and Yount (1976) have reported that chemical modification of the single serine residue in the ELC of skeletal and cardiac muscle inhibits both ATP hydrolysis and actin binding. Wagner *et al.* (1979) have analyzed the possible role of the alkali light chains in the actin-activated ATPase of myosin subfragment. They have cautiously suggested that the ELC may play a role in influencing the kinetic properties of the actin-activated ATPase.

  f. Intestinal Ca^{2+} Binding Proteins (ICBP). That vitamin D could stimulate the synthesis of a Ca^{2+} binding protein of bovine intestinal mucosa was first reported by Wasserman and Taylor (1966). It is now ap-parent that this protein is located in a variety of animal tissues (Table I) including bovine intestine, kidney, and brain as well as avian in intes-tine, kidney, brain, and shell gland (Wasserman and Feher, 1977).

  While the exact cellular location of the ICBP has not been resolved a partly particulate (5%) and partly soluble (95%) subcellular distribution has been reported for the chick gut protein (Feher and Wasserman, 1976). A molecular weight of 27,000 has been reported for the chick pro-tein, and the protein contains four Ca^{2+} binding sites (K_a-$2\mu M$).

  Analysis of the ICBP of the rat small intestine has revealed the presence of two soluble vitamin-D-dependent ICBP. One is found predominately in the jejunum and ileum. It has a molecular weight of 27,000. The other, associated primarily with the duodenum has a molecular weight of 12,500 (Wasserman and Feher, 1977). Presumably, the later protein is similar to the 9700 dalton ICBP of bovine intestine sequenced by Hofman *et al.* (1977). This protein was also found to bind 2 mol Ca^{2+}, K_a 10^{-6}–10^{-7}. Besides the soluble ICBP of rat intestine Miller *et al.* (1979) have reported the existence of a particulate protein located in the brush borders of MW 18,500. They have suggested that this protein may be dif-ferent than the soluble ICBP. Ueng and Bronner (1979) have used the counter ion electrophoresis to identify the ICBP of rat intestine and have concluded that under conditions in which proteolysis is controlled only one soluble ICBP may exist. This result suggests that the 10,000 MW ICBP may be a fragment of the 27,000 MW protein.

  The ICBP were first postulated to mediate the vitamin D stimulation of mucosal Ca^{2+} entry (Wasserman, 1977). However, the demonstration that vitamin D stimulates Ca^{2+} transcellular transport before increase the synthesis of ICBP (Thomasset *et al.*, 1979) has ruled out this suggestion. It is possible that ICBP may effect Ca^{2+} transport once the Ca^{2+} has entered the intestinal cell.

g. *Parvalbumin.*   Parvalbumins are small (MW 12,000) highly acidic (pI 4.0) Ca^{2+} binding proteins found in all vertebrates including fish, birds, amphibians, reptiles, mammals (Benzonana *et al.*, 1972; Heizmann *et al.*, 1977), and in the white leg muscle of the invertebrate limulus (Anderson *et al.*, 1978). They are present in especially large amounts in the skeletal muscles of vertebrates (Table I). Results of tissue distribution studies (Baron *et al.*, 1975) have suggested that the majority of parvalbumin molecules within an organism are located in the white muscle, but are not restricted to this tissue. Analysis of the a.a. sequence of a variety of parvalbumins has revealed that they are isostructural (Kretsinger, 1980).

The physiological function of parvalbumin is at present unknown. Potter *et al.* (1977) have suggested that parvalbumin may play a role in the activation of PDE. LeDonne and Coffee (1979) have demonstrated that pure parvalbumin does not activate PDE in a calcium-dependent fashion and that the results of Potter *et al.* (1977) were due to contamination of parvalbumin by calmodulin.

Pechère *et al.* (1975) and Gillis and Gerday (1977) have suggested that parvalbumin may play a role in the relaxation cycle of white muscle. In particular, it has been suggested that parvalbumins may play the role of a shuttle mechanism for Ca^{2+} between myofibrils and the SR. In support of this suggestion is the observation that Ca^{2+} accumulation by SR is not fast enough to account for the rate of relaxation of a living muscle (Ebashi, 1976).

F. Modulation

Once the second messenger has bound to its receptor protein, the question then becomes the matter of how the message is transduced into response.

The mechanisms of modulation of the cAMP message and the calcium message (via calmodulin) are shown in Fig. 7. In the case of the cAMP system, the receptor protein (R) is bound to the catalytic subunit (C) of the protein kinase. In this state the kinase is inactive. When the cAMP content of the cell cytosol rises, cAMP binds to R and causes its dissociation from C. Free C is now an active protein kinase which catalyzes the phosphorylation of a variety of proteins.

At present this is the only known modulating mechanism in the cAMP

a) $R_2C_2 + 4\ cAMP \rightleftharpoons R_2 \cdot cAMP + 2C$
　(inactive)　　　　　　　　　　　　　(active)

Corbin and Lincoln (1978)

b) $E_2 + 2\ cGMP \rightleftharpoons E_2 \cdot cGMP_2$
　(inactive)　　　　　　　(active)

c) $Ca^{2+} + CAL \rightleftharpoons Ca \cdot CAL \rightleftharpoons caCAL^*$　　　　　　Wang *et al.* (1975)
　　　　　(inactive)　(inactive)　(active)

$Ca \cdot CAL + E_3 \rightleftharpoons Ca \cdot CAL \cdot E_3 \rightleftharpoons Ca \cdot CAL^* \cdot E_3^+$
(active)　　(inactive)

d) $E_4 \cdot CAL + Ca^{2+} \rightleftharpoons E_4 \cdot CAL \cdot Ca^{2+}$　　Cohen *et al.* (1978)
　(inactive)　　　　　　　(active)　　　　Waisman (1979)

Fig. 7. Mechanism of transduction of second messengers. E, Enzyme; R, regulatory subunit of cAMP-dependent protein kinase; C, catalytic subunit cAMP-dependent protein kinase; CAL, calmodulin; (*, +), conformation states.

system. However, there are membrane-bound as well as soluble cAMP-dependent protein kinases. It is not yet known how these are activated by cAMP, but it is possible that they do not involve a dissociation of R from C.

At least two mechanisms are known by which the calmodulin–calcium complex are involved in intracellular modulation (Fig. 7). The first of these is exemplified by the calmodulin-dependent activation of phosphodiesterase. In this case, in the absence of calcium, calmodulin and phosphodiesterase are separate. A rise in calcium ion content leads to the formation of a calcium–calmodulin complex. The binding of calcium to calmodulin leads to a conformation change in the molecule, which in turn leads to its association with the phosphodiesterase. This complex, calcium · calmodulin · phosphodiesterase, is the activated form of the enzyme.

In another system, e.g., phosphorylase kinase, calmodulin is a subunit of this oligomeric protein. In this case, allosteric modification of the bound subunit, calmodulin, leads to a calcium-dependent activation of the enzyme.

It is likely that in still other systems calmodulin will be found to be a bound inhibitor in the absence of calcium, and its calcium-dependent dissociation lead to an activation of a particular enzyme. In any case, present data support the view that in both the cAMP and the calcium messenger systems, the interaction of messenger with receptor protein leads to a conformational change in the structure of the receptor protein, and this change alters the nature of the interactions between receptor proteins and response elements. These altered interactions may lead to either activation or depression of the response element.

1. Determinants of Modulation

In describing cellular control systems in terms of information flow, it is generally believed that messenger-mediated cellular response is a consequence of an increase in strength of the message, i.e., an increase in the concentration of either calcium and/or cAMP in the cell cytosol. However, this is not the only means of inducing response. A change in the affinity (sensitivity) of the receptor either for the message or for the response element can alter response. Examples of this type of control are known in both the calcium and cAMP messenger systems. The situation with phosphorylase kinase exemplifies this situation in the calcium control system. This enzyme is a calcium-dependent protein kinase which can exist either in a phosphorylated (so-called active) and non-phosphorylated (so-called inactive) form. However, in either form its activity depends upon the presence of calcium. The difference is that the concentration of calcium required for the active form is 0.5 μM and that for the inactive form 3 μM. The most interesting aspect of this case is the fact that the phosphorylation of the inactive form by the cAMP-dependent protein kinase leads to the phosphorylation of subunits of the enzyme other than the calcium binding subunit. This phosphorylation, nonetheless, alters the sensitivity of the enzyme to calcium. Hence, when epinephrine acts upon resting skeletal muscle, the resulting increase in [cAMP] leads to a conversion of phosphorylase *b* kinase from inactive to active form. The latter is now receptive to the calcium concentration of the cytosol of the resting muscle, hence its activity increases, but the activity of other calcium-responsive systems do not change because the strength of the calcium signal has not changed.

The opposite type of sensitivity modulation has been discussed in the cAMP messenger system. It is known that administration of insulin modifies the subsequent hepatic response to glucagon without altering the glucagon-dependent rise in [cAMP]. Even though the [cAMP] rises to the same extent, in the presence and absence of insulin, the activation of both glycogenolysis and of gluconeogenesis are inhibited. Insulin shifts the apparent dose-response curve to the right, i.e., there is less activation of the process at any given glucagon or cAMP concentration. Walkenbach *et al.* (1978) have recently shown that the effect of insulin is to reduce the sensitivity of the cAMP-dependent protein kinase to cAMP. Thus, a higher concentration of cAMP is required to induce the dissociation of RC into C and R · cAMP.

These two examples demonstrate that control of cellular response by either the calcium or the cAMP messenger system can be achieved directly by altering the amplitude of the message, i.e., change the concentration of calcium ion or cAMP; or indirectly by sensitivity modulation, i.e., change the affinity of the response element for the message.

G. RESPONSE

The final consequence of information transfer in these cellular control systems is cellular response. Response depends upon the interaction of the intracellular receptor proteins with response elements within the cell.

In the case of the cAMP messenger system, the only presently identified type of response element is protein kinase (Robison *et al.*, 1971). The immediate molecular response is a change in the state of phosphorylation of a variety of proteins leading to a change in their activity which is eventually expressed as a change in cell function.

1. Calmodulin Response Elements

In the case of the calcium system, a variety of response elements have been identified. These include general and specific protein kinase, calcium transport systems, and microtubule assembly. The various functions of the calcium receptor protein, calmodulin, or CDR, are represented schematically in Fig. 8. Several of these specific response elements will be discussed briefly (Table II).

a. Cyclic Nucleotide Phosphodiesterase. Cyclic nucleotide phosphodiesterase represents the only enzymatic mechanism for the hydrolysis of cAMP and cGMP. The presence of multiple forms of cyclic nucleotide phosphodiesterase was reported by Thompson and Appleman (1971).

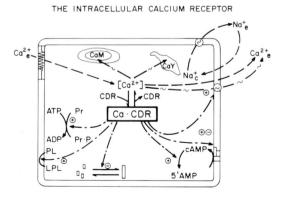

FIG. 8. The role of the calcium–CDR (calmodulin) complex in the regulation of cellular metabolism. See text for discussion.

Chromatography on DEAE-cellulose columns of extracts from a variety of tissues including liver (Russel *et al.*, 1973), heart, kidney, mammary gland, lung, and brain (Appleman and Terasaki, 1975) has resolved three discrete active fractions of phosphodiesterase activity referred to as D-I, D-II, and D-III according to their elution from the column by a salt gradient. The kinetic properties of the enzyme activities have been examined; D-III appears to be a low K_m (cAMP) particulate enzyme, D-II is a soluble enzyme possessing equal activity toward cAMP and cGMP. D-I is a low K_m (cGMP) high K_m (cAMP) enzyme and because of the Ca^{2+} dependence of this enzyme its properties will be discussed further.

The separation of soluble phosphodiesterase into Ca^{2+} sensitive and Ca^{2+} insensitive forms was initially reported in rat brain by Kakiuchi *et al.* (1971). Later it was shown that the activation of this enzyme by Ca^{2+} was mediated by calmodulin (Kakiuchi *et al.*, 1973). The kinetic properties of the calmodulin-dependent partially purified phosphodiesterase of brain and heart has been characterized kinetically in many laboratories (Teo *et al.*, 1973; Ho *et al.*, 1977; Wallace *et al.*, 1978; Klee *et al.*, 1978). The enzyme catalyzes the hydrolysis of both cAMP and cGMP. Ho *et al.* (1976) have suggested that the activation of bovine heart phosphodiesterase by calmodulin results in a fivefold increase in V_{max} and a decrease of about 90% in the K_m (from 1.5 mM to 0.2 mM) when cAMP is used as substrate (Fig. 9). Similar results have been reported by Klee *et al.* (1978). When cGMP is used as substrate a decrease in K_m of about 50-fold

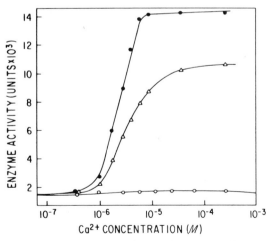

Fig. 9. The activation of cyclic nucleotide phosphodiesterase by Ca^{2+} in absence (o) or presence of 1.4 (△) or 13 (•) units of calmodulin. (From Teo *et al.*, 1973, reproduced with permission.)

(0.26 mM to 9 μM) and no change in V_{max} (remains at about 30% of the V_{max} for cAMP) was reported by Ho *et al.* (1976).

  b. Adenylate Cyclase.   The hormonal stimulation of the adenylate cyclase of the plasmalemma is believed to be responsible for activation of the cAMP second messenger system. That Ca^{2+} might be involved in its regulation was suggested by Birnbaumer (1973) who demonstrated that the adenylate cyclase derived from a variety of tissues was strongly inhibited by low concentrations of Ca^{2+}. Brain tissue on the other hand has been shown to possess adenylate cyclase activity which exhibits a biphasic response to Ca^{2+}; low Ca^{2+} concentrations activate and higher concentrations inhibit the enzyme. An examination of brain tissue by Brostrom *et al.* (1975) and Cheung *et al.* (1975) has revealed that calmodulin stimulates that adenylate cyclase activity. Cheung *et al.* (1978) have demonstrated the existence of calmodulin-dependent adenylate cyclase activity in all areas of rat brain, in human neuroblastoma and in a glioma cell line. An examination of porcine kidney medulla, frog erythrocyte, and rat and rabbit heart failed to reveal calmodulin-stimulated adenylate cyclase. On the other hand, Valverde *et al.* (1979b) have reported the presence of calmodulin stimulated adenylate cyclase in pancreatic islets.

  The biphasic response of brain adenylate cyclase to Ca^{2+} has been examined by Brostrom *et al.* (1977) and Westcott *et al.* (1979). Their results suggest that brain contains separate calmodulin—sensitive and—insensitive forms of adenylate cyclase. The calmodulin insensitive form has been shown to be inhibited by Ca^{2+}. The calmodulin sensitive adenylate cyclase displayed biphasic response to Ca^{2+} (Brostrom *et al.*, 1978), stimulation at low Ca^{2+} [K_m (Ca^{2+}) 2.5 μM] and inhibition at higher Ca^{2+} [K_m (Ca^{2+}) 200 μM].

  Gnegy *et al.* (1976) have reported that calmodulin regulates the stimulation of adenylate cyclase activity by the putative neurotransmitter dopamine. Brostrom *et al.* (1979) have analyzed the possible role of calmodulin in the regulation of cAMP production in response to norepinephrine in intact glial tumor cells. The results suggest that in these cells calmodulin mediates the β-adrenergic receptor stimulated cAMP production.

  In conclusion, it appears that in many tissues agents influencing Ca^{2+} concentration could regulate cAMP synthesis in a reciprocal fashion, i.e., agents that increase Ca^{2+} would be expected to inhibit cAMP synthesis. Presumably, this mechanism does not require calmodulin. In other tissues such as brain, Ca^{2+} (mediated by calmodulin) appears to be essential for the activation of neurotransmitter-stimulated adenylate cyclase. In the absence of Ca^{2+} and calmodulin transmitter activation of adenylate cyclase is greatly reduced.

c. *Ca^{2+} Pumps.*   The maintenance of low cytosolic Ca^{2+} concentrations is the function of the membrane Ca^{2+} pumps. Three subcellular locations have been reported for these pumps, the plasmalemma, the mitochondria, and the microsomes. The plasmalemma Ca^{2+} pumps of the human red blood cell and the canine heart microsomal pump have been well characterized and have been found to be regulated by calcium.

The red blood cell plasmalemma Ca^{2+} pump catalyzes the energy-dependent uphill transport of Ca^{2+} from the cytosol ($[Ca^{2+}] 0.1 \mu M$) to the extracellular fluid ($[Ca^{2+}]$ 1 mM) (Schatzmann and Vincenzi, 1969). The isolation of highly purified inside–out vesicles composed of plasma membrane has allowed characterization of the red blood cell Ca^{2+} pump. An apparent K_m (Ca^{2+}) of 0.8 μM has been reported by Waisman *et al.* (1980), a value in accordance with the physiological concentration of Ca^{2+} in these cells. The stimulation of Ca^{2+} pumping by calmodulin in inside–out red blood cell membrane vesicles (Fig. 10) has been reported by several groups (MacIntyre and Green, 1978; Hinds *et al.*, 1978; Larson and Vincenzi, 1979; Waisman *et al.*, 1980). The mediation of the Ca^{2+}-linked regulation of this pump by Ca^{2+} suggests the role of calmodulin as a cytosolic Ca^{2+} sensor, increases in cytosolic Ca^{2+} will result in calmodulin-stimulated pump activity which will return the Ca^{2+} concentration to resting levels. Recently Kuo *et al.* (1979) have demonstrated the regulation of the synaptic plasmalemma Ca^{2+} pump by calmodulin.

Hormonal regulation of the red blood cell or synaptic Ca^{2+} pump has not been reported. However, Pershadsingh and McDonald (1979) have reported that the adipocyte plasmalemma Ca^{2+} pump is inhibited by physiological concentrations of insulin. The mechanism of insulin inhibition was not reported. Ziegelhoffer *et al.* (1979) have observed the phos-

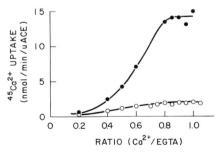

FIG. 10.   The effect of calmodulin on the active transport of calcium across the plasma membrane. Inside–out vesicles prepared from human erythrocyte show an ATP-dependent uptake of Ca^{2+} as a function of Ca^{2+} concentration. Ca^{2+}/EGTA buffers (final concentration EGTA 1 mM) were used to vary free Ca^{2+} concentration and Ca^{2+} uptake into inside–out vesicles in the presence (o) and absence (o) of calmodulin. (From Waisman *et al.*, 1980.)

phorylation and activation of the heart sarcolemmal Ca²⁺ pump by the cAMP-dependent protein kinase. Together these results suggest that the plasmalemmal Ca^{2+} pump may represent a target for both cAMP and calcium-dependent protein kinase.

LePeuch *et al.* (1980) have examined the possible role of calmodulin and cAMP in the regulation of the cardiac sarcoplasmic reticulum Ca^{2+} transport. They have shown that the regulatory protein of the Ca^{2+} pump, phospholamban, is phosphorylated at different sites by a calmodulin-stimulated protein kinase and the cAMP-dependent protein kinase. Calmodulin-dependent phosphorylation is capable of activating sarcoplasmic Ca^{2+} uptake. The cAMP-dependent phosphorylation does not activate Ca^{2+} uptake in the absence of calmodulin but amplifies the activation brought about by calmodulin-dependent phosphorylation.

The microsomal Ca^{2+} pump may be regulated by hormones. Waltenbaugh and Friedmann (1978) have reported that glucagon increased the Ca^{2+} uptake of liver microsomes. In contrast, insulin was capable of inhibiting Ca^{2+} uptake and blocking the glucagon effect.

The Ca^{2+}-stimulated Mg ATPase of membranous preparations has been generally interpreted to be associated with Ca^{2+} transport (Schatzmann and Vincenzi, 1969). Ca^{2+}/Mg^{2+} ATPase have been demonstrated in a variety of tissues including the microsomes of brain (Saermark and Vilhardt, 1979), liver (Waltenbaugh and Friedmann, 1978), adipose (Bruns *et al.*, 1977), and kidney (Moore and Landon, 1979), as well as the plasma membrane of red blood cell (Schatzmann and Vincenzi, 1969), heart (Ziegelhoffer *et al.*, 1979), kidney (Moore *et al.*, 1974), pancreas (Lambert and Christophe, 1978), adipocyte (Pershadsingh and McDonald, 1979), and synaptosomes (Ohashi *et al.*, 1970). It would, therefore, appear that the microsomal and plasmalemma Ca^{2+} pump are a common feature of most cells. If these pumps are regulated by similar mechanisms as the red blood cell plasmalemma and the cardiac microsomal pump, then it is reasonable to suggest that (a) calmodulin acts as a cytosolic Ca^{2+} sensor which activates the Ca^{2+} pumps and terminates the Ca^{2+} second message, (b) hormones that act to stimulate or inhibit the Ca^{2+} pumps (e.g., via cAMP) could alter the duration of the Ca^{2+} message, stimulation of the Ca^{2+} pumps would shorten the duration of the message, inhibition of the pumps would lengthen it.

d. Protein Kinases.   The potential involvement of Ca^{2+} in membrane function has been suggested by the work of Schulman and Greengard (1978) who have reported the existence of a Ca^{2+}-and-calmodulin-stimulated protein kinase in the particulate fraction (105,000 g pellet) of a number of tissues including spleen, skeletal muscle, heart, vas deferens, adrenals, and lung. Interestingly, a comparison of the phosphoproteins by SDS gel electrophoresis has revealed a dissimilar pattern of phospho-protein bands for each tissue examined. This result suggests that tissue specific regulatory effects of the calmodulin stimulated protein kinase may be partly achieved by the varied tissue distribution of the substrates for this kinase. Carstens and Willer (1979) have reported a similar multifunctional protein kinase that is activated by cAMP in the membranes of a variety of tissues.

An example of the role of the calmodulin-stimulated protein kinase in the regulation of membrane function has been revealed from the studies of brain synaptosomes (functionally intact pinched off nerve endings). DeLorenzo and Freedman (1977a,b) first suggested that the molecular mechanisms mediating the effects of Ca^{2+} on neurotransmitter release could involve the action of Ca^{2+}-dependent synaptic vesicle protein phosphorylation. DeLorenzo and Freedman (1978) have demonstrated a direct correlation between Ca^{2+}-specific synaptosomal phosphorylation and Ca^{2+}-specific transmitter release. The regulation of these events was subsequently shown to be mediated by calmodulin (DeLorenzo *et al.*, 1979). Besides the calmodulin-dependent regulation of synaptosomal membrane phosphorylation and norepinephrine release these investigators have also implicated calmodulin in the release of acetylcholine and dopamine. It is interesting to note that calmodulin-stimulated phosphorylation of synaptosomal membranes produces only two phosphoproteins of molecular weight 80,000 and 86,000 (Krueger *et al.*, 1977) which are found only in nerve tissues (Sieghart *et al.*, 1979). Sieghart *et al.* (1979) also report that these phosphoproteins can be phosphorylated at different sites by cAMP and Ca^{2+}-dependent protein kinase. These results suggest the involvement of both cAMP and Ca^{2+} in the regulation of neurotransmitter release.

Garrison *et al.* (1979) have reported that angiotensin II and vasopressin stimulate the phosphorylation of 10 to 12 soluble hepatic proteins by a mechanism that requires Ca^{2+} and is independent of changes in cAMP or the activity of the cAMP-dependent protein kinase. The proteins whose phosphorylation is stimulated by this mechanism have molecular weights that are identical with those whose phosphorylation is increased by glucagon through an activation of the cAMP-dependent protein kinase (a mechanism which is not dependent on the presence of extracellular Ca^{2+}) or by catecholamines via the α-adrenergic cAMP-independent mechanism. The results suggest that the activity of many soluble proteins may be regulated by a common biochemical mechanism involving Ca^{2+} and cAMP-dependent protein phosphorylation.

e. Phosphorylase b Kinase.   Phosphorylase *b* kinase has been shown to contain three types of subunits termed α, β, γ_4 (Cohen, 1973).

The enzyme can be activated covalently or allosterically. The covalent activation involves phosphorylation of the enzyme, a process which is catalyzed by four different kinases; they are the cAMP-dependent protein kinase (Walsh *et al.*, 1971), cGMP-dependent protein kinase (Khoo *et al.*, 1977), a Ca^{2+}-protease-activated protein kinase (Kishimoto *et al.*, 1977), and phosphorylase kinase itself (Walsh *et al.*, 1971).

Alternately phosphorylase kinase can be regulated allosterically by Ca^{2+} (Fig. 11). Meyer *et al.* (1964) were the first to report that calcium ion is an absolute requirement for phosphorylase kinase activity. Brostrom *et al.* (1971) have examined the Ca^{2+} requirement of the nonactivated (unphosphorylated) and activated (phosphorylated) enzyme. They have concluded that covalent activation of the enzyme results in a decrease in the apparent K_m (Ca^{2+}) of the enzyme from 3 μM (nonactivated) to 0.5 μM (activated). Kilimann and Heilmeyer (1977) have examined the Ca^{2+} binding properties of nonactivated phosphorylase kinase. They reported that phosphorylase kinase binds 8 mol Ca^{2+}/mol enzyme, K_{diss} 0.55 μM. In the presence of 20 mM Mg^{2+} two classes of Ca^{2+} binding sites are present: a high-affinity class of 8 mol/mol enzyme (K_{diss} 3 μM) and a low-affinity class of 4 mol (K_{diss} 35 μM).

The involvement of calmodulin in the regulation of phosphorylase kinase by Ca^{2+} has been reported by several groups (Cohen *et al.*, 1978; Wang and Waisman, 1979; DePaoli-Roach *et al.*, 1979). The allosteric activation of phosphorylase kinase by calmodulin involves two distinct mechanisms. As shown in Fig. 12 the addition of exogenous calmodulin results in threefold activation of phosphorylase kinase compared to the

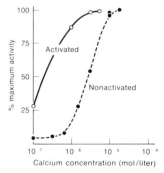

Fig. 11. Calcium sensitivity of the phosphorylated (active) and nonphosphorylated forms of phosphorylase kinase. The phosphorylated form of the enzyme shows greater affinity for Ca^{2+} than the nonphosphorylated enzyme. The phosphorylated form has been covalently modified by the action of the cAMP-dependent protein kinase. (See Meyer *et al.*, 1964; Kilimann and Heilmeyer, 1977.)

rate-limiting enzyme in the biosynthesis of serotonin in brain (Grahme-Smith, 1964). Kuhn *et al.* (1978) and Hamon *et al.* (1977) have presented evidence that tryptophan 5-monooxygenase of rat brain extracts is activated by a Ca^{2+}-stimulated protein kinase. Recently, Yamauchi and Fujisawa (1979) have suggested that rat brain tryptophan 5-monooxygenase is controlled by a calmodulin-regulated protein kinase. Characterization of this kinase is presently underway.

The results suggest that Ca^{2+} and calmodulin may be involved in the regulation of neurotransmitter synthesis. Interestingly, not only serotonin synthesis may be regulated by Ca^{2+}. Morgenroth *et al.* (1975) have observed a reversible fourfold increase in tyrosine hydroxylase activity (the rate-limiting enzyme of catecholamine synthesis) in rat brain extracts with an apparent pK_d (Ca^{2+}) of 5.9. Whether calmodulin is involved in the regulation of this enzyme remains to be tested. However, tyrosine hydroxylase has been shown to be allosterically regulated by Ca^{2+} and covalently by cAMP-dependent phosphorylation (Yamauchi and Fujisawa, 1978), and it is likely that this calcium-mediated change in enzyme function is calmodulin mediated.

i. Guanylate Cyclase.   Guanylate cyclase catalyzes the formation of cGMP from GTP. The enzyme has been demonstrated in a variety of tissues and shown to exist in membrane-bound and soluble forms (Hardman and Sutherland, 1969). Since the antibody produced against particulate guanylate cyclase does not cross-react with the soluble enzyme (Garbers, 1978), it is suspected that the particulate form of the enzyme is different from the soluble form. Kinetic studies have also confirmed this distinction (Garbers *et al.*, 1974; Neer and Sukiennik, 1975).

Various agents have been reported to activate guanylate cyclase including nonionic detergents (Ishikawa *et al.*, 1969), azide or hydroxylamine (Deguchi, 1977), hydrogen peroxide (White *et al.*, 1976), and free fatty acids (Wallach and Pastan, 1976). However, muscarinic agents, which are known to increase cGMP levels in tissues (Goldberg *et al.*, 1973), cannot activate either cell-free preparations of guanylate cyclase or purified enzyme preparation (White and Aurbach, 1969).

Nagao *et al.* (1979) have reported the activation of particulate-bound guanylate cyclase by a Ca^{2+} binding protein in the protozoan *Tetrahymena pyriformis*. In particular, it was shown that the Ca^{2+} binding protein enhanced about 20-fold the activity of the particulate guanylate cyclase. The enzyme activation was Ca^{2+} dependent and reversible. The apparent K_m (Ca^{2+}) of activation was 8 μM. The calcium binding activation protein has been isolated from *Tetrahymena* by Suzuki *et al.* (1979). Preliminary results suggest that this protein is calmodulin. The report of other Ca^{2+}-dependent guanylate cyclase in rat adipocyte plasma membrane (Levilliers *et al.*, 1978) and fibroblast membranes (Wallach and

Pastan, 1976) raises the possibility that vertebrate particulate guanylate cyclase may be also regulated by Ca^{2+} and calmodulin.

j. Microtubule Assembly.   Tubulin, the subunit protein of micro-tubules is a heterodimer composed of two polypeptide chains (α and β) of 55,000 molecular weight each. It has been demonstrated to exist in the cytosol as well as to be associated with membranous structures such as presynaptic membranes (Kornguth and Sunderland, 1975). Cytoplasmic microtubules may play a role in the intracellular transport of the secretory granules toward the cell apex during protein secretion (Rossignol *et al.*, 1977). Together with the microfilaments framed from actin, microtubules comprise the cytoskeleton and are thought to be essential for cell motility and mitosis.

A role for Ca^{2+} in the regulation of microtubule assembly was first suggested by Olmsted and Borisy (1973) who demonstrated the *in vitro* in-hibition of microtubule polymerization by Ca^{2+}. Later, Salmon and Jenkins (1977) reported the stimulation of *in vitro* depolymerization of microtubules by Ca^{2+}. Nishida and Sakai (1977) reported that porcine brain extracts contain a factor that is capable of confering Ca^{2+} sensitivity to the microtubule assembly process. In the presence of this factor micro-molar levels of Ca^{2+} were required to inhibit microtubule assembly or promote microtubule disassembly. Marcum *et al.* (1978) identified calmodulin as the factor which conferred Ca^{2+} sensitivity to microtubule assembly. They found that 10 μM Ca^{2+} and an eightfold molar excess of calmodulin over tubulin was required to completely inhibit microtubule assembly. Nishida *et al.* (1979) and Kumagai and Nishida (1979) have ex-amined the involvement of calmodulin in microtubule assembly–disas-sembly. At physiological ionic strength a calcium concentration of 1 μM was found to be necessary to completely inhibit microtubule assembly. Under these conditions a ratio of calmodulin/tubulin of 1.5/1.0 was reported. Furthermore, a Ca^{2+}-dependent binding of calmodulin to tubulin dimer was reported. It was therefore concluded that the Ca^{2+}-dependent binding of calmodulin to tubulin was the event responsible for inhibition of polymerization or promotion of depolymerization.

The physiological significance of calmodulin regulated microtubule assembly–disassembly has been investigated by comparing the cellular distribution of fluorescent antibodies to calmodulin and tubulin during mitosis (Andersen *et al.*, 1978; Welsh *et al.*, 1978, 1979). Parallel studies with tubulin and calmodulin antibodies show that calmodulin does not accompany all microtubular profiles during mitosis, but appears to be localized in specific areas of the mitotic apparatus which demonstrate microtubule fluorescence. For instance, at metaphase tubulin antibodies decorate the complete spindle and show bundles passing from spindle poles to chromosomes, and also transversing the metaphase plate, whereas calmodulin is concentrated near the spindle poles with strands projecting to the chromosomes. Since the spindle poles are thought to act as nucleating sites for microtubule assembly–disassembly, it is possible that calmodulin is restricted to these areas because these are the regulatory sites of microtubule assembly–disassembly.

k. NAD Kinase. NAD kinase is a regulatory enzyme in higher plants which catalyzes the conversion of NAD to NADP, and is, therefore, important in the regulation of the relative concentrations of NAD and NADP.

Oh-Hama and Miyachi (1960) have reported that illumination of either intact or sonicated plant cells results in an increased conversion of NAD to NADP and suggested that NAD kinase might be controlled by phytochromes. Muto and Miyachi (1977) discovered the dependence of partially purified NAD kinase activity on an endogenous heat-stable activator protein. This heat-stable activator protein was identified by Anderson and Cormier (1978) to be calmodulin.

The discovery of calmodulin-regulated NAD kinase in plants suggest that Ca^{2+} may play a role in certain phytochemical reactions and raised the possibility that Ca^{2+} may serve an important second messenger function in the intermediary metabolism of plants.

l. Calmodulin Binding Proteins. Recently two proteins capable of Ca^{2+}-dependent and reversible interaction with calmodulin have been identified in bovine brain. These proteins have been called the modulator binding protein (MBP) I and II, according to the nomenclature of Wang and Waisman (1979). As yet no catalytic function has been reported for these proteins, and their physiological function remains a mystery.

Among the known soluble calmodulin-regulated proteins in bovine brain modulator binding protein I is by far the most abundant. On a molar basis it is at least 10-fold greater in concentration than any of the other known calmodulin regulated proteins. This protein which was originally discovered by Wang and Desai (1976) is composed of two subunits, α (60,000) and β (14,500). The subunit structure is suggested to be $\alpha(\beta)_2$ (85,000) (Sharma *et al.*, 1979). Of the two subunits only the α subunit has been shown to bind calmodulin (Sharma *et al.*, 1979)

MBP-II was originally discovered by Sharma *et al.* (1978) and a heart stable protein of MW 70,000 which was capable of Ca^{2+}-dependent and reversible interaction with calmodulin. Although on a molar basis this protein is present in brain tissue at approximately 1/200 the amount of MBPI it appears to bind calmodulin more tightly than MBP-I; in fact, the specific activity of MBP-II is about 20-fold higher than MBP-I (Sharma *et al.*, 1979).

The function of neither of these proteins is presently known. They may represent response elements the nature of which remains to be identified, or they may, in fact, play a role in modulating the function of calmodulin as their names imply.

V. INTERRELATIONSHIPS BETWEEN CALCIUM AND CYCLIC NUCLEOTIDES IN STIMULUS–RESPONSE COUPLING

The original concepts that calcium ion was the coupling factor between excitation and response in excitable tissues; and that cAMP is *the* second messenger in peptide and amino hormone action are incorrect. Stimulus–response coupling in nearly all animal cells involves the interrelated actions of calcium and cAMP. This nucleotide is just as important a second messenger in the nervous as in the endocrine systems. Equally, calcium serves to couple not only stimulus to contraction, but also to secretion and metabolism. The central facts that have emerged in the past decade point clearly to the conclusion that in nearly all cells, a true understanding of the complexities of stimulus–response coupling requires an understanding of the messenger roles of both cAMP and calcium, and in particular the way in which these two messenger systems interact (Berridge *et al.*, 1975; Rasmussen and Goodman, 1977).

At this point in our discussion, the nature and complexities of these interactions will be summarized so that the reader appreciates the full extent of their interrelatedness. Specific aspects of their interactions will be discussed in more detail in the later sections of this chapter dealing with stimulus–response coupling in specific cellular systems.

The various interrelationships between these two messengers are summarized in Table IV. There are in general three general themes in these relationships (1) calcium regulates cAMP metabolism thereby controlling the cytosolic [cAMP] increases or decreases; (2) cAMP regulates calcium metabolism extending or restricting the calcium domain; and (3) the two messengers act either coordinately and/or sequentially to control eventual cellular response.

The specific types of controls of calcium metabolism by cAMP and of cAMP metabolism by calcium in any particular cell type define the relationship between these two messengers within a given cell. In some cells a rise in [Ca^{2+}] leads to a rise and in other a fall in [cAMP], and in still others a biphasic response depending on the magnitude of the change in [Ca^{2+}]. The converse is also true.

The ways in which these two messengers control cellular response are

TABLE IV

INTERRELATIONSHIPS BETWEEN CALCIUM AND cAMP IN CELLULAR CONTROL SYSTEMS

I.   Control of cAMP metabolism or action by calcium ion
   A. Increase phosphodiesterase activity
   B. Increase adenylate cyclase activity
   C. Decrease adenylate cyclase activity
   D. Alter sensitivity of cAMP-dependent activation of phosphodiesterase
II. Control of calcium metabolism or action by cAMP
   A. Increase uptake by ER
   B. Increased activity of plasma membrane pump
   C. Increased permeability of plasma membrane
   D. Decreased permeability of plasma membrane
   E. Increased efflux from cells
   F. Altered mitochondrial calcium exchange
   G. Alter sensitivity of calcium receptor protein
   H. Alter binding of calmodulin to plasma membrane
III. A. Sequential control
   B. Coordinate control
   C. Independent control
   D. Redundant control

also diverse. In some systems they exert sequential control of successive steps in an enzyme pathway, e.g., glycogenolysis. In others, coordinate control of two components of the response element, e.g., the control of a K^+ pump by cAMP and of Cl^- permeability of the luminal membrane by Ca^{2+} in the fly salivary gland. In others apparently control of the response involves only the single messenger system, e.g., calcium alone couples excitation to response in skeletal muscle. Finally, in some cells, a single response, and the various response elements involved in it, is regulated independently by the two separate messenger systems so as to provide a redundancy of control, e.g., the hormonal regulaton of hepatic glycogenolysis and gluconeogenesis. The properties of some of these systems will be discussed more fully in succeeding sections.

VI. CALCIUM AS MESSENGER IN SPECIFIC SYSTEMS

Having considered various aspects of cellular calcium metabolism and the properties of the calcium signalling system, it is now possible to consider the coupling or messenger function in a number of specific systems. In doing so only a few of a large number of systems have been chosen for analysis. Each one chosen was selected because it exemplifies some variation on the universal theme: stimulus–response coupling in nearly all excitable as well as nonexcitable tissues involves the coordinate participation of both the calcium and cAMP messenger systems.

A. Steroid Hormone Production in the Adrenal Cortex

Shortly after Rall *et al.* (1957) discovered the role of cAMP in the control of hepatic glycogenolysis, Haynes and Berthet (1957) found that cAMP was involved in the ACTH-mediated increase in adrenal steroid hormone production. Originally, Haynes (1958) proposed that the mechanism by which cAMP mediated the increase in steroid hormone production was by enhancing glycogen breakdown which by increasing the concentration of glucose 6-phosphate increased the flux of carbon through the hexose monophosphate shunt thereby increasing the supply of NADPH for steroid hormone synthesis. However, work since then has shown that ACTH has multiple effects upon adrenal cell function (Garren *et al.*, 1971; Mahaffee *et al.*, 1974; Robison *et al.*, 1971) including (1) increased glycogen phospholysis; (2) increased cholesterol synthesis; (3) increased cholesterol ester hydrolysis; (4) increased cholesterol uptake; (5) increased rate of cholesterol synthesis from cytosol to mitochondria; (6) a decrease in ascorbic acid content; (7) an activation of the hexose monophosphate shunt; and (8) an increase in the intramitochondrial conversion of cholesterol to pregnenolone. There is now a nearly universal consensus that the rate-limiting step in steroid hormone biosynthesis is the intramitochondrial conversion of cholesterol to pregnenolone (Stone and Hechter, 1954; Karaboyas and Koritz, 1965; Hall, 1966; Garren *et al.*, 1965). The precise mechanism by which it is controlled is not known and will not be discussed because our major focus in this brief discussion is upon the messengers involved in ACTH action.

Following the lead of Haynes (1958), a number of workers have investigated the second messenger function of cAMP in ACTH action (Grahame-Smith *et al.*, 1967; Hayashi *et al.*, 1979; Robison *et al.*, 1971). This system was found to meet all the criteria established by Sutherland and co-workers (1) ACTH addition causes an increase in cAMP content in the intact tissue; (2) a particulate cyclase that is activated by ACTH is present; (3) inhibitors of phosphodiesterase enhance the effect of ACTH; (4) exogenous cAMP or dibutyryl cAMP stimulate hormone synthesis and release; and (5) there is a cAMP-dependent protein kinase in this tissue which becomes catalytically active after ACTH addition. From these observations it has been concluded that ACTH mediates steroid hormone production via the second messenger cAMP, i.e., this systems represent a classic example of the second messenger model of horomone action. There are, however, considerable data indicating that the system is more complex than this, and that calcium ions also play an important messenger role in this tissue. Also, in the case of the messenger function of cAMP a problem existed: the problem of a lack of correlation between cAMP production and steroidogenesis (Beall and Sayers, 1972; Nakamura *et al.*, 1972; Moyle *et al.*, 1973; Perchellet *et al.*, 1978; Saez *et al.*, 1978; Mackie *et al.*, 1977; Bowyer and Kitabchi, 1974; Honn and Chavin, 1977; Sharma *et al.*, 1976).

A plot of steroid production by and change in cAMP content of adrenal steroid tissue versus the concentration of ACTH in the medium (Fig. 13) illustrates the problem. The peptide hormone stimulates steroidogenesis at lower concentrations than those needed to stimulate cAMP production. For example, at an ACTH concentration sufficient to stimulate steroid production to approximately one-third the maximal rate, there is no detectable rise in cAMP content, and when steroid hormone production is near maximal the rise in cAMP is less than 10% of the maximal possible rise. In the original studies of ACTH binding to this tissue, it was found that hormone binding correlated with changes in cAMP concentration and not with changes in rate of steroidogenesis. From these findings arose the concept of spare receptors. This explanation of the discrepancy

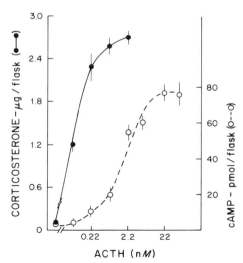

Fig. 13. A plot of corticosteroid production (•——•) and cAMP concentration (o——o) as a function of ACTH concentration in isolated adrenal tissue. (Replotted from Moyle *et al.*, 1973.)

between tissue response and second messenger production was that the cell was endowed with a large number of spare receptors hence only a very small proportion of the total receptors had to be occupied in order to obtain a maximal physiological response. However, the utility of this type of organizational arrangement is not clear. Furthermore, Moyle *et al.* (1973) found that the *o*-nitrophenyl sulfenyl derivative of ACTH induced a significant stimulation of steroid hormone production but a barely detectable increase in tissue cAMP content even at very high concentration. So with this hormone analog, an even greater discrepancy between steroid production and tissue [cAMP] was seen.

These observations have led to a re-evaluation of the mechanism of ACTH action. Recent studies have established the fact that rather than a single set of receptors, this tissue possesses two sets of receptors; one of high affinity and low capacity, and the other of lower affinity but high capacity (Lefkowitz *et al.*, 1971; Wolfsen *et al.*, 1972; McIlhinney and Schulster, 1975; Yanagibashi *et al.*, 1978). The range of concentration of ACTH over which binding to the high-affinity sites is similar to the range over which binding to the high-affinity sites is similar to the range over which steroid hormone production is activated, and the range over which binding to the lower affinity sites is similar to the range over which adenylate cyclase is activated. These data suggest that the high-affinity receptors are coupled to hormone production by a second messenger other than cAMP. A considerable mass of recent data indicate that this second messenger is calcium ion (Birmingham *et al.*, 1953; Farese, 1971a,b; Farese and Prudente, 1977; Yanagibashi, 1979; Haksar and Peron, 1972; Jaanus *et al.*, 1970). Thus, in this tissue there appear to be separate receptors possessing differing affinities for the same extracellular messenger; one coupled to the calcium and the other to the cAMP signaling system (Fig. 14).

At present one can only speculate on the purpose of, or need for such a hierarchical control system. Perhaps of first consideration is the misplaced bias that peptide hormone such as ACTH have only a single physiological effect on adrenal cells, i.e., that of stimulating hormone release. This is not so. Chronic exposure of the gland to this hormone leads to three important changes: hypertrophy, hyperplasia, and an increased capacity to produce steroids. Hence, a complex signaling signal of the type found is central both to the immediate and long-term effects of the trophic hormone. Most biochemical studies have focused only on the short-term response, and philosophic discussions of the relationship of messenger function to response have largely ignored the equally important long-term response.

The precise mechanism by which calcium mediates the increase in

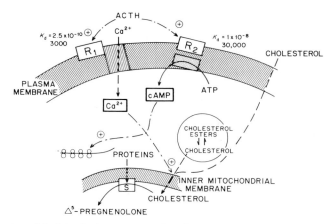

Fig. 14. A model of the dual messenger roles of calcium and cAMP in the action of ACTH upon the adrenal cortex.

steroid hormone production is not known. It may exert a variety of direct effects via calmodulin, or its effects may be indirect and be mediated largly by cGMP. The latter possibility is raised by the studies of Perchellet, Sharma, and their collaborators (Sharma *et al.*, 1976; Perchellet *et al.*, 1978; Perchellet and Sharma, 1979; Sharma and Sawhney, 1978), who in confirmation of others found that the effect of ACTH upon steroidogenesis is directly dependent upon the calcium ion content of the extracellular medium. However, they further showed that ACTH induces an increase in cGMP concentration; that the effect of ACTH upon cGMP production depends upon the extracellular calcium ion concentration; and that exogenous cGMP or dibutryl cGMP will induce steroidogenesis. From these data they were led to propose that the major means by which calcium regulated steroid hormone production was by controlling the activity of guanylate cyclase. On the other hand, their own data clearly show that the effects of exogenous cGMP are dependent on the extracellular calcium ion concentration so that it seems likely that calcium controls intracellular events at several different sites. Furthermore, Hayashi *et al.* (1979) report that the cGMP accumulates largely if not entirely in the extracellular space.

Up to this point, only the response of the zona fasiculata to ACTH has been considered. There is another important zone of the adrenal cortex, the zona glomerulosa, which differs from the fasiculata. Most crucial are that the fasiculata synthesizes corticosteroids, the glomerulosa aldosterone, and that ACTH regulates steroid synthesis in both zones, but additional extracellular messengers, angiotensin and K^+, also regulate aldosterone production in the glomerulosa (Davis, 1961; Ganong *et al.*, 1966; Aguilera and Catt, 1978; Muller, 1971; Rosenkrantz, 1959; Saruta *et al.*, 1972; Kaplan, 1965; Boyd *et al.*, 1973; Mackie *et al.*, 1977; Douglas *et al.*, 1978; Fredlund *et al.*, 1977; Fujita *et al.*, 1979; Foster *et al.*, 1979; Fakunding, 1979; Peach, 1977; Tait and Tait, 1976; Williams and Dluhy, 1972). In the zona glomerulosa, angiotensin and K^+ seem to operate via a similar messenger system that differs from the one utilized by ACTH.

If we first consider ACTH, the evidence presently available shows that ACTH stimulates cAMP synthesis. The effect of ACTH on cAMP production is correlated with its effect on steroid hormone secretion. However, removal of extracellular calcium reduces both the ACTH-mediated rise in cAMP and in aldosterone production. Also, the increase in steroid hormone production induced by choleragen, which induces a calcium-independent increase in cAMP, is blunted in the absence of extracellular calcium. Hence, in the case of ACTH a major second messenger appears to be cAMP but both its ACTH-induced synthesis and final expression of its intracellular effects are calcium dependent.

Studies of the messenger system involved in the actions of K^+ and angiotensin have led to the conclusion that neither agonist stimulates the production of cAMP. On the other hand, the effect of both agonists is critically dependent upon the extracellular calcium ion concentration. In the absence of extracellular calcium neither agent stimulates aldosterone secretion even though the absence of Ca^{2+} does not alter the binding of angiotensin to its receptor. Furthermore, the divalent cation ionophore, A23187, mimics the effect of angiotension upon aldosterone biosynthesis. These results are consistent with the hypothesis that a rise in the extracellular K^+ or angiotensin II concentration causes an increase in calcium influx across the plasma membrane of the cell leading to a rise in the cytosolic calcium ion concentration sufficient to stimulate steroid hormone production. The intracellular site of action of Ca^{2+} is not known, but a major site is presumed to be the intramitochondrial conversion of cholesterol to pregnenelone.

In the zona glomerulosa, plasticity of control of aldosterone secretion appears to be achieved by a hierarchical control system in which different extracellular messengers regulate the activity of the cAMP and calcium messengers systems independently. Yet even in this case the expression of the ultimate cAMP effect is calcium dependent. No critical evaluation of the alternate possibility, i.e., the ultimate effect of Ca^{2+} is cAMP dependent, has been carried out.

B. INSULIN SECRETION

The control of insulin secretion from the beta cells of the islets of Langerhans is achieved by a variation of the type of hierarchical control seen in the adrenal cortex. In this variation separate extracellular messengers control the two separate intracellular signaling systems, and these two intracellular signals operate in a strict hierarchical sense. In addition, the calcium signal is generated by a change in the concentration of some intracellular metabolite rather than being directly coupled to a surface receptor for the extracellular messenger.

The control of insulin secretion has been more thoroughly studied than the control of secretion of any other peptide hormone (Grill and Cerasi, 1973; Grodsky, 1970, 1972; Grodsky and Bennett, 1966; Hales and Milner, 1968; Hellman, 1975; Henquin and Lambert, 1974; Kuo *et al.*, 1973; Malaisse *et al.*, 1973, 1974, 1978a,b, 1979c; Malaisse-Lagae and Malaisse, 1971; Matschinsky and Ellerman, 1973; Matschinsky *et al.*, 1971; Matthews, 1970, 1975; Gerich *et al.*, 1976; Lambert, 1976; Montague, 1977; Curry *et al.*, 1968; Floyd *et al.*, 1966; Grodsky *et al.*, 1967; Matthews and Sakamoto, 1975; Milner and Hales, 1968; Malaisse, 1973; Malaisse *et al.*, 1978a,b,c,d; Montague *et al.*, 1976; Unger, 1967; Howell *et al.*, 1975; Täljedal, 1978; Charles *et al.*, 1975; Sehlin and Täljedal, 1975; Sugden *et al.*, 1979; Valverde *et al.*, 1979a; Karl *et al.*, 1975; Brisson *et al.*, 1977; Brisson and Malaisse, 1973; Dean and Matthews, 1970a,b, 1972; Montague and Cook, 1971; Montague and Howell, 1973; Sharp *et al.*, 1975). Two types of control have been recognized: short-term minute-to-minute control determined by the fluctuations in the concentrations of extracellular metabolites and hormones; and long-term changes determined by dietary or physiological status of the organism.

Studies of the short-term control have defined three types of extracellular signals (Table V). The first has been called primary signals or initiators of the second secondary signals or potentiators and the third inhibitors of insulin secretion. In defining any of these, a key point is that all known physiological stimuli requires the presence of extracellular calcium and the normal metabolism of glucose in order to stimulate insulin release. The distinction between primary and secondary stimulators is that none of the agents shown to be secondary stimulators will stimulate insulin release from islets incubated in a solution lacking a primary stimulator. In most instances this has meant glucose. Thus, glucagon enhances the rate of insulin secretion at any fixed, submaximal concentration of extracellular glucose, but does not stimulate insulin

TABLE V
REGULATORS OF INSULIN SECRETION

A. Primary signals or initiators
   1. Glucose
   2. Mannose
   3. Glyceraldehyde
   4. Leucine
   5. Arginine
   6. Sulfonylurea
B. Secondary signals or potentiators
   1. Glucagon
   2. Secretin
   3. ACTH
   4. Pancreozymin
   5. Theophylline
   6. Cholera toxin
C. Inhibitors
   1. Verapramil
   2. Imidazole
   3. Epinephrine
   4. Mannoheptulose
   5. Iodoacetamide
   6. Menadione
   7. Somatostatin
   8. Phenothiazines

release if glucose is absent. As will be developed in the ensuing discussion, this physiological distinction between initiators and potentiators of insulin release has its messenger system counterpart. Initiators alter primarily cellular calcium metabolism. Potentiators primarily cAMP metabolism.

In addition to these two classes of stimulators a group of agents have been identified which act as inhibitors of insulin secretion (Table V). These agents can be shown to alter the metabolism of either calcium, cAMP or glucose, or to change the redox state of the cell membrane.

In the absence of extracellular glucose, the intact beta cell releases little insulin. As the glucose concentration is raised from 2.7 to 27.7 mM, there is a dose-dependent increase in insulin secretion. The steepest portion of this dose-response curve is between 4 and 10 mM glucose which is the normal physiological range of plasma glucose concentration. Although there are reports that under some circumstances, glucose addition to isolated or perfused islets causes an increase in intracellular cAMP concentration, the general consensus is that at physiological concentrations of glucose and extracellular calcium ion there is little or no increase in cAMP content of the islet cells. The major effects of physiological concentrations of glucose are upon ion fluxes across the plasma membrane of the cell. It induces an increase in Ca^{2+} influx and a decrease in both K^+ and Ca^{2+} efflux, and has a slight effect on Na^+ fluxes.

The elegant studies of Matthews (1975) and colleagues (Dean and Matthews, 1970a,b) have demonstrated that the addition of glucose to pancreatic islet cells causes a slight depolarization of the membrane, but also a train of spike or action potentials. There is a dose-dependent increase in the number of cells exhibiting action potentials as the glucose concentration is raised from 3 and 12 mM, i.e., the same range over which there is a glucose-dependent increase in insulin release. Exploration of the characteristics of these current pulses showed that (1) they were enhanced by a hyperpolarizing current induced by intracellular current injection, and reduced by depolarizing current; (2) current injection evoked a spike potential in the absence of glucose, but not in the absence of extracellular calcium (i.e., these cells are electrically excitable); (3) low extracellular calcium or addition of D-600 (a calcium channel blocker) abolished the spike potentials; (4) low extracellular Na^+ concentration or tetrodotoxin (a sodium channel blocker) enhanced the spike potentials; and (5) inhibitors of glucose metabolism prevent glucose-induced action potentials. These data indicate that beta cells exhibit the other characteristic of an excitable tissue, regenerative action potential, i.e., a cycle of depolarization followed by repolarizaiton.

From these data Matthews (1975) concluded that the spike potentials were primarily calcium currents. He proposed a model to account for these currents and their regenerative nature. In this model, the primary effect of glucose (exerted via one of its metabolites—see below) is to decrease K^+ efflux leading to a depolarization of the plasma membrane sufficient to lower the threshold of a voltage-dependent calcium ion channel and lead thereby to an increase in calcium entry into the cell. The rise in calcium ion content on the inside surface of the cell membrane would in turn increase the K^+ permeability of the plasma membrane and act to repolarize the membrane, and close the voltage-dependent calcium channel. Studies by a number of other investigators provide considerable direct support for this hypothesis (Sehlin and Taljedal, 1975; Malaisse *et al.*, 1978a; Valverde *et al.*, 1979a,b; Henquin and Lambert, 1974).

There is a considerable amount of data obtained by a variety of experimental techniques and under a host of different experimental conditions all of which support the concept that the primary signal generated when glucose acts upon the beta cell is a rise in the calcium ion content of the cell cytosol or at least some domain of this cellular compartment. A summary of the salient facts supporting this conclusion is shown in Table VI.

In addition to the data from electrophysiological studies of islet cell calcium metabolism has been analyzed using isotopic techniques. Glucose addition to incubated islets has been shown to have two effects upon cellular calcium exchange. It stimulates net calcium accumulation and inhibits calcium efflux. The magnitude of the calcium accumulation is a function of both the glucose and external calcium ion concentration. Furthermore, the extent of calcium accumulation correlates with the magnitude of the insulin released.

Studies of the effects of the calcium channel blockers, Verapramil and D-600 or cobalt on insulin release and calcium uptake also support the view that calcium is the messenger. Verpramil, D-600 or Co^{2+}, block the electrical excitability (i.e., glucose-induced spike potentials), calcium accumulation, and insulin release. Their inhibitory actions can be reversed

TABLE VI

EVIDENCE THAT CALCIUM ION IS PRIMARY MESSENGER IN GLUCOSE-INDUCED
INSULIN RELEASE

1. Glucose effect depends upon external calcium
2. At a fixed external glucose concentration the rate of insulin secretion is a function of the external calcium concentration
3. Glucose stimulates calcium uptake into and calcium efflux from beta cells
4. Glucose induces membrane depolarization and regenerative calcium currents across beta cell plasma membrane
5. Correlation between calcium current intensity and rate of insulin release
6. Depolarization by high external K^+ induces calcium uptake and insulin release
7. Depolarization by vertridine and Na^+ induces calcium uptake and insulin release
8. Calcium ionophore A23187 stimulates calcium uptake and insulin release
9. Agents that block the voltage-dependent calcium channel (Verapramil, D-600, cobalt) block calcium uptake and insulin release
10. When physiological concentrations of extracellular calcium and glucose are employed, glucose does not cause an increase in the cAMP content of the beta cell
11. There is a high concentration of the calcium receptor protein, calmodulin, in beta cells
12. Under pharmacological conditions insulin secretion can be stimulated without an evident increase in the uptake of calcium by the beta cell, but in all of these conditions there is evidence for a mobilization of calcium from an intracellular pool
13. The amount of calcium normally taken up by the glucose-stimulated cell is sufficient to increase the calcium ion content of the cytosol into the calcium control range
14. Other primary initiators of insulin secretion stimulate calcium uptake
15. Close structural analogs of glucose that do not stimulate insulin release do not stimulate calcium currents or uptake

by increasing the extracellular calcium ion concentration. Conversely, addition of the calcium ionophore A23187 leads to a nonglucose-dependent influx of calcium into the islet cell and a calcium-dependent release of insulin. Finally, as noted above (Table V) the phenothiazines have been shown to inhibit insulin release. Weiss and Putney (1978) have shown that a major site of action of this class of compounds is inhibition of calmodulin-mediated activities.

Even though the data in support of the calcium hypothesis, there is still the question of the role of cAMP as a second messenger in the glucose-dependent control of insulin secretion. The question is whether or not under usual physiological circumstances the concentration of cAMP increases in islets after glucose addition. The answer is that this does not usually occur. However, there are several experimental results of interest. First, under some near-physiological conditions, a glucose-dependent rise in the cAMP content is seen. Second, this rise depends upon the presence of extracellular calcium ion. Third, a similar calcium-dependent rise in cAMP content is seen after addition of the ionophore A23187. Fourth, it has been found that calcium stimulates a calmodulin-mediated activation of a particular adenylate cyclase from the islets. Fifth, glucose has never been shown to activate adenylate cyclase directly.

A logical interpretation of the observation that under some circumstances glucose induces a rise in the cAMP content of the beta cell is that such a rise is observed when glucose causes a net influx and/or accumulation of calcium into the cell above some threshold value. If this interpretation is correct, it has an important theoretical implication. It implies that under normal circumstances a small rise in the strength of calcium signal is sufficient to stimulate insulin release without activating adenylate cyclase, although both events take place at the plasma membrane, and both are mediated in all likelihood by calcium interacting with the calcium receptor protein, calmodulin. This must mean that one of two mechanisms operate to dictate a hierarchial sensitivity of final response elements to a single intracellular signal. Either the calmodulin is already bound to the response element and this binding to the element changes the calcium affinity of the calmodulin, or once calcium binds to free calmodulin, the Ca–calmodulin complex has different affinities for different response elements within the cell. In either case, the situation is operationally analogous to the difference in the sensitivity of the phosphorylated and nonphosphorylated forms of phosphorylase *b* kinase to calcium-mediated calmodulin activation.

The final point to be discussed in relation to the regulation of cellular calcium metabolism by glucose concerns the effect of glucose upon calcium efflux from cells. If glucose is added to islets prelabeled with radioactive calcium, a biphasic response ensues: first a decrease in calcium efflux rate is seen followed by a marked increase. However, if insulin secretion is blocked by prior addition of verapamil then only the first phase of the response is seen. These data have been interpreted to mean that the initial decrease in calcium efflux is due to a direct inhibitory action of glucose upon calcium efflux, and the subsequent rise in efflux is due to the release of radio calcium from secretory vesicles during the process of insulin secretion (Malaisse *et al.*, 1978).

The mechanisms by which glucose regulates membrane calcium transport is still a matter of controversy. On the one hand, it has been proposed that glucose interacts directly with a surface receptor to initiate calcium entry; on the other that it first enters the cell and undergoes metabolic transformation before exerting its effects. There is recent evidence in support of both concepts, although to date no direct demonstration of a glucose receptor has been made. In particular, no glucose receptor coupled to an adenylate cyclase has even been described.

The evidence in favor of glucose undergoing metabolic transformation is considerable, and this evidence suggests that the signal for insulin release is generated by a metabolite of glucose at or below the triosephosphate level in the glycolytic sequence. These data are (1) changes in glucose metabolism such as rate of oxidation, rate of lactate production, glucose 6-phosphate concentration show a similar dependence on extracellular glucose concentration as does insulin release; (2) when glucose-induced insulin secretion is inhibited by diazoxide, or epinephrine the metabolites of glucose above the phosphoglyceraldehyde dehydrogenase step accumulate; (3) 0.1 mM iodoacetate as inhibitor of glyceraldehyde phosphate dehydrogenase blocks glucose-induced insulin release; (4) glyceraldehyde is a potent initiator of insulin release; (5) the effect of glyceraldehyde is blocked by epinephrine or the absence of external Ca^{2+}; (6) glyceraldehyde stimulates calcium uptake by islet tissue; and (7) menadione, and other agents that alter the NADH/NAD ratio in the islet cell blocks insulin secretion induced by either glucose or glyceraldehyde but not that induced by ionophore (Malaisse *et al.*, 1978b,c,d, 1979a,b; Sener *et al.*, 1978; Sener and Malaisse, 1979).

When the menadione concentration is increased in the presence of a fixed glucose concentration there is a parallel decrease in the amount of oxidized pyridine nucleotide, the rate of insulin secretion, the rate of rubidium efflux (a measure of K^+ efflux), and in calcium uptake. These effects of menadione were seen with concentrations that did not alter the rate of the glucose utilization, lactate production, or ATP content of the islet. Menadione increased the flux through the pentose shunt pathway, and decreased the cellular content of both NADH and NADPH.

These studies are of considerable interest because they raise the possibility that the NADH dehydrogenase found in the plasma membrane of a variety of cells may exist in the beta cell and may be the means by which the glucose signal is coupled to the changes in cation fluxes (K^+ and Ca^{2+}) that initiate insulin release.

In contrast to glucose, glucagon alone will not stimulate insulin release, but its addition will potentiate the action of a given concentration of glucose. A similar effect is found with phosphodiesterase inhibitors, secretin, pancreozymin, ACTH, and β-adrenergic agonists. All of these agents cause a rise in the cAMP content of the beta cell. Conversely, the drug imidazole which stimulates phosphodiesterase and causes a fall in cAMP content, causes a decrease in the rate of glucose-induced insulin release (Montague, 1977).

These data are consistent with the concept that in the beta cell the calcium and cAMP signals are controlled by different extracellular messengers acting through different surface transducing systems. Furthermore, the two intracellular signals operate in a hierarchial and complementary fashion.

The second messenger cAMP may act in several ways to modify the behavior of the calcium signaling system. There is evidence that it causes the mobilization of calcium from an intracellular pool, possibly the mitochondrial pool (Montague, 1977). In considering the consequences of this effect, it is worth contrasting the situation in the beta cell with that in the fly salivary gland. In the latter case, the initial calcium signal is generated at the baso-lateral cell membrane, but acts on the luminal membrane to alter Cl^- permeability. In that case, a rise in cytosolic cAMP was also found to mobilize calcium from an intracellular (mitochondrial) pool, and this was seen as an essential condition for the transmission of the calcium signal from one cell surface to the other in this polar cell. In the case of the pancreatic beta cell the site of calcium entry across the plasma and its site of action in inducing exocytosis just beneath that membrane do not require the transcellular propagation of the calcium message, hence under some conditions secretion is stimulated by an influx of calcium without an associated rise in cAMP. However, when the cAMP content rises, it leads to a mobilization of intracellular calcium into the cytosol. This has the effect of propagating the calcium signal in both the temporal and spacial domains. In this view, the major effect of cAMP upon insulin release is mediated indirectly through an effect upon cellular calcium metabolism. However, it is probable that cAMP also modifies either the sensitivity of response elements to the calcium signal and/or alters the magnitude of the calcium signal to a given change in extracellular glucose concentration.

At the moment, there is no direct evidence for the first of these suggestions, but this lack of evidence may be due largely to the fact that the final calcium response element(s) has yet to be identified. On the other hand, there is evidence that suggests that cAMP may modify the glucose-induced change in cell membrane function. Before discussing this evidence it is necessary to consider another class of compounds that influence insulin release.

As noted in Table V, a variety of chemically different compounds block glucose-induced insulin release. Some, such as Verapramil do so by blocking calcium entry into the beta cell, others such as imidazole by lowering cAMP concentration, and still others such as mannoheptulose and iodoacetamide by blocking glucose metabolism. The most carefully studied natural hormonal agent known to inhibit insulin release is epinephrine (Montague, 1977). This inhibitory action is mediated through interaction of the catecholamine with an alpha receptor upon the cell surface. A major consequence of this catecholamine–receptor interaction is an inhibition of the adenylate cyclase activity with a resultant fall in the intracellular cAMP concentration. This fall is associated with a decrease in rate of insulin secretion. Data discussed above show that a rise in cAMP concentration causes a mobilization of intracellular calcium which, by extending both the temporal and spacial domains of calcium, can account for the enhanced rate of insulin secretion. If this were the sole effect of cAMP, then a fall in the cAMP content of islets should restrict the domains of calcium by allowing for its more rapid uptake into intracellular storage sites. If so, one would not expect to see a significant change in the immediate effects of glucose upon K^+ and Ca^{2+} transport across the cell membrane. However, this is not the case, prior addition of epinephrine in a dose sufficient to inhibit glucose-induced insulin release also inhibits the initiation of action potentials and the depolarization of the membrane usually seen after glucose addition (Matthews, 1975). These data argue that epinephrine alters the coupling between the glucose–metabolite receptor and the fluxes of K^+ and Ca^{2+} across the plasma membrane. It could do so by one of two mechanisms, either as a direct consequence of hormone–receptor interaction in the membrane, or indirectly via an alteration in the cellular content of cAMP. Experiments designed to distinguish between these two alternatives have not yet been carried out, but there is some evidence from another line of investigation which suggests indirectly that the effect may be mediated indirectly via cAMP. This line is the study of long-term adaptations of the pancreatic islet to altered nutritional or hormonal states (Montague, 1977).

Up to this point, the data that has been reviewed has dealt almost exclusively with the immediate effects of various stimuli on insulin release from islet prepared from fed animals, and involve the nature of the information transfer involved in the minute-to-minute control of insulin secretion. In addition to this type of data, there is data showing that long-term adaptations of the insulin secretory response occurs during starvation or pregnancy. In the former a decreased and in the latter an increased responsiveness is seen (Montague, 1977).

In islets from starved animals, the pattern of response to glucose is similar to that seen in tissues from fed animals treated with agents that lower their cAMP content. This adaptation to starvation can be prevented by intermittent administration of small amounts of glucose to the animals. Also, if islet from starved animals are treated *in vitro* with agents that increase their cAMP content, their response to glucose resembles that of islet from fed animals. These results suggested that the cAMP system plays a role in this long-term adaptation. This suggestion is supported by the observation that the cAMP content of islet from starved animals is lower than that from fed animals, and that this reduction is due to a decrease in adenylate cyclase activity. In contrast, glucose loading of animals leads to an increase in the adenylate cyclase activity and cAMP content of subsequently isolated islets. Thus, the glucose responsiveness of the insulin secretory system correlates directly with the cAMP content of the tissue. The converse is found in the pregnant animal. The response of the beta cell to glucose is enhanced, and these cells have higher cAMP contents and adenylate cyclase activities than comparable cells from nonpregnant littermates.

Given the fact that starvation (a chronic adaptation) and adrenaline administration (a short-term response) both lead to a concomitant fall in tissue content of cAMP and in the magnitude of the insulin secretory response to a standard change in extracellular glucose concentration, it seems likely that their common mechanism is a cAMP-dependent change in the membrane transduction event mediated by glucose and/or its metabolites(s).

The other conclusion from these studies is that either directly or indirectly, the extracellular glucose concentration regulates the adenylate cyclase activity of the islets. The effect appears to be a direct one because it is seen when islets are incubated for 24 hours *in vitro* in the presence of high extracellular glucose concentration. The nature of the signal mediating this long term response of the islet cell to glucose is not known.

C. Skeletal Muscle Glycogenolysis

Nearly all the glycogen in mammalian tissues is found either in liver or skeletal muscle. In the liver glycogenolysis (Section VI,D) provides glucose to maintain blood glucose levels. In muscle glycogenolysis serves

either to provide energy for muscle contraction, or to produce gluconeogenic precursor, pyruvate, lactate, alanine for hepatic gluconeogenesis.
Hormonally, epinephrine stimulates glycogenolysis in both muscle and
liver, but norepinephrine and glucagon stimulate glycogenolysis only in
liver (Robison *et al.*, 1971).

The regulation of glycogenolysis in muscle differ from that in liver. In
contrast to the α-adrenergic Ca^{2+}-dependent stimulation of hepatic glucogenolysis by epinephrine, muscle glucogenolysis is stimulated by epinephrine via an β receptor cAMP-dependent mechanism (reviewed by
Cohen, 1978). In particular epinephrine by interacting with its β receptor on the sarcolemma activates adenylate cyclase. As a result, cytosolic
cAMP levels rise leading in turn to an activation of the cAMP-dependent
protein kinase (Fig. 15). This results in (1) phosphorylation and activation of phosphorylase kinase (Walsh *et al.*, 1971); (2) phosphorylation
and inactivation of glycogen synthase (Soderling *et al.*, 1970); and (3)
phosphorylation and activation of the heat stable inhibitor of protein
phosphatase 1 resulting in the inactivation of this phosphatase (Huang
and Glinsmann, 1976). Activation of glycogen breakdown by epinephrine, therefore, effects two distinct enzymatic mechanisms, on the one
hand protein phosphorylation is turned on such that glycogen synthase
and hence glycogen synthesis is inactivated, while the activation of
phosphorylase kinase and the resultant phosphorylation and activation of
glycogen phosphorylase by this enzyme turns on glycogenolysis. On the
other hand, the protein phosphatase is inactivated, this prevents
dephosphorylation and reversal of protein phosphorylations.

The key regulatory enzyme of muscle glycogenolysis is phosphorylase
kinase and the activation of this enzyme by the cAMP-dependent protein
kinase represents the key step in the stimulation of glycogenolysis by
epinephrine. Phosphorylase kinase also phosphorylates and inactivates
glycogen synthase (Srivastava *et al.*, 1979). Furthermore, phosphorylase
kinase is a Ca^{2+}-dependent enzyme and is totally inactive in the absence
of Ca^{2+} (Meyer *et al.*, 1964). The activation of this enzyme by the cAMP-
dependent protein kinase results in an increase in its affinity for Ca^{2+}
(Fig. 11). The activation of phosphorylase kinase by Ca^{2+} is mediated by
calmodulin (Cohen *et al.*, 1978; Wang and Waisman, 1979).

These results are consistent with the model (Fig. 15) that both cAMP
and Ca^{2+} are required for the activation of glycogenolysis in muscle by
epinephrine. The source of the Ca^{2+} pool that may be involved in the activation of glycogenolysis is uncertain, the sarcoplasmic reticulum is an
unlikely candidate since cAMP and Ca^{2+} have been shown to increase
Ca^{2+} uptake by that organelle, resulting in lowering of cytosolic Ca^{2+}.
Two possibilities remain; epinephrine may promote an influx of Ca^{2+} into

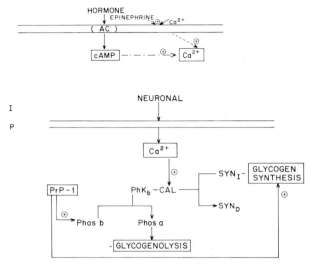

FIG. 15. Neuronal (A) and hormonal (B) activation of skeletal muscle glycogenolysis. The neuronal activation involves calcium as a messenger interacting with the calmodulin (CAL) subunit of phosphorylase b kinase (PhK$_b$) which catalyzes the phosphorylation of phosphorylase b to a (Phos b,a) thereby activating glycogenolysis. PhK$_b$-CAL also catalyzes the phosphorylation of glycogen synthase (SYN$_D$ to SYN$_I$) thereby inhibiting glycogen synthesis. A rise in calcium concentration also probably inhibits the activity of protein phosphatase 1 (PrP-1) which normally enhances the dephosphorylation of both Phos a and SYN$_I$. The hormonal activation by epinephrine involves cAMP as the major messenger although calcium may play a subsidiary role. The rise in cAMP content causes an activation of protein kinases which catalyzes the conversion of phosphorylase b kinase from its less calcium-sensitive to its more calcium-sensitive form and this form, in turn catalyzes the formation of Phos a and SYN$_I$. In addition, the cAMP-dependent protein kinase stimulates the phosphorylation of an inhibitor protein which acts to inhibit the activity of PrP-1.

the cytosol through the sarcolemma, or epinephrine or its second messenger cAMP may cause mitochondrial Ca^{2+} release. In either case, there is evidence that following epinephrine action both Ca^{2+} and cAMP serve a messenger function in this tissue.

Muscle glycogenolysis can also be activated by a calcium-dependent catecholamine-independent mechanism. The Ca^{2+}-dependent phosphorylation of phosphorylase kinase represents the mechanism by which the energy producing process of glycogenolysis is activated when skeletal muscle contracts. According to the model presented in Fig. 15, the muscle action potential causes a release of calcium from the SR, the resulting rise in the cytosolic Ca^{2+} is responsible for activation of the contractile process and simultaneously activates phosphorylase kinase allosterically. Calmodulin mediates this calcium-dependent activation. The activated phosphorylase kinase catalyzes the phosphorylation of both glycogen phosphorylase and glycogen synthase leading to both a stimulation of glycogenolysis and an inhibition of glycogen synthesis.

The enzyme cascades controlling glycogen metabolism in both skeletal muscle and liver represent prototypical cellular response elements the activities of which are regulated by changes in the strength (concentration) of the cAMP and/or calcium messages. In this case two features are noteworthy. First, the ultimate effect of the cAMP message depends upon the calcium ion concentration in the cell cytosol, but the converse is not true. Second, by utilizing dual control signals generated by different extracellular messages, a plasticity of response is possible.

D. Hepatic Glucose Production

In studying the effects of glucagon and epinephrine upon hepatic glycogenolysis, Sutherland and Rall (1958) discovered the second messenger role of cAMP. This was followed by the discovery that most, if not all, β-adrenergic effects of catecholamines are mediated by the cAMP messenger system (Robison *et al.*, 1971). In a sense, the liver system served as a benchmark against which to compare a variety of other adrenergic system. However, recent critical analyses of the hormonal control of hepatic glycogenolysis and gluconeogenesis indicate that there are two more or less separate messenger systems regulating carbohydrate metabolism: glucagon and β-adrenergic agonists operating via the cAMP messenger system; and vasopressin, angiotensin II, and α-adrenergic agonists operating via the calcium messenger system (Van de Werve *et al.*, 1977; Assimacopoulos-Jeannet *et al.*, 1977; Keppens *et al.*, 1977). However, this sharp division may not be adequate because there is evidence that glucagon also influences hepatic cellular calcium metabolism (Friedman and Park, 1968; Friedman and Rasmussen, 1970; Foden and Randle, 1978; Chen *et al.*, 1978; Waltenbaugh *et al.*, 1978; Bygrave and Tranter, 1978; Waltenbaugh and Friedmann, 1978).

In considering the messenger role of calcium in the hormonal control of hepatic metabolism, we will first discuss those hormones in which the evidence points to a calcium-dependent cAMP-independent activation of glycogenolysis and/or gluconeogenesis. Questions of central importance will be those of defining the calcium pool that serves as source of messenger in these systems, and discussing the mechanisms by which changes in calcium flux are brought about. This discussion will lead to a consideration of how the calcium message exerts its effects. Finally, a brief consideration will be given the possible messenger function of calcium ion in the mechanism of glucagon action.

Before undertaking this discussion it is necessary to point out that a number of contradictory findings exist concerning the simplest of points. Diametrically opposite results have been obtained by investigators studying the same question. In part this is a matter of technique but in part it represents an unresolved difference which makes a complete analysis of the situation impossible. For this reason our discussion will be relatively brief and will concentrate on the fact demonstrating a messenger function for calcium, how the calcium message is generated, and how it acts to alter carbohydrate metabolism.

As noted above, the hepatic response to epinephrine was the original system in which cAMP was found to serve a messenger function. This concept went unchallenged for over 10 years. Then in 1972 Sherline *et al.* raised the first serious doubts by noting that α-adrenergic agents may also stimulate hepatic glucose production. In the succeeding years Tolbert *et al.* (1973) demonstrated that if one studied the dose response characteristics of glucose production and cAMP content against agonist concentration employing the α agonist phenylephrine and the β agonist isoproterenol in the rat liver, there was no correlation between cAMP content and glucose production. In the case of phenylephrine, a concentration sufficient to produce a maximal stimulation of glucose production had practically no effect on cAMP content. Conversely, a concentration of isoproterenol that had a marked effect upon cAMP content had very little effect on glucose production. Furthermore, the α blocker phentolamine suppressed the effect of phenylephrine, but the β blocker propranolol did not. From these data, they concluded that in the rat liver catecholamines activate hepatic glucose production by an α-adrenergic cAMP-independent mechanism. More recent work has amply confirmed this conclusion, and shown in addition that both vasopressin, and angiotensin II also stimulate hepatic glucose production by a cAMP-independent mechanism (Van de Werve *et al.*, 1977; Blackmore *et al.*, 1978; Assimacopoulos-Jeannet *et al.*, 1977; Keppens *et al.*, 1977; Exton, 1979; Hutson *et al.*, 1976; Kneer *et al.*, 1974; Chan and Exton, 1978; Garrison and Borland, 1979; Jakob and Deem, 1976; Parisa *et al.*, 1977; LeCann and Freychet, 1978; Chen *et al.*, 1978; Shimazu and Amakawa, 1975; Keppens and de Wulf, 1976, 1979; Garrison *et al.*, 1979; Garrison, 1979; Hems and Whitton, 1973).

When either angiotensin II, vasopressin, or α-adrenergic agonists, e.g., phenylephrine, act upon liver they each increase the rate of glycogenolysis and gluconeogenesis. Their effects depend critically upon the calcium concentration in the external medium. In the absence of external calcium, phenylephrine and the other hormones do not stimulate glucose production (Chan and Exton, 1977; Van de Werve *et al.*, 1977; Keppens *et al.*, 1977). Also, these hormones increase the uptake of calcium into these cells (Keppens *et al.*, 1977; Foden and Randle, 1978; Assimacopoulos-Jeannet *et al.*, 1977; Chen *et al.*, 1978). These facts would suggest that the hormones cause a rise in the cytosolic calcium ion concentration primarily by increasing the rate of entry of calcium into the cell across the plasma membrane. Consistent with this view are the facts that angiotensin, vasopressin and adrenaline all stimulate phosphosinositide turnover in liver cells, but glucagon and A23187 do not. Also, A23187, a divalent cation ionophore produces a calcium-dependent stimulation of glycogenolysis. However, there are other data showing that these same hormones increase calcium efflux from a subcellular pool thought to be the mitochondrial pool (Blackmore *et al.*, 1979a,b; Exton, 1979; Chen *et al.*, 1978; Babcock *et al.*, 1979). Recent emphasis has been placed upon the role of this subcellular pool in serving as the source of cytosolic calcium. In the studies of Chen *et al.* and Blackmore *et al.* the hormone has been shown to cause a net release of cellular calcium when the cells are incubated in a calcium free medium. In contrast, Foden and Randle (1978) reported that phenylephrine caused an increase in cellular and mitochondrial calcium in cells incubated in the presence of calcium. A major problem in resolving these disparate results is the finding by Chan and Exton (1977) that when hepatocytes are incubated in calcium-free media and then exposed to phenylephrine there is a rise in the cAMP content of the cells. For the present the best evidence indicates that one effect of phenylephrine is to increase calcium uptake across the plasma membrane, and that if calcium is absent this hormone does not activate glucose release. Present evidence suggests that the hormone also mobilizes calcium from an intracellular pool but the nature of the message by which it does so is not clear. However, recent work by Nishizuka and co-workers (1979; Takai *et al.*, 1980) raise an interesting possibility related to the turnover of phosphoinositide.

An increase in the breakdown of phosphatidylinositol is a common cellular response to activation of certain types of plasmalemma receptors for either hormones and neurotransmitters, particularly receptors coupled to the calcium messenger system (Michell, 1975). Phosphatidylinosital breakdown in rat hepatocytes can be stimulated by at least three types of receptors namely α adrenergic, vasopressin, and angiotensin (DeTorrentegui and Berthet, 1966; Billah and Michell, 1979). Glucagon does not effect PI breakdown (Kirk *et al.*, 1977). Since α blockers inhibit the α-adrenergic stimulation of PI breakdown but do not effect vasopressin stimulation it appears that individual receptors for these three hormones exist and individually stimulate PI breakdown (Kirk *et al.*, 1977). The inability of the ionophore A23187 and cellular Ca^{2+} depletion to alter PI breakdown has suggested that hormone stimulated PI breakdown is not a consequence of a rise in cytosolic calcium concentration (Kirk *et al.*, 1978; Billah and Michell, 1979).

One of the consequences of PI breakdown is the release of diacylglycerol. Nishizuka *et al.* (Nishizuka *et al.*, 1977; Takai *et al.*, 1980) have found a calcium-dependent phospholipid-dependent protein kinase that is activated by diacylglycerol. Hence, as they suggest, diacylglycerol may be a second messenger that is released when the calcium channel in the plasma membrane is opened by PI turnover, and which sensitizes a specific protein kinase within the cell to the effects of Ca^{2+}.

A phenomena seen in many tissues is the rapid efflux of K^+ upon hormonal or neural stimulation. This phenomena has been investigated in detail in liver tissue by Weiss and Putney (1978). They have suggested that the K^+ permeability change evoked by angiotensin or phenylephrine is regulated by Ca^{2+}. Furthermore, phenylephrine and angiotensin can produce a single response (release of K^+ from the cell) in the absence of extracellular Ca^{2+}. A second response by either agent cannot be obtained unless Ca^{2+} is present. These results suggest that angiotensin and phenylephrine mobilize a common plasma membrane bound pool of Ca^{2+} which is responsible for the initial activation of the K^+ efflux mechanism. Normally, as a result of the hormone-induced change in membrane function, extracellular calcium enters the cell and this is responsible for the sustained increase in K^+ efflux and membrane hyperpolarization. These calcium-mediated changes in K^+ efflux have been taken to mean that this group of hormones brings about an increase in the calcium ion content of the cell cytosol.

Accepting for the present that catecholamines, vasopressin, and angiotensin II activate hepatic metabolism via a rise in the calcium ion concentration in the cell cytosol, the question which arises is the mechanism by which the increased Ca^{2+} concentration alters cell metabolism. The first point of considerable interest is that hepatic metabolism is regulated at the same control points whether Ca^{2+} or cAMP is messenger (Fig. 16). These points are (1) phosphorylase *b* (Sherline *et al.*, 1972; Van de Werve *et al.*, 1977; Hutson *et al.*, 1976; Keppens and de Wulf, 1976); (2) glycogen synthase (Hutson *et al.*, 1976); (3) pyruvate kinase (Taunton *et al.*, 1974; Chan and Exton, 1978; Stifel *et al.*, 1974; Garrison and Borland, 1979); and (4) mitochondrial pyruvate carboxylation (Foldes and Barrett, 1977; Garrison and Haynes, 1975; Garrison and Borland, 1979; Kneer *et al.*, 1979). In attempting to define the molecular basis by

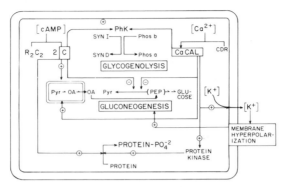

FIG. 16. The mechanisms by which calcium ion and cAMP regulate hepatic glycogenolysis and gluconeogenesis. The key point is that both messengers control the same key metabolic steps. See text for discussion. CaCAL–calcium–calmodulin complex; C, catalytic subunit of cAMP-dependent protein kinase.

which the activities of these control enzymes were brought about, Garrison (1978) compared the effects of glucagon and catecholamines upon the incorporation of radioactive phosphate into cytosolic proteins from intact rat hepatocytes. Treatment of these cells with glucagon or cAMP increased the extent of phosphorylation of 12 separate protein bands when the cytosolic proteins were analyzed on slab get electrophoresis. Treatment of similar cells with phenylephrine or other catecholamines in the presence of β antagonists led to an increase in the extent of phosphorylation of 11 of the same 12 proteins phosphorylated after glucagon. The twelfth protein was phosphorylase *b* kinase. The phosphorylation of these proteins in response to catecholamine was abolished by removal of Ca^{2+} from the external medium, but their phosphorylation in response to glucagon was not altered. Hence, the same proteins undergo phosphorylation in response to either the calcium or the cAMP message. It is not yet known if the same protein kinase is regulated by either Ca^{2+} or cAMP, or whether there are separate cAMP- and Ca^{2+}-dependent kinases. However, in view of the report by Schulman and Greengard (1978) that a calmodulin–calcium-activated protein kinase is present in many tissues, it is quite likely that Ca^{2+} and cAMP act via separate protein kinases which utilize the same cytosolic proteins as substrates. In any case, these findings point to the fact that the control of hepatic glucose production is of such critical survival values to the organism that a redundant system of control has evolved to insure its operation under any conceivable circumstances.

The site of calcium action has been approached in a different fashion by Kneer and co-workers (1979). They examined the ability of calcium to support norepinephrine-stimulated glucose formation from a variety of substrates. They found that calcium was an absolute requirement for the stimulation of glucose formation from lactate, pyruvate, glycerol, sorbitol, and xylitol, but not from fructose and dihydroxyacetone phosphate. From these results and the measurement of certain other metabolic intermediates, they concluded that calcium ion helped determine the redox state of the cell and thereby controlled gluconeogenesis. Since fructose and dihydroxyacetone phosphate do not have to be oxidized, they can be converted directly into glucose whereas those substrates that must be oxidized cannot be converted in the absence of calcium. However, an alternative possibility exists. Chan and Exton (1977) have shown that when phenylephrine or other α agonists interact with hepatocytes incubated in a calcium-free medium, these agonists activate adenylate cyclase cyclase and cause an increase in cAMP. Hence, the observations of Kneer *et al.* (1979) may be explained by an α agonist-induced rise in cAMP content. If so, then the observations of Clark and Jarrett may explain the dependency of the effects of the α agonists (in the absence of calcium) upon the redox state of the cell. Clark and Jarrett (1978) have shown that the responsiveness of the isolated hepatocyte to glucagon is controlled by the redox state of the cytosolic NAD couple. Under reduced conditions, glucagon stimulates gluconeogenesis, but under oxidized conditions it does not. The aboility of glucagon to stimulate gluconeogenesis correlated with the glucagon-dependent increase in cAMP. These workers showed that the activity of a membrane-bound phosphodiesterase was controlled by the cytosolic redox potential: NAHD inhibited the enzyme. This situation represents a particularly elegant example of metabolic control of signal termination.

These findings relating cytosolic redox state to cellular response are but one aspect of a larger question raised by the work of Friedmann and co-workers (Friedmann and Rasmussen, 1970; Friedmann and Dambach, 1973, 1980; Friedmann *et al.*, 1971). They have found that when glucagon stimulates gluconeogenesis there are changes in the rate of flux of Ca^{2+}, K^+, and Na^+ across the plasma membrane of the cell, and these changes are associated with a hyperpolarization of the plasma membrane. Furthermore, insulin in doses sufficient to block the metabolic effects of glucagon also blocks its effect upon membrane potential. Dambach and Friedmann (1974) carried out a number of manipulations including addition of tetracaine or valinomycin, and alteration of ionic environment. In confirmation of earlier work (Tolbert and Fain, 1974), they found that addition of low doses of valinomycin stimulated gluconeogenesis and caused a hyperpolarization of the membrane. Similarly,

Haylett and Jenkinson (1969) found that membrane hyperpolarization was seen following application of α-adrenergic agonists. In general, Friedmann and Dambach found a very close correlation between membrane potential and glucose production. It is not yet possible to define the mechanism by which change in membrane potential (and ion fluxes) might regulate hepatic carbohydrate metabolism but these results taken together with those of Clark and Jarrett (1978) point to the possibility of membrane potential influencing metabolism via ionic events, and metabolism influencing membrane events via redox control of membrane bound enzymes.

These results suggest that hormonal agents which increase cytosolic Ca^{2+} may regulate gluconeogenesis by means of a Ca^{2+}-stimulated K^+ efflux mechanism which serves to produce membrane hyperpolarization. Implicated in this mechanism are α agonists, vasopressin and angiotensin. Interestingly, glucagon also evokes a K^+ efflux and membrane hyperpolarization which correlates with enhanced gluconeogenesis. It is possible that glucagon achieves this effect by a similar Ca^{2+}-dependent K^+ mechanism.

Furthermore, the Ca^{2+} ionophore A23187 fails to stimulate gluconeogenesis. It is of interest that this compound also fails to activate the Ca^{2+}-dependent K^+ efflux in the liver of several species (Putney, 1979). This could be due to the inability of A23187 to increase intracellular Ca^{2+} past the threshold concentrations for K^+ efflux to occur or alternatively the K^+ channels may close rapidly after Ca^{2+} influx (Putney, 1979). In any case, even under this unusual circumstance gluconeogenesis is not activated even though glycogenolysis is. It is of considerable interest that Garrison (1978) found that A23187 induced the phosphorylation of less than half the 11–12 cytosolic proteins which are phosphorylated after either glucagon or norepinephrine action. Hence, there is something different between the effects of A23187 and α agonists upon hepatic cell calcium metabolism that determines a difference in cell response. Under a variety of circumstances the change in gluconeogenesis correlates with the change in membrane potential. It is of obvious interest to determine the link between them.

A question still to be resolved is the possible messenger role of Ca^{2+} in the action of glucagon on the liver. As discussed above, it is generally accepted that cAMP plays a major messenger in the action of this hormone on the liver. It is also evident that exogenous cAMP mimics most of the effects of glucagon. Also, in contrast to phenylephrine, vasopressin, and angiotensin, the action of glucagon is expressed even in hepatocytes incubated in calcium-free media. Hence, it would appear that calcium is not involved in glucagon action. However, there is evidence that glucagon or cAMP cause the mobilization of calcium from an intracellular pool (Friedmann and Park, 1968; Foden and Randle, 1978); that their effects are partially dependent on external calcium (Kneer *et al.*, 1979), and glucagon stimulates the uptake of calcium by liver cells (Keppens *et al.*, 1977; Assimacopoulos-Jeannet *et al.*, 1977). Thus, calcium may also play an undefined messenger role in glucagon action.

E. RENAL GLUCONEOGENESIS

Renal gluconeogenesis is a metabolic function of the proximal tubule (Guder and Wieland, 1972). Hormones capable of activating gluconeogenesis in this tissue include parathyroid hormone, catecholamines, and angiotensin II.

The observations that parathyroid hormone or exogenous cAMP stimulate renal gluconeogenesis, that parathyroid hormone can increase renal proximal tubule cAMP through the action of a parathyroid hormone sensitive adenylate cyclase, that the actions of parathyroid hormone and cAMP on renal gluconeogenesis are nonadditive, and that the concentration of parathyroid hormone required to activate cAMP is similar to the concentration of that hormone required to activate gluconeogenesis, led to the conclusion that cAMP acted as the second messenger of this hormone (Pagliara and Goodman, 1969; Nagata and Rasmussen, 1970; Baumann *et al.*, 1975).

The observation that norepinephrine and epinephrine stimulate cAMP levels in renal tubule preparations led Klahr *et al.* (1973) to postulate that catecholamines act via a β receptor and cAMP in stimulating renal gluconeogenesis. However, Guder and Rupprecht (1975) have reported that the concentration of catecholamine required to turn on gluconeogenesis is less than that required to turn on cAMP production (10 μM norepinephrine was required to half-maximally activate cAMP production while 0.05 μM was required to half-maximally stimulate gluconeogenesis). Also, the stimulation of gluconeogenesis by catecholamine was additive to that of cAMP. These results suggest that catecholamines activate gluconeogenesis by a cAMP-independent mechanism.

The exact nature of this cAMP-independent mechanism has been elucidated by the work of Guder and Rupprecht (1975) and that of Mac-Donald and Saggerson (1977). These investigators report that phentolamine (α blocker) inhibit the stimulatory effect of catecholamines on renal gluconeogenesis, whereas propranolol (β blocker) is ineffective. Also, oxymetazoline (α agonist) was found to stimulate gluconeogenesis. These observations are consistent with the suggestion that catecholamines stimulate gluconeogenesis through an α-receptor cAMP-independent event.

One possible explanation for the catecholamine-stimulated increase in cAMP levels involves possible contamination of the proximal tubules with distal tubules. Morel (1976) has microdissected rabbit kidney structures and found that the proximal tubule contained most of the parathyroid hormone-stimulated adenylate cyclase, whereas catecholamine and vasopressin-stimulated adenylate cyclase were localized in the distal convolutions and collecting duct where gluconeogenesis is not found.

Two observations appear inconsistent with the proposal that catecholamines stimulate gluconeogenesis solely by an α receptor cAMP-independent mechanism.

1. Propranolol at concentrations 50 times greater than phentolamine inhibited the stimulating of catecholamines on gluconeogenesis (Guden and Rupprecht, 1975).

2. Norepinephrine (0.1 μM) antagonized the effect of parathyroid hormone on cAMP levels. This effect was abolished by phentolamine (Guder and Rupprecht, 1976).

Since the stimulatory effect of cAMP on renal gluconeogenesis is also blocked by propranolol, observation (1) could be explained by a nonspecific effect of propranolol on gluconeogenesis. Observation (2) presents the possibility that the α adrenergic mechanism may regulate the β-adrenergic cAMP-dependent mechanism.

Angiotensin II has been reported to stimulate renal gluconeogenesis by a mechanism which does not involve cAMP (Guder and Rupprecht, 1976). Furthermore, the stimulatory effects of angiotension II are additive with those of cAMP but not with those of the catecholamines (Guder, 1979), suggesting that angiotensin II and catecholamines operate by a similar cAMP-independent mechanism.

Evidence suggests that the catecholamine and angiotensin II stimulation of gluconeogenesis is mediated by Ca^{2+}. MacDonald and Saggerson (1977) have shown that in the absence of Ca^{2+} the stimulation of gluconeogenesis by the α agonist oxymetazoline was completely blocked; however, some stimulatory effect of epinephrine was still observed. It is possible that the Ca^{2+}-independent epinephrine-dependent stimulation of gluconeogenesis represents stimulation and release of cAMP from distal tubule contamination which then acts on the proximal tubules. A Ca^{2+}-dependent α adrenergic mechanism is also suggested by the report that norepinephrine causes an increase in the efflux of ^{45}Ca from prelabeled kidneys perfused with Ca^{2+}-free solution (Harada and Rubin, 1978). This observation implies that α-adrenergic agents may trigger the release of Ca^{2+} from internal stores. The effect of Ca^{2+} omission on the stimulation of gluconeogenesis by angiotensin II has been examined by Guder (1979). Addition of 1 mM EDTA to the media completely abolished the angiotensin II effect on glucose formation. The site of regulation of renal gluconeogenesis by Ca^{2+} or cAMP has not been examined, unlike hepatic gluconeogenesis where it has been shown that cAMP- or Ca^{2+}-dependent phosphorylation of pyruvate kinase represents the major site of regulation (Section VI,A).

Thus, in the kidney as in the liver there appear to be two pathways by which gluconeogenesis is activated: one involving parathyroid hormone (PTH) and utilizing cAMP as a second messenger; the other involving epinephrine or angiotensin II and utilizing calcium as second messenger. However, the situation is more complicated because there is considerable evidence that the effect of PTH upon renal gluconeogenesis is also dependent upon, and utilizes calcium as messenger (Rasmussen, 1970; Rasmussen *et al.*, 1972; Borle, 1970; Nagata and Rasmussen, 1970; Kurokawa *et al.*, 1973).

In contrast to the liver cell, the proximal tubule cell is highly permeable to calcium. When such tubules are incubated *in vitro* the rate of gluconeogenesis from a variety of substrates (particularly Krebs cycle intermediates) is a function of the external calcium ion concentration between 0.2 and 2.0 mM. The calcium content of the tissue shows a similar dependency upon extracellular calcium concentration. Most importantly, the rate of gluconeogenesis is stimulated by the addition of parathyroid hormone. The magnitude of this stimulation is a function of the external calcium ion concentration being maximal (in terms of percentage of basal rate of gluconeogenesis) when the external calcium ion concentration is between 0.5 and 1.25 mM (the physiological range). At low external calcium concentrations (< 0.2 mM), PTH has very little effect upon glucose formation even though it still stimulates adenylate cyclase and causes an even greater than normal increase in cAMP content. The tissue is still intact under these conditions because a shift in pH from 7.4 to 6.8 induces a marked stimulation of glucose formation whether the external Ca^{2+} concentration is 0.2 or 1.2 mM. There is independent evidence that PTH stimulates the uptake of calcium into target cells (Borle, 1968; Borle and Uchikawa, 1979).

It is also evident that exogenous cAMP will stimulate gluconeogenesis and that its effects are calcium dependent (Nagata and Rasmussen, 1970; Kurokawa *et al.*, 1973). However, there are subtle differences between the effects of exogenous cAMP and those of PTH. The stimulation of the conversion of some substrates by PTH is more dependent upon calcium than is the stimulation induced by cAMP. These data suggest that both calcium and cAMP serve second messenger function in the action of PTH.

On the basis of these data, Nagata and Rasmussen (1970; Rasmussen, 1970) proposed that both calcium and cAMP served messenger functions in the PTH-induced increase in renal gluconeogenesis. It was from these studies and later those in the fly salivary gland that led to the more general formulation of the universality of the relationship of the cAMP and calcium messenger systems. The more recent work with the other hormones, catecholamines and angiotensin II, are further substantiation of the fact that Ca^{2+} can serve to couple excitation to metabolism in a variety of tissues. Yet to be resolved in the case of the kidney is whether the PTH-responsive cells on the one hand and the angiotensin II and catecholamine-responsive cells on the other are the same or different cells. If the latter, then there is a striking analogy between the situation in the renal cortex and that discussed previously in the adrenal cortex in that certain segments appear to utilize both cAMP and Ca^{2+} as messengers, and others primarily calcium.

F. Intestinal Fluid Secretion

Intestinal secretagogues have been shown to act upon the small intestine to change it from a tissue which absorbs fluid and electrolyte into one in which fluid and electrolytes are actively secreted (reviewed by Hendrix and Paulk, 1977). These secretagogues can be divided into two general catagories, those whose stimulatory effects are mediated either by cAMP or by Ca^{2+}.

Field *et al.* (1968) first demonstrated that cAMP abolished active Na and Cl absorption by rabbit ileum and elicited active Cl secretion. Later Kimberg *et al.* (1971) showed that exposure of this tissue to cholera toxin or theophylline resulted in elevated cAMP levels and active Cl secretion. Bolton and Field (1977) reported that the vasoactive intestinal peptide (VIP) and prostaglandin E_1 (PGE 1) also increase intracellular cAMP levels and stimulated Cl^- secretion. The stimulation of intracellular cAMP levels by the secretagogues cholera toxin, VIP, and PGE 1 are accomplished by the activation of the plasmalemma adenylate cyclase. On the other hand, theophylline is believed to increase cAMP levels by inhibition of phosphodiesterase.

Addition of the Ca^{2+} ionophore A23187 to the serosal side of isolated rabbit ileal mucosa (Bolton and Field, 1977) or to the mucosal side of rabbit colon (Frizzell, 1977) results in a secretory response qualitatively identical with that elicited by agents that increase intracellular cAMP concentrations. Unlike the cAMP-dependent mechanism, however, the ionophore does not increase mucosal cAMP concentration and its action is dependent on extracellular Ca^{2+}.

Bolton and Field (1977) have also reported that carbamylcholine and serotonin stimulate Cl^- secretion in ileal mucosa. The stimulation associated with these secretagogues is not associated with an increase in the cAMP concentration but is dependent on extracellular Ca^{2+}. These results suggest that carbamylcholine and serotonin may activate intestinal secretion by increasing intracellular Ca^{2+} concentration whereas VIP and cholera toxin do so by increasing cAMP concentration.

A mechanism by which Ca^{2+} and/or cAMP act to alter the tissue from an absorptive to a secretory tissue has been proposed by Frizzel *et al.* (1979) and by Naftalin and Simmons (1979). In these models NaCl enters the cell by a neutral cotransport system. This coupling insures the movement of Cl^- into the cell against its electrochemical gradient being driven by the flow of Na^+ into the cell down its electrochemical gradient. However, if agents which cause either an increase in Ca^{2+} or in cAMP within the cell are added net chloride secretion into the luminal fluid is seen. This secretion is dependent upon the presence of Na^+ in the solution bathing the contraluminal membrane. Chloride secretion is inhibited by furosemide. These facts have been used to construct a model in which a neutral NaCl entry mechanism at the baso-lateral membrane mediates the flow of Cl^- into the cell against an electrochemical gradient by coupling its flow to the influx of Na^+ down its electrochemical gradient. The Na^+ is re-extruded from the cell via the Na–K exchange pump, thereby maintaining the Na^+ gradient. Active Cl^- secretion results from the movement of Cl^- out of the cell across the luminal membrane down a favorable electrochemical gradient. Hence, at the luminal border there are two opposing forces; a Na^+ gradient, and a coupled NaCl cotransport driving Cl^- into the cell, and an electrochemical Cl^- gradient tending to drive it out of the cell into the lumen. What determines the net flux is the balance between the two processes. Of critical importance in defining this balance is the Cl^- permeability of the luminal membrane. It is thought (Frizzel *et al.*, 1979) that this is the major step at which both cAMP and/or Ca^{2+} act. By increasing Cl^- permeability, it is proposed that these agents alter the balance so that net secretion rather than net absorption of fluid and electrolytes takes place.

A possible relationship between the actions of cAMP and Ca^{2+} has been suggested by the finding that cAMP stimulates the release of ^{45}Ca from prelabeled rabbit colon mucosa (Frizzell, 1977). These results present the possibility that the secretory response due to cAMP results at least in part from a release of Ca^{2+} from internal stores and a subsequent activation of Cl secretion by the elevated cytosolic Ca^{2+}.

The observation that the drug Stelazine, a phenothiazine, blocks iono-phoretic stimulation of intestinal Cl^- secretion and has little effect on cAMP levels (Hamilton and Hamilton, 1979) has led to the suggestion that calmodulin mediates the Ca^{2+}-stimulated intestinal secretatory response. This suggestion was based on the earlier report of Levin and Weiss (1976) who showed that Stelazine binds to and inactivates the cal-modulin-mediated increase in cAMP phosphodiesterase activity.

The actual mechanism by which cAMP or Ca^{2+} turn on absorptive tissue into a secretatory tissue is unknown. However, Ilundain and Naf-talin (1979) have shown that Stelazine also blocks choleragen- and theophylline-mediated increases in tissue Cl^- flux without altering the cAMP content of the tissue. Furthermore, they showed that that both choleragen and theophylline as well as the ionophore A23187 increased the uptake of labeled Stelazine into the tissue. Based upon the observations of Levin and Weiss (1976) and Fentel and Weiss (1976) that the bind-ing of calcium to calmodulin causes an increase in the binding of Stelazine to calmodulin, Ilundain and Naftalin (1979) proposed that both choleragen and A23187 increased the intracellular calcium ion content, and that the final common mediator of the change in Cl^- permeability was a rise in the cytosolic Ca^{2+} ion content. However, in view of the fact that in other systems a cAMP-dependent phosphorylation of a protein complex leads to an increased affinity of calmodulin for Ca^{2+} one cannot rule out the possibility that cAMP does not act to raise cytosolic Ca^{2+} con-centration, but to increase the sensitivity of the cellular component con-trolling Cl^- permeability to an unchanged Ca^{2+} message. In either mechanism, however, calcium is the final mediator of response. Hence, in the intestine the situation appears to be operationally similar to that seen in a variety of other tissues, in the sense that cAMP and Ca^{2+} interact in complex ways to mediate final response.

G. Exocrine Secretion

The exocrine glands represent tissues in which a combination of neural and hormonal stimuli regulate cell function. Three of these tissues in which stimulus–response coupling has been studied in some detail are the parotid, the salivary gland of the blow fly, and the exocrine pancreas. Our discussion of each of these will be limited to the major facts relating to calcium as messenger. For more detailed discussion the reader is re-ferred to recent reviews by Butcher (1978a,b) and Case (1978).

1. Parotid Gland

Parotid secretion can be modulated by four types of receptors, the α-and β-adrenergic receptors, the muscarine cholinergic receptor, and the receptor for substance "P". Release of amylase by rat parotid, *in vitro* is strongly stimulated by β-adrenergic agonists. Schramm *et al.* (1972) have reported that norepinephrine stimulates the plasmalemma adenylate cyclase enhancing the concentration of cAMP in this tissue. The resultant activation of the cAMP-dependent protein kinase is believed to result in the activation of the process by which the secretory granules fuse with the cell membrane at the lumen (Batzri *et al.*, 1973). Monobutyryl cAMP can bypass the β-adrenergic receptor (Schramm *et al.*, 1972) and mediate the entire β-adrenergic response. The presence of Ca^{2+} in the external media is not required for the β-adrenergic response (Batzri and Selinger, 1973; Kanagasuntheram and Randle, 1976). While the β agonists can turn on protein secretion they do not activate water and ion secretion to any great extent. Injection of isoproterenol into fasted rats produces only a small volume of saliva containing large amounts of protein (Batzri *et al.*, 1973). On the other hand, injection of phenylephrine into fasted rats produces large volumes of serous saliva low in protein content (Schramm and Selinger, 1975). This result suggests the involvement of α-adrenergic receptors in the release of ions and water, and the fact that when secretion is controlled *in vivo* by the sympathetic nervous system both protein and fluid secretion are enhanced. Acetylcholine or parasympathetic stimulation also stimulate fluid and electrolytes secretion. The effects of both acetylcholine and of α-adrenergic agonists require the presence of calcium in the medium and these neurotransmitters are thought to act via the calcium messenger system.

Consistent with studies in intact parotid glands, in parotid slices activation of the α-adrenergic receptor, activation of the muscarinic receptor by acetylcholine, and activation of a distinct receptor by substance "P" results in a large efflux of K^+ by a cAMP-independent mechanism (Batzri *et al.*, 1973; Schramm and Selinger, 1975; Rudich and Butcher, 1976). These hormones as well as A23187 also release amylase, but the amount released is small compared to that released by β-adrenergic stimulation (Butcher, 1978a,b).

The involvement of Ca^{2+} as the second messenger in the activation of this tissue by α agonists, muscarinic agonists, and substance "P" has been investigated in several laboratories and is summarized as follows.

1. The release of K^+ and water by these agents is dependent on the presence of external Ca^{2+} (Selinger *et al.*, 1974; Butcher, 1978). Similar-

ily, the enhancement of cGMP concentration by carbamadrol, phenylephrine, and "P" is Ca^{2+} dependent (Butcher, 1978a,b).

2. The Ca^{2+} ionophore, A23187, mimics the action of these agents (Selinger *et al.*, 1974).

3. Substance "P", carbachol, and phenylephrine stimulate *net* release
of Ca^{2+} from preloaded parotid cells (Putney, 1977; Haddah *et al.*, 1979).
In contrast, Kanagasuntheram and Randle (1976) reported that phenylephrine and carbamoylcholine inhibited efflux of Ca^{2+} into Ca^{2+}-free
media.

4. In the absence of extracellular Ca^{2+} a prior challenge with carbachol prevents the Ca^{2+} efflux stimulated by substance "P".

5. Release of K^+ by secretagogues is biphasic, a transient phase occurs
lasting 2–4 minutes which does not require extracellular Ca^{2+} followed by
a sustained phase which is absolutely dependent on extracellular Ca^{2+}
(Putney, 1977). In Ca^{2+}-free media only one transient efflux of K^+ can be
obtained and a second challenge fails to produce a response even if an
agonist activating a different receptor is used. For a second response the
tissue must be re-incubated in Ca^{2+} containing media between the
challenges.

6. The release of minor amounts of amylase by these secretagogues
and also by A23187 is dependent on extracellular Ca^{2+} (Butcher, 1978a,b).

These results are consistent with the suggestion that α agonists, muscarinic agonists, and substance "P" mobilize a common pool of Ca^{2+}. This
Ca^{2+} pool is probably that associated with the plasma membrane. In addition, these agents increase the uptake of calcium by the cells. Hence, as
seen in several other systems, the interaction of agonists with its membrane receptor causes an initial release of calcium from a plasma membrane pool, and this is followed by an increase in Ca^{2+} influx into the cell.
In addition, mobilization of calcium from another (beside the plasma
membrane pool) intracellular pool may be a component of the sustained
response.

The possible involvement of Ca^{2+} in the β-adrenergic response has been
reexamined by Butcher (1978a,b). The following results are consistent
with a role of Ca^{2+} in the β-adrenergic response.

1. Incubation of parotid slices in Ca^{2+}-free media containing EGTA
inhibit β-adrenergic stimulation of amylase release (Butcher, 1978a,b).
Furthermore, the β-adrenergic stimulation of cAMP production is inhibited by Ca^{2+} removal.

2. Beta agonists and cAMP stimulate efflux of Ca^{2+} into Ca^{2+}-free
media. The release of Ca^{2+} precedes the release of amylase and is of

shorter duration than the release of amylase (Kanagasuntheran and Randle, 1976; Putney *et al.*, 1977).

3. Beta agonists and cAMP induce release of Ca^{2+} from mitochondria during incubation in Ca^{2+}-free media (Dormer and Ashcroft, 1974; Kanagasuntheram and Randle, 1976).

4. A23187 augments the amount of amylase released by limited concentrations of isoproterenol. Also, carbachol or phenylephrine greatly enhance amylase release by limiting amounts of isoproterenol.

5. The amount of amylase released by, e.g., carbachol and limiting amounts of isoproterenol is greater than the sum of each of these agents alone.

6. Rat parotid adenylate cyclase requires Ca^{2+} for optimal activity (Butcher, 1978a,b).

These results are consistent with a dual role of Ca^{2+} in the response of parotid to secretagogues (Fig. 17). In the β-adrenergic response Ca^{2+} appears to be essential for cAMP accumulation, i.e., a calcium-dependent activation of adenylate cyclase. On the other hand, it appears that Ca^{2+} also acts as a second messenger in the stimulation of protein secretion (a site distal to cyclase activation) by a mechanism operationally similar to the dual effects of Ca^{2+} and cAMP upon glycogenolysis. The site of action of neither Ca^{2+} nor cAMP within the cell are not yet known. Finally, as seen in other systems there is evidence that cAMP causes the mobilization

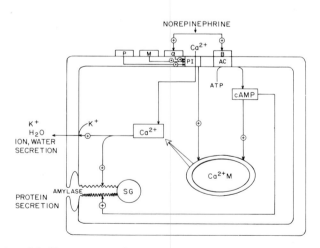

FIG. 17. A model of how norepinephrine may regulate fluid and electrolyte secretion in the mammalian salivary gland.

of calcium from an intracellular pool tentatively identified as the mito-chondrial pool.

The mechanism by which hormone–receptor interaction (in the case of α-adrenergic agonists, for example) stimulates the release of Ca^{2+} from the plasma membrane pool is unknown. It has been proposed that hydrolysis of membrane phosphatidylinositol induced by receptor activation might be directly involved in regulating both Ca^{2+} release and Ca^{2+} entry into the secretory cells (Michell, 1975).

The strongest evidence for this theory is that PI hydrolysis is stimulated only by agents which activate Ca^{2+} channels (Michell, 1975), but is unaffected by cytosolic Ca^{2+} concentrations. For instance, the Ca^{2+} ionophore A23187, which activates Ca^{2+}-dependent K^+ efflux, does not effect phosphatidylinositol breakdown. On the other hand, it has been postulated that PI breakdown does not represent the mechanism of Ca^{2+} entry into the cell but is rather a process correlated to other cellular events (Oron *et al.*, 1975).

The mechanism by which cytosolic Ca^{2+} or cAMP might control the secretory process is uncertain. The secretory apparatus responsible for exocytosis of protein is composed of the secretory granules, the apical plasma membrane–secretory granule fusion site and the contractile elements. The involvement of Ca^{2+} in exocytosis has been appreciated since the studies of Locke (1894). Within the present context it appears that Ca^{2+} can induce protein secretion in the parotid gland, however, the amount of protein released is much less than by the β-adrenergic mechanism. The β-adrenergic mechanism presumably results in elevations in both cAMP and Ca^{2+} it is reasonable to assume that both these messengers are required for exocytosis to occur, otherwise agents such as A23187 should produce a maximal response.

Two possible loci of regulation by these second messengers are the contractile elements which are thought to be responsible for transport of proteins and the apical plasma membrane–secretory granule fusion site.

The contractile elements are composed of the microtubules (composed of tubulin) and the microfilaments (composed of actin). Colchicine, which inhibits the polymerization of microtubules, does not significantly affect the muscarinic or adrenergic response, but does impair the secretation of protein in salivary glands by slowing down the intracellular transport of proteins (Rossignol *et al.*, 1977). This suggests tubulin plays a key role in the contractile elements. The polymerization of tubulin has been shown to be initiated by Ca^{2+} and calmodulin (Section IV G,l,j) and cAMP (Garland, 1979). These results would appear to contradict a role for Ca^{2+} in the transport of proteins. However, it is quite possible that a polymerization–depolymerization cycle is essential in the secretory process.

Key in the apical plasma membrane–secretatory granule fusion site is a protein called synexin which promotes the fusion of secretatory granules in the presence of micromolar Ca^{2+} (Creutz et al., 1978). This protein may represent the intracellular receptor for Ca^{2+} in the process of exocytosis in this tissue.

In conclusion, norepinephrine released at the nerve endings causes protein secretion through the β-adrenergic receptor and water secretion apparently associated with K^+ release, through the α-adrenergic receptor (Fig. 17). The β receptor activates the cAMP second messenger system while the α receptor activates the Ca^{2+} second messenger system. Muscarinic agonists and substance P work by a mechanism similar to the α adrenergic. It appears that both α- and β-adrenergic receptor activation results in a mobilization of Ca^{2+} from intracellular stores, perhaps the mitochondria. Why the β agonists cannot activate the K^+ efflux mechanism via the release of intracellular Ca^{2+} is uncertain, but the key difference is that α-adrenergic agonists cause release of plasma membrane bound Ca^{2+} and the influx of extracellular calcium whereas β agonists do not.

The second messenger cAMP presumably acting through the activation of the cAMP-dependent protein kinase can turn on the process of exocytosis, but it is likely that Ca^{2+} is also required for this process. An intriguing possibility is that cAMP promotes the phosphorylation of a regulatory protein(s) of the exocytotic process which results in an increased affinity for Ca^{2+}, therefore potentiating the stimulation of exocytosis by Ca^{2+} in analogy with the phosphorylase kinase situation.

2. Blowfly Salivary Gland

Prince et al. (1972, 1973) have described a series of studies on the respective roles of calcium and cAMP as second messengers in the action of 5-HT on the blowfly salivary gland. Before these studies Berridge (1970) had shown that the 5-HT response met several of the criteria established by Sutherland for a hormone conforming to the second messenger (cAMP) mode. Thus, exogenous cAMP was shown to mimic the effect of 5-HT on fluid secretion, and theophylline an inhibitor of phosphodiesterase, enhanced the effect of submaximal doses of 5-HT on fluid secretion. Using the newly developed Gilman assay, Prince et al. (1972) were able to show that the system met the other criteria (1) the cAMP content of the gland increased after 5-HT; (2) a hormone-sensitive adenylate cyclase was found in a particulate fraction; and (3) a cAMP-dependent protein kinase was found in the soluble fraction of the cell homogenate.

Nonetheless, when Prince began to measure the transepithelial membrane potential in these secretory cells, either 5-HT or exogenous cAMP addition led to a change in potential, but the direction of change were exactly opposite: 5-HT caused the potential to become more negative, cAMP to become more positive even though the rates and ionic compositions of the fluid being secreted were essentially the same (Prince *et al.*, 1972). The question at that point was whether this difference was an expression of a fundamental difference between how 5-HT and cAMP turned on secretion, or a trivial epiphenomenon. Additional experiments showed that (1) both 5-HT and exogenous cAMP required calcium to exert their effect on secretion; (2) both induced an efflux of calcium from an intracellular (presumably mitochondrial) pool; but only 5-HT stimulated a net influx of calcium. If 5-HT was added to the gland in the absence of calcium even though there was very little secretion it induced a rise in cAMP content, and a shift to a more positive potential just as seen after addition of exogenous cAMP in the presence of external calcium. Also, when a calcium-deprived 5-HT-stimulated gland with a positive transmembrane potential was re-exposed to calcium, the potential reversed to a negative one as seen in the normal 5-HT-stimulated gland.

These experiments demonstrated that the different effects of 5-HT and exogenous cAMP on membrane potential were related to their differing effects upon cellular calcium metabolism. They also raised the possibility that calcium ion as well as cAMP served a messenger function in this tissue. This possibility was explored by using the calcium ionophore, A23187 (Prince *et al.*, 1973). Addition of ionophore to the gland produced the following calcium-dependent changes (1) an increase in fluid secretion; (2) an increase in calcium influx; (3) an increase in calcium efflux; and (4) a more negative membrane potential. All of these changes were identical to those seen after 5-HT addition. However, A23187 caused a fall rather than a rise in cAMP content of the gland as seen after 5-HT addition. Furthermore, Berridge *et al.* (1975) adduced evidence that calcium ion had a separate effect from that of cAMP. A rise in intracellular calcium led to an increase in the chloride permeability of the luminal membrane. It was this change that accounted for the change in membrane potential seen after 5-HT and A23187. An important inference from these data and this conclusion was that the cytosolic calcium ion concentration was higher in a 5-HT-stimulated than in a cAMP-stimulated gland. Equally important these data clearly indicated that the secretory response of the salivary gland could be initiated and sustained by an increase in the cytosolic concentration of either messenger, calcium ion, or cAMP; but that under physiological circumstances, i.e., after 5-HT addition, there was a coordinate rise in the concentration of both messengers and a coordinate interaction of the two messengers with the final effector element: the luminal membrane.

The model developed to account for these data was operationally similar to that developed to account for the renal action of PTH. Each hormone induced two primary effects on its respective target cell, an increase in calcium entry and a rise in cAMP content. These two intracellular agents acting in concert controlled the final response; and each in turn controlled the concentration of the other; cAMP controlled the calcium message in a positive way by mobilizing calcium from an intracellular source, and calcium controlled cAMP content in a negative way either by inhibiting its synthesis or stimulating its hydrolysis.

These results were important also in demonstrating that the dual involvement of cAMP and calcium ion as messengers in the same cell was not restricted to cells and hormones (the renal tubule and PTH) involved in regulating extracellular mineral homeostasis.

A further difference between the action of 5-HT and exogenous cAMP has been described by Fain and Berridge (1979; Berridge and Fain, 1979). They have reported that phosphatidylinositol hydrolysis may be important in the Ca^{2+} gating actions of serotonin. The following observations have been made (1) addition of serotonin but not cAMP led to a release of inositol from glands prelabeled with [^{3}H]inositol; or ^{32}P from prelabeled phosphatidylinositol; (2) this effect was specific for phosphoinositol because 5-HT had no effect upon phosphatidylcholine or phosphatidylethanolamine; (3) ionophore A23187 stimulated Ca^{2+} influx and secretion, but did not stimulate inositol turnover and/or release; (4) inhibition of phosphodiesterase by 3-isobutyl-1-methylxanthine potentiated fluid secretion due to serotonin, but did not affect inositol release; (5) fluid secretion gradually disappeared in the absence of external Ca^{2+} but inositol release remained constant, i.e., inositol release was not calcium dependent; (6) serotonin inhibited the synthesis of phosphatidylinositol, this effect was Ca^{2+} dependent; (7) prolonged preincubation in the presence of serotonin and Ca^{2+} prevented stimulation of secretion of Ca^{2+} flux by a subsequent challenge with serotonin, and responsiveness could be restored by preincubation of glands with inositol.

These observations are consistent with the possibility that turnover of phosphatidylinositol may be a reaction intrinsic to either receptor occupation and/or activation of Ca^{2+} channels by 5-HT in the fly salivary gland as has been proposed by Michell (1975) in other tissues.

3. Exocrine Pancreas

The control of pancreatic exocrine enzyme secretion is exerted by the vagal nerve (acetylcholine) and the polypeptide hormones cholecysto-kinin–pancreozymin (CCK-Pz) and gastrin (Mellanby, 1925; Harper and Raper, 1943; Blair *et al.*, 1966). Recently Christophe *et al.* (1977) reported that the stimulation of pancreatic acinar cells by a new class of gut hormones called bombesin and caerulein. Calderon *et al.* (1979) have reported the stimulation of amylase release by secretin and vasoactive intestinal polypeptide. Unlike the parotid acinar cells the pancreas acinar cells do not release K^+ when stimulated by secretagogues.

The hormonal regulation of pancreatic secretion can be divided into three categories according to the second messenger involved:

1. Acetylcholine, bombesin, gastrin, and pancreozymin appear to employ Ca^{2+} as a second messenger and perhaps cGMP;
2. Pancreozymin employs Ca^{2+}, cAMP, and cGMP; and
3. VIP and secretin activate adenylate cyclase hence employ cAMP.

The involvement of Ca^{2+} as a second messenger for pancreatic cellular activation has been suggested from the following observations:

1. omission of Ca^{2+} from the extracellular medium reduces the stimulation of amylase by CCK-Pz (Hokin, 1966);
2. A23187 stimulates the secretion of amylase in pancreatic slices (Selinger *et al.*, 1974);
3. Secretagogues acetylcholine, bombesin, and gastrin have no effect on pancreatic intracellular cAMP concentration (Christophe *et al.*, 1977; Gardner *et al.*, 1977);
4. Secretagogues stimulate release of Ca^{2+} from pre-equilibrated pancreatic acinar cells (Clemente and Meldolesi, 1975) into Ca^{2+}-free media. Among the cell fractions examined only the mitochondria exhibited lower Ca^{2+} relative to unstimulated controls;
5. Secretagogues stimulate a net efflux of Ca^{2+} (Gardner and Hayne, 1977; Clemente and Meldolesi, 1975);
6. Stimulation of Ca^{2+} outflow by maximally effective concentrations of CCK-Pz plus carbamylcholine is identical to that produced by maximal concentrations of either agonist alone (Gardner *et al.*, 1977);
7. carbamylcholine, and CCK-Pz stimulate an increase in cGMP levels; and
8. when acetylcholine is applied to acinar cells there is an electrical uncoupling of adjacent acinar cells which has been taken to mean that the calcium ion content of the cell cytosol has increased (Petersen and Iwatsuki, 1978).

These results suggest that the pancreatic secretagogues, acetylcholine, bombesin, CCK-Pz, gastrin, and caerulein mobilize intracellular Ca^{2+} stores, probably the mitochondria, which then activates the secretory process. The rise in cytosoli Ca^{2+} concentration is also responsible for increasing cGMP. The messenger role of cGMP remains to be determined.

The pancreatic acinar cell is also regulated by secretagogues which activate cAMP. The adenylate cyclase activity of purified pancreatic plasma membranes respond to caerulein, CCK-Pz, secretin and the vasoactive intestinal polypeptide (VIP). Unlike CCK-Pz, VIP and secretin influence neither Ca efflux or cGMP levels. Interestingly, Christophe *et al.* (1977) have reported that bombesin inhibited secretin-stimulated rise in cAMP levels and the secretory effect of bombesin partially added to that of secretin but not to that of caerulein. This suggests that Ca^{2+} inhibits cAMP production in this tissue, and both cAMP and Ca^{2+} may stimulate exocytosis at distinct sites. This is in contrast to the parotid system.

One important locus for Ca^{2+} mediation of the secretatory process appears to be the apical membrane–secretory granule fusion site. Schultz *et al.* (1977) have reported that Ca^{2+} is required for the fusion process. The K_m (Ca^{2+}) was determined to be 6 μM. The addition of EGTA resulted in only 30% reversal of said process indicating that a major part of the secretatory granule–membrane binding is not reversible by Ca^{2+} removal.

Thus, present evidence strongly supports the concept that calcium is the major second messenger involved in stimulus–secretion coupling in the exocrine pancreas; and that the major source of calcium for this coupling function is an intracellular, possibly mitochondria, pool. Very little is yet known of the mechanism by which this calcium pool is mobilized following stimulation. However, even in this tissue more recent evidence suggests that cAMP may also serve a messenger function in stimulus–response coupling. However, this tissue is composed of both acinar and ductal cells so it is possible that different cell types responsible for different aspects of the total secretory response utilize different messenger systems to control the integrated tissue response.

VII. CONCLUSIONS

Evidence in the past decade has firmly established that both calcium and cAMP serve nearly universal messenger functions in coupling stimulus to response in both excitable and nonexcitable tissues. However, more than the fact that both serve in nearly all cells is that their functions are intimately related so that a complete understanding of stimulus–response coupling in nearly any tissue requires an understanding of the roles of both messenger systems in the control of cellular response. This conclusion means that the classical second messenger concept involving cAMP as the principal intracellular mediator of cellular responses is an incomplete description of events in nearly all the tissues in which it has been considered to operate. Stated most concisely, it now appears that nearly all cell types employ a single nearly universal messenger system involving the interacting and integrated messengers, calcium ion, and cAMP, when the cell is stimulated to respond by the interaction of surface receptor with extracellular messengers. Not all of the evidence, from particular cell types, in support of this concept has been reviewed in this article. Nor does this conclusion mean that surface receptors may not cause the generation of other second messengers. It does mean that it is rare indeed when either calcium or cAMP act alone to couple stimulus to response. In order to emphasize the nearly universal existence of this system for coupling excitation to response, we have given (Rasmussen, 1979) this cellular control system *synarchy*, meaning that the two intracellular messengers regulate intracellular events by acting in concert. In particular it seems that synarchic messengers are involved in coupling stimulus to response in most differentiated cells when these cells are activated to perform their specialized functions.

The thesis can be most simply stated in the form of a schematic model (Fig. 18). In this model, extracellular messengers interacting with receptors on the cell surface lead to one or both of two changes either an increase in cAMP or of calcium ion in the cell cytosol.

In those systems in which the concentration of both messengers rise in response to the same extracellular messenger, it is quite clear that there is a direct relationship between the two messenger systems at the very beginning of the stimulus–response coupling. This relationship becomes even more readily apparent when the subsequent intracellular events are analyzed. Each of the two messages interacts with one or more elements in the cell to control the others concentration, i.e., there is a dialogue between the two. Each alters the sensitivity of response elements to the effects of the other. Each regulates the same class of enzymes, protein kinases, and these in turn may regulate the activity of the same phosphoprotein effectors to determine the ultimate cellular response. Plasticity is built into the system by the fact that each messenger controls the activity of one or more response element not influenced by the other.

In those systems in which different extracellular messengers give rise to the two different intracellular messengers, cAMP and calcium, it is not immediately obvious that one is dealing with a universal system. However, when one analyzes the intracellular interactions between the two messenger systems in such cells, the commonality and universality

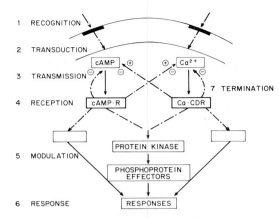

FIG. 18. A schematic representation of the synarchic regulation illustrating the bimodal control of cell function by cAMP and calcium. These two messengers may be altered by separate, or the same extracellular messenger, they often regulate the same common metabolic pathways, they regulate their own and each other's concentration. The -•→ lines illustrate the flow of information. The ——→ lines represent the sequence of events in the final response elements. The response of a cell can be broken down into a sequence of first messenger recognition; plasma membrane transduction; intracellular transmission of the message; recognition of the intracellular message; modulation of the intracellular message; response of the control.

becomes evident because the interrelated roles of the two messengers in stimulus–response coupling in these cells are identical to those just summarized for cells in which both messengers increase in response to a single extracellular messenger.

The systems in which separate first messengers give rise separately to the calcium or the cAMP message within the cell use these two systems to control the same basic process, but use them in either a complimentary manner thereby lending further plasticity to the range of control possibilities; or in an antagonist fashion to balance cell response between two extremes of cell behavior. In this regard, one additional modality of control not illustrated in the model is that of a suppression of cAMP production or a decrease in calcium entry into the cytosol as a consequence of first messenger action. Such controls do not invalidate the basic model but extend into another domain. Primary controls of this negative or inhibitory type appear less common than the more usual positive or stimulatory controls. However, a less systematic search for this type of regulation has been made, hence they may be considerably more common than presently realized.

The point that is likely to be questioned immediately is the fact that, as depicted, the calcium message arises from a transduction event (an increase in the permeability of a calcium channel) in the plasma membrane. Yet as has been made clear in the previous discussion the calcium signal may arise either from the extracellular pool as depicted in Fig. 18, or from one or more intracellular pools, e.g., from the SR in the case of skeletal muscle. However, if one views the situation in the model (Fig. 18) in a less literal sense, then the model represents the essential truth which is: there is an operational similarity between all cell systems in which calcium is used as messenger, the rise in cytosolic calcium ion concentration is a direct consequence of the excitatory event at the cell surface membrane. This event may cause a release of calcium from and/or a change in calcium permeability in this membrane, or given rise to some signal (chemical or electrical) that causes a release from and/or a change in calcium permeability of an intracellular membrane. The model emphasizes this operational similarity, but it is obvious that in terms of a particular system under study, it is necessary to define the precise details of this transduction event.

The second general point concerns the respective modes by which the cAMP receptor protein and the calcium receptor protein, calmodulin, regulate cell function. Both are capable of regulating the activity of an important class of regulatory proteins, protein kinases. This appears to be the only means by which the cAMP receptor protein regulates cell function. Calmodulin, on the other hand, regulates a number of other calcium-dependent processes that do not involve activation of this class of enzymes. This would appear to be a significant difference between the modulating function of these two messengers. However, the possibility that the cAMP–receptor protein complex may regulate the function of proteins other than protein kinase has not been critically evaluated. It seems likely that when it is effector elements will be discovered that respond to cAMP·R.

A third point concerns the illustration of a single calcium receptor protein, calmodulin, when in fact there are several others, parvalbumin, leiotonin C, and troponin C. Again this is a detail of minor importance. All four proteins are structurally and operationally similar. It will be of interest to see that if in time more than one cAMP receptor protein is discovered.

Fourth, as illustrated, a single class of enzymes, the protein kinases, are shown to be activated by either cAMP or calcium. The implication here is not necessarily that the identical enzymes are involved. Clearly, in the case of the phosphorylase system the cAMP-sensitive protein kinase, and the calcium-sensitive one are different enzymes, and both can catalyze the phosphorylation of a specific substrate, e.g., glycogen synthase. However, in a situation such as the hepatic responses to nor-epinephrine and glucagon where the same 10 proteins are phosphory-lated whether calcium or cAMP, respectively, serves as primary messengers, it is not clear if the same or different enzymes are involved. One of at least four possibilities can be considered: (1) the ultimate protein kinase is calcium dependent and cAMP changes the sensitivity of the system to calcium; (2) the ultimate protein kinase is cAMP dependent and calcium changes the sensitivity of the system to cAMP; (3) each messenger acts on a different protein kinase and each kinase the same proteins as substrates; or (4) the two different messengers act on the same protein kinase. Regardless of which of these mechanisms operate, the operational result in terms of information flow is comparable.

The final point concerns the interrelationships between calcium and cAMP in terms of regulating each other's concentration. These are the least stereotyped aspect of their relationship. Calcium can stimulate either cAMP synthesis or hydrolysis. Cyclic AMP can stimulate either a rise or fall in the intracellular calcium ion concentration by affecting calcium exchange across any or all three calcium transporting mem-branes: plasma membrane, endoplasmic reticulum, and inner mitochon-drial membrane.

In closing, it is necessary to anticipate another objection to the model: its failure to include cGMP, guanylate cyclase, and cGMP phosphodies-terase. The problem is that the role of cGMP remains elusive. The more we learn the less we know. In some respects, it appears to be a variant of the cAMP system, but in others it is quite different. A major problem is that some guanylate cyclases are particulate, others soluble. In some cases, these cyclases, particularly the soluble ones, appear to be activated by calcium ion. It is not yet clear what role the calcium-mediated rise in cGMP plays in excitation–response coupling. There are several examples of cGMP-dependent protein kinases but as yet no definition, in physio-logically meaningful terms, of the function of the phosphorylated pro-ducts. A major type of experimental observation that helped define the role of cAMP was the fact that when exogenous cAMP or one of its analogs is added to many hormonally responsive cells, the exogenous nucleotide mimics many of the effects normally produced by the usual first messenger in the same tissue. This approach has been nowhere near as successful with cyclic GMP. In some tissues its addition alters cell behavior, but, for example, in the liver the change in behavior is similar to that seen after cAMP addition.

Present data do not yet allow one to formulate a general model for the role of the cGMP system. It is the authors' belief that eventually cGMP will be found to function in some general capacity as a modifier of the generation, propagation, and reception of the two universal messengers, calcium and cAMP.

REFERENCES

Adelstein, R. S., Conti, M. A., Hathaway, D. R., and Klee, C. B. (1978). *J. Biol. Chem.* **253**, 8347.

Aguilera, G., and Catt, K. J. (1978). *Proc. Natl. Acad. Sci. U.S.A.* **75**, 4057.

Ahlquist, R. P. (1959). *Pharmacol. Rev.* **11**, 441.

Anderson, B., Nelson, D. J., Brittain, H. G., and Jones, W. C. (1977). *Proc. 2nd Maine Biomed. Sci. Symp., University of Maine Press, Orono.*

Anderson, B., Osborn, M., and Weber, K. (1978). *Eur. J. Cell Biol.* **17**, 354.

Anderson, J. M., and Cormier, M. J. (1978). *Biochem. Biophys. Res. Commun.* **84**, 595.

Appelman, M. M., and Terasaki, W. L. (1975). *Adv. Cyclic Nucleotide Res.* **5**, 153.

Assimacopoulos-Jeannet, F. D., Blackmore, P. F., and Exton, J. H. (1977). *J. Biol. Chem.* **252**, 2662.

Babcock, D. F., Chen, J.-L., Yip, B. P., and Lardy, H. A. (1979). *J. Biol. Chem.* **254**, 8117.

Baker, P. F. (1973). *Fed. Proc., Fed. Am. Soc. Exp. Biol.* **32**, 1944.

Baker, P. F. (1976). *Symp. Soc. Exp. Biol.* **30**, 67.

Baker, P. F. (1978). *Ann. N.Y. Acad. Sci.* **307**, 250.

Bárány, K., Bárány, M., Gillis, M. J., and Kushmerick, M. J. (1979). *J. Biol. Chem.* **254**, 3617.

Barker, W. C., Ketcham, L. K., and Dayhoff, M. O. (1977). *In* "Calcium Binding Proteins and Calcium Function in Health and Disease" (R. H. Wasserman *et al.*, eds.), p. 110. Am. Elsevier, New York.

Baron, G., Damaille, J., and Dutruge, E. (1975). *FEBS Lett.* **56**, 156.

Barrantes, F. J., Changeux, J. P., Lunt, G. G., and Sobel, A. (1975). *Nature (London)* **256**, 325.

Barron, J. T., Bárány, M., and Bárány, K. (1979). *J. Biol. Chem.* **254**, 4954.

Batzri, S., and Selinger, Z. (1973). *J. Biol. Chem.* **248**, 356.

Batzri, S., Selinger, Z., Schramm, M., and Rabinovitch, M. R. (1973). *J. Biol. Chem.* **248**, 361.

Baumann, K., Chan, H. L., Bode, F., Papavassilious, F., and Wagner, M. (1975). *In* "Biochemical Aspects of Renal Function" (Angielski *et al.*, eds.), p. 223. Bern/Stuttgart, Wein.

Beall, R. J., and Sayers, G. (1972). *Arch. Biochem. Biophys.* **148**, 70.

Benzonana, G., Capony, J.-P., and Pechère, J.-F. (1972). *Biochim Biophys. Acta* **278**, 110.

Bergstrom, S., Danielsson, H., Klemberg, D., and Samuelsson, B. (1964). *J. Biol. Chem.* **239**, 4006.

Berridge, M. J. (1970). *J. Exp. Biol.* **53**, 171.

Berridge, M. J. (1977). *In* "Transport of Ions and Water in Animals" (B. L. Gupta *et al.*, eds.), p. 75. Academic Press, New York.

Berridge, M. J., and Fain, J. N. (1979). *Biochem. J.* **178**, 59.

Berridge, M. J., and Prince, W. T. (1973). *Adv. Insect Physiol.* **9**, 1.

Berridge, M. J., Oschman, J. L., and Wall, B. J. (1975). *In* "Calcium Transport in Contractions and Secretion" (E. Carafoli, F. Clementi, W. Drabikowsky, and A. Margreth, eds.), p. 131. North-Holland Publ., Amsterdam.

Billah, M. M., and Michell, R. H. (1979). *Biochem. J.* **182**, 661.

Birmingham, M. K., Elliot, F. H., and Valere, P. H. C. (1953). *Endocrinology* 53, 687.
Birnbaumer, L. (1973). *Biochim. Biophys. Acta* 300, 129.
Blackmore, P. F., Brumley, F. T., Marks, J. L., and Exton, J. H. (1978). *J. Biol. Chem.* 253, 4851.
Blackmore, P. F., Assimacopoulos-Jeannet, F., Chan, T. M., and Exton, J. H. (1979a). *J. Biol. Chem.* 254, 2828.
Blackmore, P. F., Dehaye, J.-P., and Exton, J. H. (1979b). *J. Biol. Chem.* 254, 6945.
Blair, E. L., Brown, J. C., Harper, A. A., and Scratcherd, T. (1966). *J. Physiol. (London)* 184, 812.
Blaustein, M. P. (1974). *Ergeb. Physiol., Biol. Chem. Exp. Pharmakol.* 70, 33.
Blaustein, M., Ratztaff, R. W., and Kendrick, N. K. (1978). *Ann. N.Y. Acad. Sci.* 307, 195.
Blinks, J. R., Prendergast, F. G., and Allen, D. G. (1976). *Pharmacol. Rev.* 28, 1.
Bolton, J. E., and Field, M. (1977). *J. Membr. Biol.* 35, 159.
Bolton, T. B. (1979). *Physiol. Rev.* 59, 607.
Borle, A. B. (1968). *Endocrinology* 83, 1316.
Borle, A. (1970). *J. Gen. Physiol.* 55, 163.
Borle, A. (1973). *Fed. Proc., Fed. Am. Soc. Exp. Biol.* 32, 1944.
Borle, A. B., and Uchikawa, T. (1978). *Endocrinology* 102, 1725.
Borle, A. B., and Uchikawa, T. (1979). *Endocrinology* 104, 122.
Bourne, H. R., Lichtenstein, L. M., Melmor, K. L., Henney, C. S., Wernstein, Y., and Shearer, G. M. (1974). *Science* 184, 19–28.
Bowyer, F., and Kitabchi, A. E. (1974). *Biochem. Biophys. Res. Commun.* 57, 100.
Boyd, J., Mulrow, P. J., Palmore, W. P., and Silva, P. (1973). *Circ. Res.* 32, Suppl. 1, 29.
Brinley, F. J., Jr. (1978). *Annu. Rev. Biophys. Bioeng.* 7, 363.
Brisson, G. R., and Malaisse, W. J. (1973). *Metab., Clin. Exp.* 22, 455.
Brisson, G. R., Malaisse-Lagae, F., and Malaisse, W. K. (1977). *J. Clin. Invest.* 51, 232.
Brostrom, C. O., Hunkeler, F. L., and Krebs, E. G. (1971). *J. Biol. Chem.* 246, 1961.
Brostrom, C. O., Brostrom, M. A., and Wolff, D. J. (1977). *J. Biol. Chem.* 252, 5677.
Brostrom, M. A., Brostrom, C. O., Breckenridge, B. M., and Wolff, D. J. (1975). *Proc. Natl. Acad. Sci. U.S.A.* 72, 64.
Brostrom, M. A., Brostrom, C. O., Breckenridge, B. M., and Wolff, D. J. (1978). *Adv. Cyclic Nucleotide Res.* 9, 85.
Brostrom, M. A., Brostrom, C. O., and Wolff, D. J. (1979). *J. Biol. Chem.* 254, 7548.
Bruns, D. E., Black, B., McDonald, J. M., and Jarett, L. (1977). *In* "Calcium Binding Proteins and Calcium Function in Health and Disease" (R. H. Wasserman *et al.*, eds.), p. 181. Am. Elsevier, New York.
Butcher, F. R. (1978a). *Adv. Cyclic Nucleotide Res.* 9, 707.
Butcher, F. R. (1978b). *In* "Biochemical Actions of Hormones" (G. Litwack, ed.), Vol. 5, p. 54. Academic Press, New York.
Butcher, F. R., Goldman, J. A., and Memerovsi, M. (1975). *Biochim. Biophys. Acta* 392, 82.
Bygrave, F. L., and Tranter, C. J. (1978). *Biochem. J.* 174, 1021.
Calderon, P., Furnelle, J., and Christophe, J. (1979). *Biochim. Biophys. Acta* 574, 391.
Carafoli, E., and Crompton, M. (1978). *Curr. Top. Membr. Transp.* 10, 151–216.
Carstens, M., and Weller, M. (1979). *Biochim. Biophys. Acta* 551, 420.
Case, R. M. (1978). *Biol. Rev. Cambridge Philos. Soc.* 53, 211.
Case, R. M., Johnson, M., Scratcherd, T., and Sherratt, H. S. A. (1972). *J. Physiol. (London)* 223, 669.
Chan, T. M., and Exton, J. H. (1977). *J. Biol. Chem.* 252, 8645.
Chan, T. M., and Exton, J. H. (1978). *J. Biol. Chem.* 253, 6393.

Chang, H. W. (1974). *Proc. Natl. Acad. Sci. U.S.A.* **71**, 2113.

Changeux, J. P., Thiery, J., Tung, T., and Kittel, C. (1967). *Proc. Natl. Acad. Sci. U.S.A.* **57**, 335.

Changeux, J. P., Podleski, T. R., and Meunier, J. C. (1969). *J. Gen. Physiol.* **54**, 2255.

Changeux, J. P., Meunier, J. C., and Huchet, M. (1971). *Mol. Pharmacol.* **7**, 538.

Changeux, J. P., Kasai, M., and Lee, C. Y. (1970). *Proc. Natl. Acad. Sci. U.S.A.* **67**, 1241.

Changeux, J. P., Benedetti, L., Bourgeois, J. P., Brisson, A. D., Cartand, J., Devaux, P., and Grünhagen, H. H. (1976). *Cold Spring Harbor Symp. Quant. Biol.* **40**, 211.

Charbonneau, H., and Cormier, M. J. (1979). *Biochem. Biophys. Res. Commun.* **90**, 1039.

Charles, M. A., Lawecki, J., Picket, R., and Grodsky, G. M. (1975). *J. Biol. Chem.* **250**, 6134.

Chen, J. J., Babcock, D. F., and Lardy, H. A. (1978). *Proc. Natl. Acad. Sci. U.S.A.* **75**, 2234.

Cheung, W. H., Gradham, L. S., Lynch, T. J., Lin, H. M., and Tallant, E. A. (1975). *Biochem. Biophys. Res. Commun.* **66**, 1055.

Cheung, W. H., Lynch, T. J., and Wallace, R. W. (1978). *Adv. Cyclic Nucleotide Res.* **9**, 233.

Cheung, W. Y. (1970). *Biochem. Biophys. Res. Commun.* **38**, 533.

Christophe, J., Deschodt-Lanckman, M., Adler, N., and Robberecht, P. (1977). *In* "Hormonal Receptors in Digestive Tract Physiology" (S. Bonfils *et al.*, eds.), p. 247. North-Holland Publ., Amsterdam.

Claret-Berthon, B., Claret, M., and Mazet, J. L. (1977). *J. Physiol. (London)* **272**, 529.

Clark, M. G., and Jarrett, J. G. (1978). *Biochem. J.* **176**, 805.

Clarke, W. R., Jones, L. R., and Lefkowitz, R. J. (1978). *J. Biol. Chem.* **253**, 5975.

Clemente, F., and Meldolesi, J. (1975). *Br. J. Pharmacol.* **55**, 369.

Cochrane, D. E., and Douglas, W. W. (1974). *Proc. Natl. Acad. Sci. U.S.A.* **71**, 408.

Cohen, P. (1973). *Eur. J. Biochem.* **34**, 1.

Cohen, P. (1978). *Curr. Top. Cell. Regul.* **14**, 117.

Cohen, P., Burchell, A., Foulkes, J.-G., Cohen, P. T. W., Vanaman, T. C., and Nairn, A. C. (1978). *FEBS Lett.* **92**, 287.

Collins, J. H. (1976). *Nature (London)* **259**, 699.

Collins, J. H., Potter, J. D., Horn, M. J., Wilshire, G., and Jackson, N. (1973). *FEBS Lett.* **36**, 268.

Corbin, J. D., and Lincoln, T. M. (1978). *Adv. Cyclic Nucleotide Res.* **9**, 159.

Creutz, C. E., Pazoles, C. J., and Pollard, H. B. (1978). *J. Biol. Chem.* **298**, 289.

Curry, D. L., Bennett, L. L., and Grodsky, G. M. (1968). *Am. J. Physiol.* **214**, 174.

Dabrowska, R., and Hartshorne, D. J. (1978). *Biochem. Biophys. Res. Commun.* **85**, 1352.

Dabrowska, R., Aramatorio, D., Sherry, J. M. F., and Hartshorne, D. J. (1978). *Biochemistry* **17**, 253.

Dambach, N. G., and Friedmann, N. (1974). *Biochim. Biophys. Acta* **332**, 374.

Danforth, W. H., Helmreich, E., and Cori, C. F. (1962). *Proc. Natl. Acad. Sci. U.S.A* **48**, 1191.

Davis, J. O. (1961). *Recent Prog. Horm. Res.* **17**, 293.

Dean, P. M., and Matthews, E. K. (1970a). *J. Physiol. (London)* **210**, 255.

Dean, P. M., and Matthews, E. K. (1970b). *J. Physiol. (London)* **210**, 265.

Dean, P. M., and Matthews, E. K. (1972). *Diabetologia* **8**, 173.

Dedman, J. R., Potter, J. D., and Means, A. R. (1977a). *J. Biol. Chem.* **252**, 2437.

Dedman, J. R., Potter, J. D., Jackson, R. L., Johnson, J. D., and Means, A. R. (1977b). *J. Biol. Chem.* **252**, 3415.

Dedman, J. R., Jackson, R. L., Schreiber, W. E., and Means, A. R. (1978). *J. Biol. Chem.* **253**, 343.

Deguchi, T. (1977). *J. Biol. Chem.* **252**, 596.
DeLorenzo, R. J., and Freedman, S. D. (1977a). *Biochem. Biophys. Res. Commun.* **77**, 1036.
DeLorenzo, R. J., and Freedman, S. D. (1977b). *Epilepsia* **18**, 357.
DeLorenzo, R. J., and Freedman, S. D. (1978). *Biochem. Biophys. Res. Commun.* **80**, 183.
DeLorenzo, R. J., Freedman, S. D., Yohe, W. B., and Maurer, S. C. (1979). *Proc. Natl. Acad. Sci. U.S.A.* **76**, 1838.
DePaoli-Roach, A. A., Roach, P. J., and Larner, J. (1979). *J. Biol. Chem.* **254**, 4212.
Deth, R., and van Breeman, C. (1977). *J. Membr. Biol.* **30**, 363.
DeTorrentegui, G., and Berthet, J. (1966). *Biochim. Biophys. Acta* **116**, 467.
Dormer, R. L., and Ashcroft, S. J. H. (1974). *Biochem. J.* **144**, 543.
Douglas, J., Aguilera, G., Kondo, T., and Catt, K. J. (1978). *Endocrinology* **102**, 685.
Douglas, W. W., and Rubin, R. P. (1961). *J. Physiol. (London)* **159**, 40.
Douglas, W. W., and Veda, Y. J. (1973). *J. Physiol. (London)* **234**, 97P.
Drabikowski, W., Grabarek, Z., and Barylko, B. (1977). *Biochim. Biophys. Acta* **490**, 216.
Ebashi, S. (1976). *Annu. Rev. Physiol.* **38**, 293.
Ebashi, S., Endo, M., and Ohtsuki, I. (1969). *Q. Rev. Biophys.* **2**, 351.
Eldefrawi, M. E., Eldefrawi, A. T., and O'Brien, R. D. (1971). *Proc. Natl. Acad. Sci. U.S.A.* **68**, 1047.
Exton, J. H. (1979). *Biochem. Pharmacol.* **28**, 2237.
Exton, J. H., and Harper, S. C. (1975). *Adv. Cyclic Nucleotide Res.* **5**, 519.
Exton, J. H., Robison, G. A., Sutherland, E. W., and Park, C. R. (1971). *J. Biol. Chem.* **246**, 6166.
Fabiato, A., and Fabiato, F. (1978). *Ann. N.Y. Acad. Sci.* **307**, 491.
Fain, J. N. (1978). *Recept. Recognition, Ser. A.* **6**, 3.
Fain, J. N., and Berridge, M. J. (1979). *Biochem. J.* **178**, 45.
Fakunding, J. L. (1979). *Endocrinology* **105**, 327.
Fambrough, D. M., and Hartzell, H. C. (1972). *Science* **176**, 189.
Farese, R. V. (1971a). *Endocrinology* **89**, 1057.
Farese, R. V. (1971b). *Endocrinology* **89**, 1064.
Farese, R. V. (1971c). *Science* **173**, 447.
Farese, R. V., and Prudente, W. J. (1977). *Biochim. Biophys. Acta* **497**, 386.
Feher, J. J., and Wasserman, R. H. (1976). *Fed. Proc., Fed. Am. Soc. Exp. Biol.* **35**, 339.
Fentel, R. M., and Weiss, B. (1976). *Mol. Pharmacol.* **12**, 678.
Field, M., Plotkin, G. R., and Silen, W. (1968). *Nature (London)* **217**, 469.
Fine, R., Lehman, W., Head, J., and Blitz, A. (1975). *Nature (London)* **258**, 260.
Fischer, E. H., Heilmeyer, M. G., and Haschke, R. H. (1971). *Curr. Top. Cell. Regul.* **4**, 211.
Florio, V. A., and Twible, D. A. (1979). *J. Biol. Chem.* **254**, 7147.
Floyd, J. J., Jr., Fajans, S. S., Conn, J. W., Knoff, R. F., and Rull, J. (1966). *J. Clin. Invest.* **45**, 1487.
Foden, S., and Randle, P. J. (1978). *Biochem. J.* **170**, 615.
Foldes, M., and Barrett, G. J. (1977). *J. Biol. Chem.* **252**, 5372.
Foreman, J. C., and Mongar, J. L. (1975). *In* "Calcium Transport in Contractions and Secretion" (E. Carafoli, F. Clementi, W. Drabikowski, and A. Margreth, eds.), p. 175. North-Holland Publ., Amsterdam.
Foreman, J. C., Mongar, J. L., and Comperts, B. P. (1973). *Nature (London)* **245**, 249.
Foster, R., Lobo, M. V., and Marusic, E. T. (1979). *Am. J. Physiol.* **237**, E363.
Fredlund, P., Saltman, S., Kondo, T., Douglas, J., and Catt, K. J. (1977). *Endocrinology* **100**, 481.
Friedmann, N., and Dambach, G. (1973). *Biochim. Biophys. Acta* **307**, 339.

Friedmann, N., and Dambach, G. (1980). *Biochim. Biophys. Acta* (in press).

Friedmann, N., and Park, C. R. (1968). *Proc. Natl. Acad. Sci. U.S.A.* **61**, 584.

Friedmann, N., and Rasmussen, H. (1970). *Biochim. Biophys. Acta* **222**, 41.

Friedmann, N., Somlyo, A. V., and Somlyo, A. P. (1971). *Science* **171**, 400.

Frizzell, R. A. (1977). *J. Membr. Biol.* **35**, 175.

Frizzell, R. A., Field, M., and Schultz, S. G. (1979). *Am. J. Physiol.* **236**(1), F(1).

Fujita, K., Aguilera, G., and Catt, K. J. (1979). *J. Biol. Chem.* **254**, 8567.

Ganong, W. F., Biglieri, E. F., and Mulrow, P. J. (1966). *Recent Prog. Horm. Res.* **22**, 381.

Gardner, J. D., and Hahne, W. F. (1977). *Biochim. Biophys. Acta* **471**, 466.

Gardner, J. D., Christophe, J. P., Conlon, T. P., and Fransen, E. K. (1977). *In* "Hormonal Receptors in Digestive Tract Physiology" (S. Bonfils *et al.*, eds.), p. 237. North-Holland Publ., Amsterdam.

Garland, D. L. (1979). *Arch. Biochem. Biophys.* **198**, 335.

Garren, L. D., Ney, R. L., and Davis, W. W. C. (1965). *Proc. Natl. Acad. Sci. U.S.A.* **53**, 1443–1450.

Garren, L. D., Gill, G. N., Masui, H., and Walton, G. M. (1971). *Recent Prog. Horm. Res.* **27**, 433.

Garrison, J. C. (1978). *J. Biol. Chem.* **253**, 7091.

Garrison, J. C., and Borland, M. K. (1979). *J. Biol. Chem.* **254**, 1129.

Garrison, J. C., and Haynes, R. C. (1975). *J. Biol. Chem.* **250**, 2769.

Garrison, J. C., Borland, K., Florio, V. A., and Twible, D. A. (1979). *J. Biol. Chem.* **254**, 7147.

Gerbers, D. L. (1978). *J. Biol. Chem.* **253**, 1898.

Gerbers, D. L., Hardman, J. G., and Rudolph, F. B (1974). *Biochemistry* **13**, 4166.

Gerich, J. E., Charles, M. A., and Grodsky, G. M. (1976). *Annu. Rev. Physiol.* **38**, 353.

Gillis, J. M., and Gerday, C. C. (1977). *In* "Calcium Binding Proteins and Calcium Function in Health and Disease" (R. H. Wasserman *et al.*, eds.), p. 193. Am. Elsevier, New York.

Gnegy, M. E., Uzunov, P., and Costa, E. (1976). *Proc. Natl. Acad. Sci. U.S.A.* **73**, 3887.

Goldberg, N. D., O'Dea, R. F., and Haddox, M. K. (1973). *Adv. Cyclic Nucleotide Res.* **3**, 155.

Grahme-Smith, D. G. (1964). *Biochem. Biophys. Res. Commun.* **16**, 586.

Grahme-Smith, D. G., Butcher, R. W., New, R. L., and Sutherland, E. W. (1967). *J. Biol. Chem.* **242**, 5535.

Grand, R. J. A., Perry, S. V., and Weeks, R. A. (1979). *Biochem. J.* **177**, 521.

Grill, V., and Cerasi, E. (1974). *J. Biol. Chem.* **249**, 4196.

Grodsky, G. M. (1970). *Vitam. Horm. (N.Y.)* **28**, 37.

Grodsky, G. M. (1972). *Diabetes* **21**, Suppl. 2, 584.

Grodsky, G. M., and Bennett, L. L. (1966). *Diabetes* **15**, 910.

Grodsky, G. M., Bennett, C. L., Smith, D. F., and Schimid, F.G. (1967). *Metab. Clin. Exp.* **16**, 222.

Guder, W. G. (1979). *Biochim. Biophys. Acta* **584**, 507.

Guder, W. G., and Rupprecht, A. (1975). *Eur. J. Biochem.* **52**, 283.

Guder, W. G., and Rupprecht, A. (1976). *In* "Use of Isolated Liver Cells and Kidney Tubules in Metabolic Studies" (J. M. Tager *et al.*, eds.). p. 75. North-Holland Publ., Amsterdam.

Guder, W. G., and Wieland, O. H. (1972). *Eur. J. Biochem.* **31**, 69.

Haddah, R. A., Landis, C. A., and Putney, J. W. (1979). *J. Physiol. (London)* **291**, 457.

Haksar, A., and Peron, F. G. (1972). *Biochem. Biophys. Res. Commun.* **47**, 445.

Hales, C. N., and Milner, R. D. G. (1968). *J. Physiol. (London)* **199**, 177.

Hall, P. F. (1966). *Endocrinology* **78**, 690.

Hamilton, M. N., and Hamilton, R. T. (1979). *Nature (London)* **279**, 446.

Hamon, M., Bourgoin, S., Artaud, F., and Hery, F. (1977). *J. Neurochem.* **28**, 811.

Harada, E., and Rubin, R. P. (1978). *J. Physiol. (London)* **274**, 367.

Hardman, J. G., and Sutherland, E. W. (1969). *J. Biol. Chem.* **244**, 6363.

Harper, A. A., and Raper, H. S. (1943). *J. Physiol. (London)* **102**, 115.

Hathaway, D. R., and Adelstein, R. S. (1979). *Proc. Natl. Acad. Sci. U.S.A.* **76**, 1653.

Hayashi, K., Sala, G., Catt, K., and Dafau, M. L. (1979). *J. Biol. Chem.* **254**, 6678.

Haylett, D. G., and Jenkinson, D. H. (1969). *Nature (London)* **224**, 80.

Haynes, R. C. (1958). *J. Biol. Chem.* **233**, 1220.

Haynes, R. C., and Berthet, L. (1957). *J. Biol. Chem.* **225**, 115.

Hazelbauer, J., and Changeux, J. P. (1974). *Proc. Natl. Acad. Sci. U.S.A.* **71**, 1479.

Head, J. F., Weeks, R. A., and Perry, S. V. (1977). *Biochem. J.* **161**, 465.

Hechter, O. (1955). *Vitam. Horm. (N.Y.)* **13**, 293.

Heilbrunn, L. V., and Wiercenski, F. J. (1947). *J. Cell. Comp. Physiol.* **29**, 15.

Heilmeyer, L. M. G., Jr., Meyer, F., Haschke, R. H., and Fisher, E. H. (1970). *J. Biol. Chem.* **245**, 6649–6656.

Heizmann, C. W., Haeuptle, M. T., and Eppenberger, H. M. (1977). *Eur. J. Biochem.* **80**, 433.

Hellman, B. (1975). *Endocrinology* **97**, 392.

Hems, D. A., and Whitton, P. D. (1973). *Biochem. J.* **136**, 705.

Hendrix, T. R., and Paulk, H. T. (1977). *In* "International Review of Physiology. Gastrointestinal Physiology II" (R. K. Crane, ed.), Vol. 12, p. 257. University Park Press, Baltimore, Maryland.

Henquin, J. C., and Lambert, A. E. (1974). *Diabetologia* **10**, 368.

Henquin, J. C., and Lambert, A. E. (1976). *J. Physiol. (Paris)* **72**, 747.

Hidaka, H., Yamaki, T., Totsuka, T., and Masahisa, A. (1979). *Mol. Pharmacol.* **15**, 49.

Hinds, T. R., Larsen, F. L., and Vincenzi, F. F. (1978). **81**, 455.

Ho, H. C., Desai, R., and Wang, J. H. (1975). *FEBS Lett.* **50**, 374.

Ho, H. C., Teo, T. S., Desai, R., and Wang, J. H. (1976). *Biochim. Biophys. Acta* **429**, 461.

Ho, H. C., Wirch, E., Stevens, F. C., and Wang, J. H. (1977). *J. Biol. Chem.* **252**, 43.

Hofman, T., Kawakami, M., Morris, H., Hitchman, A. J. W., Harrison, J. E., and Dorrington, K. J. (1977). *In* Calcium Binding Proteins and Calcium Function in Health and Disease" (R. H. Wasserman *et al.*, eds.), p. 373. Am. Elsevier, New York.

Hokin, L. E. (1966). *Biochim. Biophys. Acta* **115**, 219.

Holroyde, M. J., Potter, J. D., and Solaro, R. J. (1979). *J. Biol. Chem.* **254**, 6478.

Honn, K. V., and Chavin, W. (1977). *Acta Endocrinol. (Copenhagen)* **85**, 823.

Howell, S. L., Montague, W., and Tyhurst, M. (1975). *Cell Sci.* **19**, 395.

Huang, F. L., and Ginsmann, W. H. (1976). *FEBS Lett.* **62**, 326.

Hutson, N. J., Brumley, F. T., and Assimacopoulos, F. D., Harper, S. C., and Exton, J. H. (1976). *J. Biol. Chem.* **251**, 5200.

Ilundain, A., and Naftalin, R. J. (1979). *Nature (London)* **279**, 446.

Ishikawa, E., Ishikawa, S., Davis, J. W., and Sutherland, E. W. (1969). *J. Biol. Chem.* **244**, 6371.

Jaanus, S. D., Rosenstein, M. J., and Rubin, R. P. (1970). *J. Physiol. (London)* **209**, 539.

Jackson, R. L., Dedman, J. R., Schreiber, W. E., Bhatnagar, P. K., Knapp, R. D., and Means, A. R. (1977). *Biochem. Biophys. Res. Commun.* **77**, 723.

Jakob, A., and Diem, S. (1976). *Biochim. Biophys. Acta* **404**, 57.

Jarrett, H. W., and Kyte, J. (1979). *J. Biol. Chem.* **254**, 8237.

Kakiuchi, S., and Yamazaki, R. (1970). *Biochem. Biophys. Res. Commun.* **41**, 1104.

Kakiuchi, S., Yamazaki, R., and Teshima, H. (1971). *Biochem. Biophys. Res. Commun.* **42**, 968.

Kakiuchi, S., Yamazaki, R., Teshima, H., and Menishi, K. (1973). *Proc. Natl. Acad. Sci. U.S.A.* **70**, 3526.

Kanagasuntheram, P., and Randle, P. J. (1976). *Biochem. J.* **160**, 547.

Kanno, T., Cochrane, D. E., and Douglas, W. W. (1973). *Can. J. Physiol. Pharmacol.* **51**, 1001.

Kaplan, N. M. (1965). *J. Clin. Invest.* **44**, 2029.

Karaboyas, G. C., and Koritz, S. B. (1965). *Biochemistry* **4**, 462.

Karl, R. C., Zawalich, W. S., Ferrendelli, J. A., and Matschinsky, F. M. (1975). *J. Biol. Chem.* **250**, 4575.

Karlin, A. (1974). *Life Sci.* **14**, 1385.

Katz, A. M., Tada, M., and Kirchberger, M. (1975). *Adv. Cyclic Nucleotide Res.* **5**, 453.

Katz, B. (1966). "Nerve, Muscle and Synapse." McGraw-Hill, New York.

Katz, B., and Miledi, R. (1967). *J. Physiol. (London)* **189**, 535.

Keppens, S., and de Wulf, H. (1976). *FEBS Lett.* **68**, 279.

Keppens, S., and de Wulf, H. (1979). *Biochim. Biophys. Acta* **588**, 63.

Keppens, S., Vandenhude, J. R., and DeWulf, H. (1977). *Biochim. Biophys. Acta* **496**, 448.

Khoo, J. C., Sperry, P. J., Gill, G. N., and Steinberg, D. (1977). *Proc. Natl. Acad. Sci. U.S.A.* **74**, 4843.

Kilimann, M., and Heilmeyer, L. M. G. (1977). *Eur. J. Biochem.* **73**, 191.

Kimberg, D. V., Field, M., Johnson, J., Henderson, A., and Gershon, E. (1971). *J. Clin. Invest.* **50**, 1218.

Kirk, C. J., Verrinder, T. R., and Hems, D. A. (1977). *FEBS Lett.* **83**, 267.

Kirk, C. J., Verrinder, T. R. and Hems, D. A. (1978). *Biochem. Soc. Trans.* **6**, 1031.

Kishimoto, A., Takai, H., and Nishizuka, H. (1977). *J. Biol. Chem.* **252**, 7449.

Klahr, S., Nawar, T., and Schoolwerth, A. C. (1973). *Biochim. Biophys. Acta* **304**, 161.

Klee, C. B. (1977). *Biochemistry* **16**, 1017.

Klee, C. B., Crouch, T. H., and Krinks, M. H. (1978). *Fed. Proc., Fed. Am. Soc. Exp. Biol.* **37**, 188.

Kneer, N. M., Bosch, A. L., Clark, H. G., and Lardy, H. A. (1974). *Proc. Natl. Acad. Sci. U.S.A.* **71**, 4523.

Kneer, N. M., Wagner, M. J., and Lardy, H. A. (1979). *J. Biol. Chem.* **254**, 12160.

Kornguth, S. E., and Sunderland, E. (1975). *Biochim. Biophys. Acta* **393**, 100.

Kretsinger, R. H. (1972). *Nature (London)* **240**, 85.

Kretsinger, R. H. (1976). *Annu. Rev. Biochem.* **56**, 239.

Kretsinger, R. H. (1980). *CRC Crit. Rev.* (in press).

Kretsinger, R. H., and Nockolds, C. E. (1973). *J. Biol. Chem.* **248**, 3313.

Krueger, B. K., Forn, J., and Greengard, P. (1977). *J. Biol. Chem.* **252**, 2764.

Kuhn, D. M., Vogel, R. L., and Lovenberg, W. (1978). *Biochem. Biophys. Res. Commun.* **82**, 759.

Kumagi, H., and Nishida, E. (1979). *J. Biochem. (Tokyo)* **85**, 1267.

Kuo, C.-H., Ichida, S., Matsuda, T., Kakuichi, S., and Yoshida, H. (1979). *Life Sci.* **25**, 235.

Kuo, I. C. Y., and Coffee, C. J. (1976). *J. Biol. Chem.* **251**, 1603.

Kuo, J. F., and Greengard, P. (1969). *Proc. Natl. Acad. Sci. U.S.A.* **64**, 1349.

Kuo, W. N., Hodgins, O. S., and Kuo, J. F. (1973). *J. Biol. Chem.* **248**, 2705.

Kurokawa, K., Ohno, T., and Rasmussen, H. (1973). *Biochim. Biophys. Acta* **313**, 32.

Kuwayma, H., and Yagi, K. (1979). *J. Biochem. (Tokyo)* **85**, 1245.

Lambert, A. (1976). *Ergeb. Physiol., Biol. Chem. Exp. Pharmakol.* **75**, 98.

Lambert, M., and Christophe, J. (1978). *Eur. J. Biochem.* **91**, 485.

Larsen, F. L., and Vincenzi, F. F. (1979). *Science* **204**, 306.

LeCann, A., and Freychet, P. (1978). *Endocrinology* 102, 379.
LeDonne, N. C., and Coffee, C. J. (1979). *J. Biol. Chem.* 254, 4317.
Lefkowitz, R. J., Roth, J., and Pastan, I. (1971). *Ann. N.Y. Acad. Sci.* 185, 195.
Lehman, W., and Szent-Györgyi, A. G. (1972). *J. Gen. Physiol.* 59, 375.
LePeuch, C. J., Haiech, J., and Demaille, J. G. (1980). *Biochemistry* 91, 485.
Levilliers, J., Lecot, F., and Pairault, J. (1978). *Biochem. Biophys. Res. Commun.* 84, 727.
Levin, R. M., and Weiss, B. (1976). *Mol. Pharmacol.* 12, 581.
Lichtenstein, L. M., Ishizaka, K., Norman, P. S., Sobotka, A. K., and Hill, B. M. (1973) *J. Clin. Invest.* 52, 472.
Lin, Y. M., Liu, Y. P., and Cheung, W. Y. (1974). *J. Biol. Chem.* 249, 4943.
Liu, Y. P., and Cheung, W. Y. (1976). *J. Biol. Chem.* 251, 4193.
Locke, F. S. (1894). *Zentralbl. Physiol.* 8, 166.
Lowenstein, W. R., and Rose, B. (1978). *Ann. N. Y. Acad. Sci.* 307, 285.
MacDonald, D. W. R., and Saggerson, D. E. (1977). *Biochem. J.* 168, 33.
McGowen, E. B., Speiser, S., and Stracher, A. (1976). *Biophys. J.* 16, 162a.
McIhinney, J., and Schulster, D. (1975). *J. Endocrinol.* 64, 175.
MacIntyre, J. D., and Green, J. W. (1978). *Biochim. Biophys. Acta* 510, 373.
Mackie, C. M., Simpson, E. R., Mee, M. S. R., Tait, S. A. S., and Tait, J. F. (1977). *Clin. Sci. Mol. Med.* 53, 289.
Mahafee, D., Reitz, R. C., and Ney, R. L. (1974). *J. Biol. Chem.* 249, 227.
Malaisse, W. J. (1973). *Diabetologia* 9, 167.
Malaisse, W. J., and Boschero, A. C. (1979). *Am. J. Physiol.* 236(2), E139.
Malaisse, W. J., Brisson, G. R., and Baird, L. E. (1973). *Am. J. Physiol.* 224, 389.
Malaisse, W. J., Devis, G., Pipeleers, D. G., Somers, G., and van Obberghen, E. (1974). *Diabetologia* 10, 379.
Malaisse, W. J., Boschero, A. C., Kawazu, S., and Hutton, C. (1978a). *Pfluegers Arch.* 373, 237.
Malaisse, W. J., Herchuelz, A., Devis, G., Somers, G., Boschero, A. C., Hutton, J. C., Kawazu, S., Sener, A., Atwater, I. J., Duncan, G., Ribalet, B., and Rojas, E. (1978b). *Ann. N.Y. Acad. Sci.* 307, 562.
Malaisse, W. J., Sener, A., Boschero, A. C., Kawazu, S., Devis, G., and Somers, G. (1978c). *Eur. J. Biochem.* 87, 111.
Malaisse, W. J., Hutton, J. C., Kawazu, S., and Sener, A. (1978d). *Eur. J. Biochem.* 87, 121.
Malaisse, W. J., Hutton, J. C., Kawazu, S., Herchuelz, A., Valverde, I., and Sener, A. (1979a). *Diabetologia* 16, 331.
Malaisse, W. J., Kawazu, S., Herchuelz, A., Hutton, J. C., Somers, G., Devis, G., and Sener, A. (1979b). *Arch. Biochem. Biophys.* 194, 1.
Malaisse, W. J., Sener, A., Herchuelz, A., and Hutton, J. C. (1979c). *Metabl. Clin. Exp.* 28, 373.
Malaisse-Lagae, F., and Malaisse, W. J. (1971). *Endocrinology* 88, 72.
Marcum, J. M., Dedman, J. R., Brinkley, B. R., and Means, A. R. (1978). *Proc. Natl. Acad. Sci. U.S.A.* 75, 3771.
Martinosi, A. N., Chyn, T. L., and Schibeci, A. (1978). *Ann. N.Y. Acad. Sci.* 307, 148.
Matchinsky, F. M., and Ellerman, J. (1973). *Biochem. Biophys. Res. Commun.* 50, 193.
Matchinsky, F. M., Ellerman, J. E., Kranowski, J., Kotler-Brajtburg, J., Landgraf, R., and Fertel, R. (1971). *J. Biol. Chem.* 246, 1007.
Matthews, I. K. (1970). *Acta Diabetol. Lat.* 7, Suppl., 83.
Matthews, E. K. (1975). *In* "Calcium Transport in Contractions and Secretion" (E. Carafoli, F. Clementi, W. Drabikowski, and A. Margreth, eds.), p. 203. North-Holland Publ., Amsterdam.
Matthews, E. K., and Sakamoto, Y. (1973). *J. Physiol. (London)* 230, 35.

Matthews, E. K., and Sakamoto, Y. (1975). *J. Physiol. (London)* **246**, 421.
Mellanby, J. (1925). *J. Physiol. (London)* **60**, 85.
Meunier, J. C., Olsen, R., Sealock, R., and Changeux, J. P. (1974). *Eur. J. Biochem.* **45**, 371.
Meyer, W. L., Ficher, E. H., and Krebs, E. G. (1964). *Biochemistry* **3**, 1033.
Michaelson, D. M., and Raftery, M. A. (1974). *Proc. Natl. Acad. Sci. U.S.A.* **71**, 4768.
Michell, R. H. (1975). *Biochim. Biophys. Acta* **415**, 81.
Miller, A., Ueng, T. H., and Bronner, F. (1979). *FEBS Lett.* **103**, 319.
Milner, R. D. G., and Hales, C. N. (1968). *Biochim. Biophys. Acta* **150**, 165.
Miyake, M., and Kakiuchi, S. (1978). *Brain Res.* **139**, 378.
Moews, P. C., and Kretsinger, R. H. (1975). *J. Mol. Biol.* **91**, 201.
Montague, W. (1977). *In* "Cyclic 3′5′-Nucleotides: Mechanisms of Action" (H. Cramer and J. Schultz, eds.), chapter 8 p. 133. Wiley, New York.
Montague, W., and Cook, J. R. (1971). *Biochem. J.* **122**, 115.
Montague, W., and Howell, S. L. (1973). *Biochem. J.* **134**, 321.
Montague, W., Green, I. C., and Howell, S. C. (1976). *In* "Eukaryotic Cell Function and Growth," p. 609.
Moore, L., and Landon, E. (1979). *Life Sci.* **25**, 1029.
Moore, L., and Pastan, I. (1978). *Ann. N.Y. Acad. Sci.* **307**, 177.
Moore, L., Fitzpatrick, D. F., Chen, T. S., and Landon, E. J. (1974). *Biochim. Biophys. Acta* **345**, 405.
Moreau, M., Popot, J. L., Sobel, A., and Weber, M. (1976). *Cold Spring Harbor Symp. Quant. Biol.* **40**, 211.
Morel, F. (1976). *In* "Use of Isolated Liver Cells and Kidney Tubules in Metabolic Studies" (J. M. Tager *et al.*, eds.), p. 161. North-Holland Publ., Amsterdam.
Morgenroth, V. H., Boadle-Berber, M. C., and Roth, R. H. (1975). *Mol. Pharmacol.* **11**, 427.
Morimoto, K., and Harrington, W. F. (1974). *J. Mol. Biol.* **88**, 693.
Moyle, W. R., Kong, Y. C., and Ramachandran, J. (1973). *J. Biol. Chem.* **248**, 2409.
Muller, J. (1971). "Regulation of Aldosterone Biosynthesis." Springer-Verlag, Berlin and New York.
Muto, S., and Miyachi, S. (1977). *Plant Physiol.* **59**, 55.
Mutsuda, G., Maita, T., Suyama, Y., Setoguchi, M., and Klmegane, T. (1977). *J. Biochem. (Tokyo)* **81**, 809.
Naftalin, R. J., and Simmons, N. L. (1979). *J. Physiol. (London)* **290**, 331.
Nagao, S., Suzuki, Y., Watanabe, Y., and Nozawa, Y. (1979). *Biochem. Biophys. Res. Commun.* **90**, 261.
Nagata, N., and Rasmussen, H. (1970). *Proc. Natl. Acad. Sci. U.S.A.* **65**, 368.
Nakamura, M., Ide, M., Okabayashi, T., and Tanaka, A. (1972). *Endocrinol. Jpn.* **19**, 443.
Namm, D. H., Mayer, S. E., and Maltbie, M. (1968). *Mol. Pharmacol.* **4**, 522.
Natori, R. (1954). *Jikeikai Med. J.* **1**, 119.
Nicholls, D. G. (1978a). *Biochem. J.* **170**, 511.
Nicholls, D. G. (1978b). *Biochem. J.* **176**, 463.
Neer, E. J., and Sukiennik, E. A. (1975). *J. Biol. Chem.* **250**, 7905.
Niggli, V., Penniston, J. T., and Carafoli, E. (1979). *J. Biol. Chem.* **254**, 9955.
Nishida, E., and Sakai, H. (1977). *J. Biochem. (Tokyo)* **82**, 303.
Nishida, E., Kumagai, H., Ohtsuki, I., and Sakai, H. (1979). *J. Biochem. (Tokyo)* **85**, 1257.
Nishizuka, Y., Takai, G., Hashimoto, E., Kishimoto, A., Kuroda, Y., Sakai, K., and Yamamura, H. (1979). *Mol. Cell. Biochem.* **23**, 153.

Oh-Hama, T., and Miyachi, S. (1960). *Plant Cell Physiol.* 1, 155.
Ohashi, T., Uchida, S., Nagai, K., and Yoshida, H. (1970). *J. Biochem. (Tokyo)* 67, 635.
Olmsted, J. B., and Borisy, G. G. (1973). *Annu. Rev. Biochem.* 42, 507.
Oron, Y., Löwe, M., and Selinger, Z. (1975). *Mol. Pharmacol.* 11, 79.
Pagliara, A. S., and Goodman, A. D. (1969). *J. Clin. Invest.* 48, 1408.
Papahadjopoulos, D., Poste, G., Schaeffer, G. E., and Vail, W. (1974). *Biochim. Biophys. Acta* 352, 10.
Parisa, M. W., Butcher, F. R., Becker, J. E., and Potter, V. R. (1977). *Proc. Natl. Acad. Sci. U.S.A.* 74, 234.
Patrick, J., and Lindstrom, J. (1973). *Proc. Natl. Acad. Sci. U.S.A.* 70, 3334.
Peach, M. J. (1977). *Physiol. Rev.* 57, 313.
Pechère, J.-F., Damaille, J., Dutruge, E., Capony, J.-P., Baron, G., and Pina, C. (1975). *In* "Calcium Transport in Contractions and Secretion" (E. Carafoli, F. Clementi, W. Drabikowski, and A. Margreth, eds.), p. 459. North-Holland Publ., Amsterdam.
Perchellet, J.-P., and Sharma, R. K. (1979). *Science* 203, 1259.
Perchellet, J.-P., Shanker, G., and Sharma, R. K. (1978). *Science* 199, 311.
Perry, S. V. (1979). *Cyclic Nucleotide Cell. Regul.* 54, 1.
Pershadsingh, H. A., and McDonald, J. M. (1979). *Nature (London)* 281, 495.
Peterson, O. H., and Iwatsuki, N. (1978). *Ann. N.Y. Acad. Sci.* 307, 599.
Pointer, R. H., Butcher, F. R., and Fain, J. N. (1976). *J. Biol. Chem.* 251, 2987.
Portis, A., Newton, C., Pangborn, W., and Paphadjopoulos, D. (1979). *Biochemistry* 18, 780.
Posner, J. B., Stern, R., and Krebs, E. G. (1965). *J. Biol. Chem.* 240, 982.
Poste, G., and Allison, A. C. (1973). *Biochim. Biophys. Acta* 300, 421.
Potter, J. D., and Gergely, J. (1975). *J. Biol. Chem.* 250, 4628.
Potter, J. D., Johnson, J. D., Dedman, J. R., Schreiber, F. M., Jackson, R. L., and Means, A. R. (1977). *In* "Calcium Binding Proteins and Calcium Function in Health and Disease" (R. H. Wasserman *et al.*, eds.), p. 239. Am. Elsevier, New York.
Prince, W. T., and Berridge, M. J. (1973). *J. Exp. Biol.* 58, 367.
Prince, W. T., Berridge, M. J., and Rasmussen, H. (1972). *Proc. Natl. Acad. Sci. U.S.A.* 69, 553.
Prince, W. T., Rasmussen, H., and Berridge, M. J. (1973). *Biochim. Biophys. Acta* 329, 98.
Putney, J. W. (1977). *J. Physiol. (London)* 268, 139.
Putney, J. W. (1979). *Pharmacol. Rev.* 30, 209.
Putney, J. W., Weiss, S. J., Leslie, B. A., and Marier, S. H. (1977). *J. Pharmacol. Exp. Ther.* 203, 144.
Rall, T. W., Sutherland, E. W., and Berthet, J. (1957). *J. Biol. Chem.* 224, 463.
Rasmussen, H. (1970). *Science* 170, 404.
Rasmussen, H., and Bikle, D. D. (1975). *In* "Calcium Transport In Contractions and Secretion" (E. Carafoli, F. Clementi, W. Drabikowski, and A. Margreth, eds.), p. 111. North-Holland Publ., Amsterdam.
Rasmussen, H., and Clayberger, C. (1979). *In* "Membrane Transduction Mechanisms" (R. A. Cone and J. E. Downling, eds.), Sect. Gen. Physiol. Ser., Vol. 33, p. 139. Raven, New York.
Rasmussen, H., and Goodman, D. B. P. (1977). *Physiol. Rev.* 57, 421.
Rasmussen, H., and Gustin, M. (1978). *Ann. N.Y. Acad. Sci.* 307, 391.
Rasmussen, H., and Tenenhouse, A. (1968). *Proc. Natl. Acad. Sci. U.S.A.* 59, 1364.
Rasmussen, H., Goodman, D. B. P., and Tenenhouse, A. (1972). *CRC Crit. Rev. Biochem.* 1, 95.
Reed, K., Vandlen, R., Bode, J., Duguid, J., and Raftery, M. A. (1975). *Arch. Biochem. Biophys.* 167, 138.

Rink, T. J., and Baker, P. F. (1975). *In* "Calcium Transport In Contractions and Secretion" (E. Carafoli, F. Clementi, W. Drabikowski, and A. Margreth, eds.), p. 235. North-Holland Publ., Amsterdam.

Rittenhouse-Simmons, S., Russel, F. A., and Deykin, D. (1977). *Biochim. Biophys. Acta* **488**, 370.

Roach, P. J., DePaoli-Roach, A. A., and Lerners, J. (1978). *J. Cyclic Nucleotide Res.* **4**, 245.

Robison, G. A., Butcher, R. W., and Sutherland, E. W. (1971). "Cyclic AMP." Academic Press, New York.

Rodbell, M., Liu, M. C., Salomon, Y., Louclos, C., Harwood, J. P., Martin, B. R., Rendell, M., and Berman, M. (1975). *Adv. Cyclic Nucleotide Res.* **5**, 3.

Rosenkrantz, H. (1959). *Endocrinology*, **64**, 355.

Rossignol, B., Keryer, G., Herman, G., Chambaut-Guérin, A. M., and Cahoreau, C. (1977). *In* "Hormonal Receptors in Digestive Tract Physiology" (S. Bonfils *et al.*, eds.), p. 311. North-Holland Publ., Amsterdam.

Roth, J. (1973). *Metab., Clin. Exp.* **22**, 1059.

Rudich, L., and Butcher, F. R. (1976). *Biochim. Biophys. Acta* **444**, 701.

Russel, T. R., Terasaki, W. L., and Appleman, M. M. (1973). *J. Biol. Chem.* **248**, 1334.

Saermark, T., and Vilhardt, H. (1979). *Biochem. J.* **181**, 321.

Saez, J. M., Evans, D., and Gallet, D. (1978). *J. Cyclic Nucleotide Res.* **4**, 311.

Sakai, K., Matsumura, S., Ohimura, Y., Yamamura, H., and Nishizuka, Y. (1979). *J. Biol. Chem.* **254**, 6631.

Salmon, E. D., and Jenkins, R. C. (1977). *J. Cell Biol.* **75**, 295a.

Sandow, A. (1952). *Yale J. Biol. Med.* **24**, 176.

Sandow, A. (1965). *Pharmacol. Rev.* **17**, 265.

Saruta, T., Cook, R., and Kaplan, N. M. (1972). *J. Clin. Invest.* **51**, 2239.

Sato, T., and Fujii, T. (1974). *Chem. Pharm. Bull.* **22**, 368.

Scarpa, A. (1979). *In* "Membrane Transport In Biology" (G. Briebisch, D. C. Tosteson, and H. H. Ussing, eds.), Chapter 7. p. 263. Springer-Verlag, Berlin and New York.

Schatzmann, H. J., and Vincenzi, F. F. (1969). *J. Physiol. (London)* **201**, 369.

Schramm, M., and Nairn, E. (1970). *J. Biol. Chem.* **245**, 3225.

Schramm, M., and Selinger, Z. (1976). "Stimulus Secretion Coupling in the 61 Tract" (R. M. Case and H. Goebell, eds.), p. 49. MTP, London.

Schramm, M., Selinger, Z., Solomon, Y., Eytan, E., and Batzri, S. (1972). *Nature (London)* **240**, 203.

Schulman, H., and Greengard, P. (1978). *Nature (London)* **271**, 478.

Schultz, I., Kondo, S., Sachs, G., and Milutinovíc, S. (1977). *In* "Hormonal Receptors in Digestive Tract Physiology" (Bonfils *et al.*, eds.), p. 275. North-Holland Publ., Amsterdam.

Selinger, Z., Eimerl, S., and Schramm, M. (1974). *Proc. Natl. Acad. Sci. U.S.A.* **71**, 128.

Sener, A., and Malaisse, W. J. (1979). *Eur. J. Biochem.* **98**, 141.

Sener, A., Hutton, J. C., Kawazu, S., Boschero, A. C., Somers, G., Herchuelz, A., and Malaisse, W. I. (1978). *J. Clin. Invest.* **62**, 868.

Sharma, R. K., and Sawhney, R. S. (1978). *Biochemistry* **17**, 316.

Sharma, R. K., and Wirch, E. (1979). *Biochem. Biophys. Res. Commun.* **91**, 338.

Sharma, R. K., Ahmed, N. K., and Shanker, G. (1976). *Eur. J. Biochem.* **70**, 427.

Sharma, R. K., Wirch, E., and Wang, J. H. (1978). *J. Biol. Chem.* **253**, 3575.

Sharma, R. K., Desai, R., Waisman, D. M., and Wang, J. H. (1979). *J. Biol. Chem.* **254**, 4276.

Sharp, G. W. G., Wollheim, C., Muller, W. A., Gutzeit, A., Trueheart, P. A., Blondel, B., Orci, L., and Renold, A. E. (1975). *Fed. Proc., Fed. Am. Soc. Exp. Biol.* **34**, 1537.

Sherline, P., Lynch, A., and Glinsmann, E. (1972). *Endocrinology* **91**, 680.
Sherry, J. M. F., Gorecka, A., Oksay, M. O., Dabrowska, R., and Hartshorne, D. J. (1978). *Biochemistry* **17**, 4411.
Shibata, S., and Briggs, A. H. (1966). *J. Pharmacol. Exp. Ther.* **153**, 466.
Shimazu, T., and Amakawa, A. (1975). *Biochim. Biophys. Acta* **385**, 242.
Sieghart, W., Forn, J., and Greengard, P. (1979). *Proc. Natl. Acad. Sci. U.S.A.* **76**, 2475.
Silver, P. J., and DiSalvo, J. (1979). *J. Biol. Chem.* **254**, 9951.
Smoake, J. A., Song, S. Y., and Cheung, W. T. (1974). *Biochim. Biophys. Acta* **341**, 402.
Sobieszek, A. (1977). *Eur. J. Biochem.* **73**, 477.
Soderling, T. R., Hickenbottom, J. P., Reimann, E. M., Hunkeler, F. L., Walsh, D. A., and Krebs, E. G. (1970). *J. Biol. Chem.* **245**, 6317.
Stephenson, E. W., and Podolsky, R. J. (1978). *Ann. N.Y. Acad. Sci.*   , 307.
Stevens, F. C., Walsh, M., Ho, H.-C., Teo, T. S., and Wang, J. H. (1976). *J. Biol. Chem.* **251**, 4495.
Stifel, F. B., Taunton, O. D., Greene, H. L., and Herman, R. H. (1974). *J. Biol. Chem.* **249**, 7240.
Stone, D., and Hechter, O. (1954). *Arch. Biochem. Biophys.* **51**, 457.
Sugden, M. C., Christh, M. R., and Ashcroft, S. J. H. (1979). *FEBS Lett.* **105**, 1.
Sutherland, E. W., and Rall, T. W. (1958). *J. Biol. Chem.* **232**, 1065.
Sutherland, E. W., and Rall, T. W. (1960). *Pharmacol. Rev.* **12**, 265.
Sutherland, E. W., Robison, G. S., and Butcher, R. W. (1968). *Circulation* **37**, 279.
Suzuki, Y., Hirabayashi, T., and Watanabe, Y. (1979). *Biochem. Biophys. Res. Commun.* **90**, 253.
Szász, I., Sarkadi, B., and Gárdos, G. (1977). *J. Membr. Biol.* **35**, 75.
Tait, J. F., and Tait, S. A. S. (1976). *J. Steroid Biochem.* **7**, 687.
Takai, Y., Kishimoto, A., Kikkawa, U., Mori, T., and Nishizuka, (1980). *Biochem. Biophys. Res. Commun.* (in press).
Täljedal, I. B. (1978). *J. Cell Biol.* **76**, 652.
Taunton, O. D., Stifel, F. B., Greene, H. L., and Herman, R. H. (1974). *J. Biol. Chem.* **249**, 7228.
Teo, T. S., Wang, T. H., and Wang, J. H. (1973). *J. Biol. Chem.* **248**, 588.
Thomasset, M., Cuisinier-Gleizes, P., and Mathieu, H. (1979). *FEBS Lett.* **107**, 91.
Thompson, W. J., and Appleman, M. M. (1971). *Biochemistry* **10**, 311.
Tolbert, M. E. M., and Fain, J. N. (1974). *J. Biol. Chem.* **249**, 1162.
Tolbert, M. E. M., Butcher, F. R., and Fain, J. N. (1973). *J. Biol. Chem.* **248**, 5686.
Tufty, R. M., and Kretsinger, R. H. (1975). *Science* **187**, 167.
Ueng, T. H., and Bronner, F. (1979). *Arch. Biochem. Biophys.* **197**, 205.
Unger, R. H., Keherer, H., Dupre, J., and Eisentraut, A. M. (1967). *J. Clin. Invest.* **46**, 630.
Valverde, I., Vandermeers, A., Anjaneyulu, R., and Malaisse, W. J. (1979a). *Science* **206**, 12.
Valverde, I., Wandermeers, A., Anjaneyulu, R., and Malaisse, W. J. (1979b). *Science* **206**, 925.
Vanaman, T. C., Hanelson, W. G., and Watterson, D. M. (1975). *Fed. Proc., Fed. Am. Soc. Exp. Biol.* **34**, 307.
Vanaman, T. C., Shariel, F., and Watterson, D. M. (1977). *In* "Calcium Binding Proteins and Calcium Function in Health and Disease" (R. H. Wasserman *et al.*, eds.), p. 107. Am. Elsevier, New York.
Van Breemen, C., Farinas, B.T., Gerba, P., and McNaughton, E. D. (1972). *Circ. Res.* **30**, 44.
Van de Werve, G., Hue, L., and Hers, H. (1977). *Biochem. J.* **162**, 135.

Verna, M. J., Dabrowska, R., Hartshorne, D. J., and Goldman, R. C. (1979). *Proc. Natl. Acad. Sci. U.S.A.* **76**, 184.

Wagner, P. D., and Yount, R. G. (1976). *J. Biol. Chem.* **251**, 5424.

Wagner, P. D., Slater, C. S., Pope, B., and Weeds, A. G. (1979). *Eur. J. Biochem.* **99**, 385.

Waisman, D. M. (1979). A ubiquitous Ca^{2+} binding protein and its possible physiological functions. Ph.D. Thesis, University of Manitoba, Winnipeg, Manitoba, Canada.

Waisman, D. M., Stevens, F. C., and Wang, J. H. (1975). *Biochem. Biophys. Res. Commun.* **65**, 975.

Waisman, D. M., Stevens, F. C., and Wang, J. H. (1978a). *J. Biol. Chem.* **253**, 1106.

Waisman, D. M., Singh, T. J., and Wang, J. H. (1978b). *J. Biol. Chem.* **253**, 3387.

Waisman, D. M., Gimble, J., Goodman, D. P. B., and Rasmussen, H. (1980). *J. Biol. Chem.* (in press).

Walkenbach, R. J., Hazen, R., and Lainer, J. (1978). *Mol. Cell. Biochem.* **19**, 31.

Wallace, R. W., Lynch, T. J., Tallant, E. A., Maclead, R. M., and Cheung, W. Y. (1978) *Fed. Proc., Fed. Am. Soc. Exp. Biol.* **37**, 1302.

Wallach, D., and Pastan, I. (1976). *Biochem. Biophys. Res. Commun.* **72**, 859.

Walsh, D. A., Ashby, C. D., Gonzalez, C., Calkins, D., Fisher, E. H., and Krebs, E. G. (1971). *J. Biol. Chem.* **246**, 1977.

Walsh, M., and Stevens, F. C. (1977). *Biochemistry* **16**, 2742.

Walsh, M., Stevens, F. C., Kuznicki, J., and Drabikowski, W. (1977). *J. Biol. Chem.* **252**, 7440.

Walsh, M., Stevens, F. C., Oikawa, K., and Kay, C. M. (1978). *Biochemistry* **17**, 3924.

Waltenbaugh, A., Kimura, S., Wood, J., Divakaray, P., and Friedmann, N. (1978). *Life Sci.* **23**, 2437.

Waltenbaugh, A.-M. A., and Friedmann, N. (1978) *Biochem. Biophys. Res. Commun.* **82**, 603.

Wang, J. H. (1976). *Annu. Rev. Biochem.* **45**, 239.

Wang, J. H., and Desai, R. (1976). *Biochem. Biophys. Res. Commun.* **72**, 926.

Wang, J. H., and Waisman, D. M. (1979). *Curr. Top. Cell. Regul.* **15**, 47.

Wang, T. H., Teo, T. S., Ho, H. C., and Stevens, F. C. (1975). *Adv. Cyclic Nucleotide Res.* **5**, 179.

Wasserman, R. H. (1977). *3rd Annu. Workshop Vitam. D, Asilomar Conf., 1977.*

Wasserman, R. H., and Feher, J. T. (1977). *In* "Calcium Binding Proteins and Calcium Function in Health and Disease" (R. H. Wasserman *et al.*, eds.), p. 293. Am. Elsevier, New York.

Wasserman, R. H., and Taylor, A. N. (1966). *Science* **152**, 791.

Watterson, D. M., and Vanaman, T.-C. (1976). *Biochem. Biophys. Res. Commun.* **73**, 40.

Weber, A., and Murray, J. M. (1973a). *Physiol. Rev.* **53**, 612.

Weber, A., and Murray, J. M. (1973b). *Physiol. Rev.* **53**, 613.

Weeds, A., and McLachlan, A. (1974). *Nature (London)* **252**, 646.

Weeds, A., Wagner, P., Jakes, R., and Kendrick-Jones, J. (1977). *In* "Calcium Binding Proteins and Calcium Function in Health and Disease" (R. H. Wasserman *et al.*, eds.), p. 222. Am. Elsevier, New York.

Weiss, B., and Levin, R. M. (1978). *Adv. Cyclic Nucleotide Res.* **9**, 285.

Weiss, S. J., and Putney, J. W., Jr. (1978). *J. Pharmacol. Exp. Ther.* **207**, 669.

Welsh, M. J., Dedman, J. R., Brinkley, B. R., and Means, A. R. (1978). *Proc. Natl. Acad. Sci. U.S.A.* **75**, 1867.

Welsh, M. J., Dedman, J. R., Brinkley, B. R., and Means, A. R. (1979). *J. Cell Biol.* **81**, 624.

Westcott, K. R., LaPoute, D. C., and Storm, D. R. (1979). *Proc. Natl. Acad. Sci. U.S.A.* **76**, 204.

White, A. A., and Aurbach, G. D. (1969). *Biochim. Biophys. Acta* **191**, 686.

White, A. A., Crawford, K. M., Patt, C. S., and Lad, P. J. (1976). *J. Biol. Chem.* **251**, 7304.

Williams, G. H., and Dluhy, R. G. (1972). *Am. J. Med.* **53**, 595.

Wolff, D. J., Poirier, P. G., Brostrom, C. O., and Brostrom, M. A. (1977). *J. Biol. Chem.* **252**, 4108.

Wolfsen, A. R., McIntyre, H. B., and Odell, W. D. (1972). *J. Clin. Endocrinol. Metab.* **34**, 684.

Wong, P. Y., and Cheung, W. Y. (1979). *Biochem. Biophys. Res. Commun.* **90**, 473.

Yagi, K., Yazawa, M., Kakiuchi, S., Ohshima, M., and Uenishi, K. (1978). *J. Biol. Chem.* **253**, 1338.

Yamauchi, T., and Fujisawa, H. (1978). *Biochem. Biophys. Res. Commun.* **82**, 514.

Yamauchi, T., and Fujisawa, H. (1979). *Biochem. Biophys. Res. Commun.* **90**, 28.

Yanagibashi, I. (1979). *Endocrinol. Jpn.* **26**, 227.

Yanagibashi, K., Kamiya, N., Lin, G., and Matsuba, M. (1978). *Endocrinol. Jpn.* **25**, 545.

Ziegelhoffer, A., Anad-Srivastava, A., Khandelwal, R. L., and Dhalla, N. S. (1979). *Biochem. Biophys. Res. Commun.* **89**, 1073.

CHAPTER 2

Neuronal Regulation of Blood Pressure

Judith Juskevich
and Walter Lovenberg

Blood pressure regulation is a highly complex integration of peripheral vascular, renal, hormonal, chemical, neural, and central nervous system components. No single component can be defined as the most critical for the regulation of arterial pressure, because of the extensive integration achieved through various feedback loops. Since the system is so complex, it is often necessary and valuable to study isolated parts of the system in order to gain an understanding of the function of the system as a whole. Several reviews have been written on the different aspects of blood pressure regulation with emphasis on peripheral (Guyton *et al.*, 1972, 1973), spinal (Koizumi and Brooks, 1972), or the central nervous system components (Korner, 1971; Calaresu *et al.*, 1975; Chalmers, 1975).

This chapter will be concerned with neuronal aspects of blood pressure regulation and the interaction between neuronal and humoral regulation. The possible contributions of these systems to the development of hypertension will also be discussed.

I. ORGANIZATION OF CENTRAL NERVOUS SYSTEM AREAS REGULATING BLOOD PRESSURE

The interconnections of central nervous system (CNS) areas involved in blood pressure regulation have been studied using anatomical and electrophysiological techniques. Anatomical methods utilize degeneration studies, retrograde transport of the enzyme horseradish peroxidase and anterograde transport of radioactive amino acids. These studies are limited to establishing monosynaptic projections. Since an area may subserve functions other than blood pressure regulation, anatomical studies do not necessarily provide information on whether these primary connections are actually involved in the control of blood pressure.

Neurophysiological studies provide more varied information than anatomical techniques. Electrophysiological studies can be used to map multisynaptic pathways as well as define monosynaptic connections. In addition excitatory and inhibitory areas and pathways can be distinguished. Iontophoresis of putative neurotransmitters onto vasomotor areas of the CNS have provided some information as to the transmitters involved in vasopressor and depressor pathways. There are several limitations in interpreting electrophysiological data; for example, it has been shown that the exact site of stimulation, the stimulation parameters used, and the anesthetic employed may result in confusion in identifying pressor and depressor areas (Faiers *et al.*, 1975, 1976).

Combining data obtained using different techniques can overcome some of the limitations of any particular technique, and present a clearer picture of the pathways involved in regulation of blood pressure. A diagram of some of the interconnections in the central nervous system compiled from both anatomical and electrophysiological studies is shown in Fig. 1.

The primary afferents of the blood pressure regulatory system are the carotid sinus and aortic depressor nerves which carry information from the baro- and chemoreceptors. The first synapse in the CNS has been shown to be the nucleus tractus solitarius (NTS) (Miura and Reis, 1969, 1972; Hildebrandt, 1974; Spyer, 1975). Other areas receiving primary input are the medullae oblongatae centralis (MOC) (Miura and Reis, 1969), the parahypoglossal area (PHA) (Spyer, 1975), and possibly the

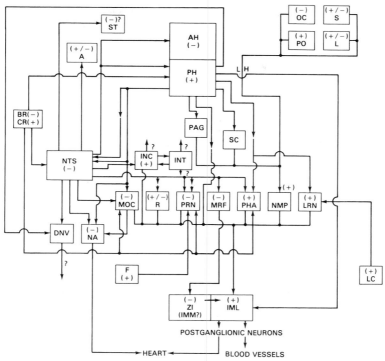

FIG. 1. Interconnections of some of the central nervous system areas involved in cardio-vasuclar regulation. (+) indicates stimulation of an area results in an increase in blood pressure; (−) indicates stimulation results in a decrease in blood pressure; (+/−) indicates that both increases and decreases in blood pressure have been reported following stimulation of an area. Abbreviations: A, amygdala; AH, anterior hypothalamus; BR, baroreceptors; CR, chemoreceptors; DNV, dorsal motor nucleus of the vagus; F, fastigial nucleus; IML, intermediolateral nucleus; IMM, intermediomedial nucleus; INC, intercalate nucleus; INT, intermediate nucleus; L, limbic system; LC, locus coeruleus; LH, lateral hypothalamus; LRN, lateral reticular nucleus; MOC, medullae oblongatae centralis; MRF, medial reticular formation; NA, nucleus ambiguus; NMP, nucleus mesencephalus profundus; NTS, nucleus tractus solitarius; OC, orbital cortex; PAG, periaqueductal gray; PH, posterior hypothalamus; PHA, parahypoglossal area; PO, preoptic area; PRN, paramedian reticular nucleus; R, raphé nuclei; S, septal nuclei; SC, superior colliculus; ST, stria terminalis; ZI, zona intermedia.

paramedian reticular nucleus (PRN) (Miura and Reis, 1969; Hilde-brandt, 1974), although the latter finding has been questioned by others (Spyer, 1975). The carotid sinus nerve also has multisynaptic input to the PRN and the raphé nuclei (Miura and Reis, 1969). In addition, Thomas and Calaresu (1972) studied the response of single units in the hypotha-lamus to carotid sinus nerve stimulation and found that baroreceptor af-ferents had an inhibitory and chemoreceptor afferents an excitatory ef-fect.

Projections from the NTS, which appears to be the primary site of baro- and chemoreceptor input, include the MOC (Calaresu and Thomas, 1975), the nucleus ambiguus (NA), dorsal motor nucleus of the vagus (DNV), the medial reticular formation (MRF), the nucleus inter-calatus (INC) (Cottle and Calaresu, 1975), anterior hypothalamus (AH) (Hilton and Spyer, 1971), the bed nucleus of the stria terminalus (ST), the central nucleus of the amygdala (A), and the posterior hypothalamus (PH) (Ricardo and Koh, 1978).

The hypothalamus contains two major pressor pathways, one passing through the lateral hypothalamus and one originating in the posterior hypothalamus (Enoch and Kerr, 1967a,b). The lateral pathway probably originates from several areas rostral to the hypothalamus including or-bital cortex, septal nuclei, the preoptic area, and the limbic system. It passes through the lateral hypothalamus and synapses in the n. mesen-cephalus profundus (NMP). The second pressor pathway, which origi-nates diffusely in the posterior hypothalamus, synapses in the peri-aqueductal gray and superior colliculi and then in the NMP.

The posterior hypothalamus has polysynaptic inputs to the MOC, NA, NTS, PHA, and lateral reticular n. (LRN) (Calaresu and Thomas, 1975). In addition to these polysynaptic connections it has been shown that the posterior hypothalamus has direct monosynaptic connections with the NTS (Saper *et al.*, 1976; Chiba and Kato, 1978), the DNV, and the inter-mediolateral n. (IML) in the spinal cord (Saper *et al.*, 1976). The latter connection provides evidence that the posterior hypothalamus can have a direct effect on preganglionic sympathetic neurons.

Stimulation of many other areas of the brain has been shown to pro-duce pressor or depressor responses. Although the details of these path-ways are still undefined, it appears that the regulatory systems are more complex than indicated in Fig. 1. Two areas of interest are the fastigial nucleus (FN) in the cerebellum and the locus coeruleus (LC).

Stimulation of the FN produces pressor responses and it has been shown to project to the PRN (Miura and Reis, 1970). The electrophysio-logical studies of this area are interesting in that it has been shown that the cardiovascular response to stimulation of the FN is very similar to the cardiovascular adjustments that occur due to postural changes (Doba and Reis, 1972). Therefore, it has been postulated that the FN is involved in a pathway integrating blood pressure regulation and postural changes.

The locus coeruleus is also of interest since it has such widespread connections throughout the central nervous system. It has been shown to possibly modulate both central and peripheral depressor systems (Ward and Gunn, 1976b). The main projection which seems to be important in this capacity is that to the LRN, since severing its connections to the hypothalamus, limbic system, and neocortex did not abolish the pressor responses to stimulation (Ward and Gunn, 1976a).

The spinal cord also contains a complex system for the regulation of blood pressure (Koizumi and Brooks, 1972). The location, as well as the functional characteristics of descending spinal sympathetic pathways, has been fairly well defined (Foreman and Wurster, 1973; Coote and Macleod, 1974). The MOC, LRN, PRN, and raphé nuclei project directly to the IML (Henry and Calaresu, 1974a). Projections from the LRN (Henry and Calaresu, 1974b) and raphé (Coote and Macleod, 1975) travel through the dorsolateral funiculus and projections from the raphé, PRN (Henry and Calaresu, 1974b), and medial reticular formation (MRF) (Coote and Macleod, 1975) travel through the ventrolateral funiculus.

It has also been shown that spontaneous sympathetic activity of the IML can be inhibited at the spinal level. This sympathoinhibitory pathway extends from the medulla to the medial portion of the zona intermedia [containing the intermediomedial n. (IMM)] which sends projections to the IML (McCall *et al.*, 1977).

In addition to descending pathways in the spinal cord, it has also been shown that there are ascending pathways involved in blood pressure regulation. Faden *et al.* (1979) have shown that an ascending intraspinal cardiovascular pathway is located in deep white matter adjacent to the IML. It has also been shown that somatosympathetic afferents influence blood pressure regulation at a spinal level (Jänig, 1975).

All of the areas involved in blood pressure regulation have not been included in this diagram. However, it is apparent, even with the anatomical areas included, that the neural system regulating blood pressure is complex and highly integrated. Much work has been done to elucidate the integration of blood pressure regulation at different levels (Chai and Wang, 1968; Gebber and Snyder, 1970; Hilton and Spyer, 1971; Gebber *et al.*, 1973; Snyder and Gebber, 1973) and this will be discussed in a later section.

II. PERIPHERAL REGULATION

A. PERIPHERAL SYMPATHETIC NERVES

Blood pressure is mainly affected by changes in the small resistance vessels—small arteries, arterioles, metarterioles, and the precapillary sphincters. Local regulation of tension in these vessels is controlled by chemical and humoral factors as well as by neuronal input. A wide range of humoral factors affect this category of vessels including norepinephrine (NE), epinephrine (E), dopamine (DA), serotonin (5-HT), histamine, angiotensin, acetylcholine (ACh), and kinins. In addition, some hormones such as the glucocorticoids and estrogens can modify the response to other hormones. Locally produced metabolic products, e.g., adenosine, H^+, K^+, inorganic phosphate, and Kreb's cycle intermediates also affect these vessels, generally causing vasodilation (Altura, 1971).

The sympathetic innervation of blood vessels has been studied using histochemical and electromicroscopic methods (Burnstock, 1970; Burnstock and Iwayama, 1971; Bevan and Su, 1973; Furness, 1973; Furness and Marshall, 1974) and the literature on this subject has recently been reviewed (Burnstock, 1975). It appears that there is a dense network of innervation around principal arteries and a loose network around the small arteries and terminal arterioles. There is no evidence for adrenergic innervation of precapillary sphincters in mesenteric vessels whereas they are heavily innervated in cardiac vessels. Baez *et al.* (1977) found that CNS stimulation resulted in constriction of all segments of precapillary microvessels in the mesentery—including arterioles, metarterioles, and precapillary sphincters. The responsiveness was greatest towards the end of the arteriolar tree, i.e., the percentage diameter change was greater in the smaller vessels. This suggests that although not directly innervated, constriction of metarterioles and precapillary sphincters may still be controlled to some extent by neural stimulation.

Peripheral sympathetic activity has been shown to correlate well with systemic arterial pressure (Gootman and Cohen, 1969, 1970). Spontaneous increases and decreases in splanchnic activity result in increases and decreases in blood pressure. In addition, changes in activity and pressure produced by brainstem stimulation were linearly related.

The electrophysiological activity of sympathetic nerves has been studied in order to further define the peripheral nervous system in relation to blood pressure regulation. Cohen and Gootman (1970) measured efferent splanchnic activity and found three types of periodicity: a fundamental periodicity with a frequency of 10 Hz, discharges that were synchronous with the cardiac cycle, and discharges synchronous with the central respiratory cycle. This indicates that aside from changes in basal sympathetic activity central cardiac and respiratory areas may influence levels of sympathetic activity.

It has also been shown that sympathetic neurons are spontaneously active. Using microelectrodes, Polosa (1968) measured activity in the upper thoracic spinal cord. He found that 21% of the neurons sampled were spontaneously active, with three different types of discharge patterns. Since this activity was found in decentralized deafferented segments of spinal cord, it can be assumed that this spontaneous activity is not imposed by higher medullary areas or cardiac rhythms from baroreceptor input.

It has been shown that there are regional variations in sympathetic responses to various stimuli. Löfving (1961) demonstrated opposite changes in blood flow to muscle and intestine upon stimulation of sympathoexcitatory areas of the medulla. It has also been shown that different sympathetic nerves have different basal patterns of firing as well as different responses to hypoxia and hemorrhage (Green and Heffron, 1966).

It has long been known that baro- and chemoreceptor afferents have a marked effect on peripheral sympathetic activity (Gernandt *et al.*, 1946). The baro- and chemoreceptors are the major peripheral afferents involved in blood pressure regulation. In general, stimulation of arterial chemoreceptors results in an increase in blood pressure and total peripheral resistance (Daly *et al.*, 1965; Korner, 1965; Daly and Ungar, 1966; Angell-James and Daly, 1969), whereas stimulation of baroreceptors results in a reflex inhibition of sympathetic activity and a decrease in blood pressure (Iggo and Vogt, 1962; Downing and Siegel, 1963; Okada, 1964; Green and Heffron, 1968; Kezdi and Geller, 1968).

The two carotid sinus and aortic depressor nerves are the major baroreceptor afferents involved in the regulation of blood pressure. Section of these four nerves abolishes the inhibition of sympathetic activity seen with baroreceptor activation and stimulation of these nerves individually results in a decrease in sympathetic activity (Ninomiya and Irisawa, 1969).

It has been found that the sympathetic response to baroreceptor activation or carotid sinus nerve (CSN) stimulation is dependent on the pattern of activation. Inhibition of sympathetic activity is greater when pulsatile pressure is applied to the carotid sinus compared to steady pressure (Kezdi and Geller, 1968) or when the CSN is stimulated with interrupted trains of pulses compared to continuous stimulation (Richter *et al.*, 1970). In addition, Richter *et al.* (1970) found that interrupted trains of stimulation reduced the adaptation of sympathetic activity seen during CSN stimulation.

As well as being affected by baro- and chemoreceptor input, sympathetic nerve activity is modulated by afferents from receptors in skin, viscera, muscles, and joints. Stimulation of cutaneous and muscle afferents result in increases and decreases in sympathetic activity depending on the stimulation parameters employed (Koizumi *et al.*, 1968). Koizumi *et al.* (1971) also found that background discharges and sympathetic reflexes were altered by respiratory neuron activity.

In the past it was generally accepted that sympathetic outflow was uniform to different regions. However, particularly for baroreceptor and chemoreceptor influences, it has been shown that sympathetic nerves supplying different regions can have differential responses to reflex stimuli (Ninomiya *et al.*, 1971; Iriki and Kozawa, 1975; Ninomiya and Irisawa, 1975).

More detailed information on arterial baroreceptor reflexes can be obtained from a recent review (Kirchheim, 1976). The integration of baroreceptor afferents with the central nervous system areas involved in blood pressure regulation will be discussed in a later section.

It appears that there is some baseline sympathetic activity originating at a spinal level. On top of this, however, is imposed input from higher CNS areas, as well as from peripheral afferents. Therefore, the peripheral sympathetic activity measured is a complex integration of different neuronal inputs—cardiovascular, respiratory, and somatosensory.

B. Hormonal Effects on the Sympathetic Nervous System

1. Angiotensin

Aside from its direct vasoconstrictor effects, angiotensin II (AII) also has a variety of interactions with the sympathetic nervous system including potentiation of the response to sympathetic nerve stimulation (Zimmerman and Whitmore, 1967; Nicholas, 1970; Hughes and Roth, 1971; Zimmerman *et al.*, 1972; Malik and Nasjletti, 1976; Povolny *et al.*, 1977; Zimmerman, 1978; Campbell and Jackson, 1979; Zimmerman and Kraft, 1979), enhanced synthesis of catecholamines (Roth, 1972; Boadle-Biber and Roth, 1977), increased release of transmitter (Zimmerman and Whitmore, 1967; Starke, 1970; Zimmerman *et al.*, 1972; Ackerly *et al.*, 1976), stimulation of sympathetic ganglia (Lewis and Reit, 1966; Reit, 1972), and inhibition of reuptake of norepinephrine (NE) into nerve endings (Khairallah, 1972; Malik and Nasjletti, 1976; Campbell and Jackson, 1979). Thus, it appears that AII interacts with many different aspects of peripheral catecholaminergic transmission. Although several different mechanisms may be involved, the main effect of AII is to potentiate the effects of sympathetic activation.

The effect of angiotensin II on transmitter release during sympathetic nerve stimulation has been studied in various vascular beds as well as isolated blood vessels. It has been shown that the potentiated vasoconstrictor response to nerve stimulation can be attributed to the facilitation of NE release by angiotensin during stimulation rather than to an increased responsiveness of the vasculature to NE (Zimmerman *et al.*, 1972). Starke *et al.* (1970) studied the overflow of NE due to nerve stimulation in isolated rabbit heart. Mechanical reduction of coronary flow and vasopressin decreased the output of NE. Angiotensin, however, resulted in an increase in NE overflow. They, therefore, concluded that the angiotensin effect must be due to a specific interaction with adrenergic nerves rather than an effect secondary to vasoconstriction. This increase in NE overflow by angiotensin has also been demonstrated in isolated perfused vessels (Khairallah, 1972). In this system 1-asparagine angiotensin caused an increased efflux of [^{3}H]NE. This effect was compared with the increase [^{3}H]NE release caused by tyramine. In the presence of tyramine the release was associated with muscle contraction and continued as long as tyramine was present. With angiotensin, however, NE release did not continue throughout the exposure period although the muscle contraction persisted, and lower levels of angiotensin which caused contraction did not always cause a significant increase in NE release. It can, therefore, be assumed that angiotensin releases NE by a different mechanism than that of tyramine.

Dopamine-β-hydroxylase (DBH) is released along with NE upon sympathetic nerve firing. Ackerly *et al.* (1976) found that control DBH increased after stimulation of isolated left rabbit atria. Addition of angiotensin II increased the release of DBH above control stimulated levels, providing further evidence that angiotensin II facilitates neurotransmitter release during nerve stimulation. Sar[1], Ile[8]-angiotensin II, a competitive antagonist of angiotensin II, did not change control stimulated release of DBH, but shifted the dose-response curve for angiotensin II to the right. This blockade of angiotensin's effect on nerve stimulation by angiotensin II antagonists has also been shown by others (Malik and Nasjletti, 1976; Sweet *et al.*, 1976; Zimmerman, 1973, 1978; Campbell and Jackson, 1979; Zimmerman and Kraft, 1979), and indicates that the potentiation of adrenergic transmission is mediated by angiotensin receptors.

Angiotensin has also been shown to block the reuptake of norepinephrine into adrenergic nerve terminals (Peach *et al.*, 1969; Janowsky *et al.*,

1972; Khairallah, 1972; Campbell and Jackson, 1979). The addition of angiotensin (0.05–2 ng/ml) to rabbit hearts caused a significant inhibition of [^{3}H]norepinephrine uptake. This effect appears to be specific for angiotensin since other peptides, including vasopressin, oxytocin, bradykinin, kallidin, and glucagon had no effect (Khairallah, 1972). The mechanism of action of this inhibition is not clear. It has been shown that the removal of Na$^+$, K$^+$ or Mg^{2+} abolishes the inhibition of metaraminol uptake into rat atria by angiotensin. Therefore, it is possible that angiotensin inhibits uptake of NE by affecting Na$^+$/K$^+$/Mg^{2+}-activated membrane ATPase, which is suggested to be involved in catecholamine uptake (Davila and Khairallah, 1970).

Whether the inhibition of reuptake of norepinephrine by angiotensin contributes significantly to the increased overflow of norepinephrine during nerve stimulation is not clear. Starke (1970, 1971) and Schümann *et al.* (1970) found that the facilitation of norepinephrine overflow by angiotensin in rabbit heart remained unchanged after pretreatment with cocaine or desmethylimiprimine in concentrations great enough to cause maximal inhibition of norepinephrine uptake. They, therefore, concluded that angiotensin increases norepinephrine overflow by increasing transmitter release, rather than by blocking reuptake.

These effects of angiotensin on noradrenergic nerve endings vary depending on the vascular bed studied and the type of preparation. For example, the augmentation of norepinephrine release during nerve stimulation by angiotensin is seen in the perfused dog paw, while angiotensin causes a decrease in norepinephrine release in the perfused dog muscle (Zimmerman and Whitmore, 1967). In general, angiotensin potentiates the effects of nerve stimulation on the vasculature more than effects of exogeneously administered norepinephrine (Zimmerman *et al.*, 1972; Malik and Nasjletti, 1976; Zimmerman, 1978) when studied *in situ*. However, it has been found with *in vitro* cutaneous arteries that angiotensin potentiates the response to nerve stimulation and exogenous norepinephrine to the same extent (Povolny *et al.*, 1977).

It has also been shown that the pattern of potentiation varies depending on the type of vessel studied. Constriction in cutaneous arterial and smaller vessels, caused by nerve stimulation, is potentiated to a much greater extent than constriction in these segments caused by norepinephrine. However, in cutaneous venous segments the potentiation of constriction by angiotensin is the same whether the constriction was due to nerve stimulation or exogenously administered norepinephrine (Zimmerman, 1978).

The interaction of angiotensin with the peripheral sympathetic nervous system appears to be receptor mediated since these effects are blocked by angiotensin antagonists. It is possible that angiotensin I is converted to angiotensin II in the vascular wall and the latter would then potentiate the effects of endogenously released norepinephrine by facilitating transmitter release, by increasing smooth muscle responsiveness to norepinephrine and possibly by decreasing the reuptake of norepinephrine.

The possibility that the adrenergic potentiating effects of angiotensin are of physiological significance has been demonstrated by Zimmerman and Kraft (1979). Using the isolated perfused dog paw, they found that aortic constriction above the kidneys, increased the vasoconstrictor response to nerve stimulation by 31%. Intra-arterial administration of saralasin reversed the potentiating effects of aortic constriction on nerve stimulation. They, therefore, postulated that when the renin–angiotensin system is activated by restricting renal blood flow that enough angiotensin II is formed to have a moderate adrenergic potentiating effect.

In addition to its effects on norepinephrine release, angiotensin II has been shown to increase norepinephrine synthesis (Roth, 1972; Boadle-Biber and Roth, 1977). Angiotensin was shown to increase catecholamine synthesis from [^{14}C]tyrosine in a variety of different tissues that are sympathetically innervated. This effect does not appear to be a general one, since some of the tissues tested did not show an increase (Boadle-Biber *et al.*, 1972). The increase in synthesis appeared after incubation for an hour with angiotensin II and returned to control levels after 2 hours of incubation. The increase in catecholamine synthesis was also dependent on the concentration of angiotensin in the incubation medium. For guinea-pig atria $5 \times 10^{-9}M$ angiotensin was ineffective, $5 \times 10^{-7}M$ was optimal, and $1 \times 10^{-4}M$ caused an inhibition of catecholamine synthesis.

Since using [^{14}C]dopa instead of [^{14}C]tyrosine, to measure catechol synthesis, eliminated the effect of angiotensin II, it was presumed that angiotensin affected the rate-limiting step in the synthesis of norepinephrine—tyrosine hydroxylation. The activity of tyrosine hydroxylase, the enzyme which catalyzes this reaction, can be affected in several different ways, e.g., changes in total amount of enzyme, end-product inhibition or affinity for substrate or cofactor. Since angiotensin II has been shown to affect protein synthesis (Roth, 1972) it is possible that it could increase the amount of tyrosine hydroxylase. Roth and Hughes (1972) have shown that puromycin blocks the increase in catecholamine synthesis seen with angiotensin, possibly indicating an effect on the synthesis of tyrosine hydroxylase. However, Boadle-Biber and Roth (1977) found that concentrations of angiotensin II that increased incorporation of amino acids into protein had no effect on the amount of tyrosine hydroxylase present.

Since angiotensin has been shown to facilitate release of norepinephrine during nerve stimulation it is possible that angiotensin may increase catecholamine synthesis by increasing the basal release of norepinephrine, thereby removing tyrosine hydroxylase from end-product inhibition. However, there is no indication that anigotensin increases the basal release of norepinephrine (Boadle-Biber and Roth, 1977).

Another possibility is that angiotensin activates tyrosine hydroxylase by increasing the affinity of the enzyme for substrate or cofactor. There is some indication that angiotensin may activate tyrosine hydroxylase in this manner (Boadle-Biber and Roth, 1977) but the mechanism involved is, as of yet, unclear.

Angiotensin has clearly been shown to interact with the sympathetic nervous system to modify vascular constriction. In addition to its effects on the responsiveness of vascular smooth muscle to norepinephrine, angiotensin potentiates the response to sympathetic nerve stimulation by facilitating the release of norepinephrine from nerve terminals and possibly by inhibiting the reuptake of norepinephrine. The contribution of the activation of tyrosine hydroxylase by angiotensin under physiologic conditions, to regulation of blood pressure is not known.

2. Serotonin

In addition to the effects of angiotensin it appears that other humoral agents may interact with the sympathetic nervous system. 5-Hydroxytryptamine (5-HT) has been shown to have indirect sympathomimetic effects on the isolated rabbit heart (Fozard and Mwaluko, 1976). The stimulatory effects of 5-HT are the result of norepinephrine release from nerve terminals since they are blocked by propranolol, and pretreatment with 6-hydroxydopamine greatly reduced the effect of 5-HT. The mechanism of release appears to be more similar to that of dimethylphenylpiperazinium (DMPP) (Ca^{2+}-dependent depolarization) than to that of tyramine (neuronal uptake resulting in stoichiometric displacement). The effect of 5-HT on blood vessels appears to be different from that found in the heart (McGrath, 1977). 5-HT ($10^{-8}M$) inhibits the release of norepinephrine and the increase in tension caused by transmural stimulation of the dog saphenous vein. In contrast, 5-HT causes contraction of the unstimulated vessel. 5-HT had no effect on the contraction caused by norepinephrine. At higher concentrations ($10^{-5}M$) 5-HT has a direct excitatory effect on vascular smooth muscle and also increases release of norepinephrine from sympathetic nerves. It appears that the effects of 5-HT on the sympathetic nervous system are complex and may vary depending on the organ and the basal sympathetic tone.

3. Dopamine

Dopamine has been shown to have both pressor and depressor effects when injected intravenously, depending on the concentration (Setler *et al.*, 1975). Small doses of dopamine cause a fall in pressure, reportedly due to its effect on postsynaptic vascular dopamine receptors (Setler *et al.*, 1975; Lokhandwala and Buckley, 1977). However, it has also been suggested that dopamine may exert its vasodilatory effect by interaction with presynaptic dopamine receptors, resulting in a decreased efflux of norepinephrine from nerve terminals (Lokhandwala and Buckley, 1977, 1978; Hope *et al.*, 1978; Lokhandwala and Jandhyala, 1979) or by interaction with ganglionic dopamine receptors resulting in decreased vasoconstrictor discharge (Lokhandwala and Jandhyala, 1979).

4. Histamine

Aside from its direct effect on blood vessels (see Owen, 1977), histamine has also been shown to interact with sympathetic nerves by decreasing the release of norepinephrine during nerve stimulation (McGrath and Shepherd, 1976; Lokhandwala, 1978; Powell, 1979). It appears that the inhibitory effect of histamine is mediated by presynaptic H_2 receptors since these effects of histamine were blocked by metiamide, an H_2-receptor antagonist, and mimicked by dimaprit, an H_2-receptor agonist (Powell, 1979).

Although these and other humoral agents (see Starke *et al.*, 1977) can interact with noradrenergic neurons via presynaptic receptors, the physiological significance of these actions in regards to blood pressure regulation remains unclear. It remains to be determined whether the effects of these agents on vascular resistance are a part of the basal regulation of vascular tone, whether they only come into play at higher than baseline circulating levels or whether these effects are purely experimental phenomena.

C. Involvement of the Peripheral Nervous System in Hypertension

The factors involved in the development and maintenance of essential hypertension in man are still unclear. It is obvious that there may be several contributing factors and that the causative factors might not necessarily be the same in every patient with essential hypertension (Schmid and Abboud, 1974; Frohlich, 1977; Cowley, 1978).

Any of the mechanisms involved in the normal regulation of blood pressure (e.g., vascular, neuronal, or hormonal) may be the "trigger" mechanism for the initiation of hypertension. Because of the complexity of the blood pressure regulatory system and the extensive feedback between different regulatory mechanisms it has been difficult to precisely define "trigger" mechanisms. Since the systems are so interrelated it is likely that changes in other systems set up by the initiating defect contribute to the initiation of hypertension.

Several different animals models of hypertension have been studied, including renal and DOCA-salt induced hypertension and several different strains of genetically hypertensive rats (Dahl *et al.*, 1962; Okamoto and Aoki, 1963; Phelan, 1968). The characteristics of hypertension differ in these different animal models (Fink and Brody, 1978; Ferrone *et al.*, 1979) and have varying correlation with the characteristics of human essential hypertension (Folkow *et al.*, 1973; de Champlain, 1978). These models, therefore, provide a means of studying the various factors involved in the development and maintenance of essential hypertension. The spontaneously hypertensive rat (SHR) developed by Okamoto and Aoki (1963) has, particularly, been extensively used because of its similarities to human essential hypertension (Folkow, 1975). SHR do not become overtly hypertensive until approximately 6 to 8 weeks of age, although differences between SHR and the control Wistar-Kyoto (WKY) rats can be seen as early as 3 to 4 weeks (Lais *et al.*, 1977). Therefore, using SHR it is possible to study changes in the blood pressure regulatory system before the onset of high blood pressure and possibly determine the initiating factors.

This section will discuss the peripheral nervous system and other peripheral components that may interact with it, in terms of the development of hypertension. The CNS factors affecting the development of hypertension will be discussed in a later section.

1. Peripheral Sympathetic Nerves

The vascular changes seen in hypertensive animals appear to be confined mainly to precapillary resistance vessels. The initial changes consist of an increased wall thickness, and if high blood pressure persists, an increased formation of extracellular supporting material. These changes result in an increased resistance to blood flow in hypertensive vascular beds and a steeper increase in resistance in response to norepinephrine than in control (Folkow, 1977).

Nakada and Lovenberg (1978) found an increased rate of incorporation of [³H]lysine into non-collagen protein of internal spermatic and mesenteric arteries of 8-week-old SHR when compared to WKY rats. This indicates that there is an increased protein synthesis in these arteries at an early stage of hypertension. In a previous study Yamori *et al.* (1976) demonstrated that the increased [³H]lysine incorporation in mesenteric arteries of 8-week-old SHR was abolished by treatment with hexamethonium for 2 weeks or splanchnicotomy at 6 weeks of age. Hydralazine treatment had no effect, indicating that sympathetic innervation is important for increased vascular protein synthesis at early stages of hypertension rather than, or in addition to, the increase in blood pressure. Lais and Brody (1978) found similar changes in vascular function in 3-week-old SHR as seen in SHR with established hypertension. Prehypertensive SHR had increased resistance to blood flow and the dose-response curve to norepinephrine had a steeper slope and a greater maximal response. These data indicate that there are structural changes in the vessels of SHR at an extremely early age.

From these studies it appears that vascular changes in the SHR play a role in the development, as well as the maintenance, of hypertension. Although it seems that an increase in peripheral sympathetic activity may initiate these vascular changes, the structural changes are present at such an early age that they undoubtedly also play a role in the development of hypertension in the SHR.

The structural changes in vessel walls due to high blood pressure affect other components of the peripheral blood pressure regulatory system. The baroreceptors of SHR reset to higher pressures after exposure to high blood pressure, although the carotid sinus and aortic depressor nerves are not functionally different from control animals (Nosaka and Okamoto, 1970; Nosaka and Wang, 1972). It has been shown that this resetting of baroreceptors is not responsible for the initiation of high blood pressure in the SHR (Thant *et al.*, 1969), but it obviously participates in the maintenance of hypertension. The baroreceptor resetting appears to be due to the decreased distensibility of the vascular wall, but also to adaptation of the receptor to persistent stimulation (Cowley, 1978; Sapru and Krieger, 1979). Sapru and Krieger (1979) found partial resetting of baroreceptors in SHR treated with antihypertensive agents starting at 4 weeks of age until 40 weeks of age and then withdrawn from treatment for 2 weeks. Since there was no change in vascular distensibility in these animals, it appears that the baroreceptors are capable of adapting to persistent high blood pressure.

This resetting of baroreceptors, whether due to decreased vascular wall distensibility or baroreceptor adaptation, results in decreased regulation of sympathetic activity by baroreceptor feedback. Coote and Sato (1977) compared the effects of baroreceptor stimulation on renal nerve activity in WKY and SHR. By measuring the silent period on the renal nerve produced by increases in blood pressure, they found the threshold pressure necessary to produce silence was greater in SHR, and that comparable increases in blood pressure above threshold were less effective in completely inhibiting sympathetic nerve activity in the SHR.

Increased sympathetic nervous activity appears to play an important role in the development, of at least some types, of human essential hypertension. It is difficult to get a reliable index of sympathetic activity in human patients, the usual measurement being plasma norepinephrine. Increases in plasma norepinephrine indicate that there is a selective increase in sympathetic activity to the vasculature since it is not accompanied by increase in cardiac output, heart rate or other sympathetic functions (Louis *et al.*, 1976, 1977; Miura *et al.*, 1978). However, since some hypertensive patients do not have elevated plasma norepinephrine it must be assumed that other factors also play a role.

Plasma norepinephrine and dopamine-β-hydroxylase (DBH), another index of sympathetic activity, has also been measured in the SHR. It appears that plasma norepinephrine is increased in SHR at 3 weeks of age but not at later ages (Nagaoka and Lovenberg,1976) and is increased in stroke-prone hypertensive rats (SHR-SP) at all ages (Nagaoka and Lovenberg, 1976; Schömig *et al.*, 1978). Plasma DBH is increased in 3-week-old SHR and SHR-SP (Nagaoka and Lovenberg, 1976; Nagatsu *et al.*, 1976, 1977), but not in 16-week-old SHR (Nagatsu *et al.*, 1977). Plasma DBH is also increased in rats 3 days to 11 weeks after neurogenic hypertension was induced by sinoaortic denervation (Alexander *et al.*, 1976).

It has also been suggested that ganglia of SHR are not able to modify incoming preganglionic activity as well as in WKY. The release and metabolism of dopamine, which suppresses transmission in sympathetic ganglia, is decreased in 4-week-old SHR, increases with the increase in blood pressure and at 20 weeks of age is similar to that of WKY (Lütold *et al.*, 1979). This suggests that in young SHR, the ganglionic dopaminergic differences might result in increased transmission of preganglionic activity resulting in increased postganglionic sympathetic activity.

The differences in plasma NE and DBH between WKY and SHR are usually found at an early age, before the onset of hypertension in the SHR. These parameters indicate an increased sympathetic nervous activity in the young SHR, and suggest that this could be a trigger mechanism for the increase in blood pressure. However, since nerve endings are not the only source of plasma NE and DBH these data do not yield conclusve information as to the actual state of the sympathetic nervous system of the SHR at different ages, or its involvement in the hypertensive process.

There are several other lines of more direct evidence that indicate an increase in peripheral sympathetic activity in SHR (Okamoto *et al.*, 1967; Iriuchijima, 1973; Nosaka, 1973; Judy *et al.*, 1976; Schramm and Barton, 1979). Iriuchijima (1973) cut the splanchnic nerves in 13- to 20-week-old WKY and SHR and measured the stimulation frequency necessary to restore the arterial pressure to the level before the nerves were cut. This frequency could then be used as an index of the average discharge rate in the sympathetic nerves of WKY and SHR. He found that the stimulation frequency needed to return SHR blood pressures to normal was four to five times higher than that in WKY rats, indicating that SHR have increased sympathetic tone.

Schramm and Barton (1979) have used the sympathetic silent period as an index of sympathetic tone in WKY and SHR. The silent period is a period of reduced sympathetic excitability which follows spontaneous or evoked sympathetic activation. The degree of inhibition is inversely related to the resting sympathetic activity (Sherrer, 1963). They measured evoked responses on the splanchnic nerve which were followed by decreases in spontaneous sympathetic activity and an increased threshold to stimulation. These silent periods were not caused by baroreceptor–reflex inhibition of sympathetic activity, since the latency of onset of the silent period was less than 100 milliseconds. In both 4-week-old and adult SHR the silent periods were significantly weaker than those in WKY, indicating a higher resting sympathetic tone in the SHR.

Perhaps, the most direct measurement of sympathetic activity in the SHR has been made by Judy *et al.* (1976). Nerve recordings from a branch of the greater splanchnic nerve were made in unanesthetized, 16 to 20-week-old WKY and SHR, and sympathetic activity was found to be significantly greater in the SHR. They also found that this increase in sympathetic activity appeared to be generalized since nerve activity of the splanchnic, cervical sympathetic, splenic, and renal nerves of SHR was two to three times greater than that of WKY rats. The sympathetic nerve activity in SHR increased with increasing age, with a time course the same as the increase in blood pressure. These results suggest that increased sympathetic nerve activity plays an important role in the development and maintenance of hypertension in the SHR.

It appears, therefore, that hyperactivity of the sympathetic nervous system in the SHR is intimately involved in the development of hypertension in this model. Aside from the direct effects of increased vasoconstriction it is possible that the increased sympathetic activity may modify vascular response to circulating catecholamines (Kubo, 1979). Since measurement of sympathetic activity in human patients must be measured indirectly it is not clear whether sympathetic hyperactivity plays the same role in the initiation of essential hypertension as it does in the hypertension of SHR.

Considering the apparent importance of the sympathetic nervous system in the development of hypertension in the SHR several investigators have studied the effects of removal of sympathetic input by chemical sympathectomy (Yamori *et al.*, 1972a; Honda *et al.*, 1975; Ikeda *et al.*, 1979) or denervation (Iriuchijima and Numao, 1976; Nakamura and Nakamura, 1977b; Kline *et al.*, 1978).

Generally, treatment of young SHR (6–10 weeks of age) with 6-hydroxydopamine (6-OHDA) has only a transient effect on the development of hypertension. In one experiment a marked decrease in blood pressure was noted 24 hours after a single injection of 6-OHDA, but the blood pressure slowly returned to normal over a period of 4 days. Despite the significant depletion of NE the development and maintenance of hypertension in the SHR was not significantly affected (Yamori *et al.,* 1972a).

Treatment of neonatal SHR-SP with 6-OHDA prevents the development of hypertension to some extent, in that treated animals have significantly lower pressures than untreated animals up to 23 weeks of age (Ikeda *et al.,* 1979). However, the pressures of treated animals were still definitely in the hypertensive range.

Denervation experiments have yielded similar results to those with 6-OHDA treatments. Bilateral removal of the abdominal sympathetic chain decreases SHR blood pressure to control levels, but the hypertension returns after a few days (Iriuchijima and Numao, 1976). Bilateral renal denervation delays the blood pressure increase in SHR (Liard, 1977; Kline *et al.,* 1978). Renal denervation in 8-week-old SHR reduces blood pressure by 20 mm Hg, 2–3 weeks after surgery. However, the blood pressure increases at the same rate as controls, and eventually they become hypertensive, although at a later age (Kline *et al.,* 1978). Bilateral removal of the coeliac ganglia in 5-week-old SHR does not change the development of hypertension, although it does decrease the elevated plasma NE and DBH levels (Nakamura and Nakamura, 1977b).

It is difficult to explain why seemingly drastic manipulations of the sympathetic nervous system have such little effect on the development of hypertension in the SHR. It is possible that vasoconstrictor responses depend on only a small fraction of total NE stores so that depletion of NE by 6-OHDA does not markedly reduce the effect of sympathetic nerves on the vasculature. It has also been shown that regeneration of sympathetic nerve fibers starts within 5 days after treatment (Yamori *et al.,* 1972a) and that the regeneration is faster in hypertensive than in normotensive rats (Honda *et al.,* 1975). It is also obvious that other changes might somewhat mask the effects of 6-OHDA treatment, such as increases in receptor sensitivity to NE and increased vascular tone due to structural changes.

Since most denervation experiments remove only a portion of the sympathetic system involved in blood pressure regulation, it is not surprising that SHR blood pressures are not reduced to control levels by these manipulations. However, the exact role of the increased sympathetic nerve activity in the development and maintenance remains to be determined.

It is possible that removal of sympathetic input results in only a partial alleviation of hypertension because it is only one of several factors involved in the hypertensive process.

2. *Peripheral Hormones*

The participation of the renin–angiotensin system in hypertension is difficult to assess. It appears that the renin–angiotensin system in hypertensive patients responds to physiological stimuli in the same manner as in normotensive patients (Gross, 1977). Hypertensive patients may exhibit low, normal, or high plasma renin activity, and therefore it is possible that the renin–angiotensin system may play a different role in different types of hypertension. Saralasin, an angiotensin II antagonist, and SQ 20881, which inhibits the conversion of angiotensin I to angiotensin II, have been used to determine the importance of angiotensin in these subgroups of hypertensive patients (Hulthën and Hökfelt, 1978; Soffer and Case, 1978). In low-renin hypertensive patients SQ 20881 had no effect and saralasin increased blood pressure. Normal-renin hypertensive patients showed no response to saralasin and an 8% decrease in blood pressure after SQ 20881. In contrast, both saralasin and SQ 20881 were effective in lowering blood pressure (8% and 15%, respectively) in high-renin hypertensive patients. It therefore appears that angiotensin II becomes a more important factor in hypertension as the level of plasma renin activity in patients increases.

Saralasin and converting enzyme inhibitors (SQ 20881 and SQ 14225) have also been used to determine the importance of the renin-angiotensin system in the development of hypertension in the different hypertensive animal models. Administration of intravenous (i.v.) saralasin has no effect on the blood pressure of one-clip one-kidney or two-clip renal hypertensive rats. However, in one-clip two-kidney renal hypertensive rats, which have been shown to have increased plasma levels of angiotensin II, i.v. saralasin decreases blood pressure. In both DOCA-salt hypertensive rats and SHR, saralasin causes an increase in blood pressure (Mann *et al.*, 1978). Shibota *et al.* (1979) found no effect of saralasin on the blood pressure of SHR-SP. Salt loading SHR-SP produced malignant hypertension and an increase in plasma renin activity. In these animals infusion of saralasin resulted in a decrease in blood pressure which became more prominent with increasing plasma renin activity.

The effects of SQ 14225, an angiotensin converting enzyme inhibitor, have been studied in one- and two-kidney renal hypertensive rats and SHR (Laffan *et al.*, 1978). SQ 14225 had no effect in one-kidney renal hypertensive rats but had a marked dose-related antihypertensive effect in two-kidney renal hypertensive rats. Some antihypertensive effect was seen in SHR but it was much less pronounced than in renal hypertensive rats. It can be concluded that the antihypertensive effect of SQ 14225 is due to its inhibition of angiotensin conversion since it has been shown that this compound does not interact with α-receptors, or have any ganglion blocking or smooth muscle relaxant properties.

It therefore appears that the renin–angiotensin system is involved in the development or maintenance of some types of hypertension—most notably in two-kidney renal hypertension and perhaps partially in the SHR.

It has also been suggested that vasopressin might play a role in essential hypertension since urinary excretion of vasopressin was increased in hypertensive patients (Khökkar *et al.*, 1974) and hypertensive rats showed increased vascular reactivity to vasopressin (Kubo, 1978). However, Padfield (1977) found no increase in plasma vasopressin levels in patients with essential hypertension, and was unable to raise the blood pressure of normal controls with arginine–vasopressin infusions. Both plasma and urinary vasopressin levels were greater in SHR than in WKY rats (Crofton *et al.*, 1978), however, they found no correlation between the increase in vasopressin levels and the increase in blood pressure. In addition, injection of an analog that blocks the pressor activity of vasopressin did not consistently decrease blood pressure in the SHR. It therefore appears that vasopressin plays a minor role, if any, in the development of hypertension both in humans and animal models.

III. CENTRAL NERVOUS SYSTEM REGULATION

The CNS regulation of blood pressure is obviously a very broad and complex topic. Not only is there integration of many different areas of the brain, but also areas have different functional contributions, e.g., tonic as compared to modulatory roles. Therefore, it is necessary to limit the scope of this discussion. Since much work has centered around the role of the NTS and the hypothalamus these two areas and their integration will be discussed, as well as the role of different neurotransmitter systems in CNS regulation of blood pressure.

Readers interested in other CNS areas are referred to references in the anatomical section of this chapter. Further references for specific areas are: spinal cord (Foreman and Wurster, 1973; Barman and Wurster, 1975; Geis *et al.*, 1978); hippocampus (Torii and Kawamura, 1960; Ely *et al.*, 1977); amygdala (Mogenson and Calaresu, 1973; Lang *et al.*, 1979). In addition, several review articles have been written which discuss different aspects of CNS mechanisms involved in the regulation of blood pressure (Korner, 1971, 1979; Koizumi and Brooks, 1972; Smith, 1974; Calaresu *et al.*, 1975; Simon and Riedel, 1975; Kirchheim, 1976).

A. CENTRAL NEURONAL SYSTEMS

1. NTS–Baroreceptor Reflex

The NTS is the major site of the synapse of carotid sinus and aortic baroreceptor afferents (Crill and Reis, 1968; Seller and Illert, 1969; Biscoe and Sampson, 1970; Hildebrandt, 1974; Burkhart *et al.*, 1977). As can be seen in Fig. 1, the NTS has inputs to many different areas, both medullary and diencephalic, thereby providing for integration of afferent information with both pressor and depressor pathways in the CNS. The baroreceptor reflex pathway is not the only pathway resulting in inhibition of sympathetic nerve activity (Snyder and Gebber, 1973; Barman and Gebber, 1978). A depressor pathway in the medial caudal medulla has been distinguished from that relaying baroreceptor information (Barman and Gebber, 1978) and it appears that they can also be distinguished on the basis of modulation of different pressor pathways (Snyder and Gebber, 1973). It appears that two distinct vasopressor pathways exist, and that baroreceptor activation can only inhibit sympathetic nerve responses evoked by stimulation of the more slowly conducting vasopressor pathway (Gebber *et al.*, 1973). This indicates that, although baroreceptor reflex activation plays an important role in regulation of blood pressure and modulation of pressor systems in the CNS, other pressor and depressor pathways operate independently of the depressor pathway originating in the NTS. There is also some indication that baroreceptor reflex activity is affected by higher centers in the CNS (Reis and Cuénod, 1964; Gebber and Snyder, 1970).

The role of the NTS in regulation of blood pressure has also been studied by making bilateral lesions of this nucleus. Bilateral lesions of the NTS results in abolition of the baroreceptor reflex (Doba and Reis, 1973, 1974; Nathan and Reis, 1977) and in acute fulminating hypertension in the rat (Doba and Reis, 1973, 1974; de Jong *et al.*, 1975b) and chronic labile hypertension in the cat (Nathan and Reis, 1977).

2. Hypothalamus

It has been known for some time that both the anterior and posterior hypothalamus are involved in the regulation of blood pressure (Gellhorn *et al.*, 1956). The exact role of the anterior hypothalamus in control of blood pressure and its interaction with baro- and chemoreceptor reflexes is still somewhat unclear. Stimulation of the anterior hypothalamus results in a decrease in blood pressure of approximately 30–50 mm Hg (Hilton and Spyer, 1969, 1971). In addition they showed that the pattern of the response to stimulation was similar to the response to baroreceptor stimulation. Bilateral lesions of this depressor area decreased but did not abolish, the response to baroreceptor stimulation (Hilton and Spyer, 1971). To totally abolish baroreceptor reflexes (with the NTS intact) it was necessary to lesion both the anterior hypothalamic and medullary depressor areas. These data indicate that the anterior hypothalamus participates in mediating baroreceptor reflexes.

The role of the posterior hypothalamus in the regulation of blood pressure has been more extensively studied (Okamoto et al., 1965; Cheatham and Matzke, 1966; Enoch and Kerr, 1967a,b; Djojosugito et al., 1970; Gebber and Snyder, 1970; Ninomiya et al., 1970; Achari et al., 1973; Bell et al., 1973; Gebber et al., 1973; Eferakeya and Buñag, 1974; Hilton, 1974; Reis et al., 1975; Saper et al., 1976; Smits and Struyker-Boudier, 1976).

Several studies have described the course and connections of the pressor tracts from the posterior hypothalamus (Cheatham and Matzke, 1966; Enoch and Kerr, 1967a,b). There appears to be two major pressor pathways—one originating diffusely in the posterior hypothalamus and the other originating in higher areas (septal, preoptic, and basofrontal cortex) and passing through the lateral hypothalamus. These pathways appear to be entirely independent.

Lesioning different areas of the hypothalamus can result in sustained hypertension or hypotension depending on the site of the lesion (Okamoto et al., 1965). Lesions that destroy a major part of the anterior or posterior hypothalamus result in hypertension; while lesions of the arcuate nucleus or anterodorsal hypothalamus result in sustained hypotension. These data indicate that the hypothalamus may play a role in tonic regulation of blood pressure.

Activity of the posterior hypothalamus can interact with the baroreceptor reflex. Stimulation of the baroreceptor reflex decreases the effectiveness of ongoing posterior hypothalamic stimulation, and conversely, hypothalamic stimulation blocks bradycardia evoked by carotid sinus nerve stimulation (Gebber and Snyder, 1970). However, the posterior hypothalamic pressor pathway is not homogeneous with respect to its response to baroreceptor reflex activation. Gebber et al. (1973) offer evidence to support the existence of both baroreceptor-sensitive and -insensitive pathways which have different electrophysiological characteristics.

3. CNS Transmitter Systems

a. Norepinephrine. The CNS catecholaminergic pathways and their involvement in the regulation of blood pressure have been widely studied. Both central α- (Scriabne *et al.*, 1976) and β-receptors (Sharma *et al.*, 1979), norepinephrine turnover rate (Ito *et al.*, 1975), and epinephrine (Bolme *et al.*, 1974) have been invoked to explain the varied blood pressure response to centrally administered NE. The literature has become somewhat confusing partly due to the fact that different animals have been used (rats, cats, dogs, monkeys, rabbits), NE is administered by different routes (intracerebroventricular, intracisternal, microiontophoresis, and neuroinjection into specific brain areas) and different pharmacological approaches have been employed (depletion of NE, use of sympathomimetics or sympatholytics). A summary of some of the results of various experiments is presented in Table I.

Intracerebroventricular (i.c.v.) administration of NE has been reported to produce hypertension (Forsyth and Pesout, 1978; Hoffman, 1979), hypotension (Day and Roach, 1974; Buccafusco and Brezenoff, 1977), and no effect (Haeusler *et al.*, 1972b). It is possible that at higher doses NE may leak out of the ventricles causing an increase in blood pressure via its peripheral effects (Buccafusco and Brezenoff, 1977) thereby explaining the differences in the results. However, Day and Roach (1974) used doses of NE as high as 30 μg and saw only decreases in blood pressure, indicating that some factor other than dose might come into play. In the above experiments, all responses to NE, whether increases or decreases in blood pressure, were blocked by α-receptor blockers, indicating that the effects of NE were mediated through stimulation of α-receptors. However, both α- and β-receptors appear to be involved in mediating the CNS effects of NE, and it seems that they have opposite effects on blood pressure (Day and Roach, 1974; Ito and Schanberg, 1974), with α-receptors mediating increases and β-receptors decreases in blood pressure.

Injections of 6-hydroxydopamine (6-OHDA) into the ventricles results in destruction of catecholaminergic neurons. Both increases (Lewis *et al.*, 1974), decreases (Haeusler *et al.*, 1972b; Korner *et al.*, 1978), and no change (Ogawa, 1978) in blood pressure have been seen after 6-OHDA, however, these effects are always transient and blood pressure returns to control values within a few hours. 6-OHDA administered the first and second day after birth reduces brain NE by 50% in 3-month-old rats, but has no effect on blood pressure (de Jong *et al.*, 1975b). Bilateral injections

TABLE I
Effects of Centrally Administered Adrenergic Compounds on Blood Pressure

Species	Area of Administration	NE	E	Clonidine	α-agonist	Pre-synaptic α-agonist	Post-synaptic α-agonist	β-agonist	α-blocker	β-blocker	6-OHDA	References
Monkey	3rd ventricle	↑									↓	Forsyth and Pesout (1978)
Rat	i.c.v.	↑		↓								Hoffman (1979)
Cat	i.c.v.	↓	↑↓	↓	↓			↑↓				Day and Roach (1974)
Rat	i.c.v.	↓										Buccafusco and Brezenoff (1977)
Rat	i.c.	↑						↑		↑		Ito and Schanberg (1974)
Rabbit	i.c.v.										↑	Lewis et al. (1974)
Rat	i.c.								↑		↓	Haeusler et al. (1972a)
Rabbit	i.c.								↑		↓	Korner et al. (1978)
Rat	i.c.v.										−	Ogawa (1978)
Rat	LC										↑	Ogawa (1978); Ogawa et al. (1977)
Rat	NTS	↓										de Jong et al. (1975b, 1976)

Species	Region					Reference
Rat	NTS	↓	↓			Struyker-Boudier et al. (1975)
Rat	NTS	↓	↓	↑↓	↓	Zandberg et al. (1979)
Cat	NTS		↑	—	↑↓	— ↑ –	Snyder et al. (1978)
Cat	H	↑	↑			Phillipu et al. (1971)
Cat	PH	↑	↑	↑		Bhargava et al. (1978)
Cat	PH[a] stimulation	↑	↑		→	Philippu et al. (1973) Philippu (1975)
Rat	AH	↑				Struyker-Boudier et al. (1975)
Rat	AH	↑	↑			Struyker-Boudier et al. (1974)

↑, Increase in blood pressure.
↓, Decrease in blood pressure.
–, No change.
i.c.v., Intracerebroventricular.
i.c., Intracisternal.
LC, locus coeruleus.
H, hypothalamus.
PH, posterior hypothalamus.
AH, anterior hypothalamus.
NTS, nucleus tractus solitarius.
[a] Effects on pressor response to PH stimulation.

of 6-OHDA into the locus coeruleus results in a more persistent hypertension which is accompanied by decreased NE levels in the cortex and pons-medulla (Ogawa *et al.*, 1977). This hypertension can be prevented by pretreatment with i.c.v. 6-OHDA indicating that the effect of 6-OHDA in the locus coeruleus is mediated via other catecholaminergic neurons (Ogawa, 1978).

The NTS is one of the sites where catecholamines appear to exert their modulatory effect on blood pressure. Injections of NE (de Jong *et al.*, 1975b, 1976; Struyker-Boudier *et al.*, 1975), epinephrine (E), and α-methylnorepinephrine (α-meNE) decrease blood pressure and heart rate. The receptor involved in mediating this effect is unclear since neither pre- nor postsynaptic α-agonists or β-agonists have the same effect as NE or E when injected into the NTS (Zandberg *et al.*, 1979).

Destruction of the catecholaminergic innervation of the NTS by injection of 6-OHDA results in an initial hypertension. Blood pressure returns to control levels after 48 hours, however, the blood pressure becomes extremely labile (Snyder *et al.*, 1978). Since the baroreceptor reflex is still intact, although blunted, and the hypertension is not persistent, it appears that catecholaminergic innervation modulates the activity of the NTS, rather than mediating the baroreceptor reflex. There are other indications that this is true since cutting the afferents to the NTS (Palkovits *et al.*, 1977) or decreasing blood pressure (Wijnen *et al.*, 1978a) does not affect catecholamine levels in the NTS.

Central α-adrenoreceptors are also involved in regulation of blood pressure in both the anterior and posterior hypothalamus (Kobinger, 1978). It appears that in the posterior hypothalamus both α- and β-receptors might be involved since microinjections of NE (Brezenoff and Jenden, 1969), E and isoproterenol (Bhargava *et al.*, 1978), and superfusion with NE or E (Philippu *et al.*, 1971) result in dose-dependent increases in blood pressure.

Agents which affect α-receptors have also been shown to affect the rise in blood pressure seen with posterior hypothalamic stimulation (Philippu *et al.*, 1973; Philippu, 1975). Basically, superfusion of the posterior hypothalamus with α-antagonists inhibits the pressor response to stimulation, while superfusion with an α-agonist enhances the response. It has also been shown that superfusion of the NTS with α-agonists will inhibit the response to posterior hypothalamic stimulation.

However, it appears that NE does not play an integral role in mediating the effects of posterior hypothalamic stimulation, but rather facilitates the activation. Injection of 6-OHDA into the posterior hypothalamus blunts the pressor response to stimulation, but does not abolish it. Treatment with reserpine and α-methyl-*p*-tyrosine, which depletes catecholamines, also does not abolish the increased sympathetic nerve activity seen with hypothalamic stimulation (Haeusler, 1975).

In the anterior hypothalamus/preoptic area, injections of NE result in decreases in blood pressure (Struyker-Boudier *et al.*, 1974, 1975). This effect is blocked by phentolamine, indicating that α-receptors are involved in mediating this response.

Although the results of experiments on central adrenergic control of blood pressure are somewhat confusing, and sometimes conflicting, some general statements can be made. It appears that there are two separate adrenergic systems that have opposite effects on blood pressure. The depressor system is localized in the medulla (region of the NTS) and the anterior hypothalamus/preoptic area. The pressor system is in the area of the posterior hypothalamus. Both α- and β-receptors appear to be involved, although not necessarily in the same area, and they generally have opposite effects. It also seems that catecholamines are not crucial for the expression of posterior hypothalamic or NTS activity, but rather they play a facilitory or modulatory role.

b. Dopamine. The role of dopamine (DA) in CNS cardiovascular control has not been extensively studied, although it has been suggested that dopaminergic pathways may be involved (Bolme *et al.*, 1972; Blessing and Chalmers, 1979). Intracerebroventricular injection of dopamine has been shown to cause decreases in blood pressure in anesthetized rats and cats (Baum and Shropshire, 1973; Heise and Kroneberg, 1973), increases in blood pressure in unanesthetized cats (Day and Roach, 1974), and increases in unanesthetized dogs (Lang and Woodman, 1979). Whether the differences found are due to species or anesthesia are unclear. It is also possible that the observed effects are due to a mixture of actions of DA on receptors other than dopaminergic receptors, since in some studies its effects on blood pressure were blocked by propranolol (Day and Roach, 1974) or phentolamine (Zandberg *et al.*, 1979), indicating that DA may have an effect on α- and β-adrenergic receptors.

Injection of dopamine into the NTS results in a decrease in blood pressure, which had a slower onset than that of NE and E, but was similar to that of α-methylnorepinephrine (Zandberg *et al.*, 1979). Blockade of this decrease in blood pressure required excessively large doses of the dopamine receptor antagonist, haloperidol, but the response was easily blocked by phentolamine and yohimbine. It therefore appears that these effects of dopamine are due to stimulation of noradrenergic, rather than dopaminergic receptors. From the above results (summarized in Table II) it appears that dopaminergic pathways in the CNS are involved in regulation of blood pressure. Their exact localization and role have not been determined at this time.

TABLE II

EFFECTS OF CENTRALLY ADMINISTERED DOPAMINE ON BLOOD PRESSURE

Species	Area of Administration	Preparation	DA	Reference
Cat	i.c.v.	Anesthetized	↓	Heise and Kroneberg (1973)
Rat	i.c.v.	Anesthetized	↓	Baum and Shropshire (1973)
Cat	i.c.v.	Unanesthetized	↑	Day and Roach (1974)
Dog	i.c.v.	Unanesthetized	↑	Lang and Woodman (1979)
Rat	NTS	Anesthetized	↓	Zandberg et al. (1979)

↑, Increase in blood pressure; ↓, decrease in blood pressure.
i.c.v., Intracerebroventricular.
NTS, Nucleus tractus solitarius.

c. 5-Hydroxytryptamine (Serotonin). The role of 5-hydroxytryptamine (5-HT) in central mechanisms of blood pressure regulation has not been well defined. Anatomical evidence suggests that the raphé has an inhibitory monosynaptic projection to sympathetic neurons (Cabot *et al.,* 1979). However, in rats stimulation of dorsal and median raphé nuclei result in an increase in blood pressure (Smits *et al.,* 1978; Kuhn *et al.,* 1980). It is possible, however, that different nuclei of the raphé may have different effects on blood pressure.

The effects of centrally administered 5-HT and 5-HT antagonists is summarized in Table III. There seems to be some species differences since i.c.v. 5-HT decreases blood pressure in cats (Baum and Shropshire, 1975; Nava-Félix and Hong, 1979) and dogs (Dhawan *et al.,* 1967), and increases blood pressure in rats (Lambert *et al.,* 1978). These effects of 5-HT are not very clear-cut since methysergide, a 5-HT antagonist, also decreases blood pressure in cats (Antonaccio and Taylor, 1977a) and dogs (Antonaccio *et al.,* 1975). Methysergide does have the reverse effect of 5-HT in rats (Smits and Struyker-Boudier, 1976), however *p*-chlorophenylalanine (PCPA), a 5-HT synthesis inhibitor, increases blood pressure when administered to rats (Ito and Schanberg, 1972).

Injections of 5-HT into the anterior hypothalamus/preoptic area increase blood pressure in rats (Smits and Struyker-Boudier, 1976). However, this effect was only partially blocked by i.c.v. methysergide. This may possibly be one of the sites of action of 5-HT in terms of blood pressure regulation, but it may also be involved in other areas of the brain.

While it is clear that serotonergic systems are involved in the regulation of blood pressure, the exact role of serotonin has not been defined

TABLE III
EFFECTS OF CENTRALLY ADMINISTERED SEROTONERGIC COMPOUNDS ON BLOOD PRESSURE

Species	Area of administration	5-HT	Methysergide	PCPA	Reference
Cat	i.c.v.	↓			Nava-Felix and Hong (1979)
Cat	i.c.v.	↓			Baum and Shropshire (1975)
Cat	i.c.v.		↓		Antonaccio and Taylor (1977a)
Dog	i.c.v.	↓			Dhawan *et al.* (1967)
Dog	i.c.v.		↓		Antonaccio *et al.* (1975)
Rat	i.c.v.	↑			Lambert *et al.* (1978)
Rat	i.c.v.			↑	Ito and Schanberg (1972)
Rat	i.c.v.		↓		Smits and Struyker-Boudier (1976)
Rat	AH/PO	↑			Smits and Struyker-Boudier (1976)

↑, Increase in blood pressure.
↓, Decrease in blood pressure.
i.c.v., Intracerebroventricular.
AH/PO, Anterior hypothalamus/preoptic area

and the pathways have not been delineated. The conflicting data make it difficult to understand the role of 5-HT in central cardiovascular regulation. Aside from the fact that there may be differences in the action of 5-HT among species, the similar effects on blood pressure obtained with both 5-HT receptor agonists and antagonists remain to be explained.

d. Acetylcholine.   Acethylcholine (ACh) injected into the posterior hypothalamus or i.c.v. causes an increase in blood pressure (Day and Roach, 1977; Bhargava *et al.*, 1978; Buccafusco and Brezenoff, 1979). It is unclear whether this effect is mediated by nicotinic or muscarinic receptors since the effect has been reported to be abolished by both atropine and hexamethonium (Day and Roach, 1977) or only by atropine (Buccafusco and Brezenoff, 1979). Bhargava *et al.* (1978) found that muscarinic receptors, in general, were inhibitory, but they found no muscarinic receptors in the hypothalamus. However, Philippu (1975) found that muscarinic compounds inhibit the pressor response to hypothalamic stimulation while nicotinic compounds have the reverse effect. These results are summarized in Table IV.

It seems clear that ACh itself has a pressor effect in the CNS. The cholinergic pathways have not been identified and it has been postulated that ACh may exert its central cardiovascular effects via modulation of NE release (Philippu, 1975).

e. γ-Aminobutyric Acid (GABA).   The role of GABA in the regulation of blood pressure has not been extensively studied. Intracerebroventricular injections of GABA or the GABA agonist muscimol cause de-

TABLE IV

EFFECTS OF CENTRALLY ADMINISTERED CHOLINERGIC COMPOUNDS ON BLOOD PRESSURE

Species	Area of adminis- tration	ACh	Carbachol	AChE inhibitors	Nicotine	Muscarine	Reference
Rat	PH	↑		↑			Bucafusco and Brezen- off (1979)
Cat	PH	↑			↑		Bhargava *et al.* (1978)
Cat	PH		↑			↓	Philippu (1975)
Cat	i.c.v.	↑	↑		↑↓		Day and Roach (1974)

↑, Increase in blood pressure.
↓, Decrease in blood pressure.
AChE, Acetylcholinesterase.
PH, Posterior hypothalamus.
i.c.v., Intracerebroventricular.

creases in blood pressure (Antonaccio and Taylor, 1977b; Antonaccio *et al.*, 1978). The GABA antagonist, bicuculline, has the opposite effect when administered i.c.v. (DiMicco and Gillis, 1979). The sites involved in the cardiovascular actions of GABA have not been localized, but it appears that it may act at both medullary (Guertzenstein, 1973) and supra-collicular levels (Bolme and Fuxe, 1977; DiMicco *et al.*, 1977).

It is apparent that noradrenergic and adrenergic systems are involved in the CNS regulation of blood pressure. Some of the pathways and their role are becoming more well defined, as well as the receptors involved in mediating the responses to central administration of NE and E. Dopamine, serotonin, acetylcholine, and GABA also appear to play a role in regulation of blood pressure. However, these systems are much less well defined and still require extensive study.

B. CNS–HORMONAL SYSTEMS

1. Angiotensin

The existence of an endogenous brain renin–angiotensin system has been discussed in some detail (Severs and Daniel-Severs, 1973; Ganong, 1977; Peach, 1977; Reid, 1977; Ganten, 1978; Ganten and Stock, 1978).

Evidence in favor of a brain renin–angiotensin system consists of: demonstration of renin-like activity in the brain, the presence of angiotensinogen, the presence of converting enzyme, angiotensin activity as measured by radioimmunoassay (Phillips, 1978), and the detection of AII-like material by immunohistochemical methods (Fuxe *et al.*, 1976). However, several of these findings have recently been questioned (Reid, 1977). It appears that angiotensin measurements made by radioimmunoassay may be artifactual due to the presence of angiotensinases in the brain resulting in destruction of the [^{125}I]angiotensin (Reid *et al.*, 1977). It also appears that the brain renin enzyme may not have renin-like activity *in vivo*. Injections of angiotensiogen i.c.v. do not result in increased formation of AII although increased amounts of AII are formed centrally after i.c.v. injections of exogenous renin (Reid and Moffat, 1978).

Whether the CNS has a renin–angiotensin system separate from the periphery or not, it is clear that angiotensin has an effect on blood pressure via central mechanisms. There appear to be specific, high-affinity binding sites for AII in the central nervous system. The areas of highest binding are the area postrema, lateral septum (Sirett *et al.*, 1977), and the superior colliculi (Sirett *et al.*, 1979). The main sites for the physiological effects of AII appear to be the area postrema, the nucleus submedialis in the midbrain (Barker, 1976; Buckley and Jandhyala, 1977), and the anteroventral third ventricle (AV3V) (Hoffman and Phillips, 1976).

There are two components to the increase in blood pressure seen after i.c.v. AII administration. The early fast rise in blood pressure is due to sympathetic activation since it is eliminated by peripheral sympathectomy with 6-OHDA (Hoffman *et al.*, 1977b; Falcon *et al.*, 1978) and hexamethonium (Severs *et al.*, 1970). The slower, later rise in blood pressure is due to release of antidiuretic hormone (ADH) by angiotensin and can be eliminated by hypophysectomy (Severs *et al.*, 1970).

It has been suggested that the pressor response to central administration of AII is due to vasoconstriction rather than to direct effects on neurons (Dickinson and Yu, 1967; Yu and Dickinson, 1971). However, it appears that the central effects of AII are not due to local vasoconstriction since i.c.v. papaverine has no effect on the pressor response to i.c.v. AII and the response to AII is blocked by administration of the specific AII antagonist, saralasin (Hoffman *et al.*, 1977d).

The mechanism by which i.c.v. AII produces its pressor effect is unclear, although it has been suggested that AII interacts with noradrenergic systems. Pretreatment with central 6-OHDA reduces the pressor response to i.c.v. AII, and phentolamine, an α-receptor blocker, blocked the response (Hoffman *et al.*, 1977c). However, the interaction of AII with α-receptors remains unclear, since different effects have been found with different noradrenergic agents. Phenoxybenzamine has been found to decrease the pressor response to i.c.v. AII, while tolazoline had no effect, and phentolamine enhanced the pressor response (Buckley and Jandhyala, 1977). It is difficult to reconcile the notion of AII affecting α-adrenergic receptors with the action of other α-agonists centrally, which is to decrease blood pressure, and the facilitation of NE release by angiotensin in the peripheral nervous system.

The area postrema is situated outside of the blood–brain barrier, and therefore, is in a position where it can be affected by blood-borne angiotensin. The exact role of the area postrema in the regulation of blood pressure is unclear. Stimulation of the area postrema in dogs results in an increase in blood pressure and lesions result in a transient increase in blood pressure but no large changes in resting pressure. The main effect of area postrema lesions in dogs appears to be a decrease in blood pressure lability and a significant decrease in the vasoconstrictor effect of i.v. AII. The latter result indicates that the area postrema may be involved in mediating the effects of peripheral AII on blood pressure (Ferrario *et al.*, 1979). In rats ablation of the area postrema has been reported to result in an increase in blood pressure (Hutchinson *et al.*, 1976). However, it is not always clear that lesions of the area postrema do not include a portion of the NTS, which could account for the resulting hypertension. Surgical excision of the area postrema in rats, which did not damage the NTS, has been shown to have no acute or chronic effect on blood pressure, the pressor effect of AII or reflex responses to AII (Zandberg *et al.*, 1977). It appears that the area postrema is involved in mediating the cardiovascular effects of AII in dogs (Ferrario *et al.*, 1979), but not in rats (Zandberg *et al.*, 1977; Haywood *et al.*, 1978).

It has been demonstrated that the area postrema is not involved in mediating the i.c.v. effects of AII. Lesions of the area postrema do not affect the blood pressure response to i.c.v. AII (Zandberg *et al.*, 1977; Phillips, 1978), and the response to i.c.v. AII is both qualitatively and quantitatively different from the blood pressure response after exposure of the area postrema to AII (Hutchinson *et al.*, 1976). One site of action of i.c.v. AII appears to be the nucleus submedialis (Buckley, 1972; Phillips, 1978). Bilateral lesions of the periqueductal gray decrease the pressor response to i.c.v. AII. AII administered into the cerebral aqueduct anterior to the nucleus submedialis produces marked pressor effects, these effects are lower when AII is administered posterior to the nucleus (Buckley, 1972).

Lesions of the AV3V region abolish the increase in blood pressure seen after central administration of AII and also decrease the response to i.v. AII (Buggy *et al.*, 1977a,b). The blood pressure response to i.c.v. AII, mediated by the AV3V region, is composed of both sympathetic activation and release of ADH (Hoffman and Phillips, 1976). It has been suggested that the AV3V region mediates the central component of peripheral AII in rats (Fink *et al.*, 1979). The AV3V may not be a major site for regulation of blood pressure since electrical stimulation of this area produces only small changes in blood pressure, its main effect being to reduce renal and splanchnic blood flow and increase hindlimb blood flow (Fink *et al.*, 1978).

The possibility that AII may affect cardiovascular regulation by facilitating release of NE in the CNS, as it does in the periphery, is still in question. Garcia-Sevilla *et al.* (1979) have reported that AII facilitates release of [³H]NE from rabbit hypothalamic slices exposed to high potassium or field stimulation. This effect appears to be specific, since it is blocked by saralasin, which itself has no effect on release. However, Taube *et al.* (1977) found that AII did not increase [³H]NE overflow from field-stimulated rat hypothalamus. Whether these differences are due to species differences in the role of AII in blood pressure regulation or experimental differences is unclear.

2. *Histamine*

There is evidence to suggest that histamine is involved in the CNS regulation of blood pressure. Histamine, administered i.c.v., causes dose-dependent increases in blood pressure due to central sympathetic activation. In all cases the blood pressure response is blocked by H_1-receptor antagonists but not by H_2-receptor antagonists (Finch and Hicks, 1975, 1976; Hoffman and Schmid, 1978a). The i.c.v. pressor effects of histamine are also blocked by the α-receptor antagonist, phentolamine, and greatly reduced by pretreatment with 6-OHDA. This indicates that noradrenergic systems are involved in mediating, to some extent, the effects of i.c.v. histamine (Finch and Hicks, 1975, 1976). Histamine also produces increases in blood pressure when injected into the posterior and anterior hypothalamus (Finch and Hicks, 1977; Owen, 1977). The pressor response after bilateral injection of histamine into the posterior hypothalamus is dose dependent and antagonized by mepyramine, a H_1-receptor antagonist. Phentolamine and atropine had no effect on the response to histamine. Histamine did not change blood pressure when injected into the ventromedial or lateral hypothalamus or the preoptic area (Finch and Hicks, 1977).

3. *Bradykinin*

Bradykinin also causes increases in blood pressure when administered i.c.v. (Lambert and Lang, 1970). The role of bradykinin has not been extensively studied, but its effects appear to be similar to those of angiotensin. The increase in blood pressure is due to sympathetic activation which can be blocked by phentolamine (Corrêa and Graeff, 1974; Hoffman and Schmid, 1978b) and partially blocked by H_1-receptor antagonists (Corrêa and Graeff, 1974). Lateral septal lesions abolish the response to i.c.v. bradykinin (Corrêa and Graeff, 1975).

In addition to angiotensin, histamine, and bradykinin, it has also been shown that prostaglandin E_2 produces increases in blood pressure when administered centrally (Hoffman and Schmid, 1979). All of these compounds produce pressor activity by central sympathetic activation, which appears to involve central noradrenergic systems. It is not known what their exact role is in the regulation of blood pressure, what their exact central sites of action are, or whether the central component of their action is important as compared to their peripheral effects.

C. INVOLVEMENT OF THE CNS IN HYPERTENSION

1. Central Neuronal Activity

It is obvious that several components are involved in the development and maintenance of essential hypertension. There is a good indication that a neurogenic component is involved in the DOCA/salt, renal, and spontaneously hypertensive models of hypertension (Chalmers, 1978). This increase in sympathetic activity appears to have its origin in the CNS with central noradrenergic, dopaminergic, serotonergic, and cholinergic systems being involved (Henning, 1975). The animal model most frequently used in these studies is the SHR, because of its resemblance to human essential hypertension (Folkow, 1975). Therefore, most of the results reported in this section will be from studies using the SHR.

Several different types of experiments have suggested a neurogenic basis for hypertension in adult SHR (Okamoto *et al.*, 1967; Iriuchijima, 1973; Honda *et al.*, 1975; Numao *et al.*, 1975). Direct measurement of sympathetic nerve activity shows that SHR have higher peripheral sympathetic activity than the control Wistar-Kyoto (WKY) rats (Judy *et al.*, 1976). Since preganglionic, as well as postganglionic, activity is increased, it can be assumed that this increase is due to some difference in CNS regulation of sympathetic activity, although it does not localize the specific area or areas involved.

Lesioning the hypothalamus (Buñag and Eferakeya, 1976) or separation of the connections between the hypothalamus and mesencephalon (Yamori and Okamoto, 1969) produces a significantly greater decrease in the blood pressure of SHR than WKY rats. This could be interpreted as an increased tonic pressor effect from the posterior hypothalamus. Posterior hypothalamic stimulation produces greater increases in blood pressure and sympathetic activity in the SHR than in the WKY (Buñag *et al.*, 1975; Juskevich *et al.*, 1978; Takeda and Buñag, 1978; Buñag and Takeda, 1979). This indicates that the posterior hypothalamus is hyper-active, either due to hyper-responsiveness to excitatory input or decreased inhibitory input. Since it appears that the baroreceptor reflex control of sympathetic activity, under conditions of hypothalamic activation, is actually greater in the SHR for a given pressure increase (Morrison and Whitehorn, 1978) it seems that the posterior hypothalamus in SHR is hyperexcitable.

Aside from the posterior hypothalamus, the locus coeruleus of SHR has also been shown to have a different response to stimulation than the WKY. WKY have frequency-related pressor resonses to stimulation of the locus coeruleus. However, no consistent changes in blood pressure are seen in the SHR (Kawamura *et al.*, 1978).

These experiments establish CNS differences between SHR and WKY rats, but do not provide any information as to whether these differences are involved in the initiation of hypertension, since SHR that had already developed some degree of hypertension were used. There is some difficulty in determining whether the neurogenic differences are primary defects, or secondary to the development of hypertension, since prehypertensive SHR are quite young (4–5 weeks old) and difficult to work with due to size. Nakamura and Nakamura (1977a), however, found an increase in choline acetyltransferase and tyrosine hydroxylase in the coeliac ganglia of 4- to 5-week-old SHR. This indicates that there is increased preganglionic activity in SHR prior to the development of hypertension.

Another method of studying CNS differences in the SHR apart from the hypertension, is to maintain SHR normotensive with antihypertensive therapy starting at 4 weeks of age. When SHR are maintained normotensive by chronic treatment with clonidine or hydralazine the sympathetic activity and blood pressure responses to posterior hypothalamic stimulation are the same as nontreated SHR and significantly greater than the responses seen in WKY (Juskevich *et al.*, 1978). This indicates that the hyperresponsivity of neural pathways capable of influencing blood pressure in SHR may represent a primary factor in the etiology of this type of hypertension.

The factor underlying the CNS differences in the SHR are unclear. In an attempt to delineate the central systems involved in experimental hypertension many studies have looked at the biochemistry and manipulated several of the CNS transmitters.

Central catecholaminergic neurons appear to play a role in the development of hypertension in several different experimental models. 6-OHDA administered i.c.v. prevents the development of DOCA/salt and renal hypertension, although it is ineffective once the hypertension has developed (Haeusler *et al.*, 1972a; Chalmers, 1975; Kubo *et al.*, 1978). 6-OHDA administered i.c.v. to SHR, attenuates, although it does not completely block, the development of hypertension for up to 12 weeks (Haeusler *et al.*, 1972a; Erinoff *et al.*, 1975; Kubo and Hashimoto, 1978). Again, administration of 6-OHDA to SHR with established hypertension produced only a transient decrease in blood pressure (Kubo and Hashimoto, 1978). Neither the telencephalic (Erinoff *et al.*, 1975) nor spinal (Kubo and Hashimoto, 1978) noradrenergic pathways appear to be responsible for the development of SHR hypertension, since their specific destruction did not have the same effect as i.c.v. treatment with 6-OHDA.

Compounds that alter the level of NE in the CNS also affect the blood pressure of SHR. Administration of L-dopa, after peripheral decarboxylase inhibition, reduces SHR blood pressure (Judy *et al.*, 1978) and retards the development of hypertension for at least 4 weeks (Yamori *et al.*, 1972b). Administration of L-dopa and a monoamine oxidase inhibitor, pargyline, to SHR results in a wide range of brainstem NE levels. A significant inverse correlation was found between brainstem NE and blood pressure (Yamori *et al.*, 1972b).

Intravenous administration of tyrosine results in decreases in blood pressure of up to 40 mm Hg in SHR. This effect was blocked by administration of other amino acids which decrease the uptake of tyrosine into the CNS, indicating that the effect of tyrosine was of a central origin. Since iv tyrosine increases the level of $MOPEG-SO_4$ (methoxyhydroxyphenylethylglycol sulfate), a metabolite of NE, in the brain, it has been hypothesized that tyrosine exerts in blood pressure—lowering effects via an increase in NE synthesis (Sved *et al.*, 1979).

Differences in the activity of the monoamine biosynthetic enzymes (tyrosine hydroxylase, dopa decarboxylase, dopamine-β-hydroxylase, phenylethanolamine *N*-methyltransferase) have been reported in different brain regions of the SHR (Nagatsu *et al.*, 1976; Nagaoka and Lovenberg, 1977; Nakamura and Nakamura, 1978; Renaud *et al.*, 1978). However, since it has been shown that there is significant genetic variation in the activities of these enzymes (Lovenberg *et al.*, 1973; Yamabe *et al.*, 1973), it is difficult to say whether the enzyme differences found in SHR are simply genetic variations or possibly involved in the development of hypertension. The changes in biosynthetic enzyme activities found in the SHR might also be due to compensatory change in the CNS during the development of hypertension rather than being involved in the initiation. For example, Petty and Reid (1977) found compensatory decreases in norepinephrine levels in several different areas of the brain in renovascular hypertensive rats 72 hours after surgery. This type of mechanism might also explain changes in biosynthetic enzymes as well as norepinephrine levels.

Differences in CNS levels of epinephrine and phenylethanolamine *N*-methyltransferase (PNMT) have also been reported in the SHR. Increased levels of epinephrine have been found in the NTS and A_1 region of the brainstem (Wijnen *et al.*, 1978b) as well as in the hypothalamus (Gianutsos and Moore, 1978; Wijnen *et al.*, 1978b). Increases in PNMT activity have been found in both the A_1 and A_2 regions of the brainstem (Grobecker *et al.*, 1976; Gianutsos and Moore, 1978). The exact role that adrenergic systems play in the development of hypertension is unclear. Since i.c.v. administration of epinephrine in SHR results in a decrease in blood pressure (Borkowski and Finch, 1978), it is possible that the increased levels of epinephrine seen in young SHR are involved more in maintaining a normal blood pressure rather than a causative factor in the development of hypertension.

There has been some suggestion that a CNS deficiency of 5-HT is involved in human essential hypertension (Bhargava *et al.*, 1979). Brainstem levels of 5-HT are not different in SHR as compared to WKY. However, daily treatment with PCPA did cause an increase in blood pressure in both SHR and WKY (de Jong *et al.*, 1975a).

Administration of 5,6-dihydroxytryptamine (5,6-DHT) i.c.v. causes a destruction of central 5-HT neurons, resulting in a depletion of CNS 5-HT. 5,6-DHT has no effect on renal hypertension (Chalmers, 1975), however it produces a rapid decrease in the blood pressure of DOCA/salt hypertensive rats, which lasts for at least 4 days (Finch, 1975). In SHR, i.c.v. 5,6-DHT produces only a short-lived fall in blood pressure in animals with established hypertension. However, when 6-week-old SHR are treated, 5,6-DHT retards the development of hypertension for at least 6 weeks (Buckingham *et al.*, 1976). An increased rate of 5-HT synthesis has also been found in prehypertensive SHR, indicating that 5-HT may be involved in the initiation of hypertension (Smith *et al.*, 1979).

The role of the CNS in the pathogenesis of hypertension is still being extensively studied. It appears, at least in the SHR, that there may be genetic defects which result in hyperactivity of CNS pressor pathways. Whether this increased pressor activity is due to hyper-responsivity of excitatory pathways or decreased inhibitory input to pressor areas is unclear, although, the inhibitory pathway from the baroreceptors appears to function normally in the SHR.

The physiological and biochemical factors underlying this hyperactivity have not been delineated. It appears that noradrenergic, and to a lesser extent serotonergic, pathways are involved in the development of hypertension since both 6-OHDA and 5,6-DHT are able to retard the development of hypertension. The involvement of cholinergic pathways in the pathogenesis of hypertension has not been extensively studied, although there is some indication of differences in central cholinergic mechanisms between SHR and WKY rats (Kubo and Tatsumi, 1979).

2. Central Hormonal Systems

It appears that the effects of angiotensin in the CNS may be involved in the development and/or maintenance of hypertension in some of the experimental models. It has been shown that administration of i.c.v. AII for 2 weeks, in addition to replacing drinking water with saline during the second week induces a mild hypertension in dogs characterized by an increase in vascular tone (Jandhyala *et al.*, 1979). Since central administration of angiotensin can produce some degree of hypertension it is very possible that this effect is a component of experimental hypertension.

Two methods have been used to study the role of angiotensin in different types of renal hypertension. One is the administration of AII antagonists and the other is lesioning areas involved in mediating the CNS effects of AII. In malignant hypertension produced by aortic occlusion, i.c.v. Sar^1, Ile^8-AII decreases blood pressure in a dose-dependent manner, whereas this compound was only effective at high doses when administered i.v. (Sweet *et al.*, 1976). In one-clip two-kidney hypertension, where plasma AII is increased, both i.v. and i.c.v. administration of saralasin lower blood pressure, indicating that both peripheral and central AII is involved in maintaining hypertension. In one-clip one-kidney hypertension, plasma AII is not increased and i.v. and i.c.v. saralasin had no effect on the hypertension. This would tend to indicate that AII plays a role in hypertension only when levels are measurably elevated. However, in two-clip two-kidney hypertension, where plasma AII is normal, i.c.v., but not i.v., AII antagonists lower blood pressure, indicating that central AII may be involved in the maintenance of hypertension (Mann *et al.*, 1978).

Lesions of the AV3V region prevent the development of both one-kidney and two-kidney hypertension (Brody *et al.*, 1978; Buggy *et al.*, 1977a). Lesions do not reverse the hypertension once it is established, but do prevent any further development. Since this region is thought to be involved in mediating the central effects of AII and lesions prevent the development of hypertension it seems likely that central effects of AII play an important role in the development of renal hypertension.

The role of AII in DOCA/salt hypertension is less well studied, and somewhat more confusing. DOCA/salt treatment actually suppresses the renin–angiotensin system and therefore it might be expected that manipulating central AII would have no effect. Saralasin injected i.c.v. and i.v. causes an increase in blood pressure, perhaps due to a direct agonist effect on AII receptors (Mann *et al.*, 1978). However, lesions of the AV3V region, prior to DOCA/salt treatment, prevents the development of hypertension (Brody *et al.*, 1978).

It is possible that central AII may play a role in the development of hypertension in the SHR, although the data, to date, have been conflicting. SHR respond with greater increases in blood pressure to i.c.v. AII than WKY (Hoffman *et al.*, 1977a; Johnson *et al.*, 1978). This increased response to i.c.v. AII does not appear to be due to changes in central AII receptors since there was no change in the threshold response to AII (Hoffman *et al.*, 1977a), and no differences have been found between SHR and WKY in AII receptor binding characteristics (Cole *et al.*, 1978).

It is possible that increased levels of AII could contribute to the hypertension in SHR. Increased levels of immunoreactive AII have been found in the cerebrospinal fluid of SHR (Ganten *et al.*, 1975). This increased level of AII cannot totally account for the increased blood pressure in SHR, since i.c.v. infusions of much greater quantities into normotensive rats does not increase their blood pressure to hypertensive levels (Reid, 1977). However, this does not rule out the possibility that increased AII levels may be one of the components involved in the development of hypertension in the SHR.

The effects of centrally administered AII antagonists in SHR have been studied, but again the results have been conflicting. Saralasin has been shown to decrease blood pressure, when administered i.c.v., in both SHR (Mann *et al.*, 1978) and stroke-prone SHR (Phillips *et al.*, 1977). However, other AII antagonists do not necessarily have the same effect. For example, succinamoyl[1],Val[5],phenylglycine[8]-AII decreased blood pressure in 10-week-old SHR, but increased blood pressure in 14-week-old SHR (Reid, 1977). Elghozi *et al.* (1976) found that neither Sar[1], Thr[8]-AII, nor Sar[1], Ile[8]-AII decreased blood pressure in the SHR, although they could show that both antagonists effectively blocked the effects of centrally administered AII.

AV3V lesions had no effect on the blood pressure of SHR with established hypertension, indicating that AII may not play a role in the maintenance of hypertension in this strain (Brody *et al.*, 1978). AV3V lesions have not been made in young SHR, so it is not known whether AII might be involved in the initiation and development of this type of hypertension.

It seems fairly clear that centrally mediated effects of angiotensin are involved in the development of renal hypertension, whether increased levels of plasma AII are present or not. The involvement of AII in the development of other types of experimental hypertension has not yet been well defined.

IV. CONCLUSION

The role of the nervous system in the regulation of blood pressure is still being extensively studied. Many CNS areas have been defined as being involved in cardiovascular control, and to some extent pathways are beginning to be delineated. However, with the exception of possibly the NTS and the hypothalamus, very little is known about their physiological function in terms of modulation by afferent input and other CNS areas. It seems clear that, in order to gain a better understanding of the role of the nervous system in cardiovascular control, future studies must go beyond lesioning and stimulating discrete areas of the CNS. Further work needs to be done in establishing the interconnections of CNS areas in terms of functional pathways and their contribution to changes in blood pressure during physiological responses (e.g., alerting response, defense reaction, postural changes). It is also necessary to look at the relationship between central and peripheral control since peripheral factors may affect the response to sympathetic activation both directly, via presynaptic effects on sympathetic nerves or by modulating the vascular response, and indirectly, via feedback to the CNS.

The exact involvement of the nervous system in the development and maintenance of hypertension will probably remain somewhat unclear until we have a better understanding of the normal control of the cardiovascular system. It appears that, at least in the SHR, the nervous system plays a significant role in the initiation of hypertension. Studies indicate that some CNS abnormality results in increased sympathetic activation, which is initially masked by compensatory mechanisms (prehypertensive stage) and expressed at a later age. It appears that pressor systems may be hyperexcitable, but the exact pathways involved and the underlying mechanisms have not been defined. Hopefully, defining the mechanism of high blood pressure in experimental models will shed some light on the problem of human essential hypertension. However, further work must be done to determine how closely related the disease process is in experimental models and hypertensive patients.

REFERENCES

Achari, N. D., Al-Ubaidy, S., and Downman, C. B. B. (1973). *Brain Res.* **60**, 439–447.
Ackerly, J., Blumberg, A., and Peach, M. (1976). *Proc. Soc. Exp. Biol. Med.* **151**, 650–653.
Alexander, N., McClaskey, J., and Maronde, R. F. (1976). *Life Sci.* **18**, 655–662.
Altura, B. M. (1971). *Microvasc. Res.* **3**, 361–384.
Angell-James, J. E., and Daly, M. DeB. (1969). *J. Physiol. (London)* **201**, 87–104.
Antonaccio, M. J., and Taylor, D. G. (1977a). *Eur. J. Pharmacol.* **42**, 331–338.
Antonaccio, M. J., and Taylor, D. G. (1977b). *Eur. J. Pharmacol.* **46**, 283–288.
Antonaccio, M. J., Kelly, E., and Halley, J. (1975). *Eur. J. Pharmacol.* **33**, 107–117.
Antonaccio, M. J., Kerwin, L., and Taylor, D. G. (1978). *Neuropharmacology* **17**, 783–791.
Baez, S., Feldman, S. M., and Gootman, P. M. (1977). *Am. J. Physiol.* **233**, H141–H147.
Barker, J. L. (1976). *Physiol. Rev.* **56**, 435–452.
Barman, S. M., and Gebber, G. L. (1978). *Proc. Soc. Exp. Biol. Med.* **157**, 648–655.
Barman, S. M., and Wurster, R. D. (1975). *Circ. Res.* **37**, 209–214.
Baum, T., and Shropshire, A. T. (1973). *Neuropharmacology* **12**, 49–56.
Baum, T., and Shropshire, A. T. (1975). *Neuropharmacology* **14**, 227–233.
Bell, C., Lang, W. J., and Tsilemanis, C. (1973). *Brain Res.* **56**, 392–395.
Bevan, J. A., and Su, C. (1973). *Annu. Rev. Pharmacol.* **13**, 269–285.
Bhargava, K. P., Jain, I. P., Saxena, A. K., Sinha, J. N., and Tangri, K. K. (1978). *Br. J. Pharmacol.* **63**, 7–15.
Bhargava, K. P., Raina, N., Misra, N., Shanker, K., and Vrat, S. (1979). *Life Sci.* **25**, 195–200.
Biscoe, T. J., and Sampson, S. R. (1970). *J. Physiol. (London)* **209**, 341–358.
Blessing, W. W., and Chalmers, J. P. (1979). *Neurosci. Lett.* **11**, 35–40.
Boadle-Biber, M. C., and Roth, R. H. (1977). *In* "Central Actions of Angiotensin and Related Hormones" (J. P. Buckley and C. M. Ferrario, eds.), pp. 83–103. Pergamon, Oxford.
Boadle-Biber, M. C., Hughes, J., and Roth, R. H. (1972). *Br. J. Pharmacol.* **46**, 289–299.
Bolme, P., Fuxe, K. (1977). *Med. Biol.* **55**, 301–309.
Bolme, P., Fuxe, K., and Lidbrink, P. (1972). *Res. Commun. Chem. Pathol. Pharmacol.* **4**, 657–697.
Bolme, P., Corrodi, H., Fuxe, K., Hökfelt, T., Lidbrink, P., and Goldstein, M. (1974). *Eur. J. Pharmacol.* **28**, 89–94.
Borkowski, K. R., and Finch, L. (1978). *Eur. J. Pharmacol.* **47**, 281–290.
Brezenoff, H. E., and Jenden, D. J. (1969). *Int. J. Neuropharmacol.* **8**, 593–600.
Brody, M. J., Fink, G. D., Buggy, J., Haywood, J. R., Gordon, F. J., and Johnson, A. K. (1978). *Circ. Res.* **43**, Suppl 1, I2–I12.
Buccafusco, J. J., and Brezenoff, H. E. (1977). *Neuropharmacology* **16**, 775–780.
Buccafusco, J. J., and Brezenoff, H. E. (1979). *Brain Res.* **165**, 295–310.
Buckingham, R. E., Hamilton, T. C., and Robson, D. (1976). *Eur. J. Pharmacol.* **36**, 431–437.
Buckley, J. P. (1972). *Fed. Proc., Fed. Am. Soc. Exp. Biol.* **31**, 1332–1337.
Buckley, J. P., and Jandhyala, B. S. (1977). *Life Sci.* **20**, 1485–1494.
Buggy, J., Fink, G. D., Johnson, A. K., and Brody, M. J. (1977a). *Circ. Res.* **40**, Suppl. I, I110–I117.
Buggy, J., Hoffman, W. E., and Johnson, A. K. (1977b). *Neurosci. Abstr. (Soc. Neurosci.)* **3**, 1081.

Buñag, R. D., and Eferakeya, A. E. (1976). *Cardiovasc. Res.* **10**, 663–671.

Buñag, R. D., and Takeda, K. (1979). *Am. J. Physiol.* **237**, R39–R44.

Buñag, R. D., Eferakeya, A. E., and Langdon, D. S. (1975). *Am. J. Physiol.* **228**, 217–222.

Burkhart, S. M., Funnell, L., and Ledsome, J. R. (1977). *J. Physiol. (London)* **273**, 69–81.

Burnstock, G. (1970). *In* "Smooth Muscle" (E. Bulbring, A. Brading, A. Jones, and T. Tomita, eds.), pp. 1–69. Arnold, London.

Burnstock, G. (1975). *Clin. Exp. Pharmacol. Physiol., Suppl.* **2**, 7–20.

Burnstock, G., and Iwayama, T. (1971). *Prog. Brain Res.* **34**, 389–404.

Cabot, J. B., Wild, J. M., and Cohen, D. H. (1979). *Science* **203**, 184–186.

Calaresu, F. R., and Thomas, M. R. (1975). *Brain Res.* **87**, 335–338.

Calaresu, F. R., Faiers, A. A., and Mogenson, G. J. (1975). *Prog. Neurobiol.* **5**, 1–35.

Campbell, W. B., and Jackson, E. K. (1979). *Am. J. Physiol.* **236**, H211–H217.

Chai, C. Y., and Wang, S. C. (1968). *Am. J. Physiol.* **215**, 1310–1315.

Chalmers, J. P. (1975). *Circ. Res.* **36**, 469–480.

Chalmers, J. P. (1978). *Clin. Sci. Mol. Med.* **55**, Suppl 4, 45s–56s.

Cheatham, M. L., and Matzke, H. A. (1966). *J. Comp. Neurol.* **127**, 369–380.

Chiba, T., and Kato, M. (1978). *Brain Res.* **151**, 323–338.

Cohen, M. I., and Gootman, P. M. (1970). *Am. J. Physiol.* **218**, 1092–1101.

Cole, F. E., Frohlich, E. D., and Macphee, A. A. (1978). *Brain Res.* **154**, 178–181.

Coote, J. H., and Macleod, V. H. (1974). *J. Physiol. (London)* **241**, 453–475.

Coote, J. H., and Macleod, V. H. (1975). *Pfluegers Arch.* **359**, 335–347.

Coote, J. H., and Sato, J. (1977). *Circ. Res.* **40**, 571–577.

Corrêa, F. M. A., and Graeff, F. G. (1974). *Neuropharmacology* **13**, 65–75.

Corrêa, F. M. A., and Graeff, F. G. (1975). *J. Pharmacol. Exp. Ther.* **192**, 670–676.

Cottle, M .K. W., and Calaresu, F. R. (1975). *J. Comp. Neurol.* **161**, 143–158.

Cowley, A. W., Jr. (1978). *Cardiovasc. Clin.* **9**, 1–22.

Crill, W. E., and Reis, D. J. (1968). *Am. J. Physiol.* **214**, 269–276.

Crofton, J. T., Share, L., Shade, R. E., Allen, C., and Tarnowski, D. (1978). *Am. J. Physiol.* **235**, H361–H366.

Dahl, L. K., Heine, M., and Tassinari, L. (1962). *J. Exp. Med.* **115**, 1173–1190.

Daly, M. DeB., and Ungar, A. (1966). *J. Physiol. (London)* **182**, 379–403.

Daly, M. DeB., Hazeldine, J. L., and Howe, A. (1965). *J. Physiol. (London)* **177**, 300–322.

Davila, D., and Khairallah, P. A. (1970). *Arch. Int. Pharmacodyn. Ther.* **185**, 357–364.

Day, M. D., and Roach, A. G. (1974). *Br. J. Pharmacol.* **51**, 325–333.

Day, M. D., and Roach, A. G. (1977). *Clin. Exp. Pharmacol. Physiol.* **4**, 431–442.

de Champlain, J. (1978). *Can. J. Physiol. Pharmacol.* **56**, 341–353.

de Jong, W., Nijkamp, F. P., and Bohus, B. (1975a). *Arch. Int. Pharmacodyn. Ther.* **213**, 272–284.

de Jong, W., Zandberg, P., and Bohus, B. (1975b). *Prog. Brain Res.* **42**, 285–298.

de Jong, W., Zandberg, P., Versteeg, D. H. G., and Palkovits, M. (1976). *Clin. Sci. Mol. Med.* **51**, 381s–383s.

Dhawan, K. N., Dhawan, B. N., and Gupta, G. P. (1967). *Jpn. J. Pharmacol.* **17**, 435–438.

Dickinson, C. J., and Yu, R. (1967). *Circ. Res.* **21**, Suppl. 2, 157–163.

DiMicco, J. A., and Gillis, R. A. (1979). *J. Pharmacol. Exp. Ther.* **210**, 1–6.

DiMicco, J. A., Hamilton, B. L., and Gillis, R. A. (1977). *J. Pharmacol. Exp. Ther.* **203**, 64–71.

Djojosugito, A. M., Folkow, B., Kylastra, P. H., Lisander, B., and Tuttle, R. S. (1970). *Acta Physiol. Scand.* **78**, 376–385.

Doba, N., and Reis, D. J. (1972). *J. Physiol. (London)* **227**, 729–747.

Doba, N., and Reis, D. J. (1973). *Circ. Res.* **32**, 584–593.

Doba, N., and Reis, D. J. (1974). *Circ. Res.* **34**, 293–301.

Downing, S. E., and Siegel, J. H. (1963). *Am. J. Physiol.* **204**, 471–479.

Eferakeya, A. E., and Buñag, R. D. (1974). *Am. J. Physiol.* **227**, 114–118.

Elghozi, J. L., Altman, J., Derynck, M. A., Liard, J. F., Grunfeld, J. P., and Meyer, P. (1976). *Clin. Sci. Mol. Med.* **51**, Suppl. 3, 385s–389s.

Ely, D. L., Greene, E. G., and Henry, J. P. (1977). *Physiol. Behav.* **18**, 1075–1083.

Enoch, D. M., and Kerr, F. W. L. (1967a). *Arch. Neurol. (Chicago)* **16**, 290–306.

Enoch, D. M., and Kerr, F. W. L. (1967b). *Arch. Neurol. (Chicago)* **16**, 307–320.

Erinoff, L., Heller, A., and Oparil, S. (1975). *Proc. Soc. Exp. Biol. Med.* **150**, 748–754.

Faden, A., Jacobs, T., and Woods, M. (1979). *Brain Res.* **162**, 13–20.

Faiers, A. A., Calaresu, F. R., and Mogenson, G. J. (1975). *Am. J. Physiol.* **228**, 1358–1366.

Faiers, A. A., Calaresu, F. R., and Mogenson, G. J. (1976). *Exp. Neurol.* **51**, 188–206.

Falcon, J. C., II, Phillips, M. I., Hoffman, W. E., and Brody, M. J. (1978). *Am. J. Physiol.* **235**, H392–H399.

Ferrario, C. M., Barnes, K. L., Szilagyi, J. E., and Broshnihan, K. B. (1979). *Hypertension* **1**, 235–245.

Ferrone, R. A., Walsh, G. M., Tsuchiya, M., and Frohlich, E. D. (1979). *Am. J. Physiol.* **236**, H403–H408.

Finch, L. (1975). *Clin. Exp. Pharmacol. Physiol.* **2**, 503–508.

Finch, L., and Hicks, P. E. (1975). *Br. J. Pharmacol.* **55**, 274P–275P.

Finch, L., and Hicks, P. E. (1976). *Naunyn-Schmiedeberg's Arch. Pharmacol.* **293**, 151–157.

Finch, L., and Hicks, P. E. (1977). *Neuropharmacology* **16**, 211–218.

Fink, G. D., and Brody, M. J. (1978). Fed. Proc., Fed. Am. Soc. Exp. Biol. **37**, 1202–1208.

Fink, G. D., Buggy, J., Haywood, J. R., Johnson, A. K., and Brody, M. J. (1978). *Am. J. Physiol.* **235**, H445–H451.

Fink, G. D., Haywood, J. R., Bryan, W. J., Packwood, W., and Brody, M. J. (1979). *Fed. Proc., Fed. Am. Soc. Exp. Biol.* **38**, 1233.

Folkow, B. (1975). *Clin. Sci. Mol. Med.* **48**, Suppl. 2, 205s–214s.

Folkow, B. (1977). *Contrib. Nephrol.* **8**, 81–94.

Folkow, B., Hallbäck, M., Lundgren, Y., Sivertsson, R., and Weiss, L. (1973). *Circ. Res.* **36**, Suppl. 1, 2–16.

Foreman, R. D., and Wurster, R. D. (1973). *Am. J. Physiol.* **225**, 212–217.

Forsyth, R. P., and Pesout, J. (1978). *Neuropharmacology* **17**, 103–108.

Fozard, J., and Mwaluko, G. (1976). *Br. J. Pharmacol.* **57**, 115–125.

Frohlich, E. D. (1977). *Mayo Clin. Proc.* **52**, 361–368.

Furness, J. B. (1973). *J. Anat.* **115**, 347–364.

Furness, J. B., and Marshall, J. M. (1974). *J. Physiol. (London)* **239**, 75–88.

Fuxe, K., Ganten, D., Hökfelt, T., and Bolme, P. (1976). *Neurosci. Lett.* **2**, 229–234.

Ganong, W. F. (1977). *Fed. Proc., Fed. Am. Soc. Exp. Biol.* **36**, 1771–1775.

Ganten, D. (1978). *Circ. Res.* **42**, 732–733.

Ganten, D., and Stock, G. (1978). *Klin. Wochenschr.* **56**, Suppl. 1, 31–41.

Ganten, D., Hutchinson, J. S., and Schelling, P. (1975). *Clin. Sci. Mol. Med.* **48**, Suppl. 2, 265s–268s.

Garcia-Sevilla, J. A., Dubocovich, M. L., and Langer, S. Z. (1979). *Eur. J. Pharmacol.* **56**, 173–176.

Gebber, G. L., and Snyder, D. W. (1970). *Am. J. Physiol.* **218**, 124–131.

Gebber, G. L., Taylor, D. G., and Weaver, L. C. (1973). *Am. J. Physiol.* **224**, 470–481.

Geis, G. S., Barratt, G., and Wurster, R. D. (1978). *Am. J. Physiol.* **234**, H152–H156.

Gellhorn, E., Nakao, H., and Redgate, E. S. (1956). *J. Physiol. (London)* 131, 402–423.

Gernandt, B., Liljestrand, G., and Zotterman, Y. (1946). *Acta Physiol. Scand.* 11, 230–247.

Gianutsos, G., and Moore, K. E. (1978). *Proc. Soc. Exp. Biol. Med.* 158, 45–49.

Gootman, P. M., and Cohen, M. I. (1969). *Bull. N.Y. Acad. Med.* [2] 45, 97–98.

Gootman, P. M., and Cohen, M. I. (1970). *Am. J. Physiol.* 219, 897–903.

Green, J. H., and Heffron, P. F. (1966). *J. Physiol. (London)* 185, 48P–50P.

Green, J. H., and Heffron, P. F. (1968). *Q. J. Exp. Physiol. Cogn. Med. Sci.* 53, 23–32.

Grobecker, H., Saavedra, J. M., Roizin, M. F., Weise, V., Kopin, I. J., and Axelrod, J. (1976). *Clin. Sci. Mol. Med.* 51, Suppl. 3, 377s–380s.

Gross, F. (1977). *Eur. J. Clin. Invest.* 7, 321–322.

Guerzenstein, P. G. (1973). *J. Physiol. (London)* 229, 395–408.

Guyton, A. C., Coleman, T. G., and Granger, H. J. (1972). *Annu. Rev. Physiol.* 34, 13–46.

Guyton, A. C., Coleman, T. G., Cowley, A. W., Liard, J.-F. Norman, R. A., and Manning, R. D. (1973). *Ann. Biomed. Eng.* 1, 254–281.

Haeusler, G. (1975). *Circ. Res.* 36, Suppl. 1, 223–232.

Haeusler, G., Finch, L., and Thoenen, H. (1972a). *Experientia* 28, 1200–1203.

Haeusler, G., Gerold, M., and Thoenen, H. (1972b). *Naunyn-Schmiedeberg's Arch. Pharmacol.* 274, 211–228.

Haywood, J. R., Fink, G. D., Buggy, J., Phillips, M. I., and Brody, M. J. (1978). *Fed. Proc., Fed. Am. Soc. Exp. Biol.* 37, 803.

Hiese, A., and Kroneberg, G. (1973). *Naunyn-Schmiedeberg's Arch. Pharmacol.* 279, 285–300.

Henning, M. (1975). *Clin. Sci. Mol. Med.* 48, 195s–203s.

Henry, J. L., and Calaresu, F. R. (1974a). *Exp. Brain Res.* 20, 485–504.

Henry, J. L., and Calaresu, F. R. (1974b). *Exp. Brain Res.* 20, 505–514.

Hildebrandt, J. R. (1974). *Exp. Neurol.* 45, 590–605.

Hilton, S. M. (1974). *In* "Recent Studies of Hypothalamic Function" (K. Lederic and K. E. Cooper, eds.), pp. 306–314. Karger, Basel.

Hilton, S. M., and Spyer, K. M. (1969). *J. Physiol. (London)* 200, 107p–108p.

Hilton, S. M., and Spyer, K. M. (1971). *J. Physiol. (London)* 218, 271–293.

Hoffman, W. E. (1979). *Neuropharmacology* 18, 7–12.

Hoffman, W. E., and Phillips, M. I. (1976). *Brain Res.* 110, 313–330.

Hoffman, W. E., and Schmid, P. G. (1978a). *Life Sci.* 22, 1709–1713.

Hoffman, W. E., and Schmid, P. G. (1978b). *Neuropharmacology* 17, 999–1002.

Hoffman, W. E., and Schmid, P. G. (1979). *J. Physiol. (London)* 288, 159–169.

Hoffman, W. E., Phillips, M. I., and Schmid, P. G. (1977a). *Am. J. Physiol.* 232, H426–H433.

Hoffman, W. E., Phillips, M. I., Schmid, P. G., Falcon, J., and Weet, J. F. (1977b). *Neuropharmacology* 16, 463–472.

Hoffman, W. E., Phillips, M. I., and Schmid, P. (1977c). *Neuropharmacology* 16, 563–569.

Hoffman, W. E., Schmid, P. G., and Phillips, M. I. (1977d). *Brain Res.* 126, 1376–1381.

Honda, K., Maekawa, S., Tamura, T., Uchigama, S., Suzuki, K., Yashima, D., Ozawa, M., Takahashi, E., and Kimura, T. (1975). *Jpn. Circ. J.* 39, 591–595.

Hope, W., McCulloch, M. W., Rand, M. J., and Story, D. F. (1978). *Br. J. Pharmacol.* 64, 527–537.

Hughes, J., and Roth, R. H. (1971). *Br. J. Pharmacol.* 41, 239–255.

Hulthën, L., and Hökfelt, B. (1978). *Acta Med. Scand.* 204, 497–502.

Hutchinson, J. S., Ganten, D., Schelling, P., Ylitalo, P., Möhring, J., and Kalina, M. (1976). *Acta Med. Acad. Sci. Hung.* 33, 101–109.

Iggo, A., and Vogt, M. (1962). *J. Physiol. (London)* 161, 62–72.

Ikeda, H., Shino, A., and Nagaoka, A. (1979). *Eur. J. Pharmacol.* 53, 173–179.

Iriki, M., and Kozawa, E. (1975). *Brain Res.* 87, 281–291.

Iriuchijima, J. (1973). *Jpn. Heart. J.* 14, 350–356.

Iriuchijima, J., and Numao, Y. (1976). *Jpn. Heart J.* 17, 354–355.

Ito, A., and Schanberg, S. M. (1972). *J. Pharmacol. Exp. Ther.* 181, 65–74.

Ito, A., and Schanberg, S. M. (1974). *J. Pharmacol. Exp. Ther.* 189, 392–404.

Ito, A., Tanaka, K., and Omae, T. (1975). *Jpn. Heart J.* 16, 575–582.

Jandhyala, B. S., Lokhandwala, M. F., Nandiwada, P., and Buckley, J. P. (1979). *Hypertension* 1, 219–227.

Jänig, W. (1975). *Brain Res.* 87, 305–312.

Janowsky, D. S., Davis, J. M., Fann, W. E., Freeman, J., Nixon, R., and Michelakis, A. A. (1972). *Life Sci.* 11, 1–11.

Johnson, A. K., Simon, W., Schaz, K., Ganten, U., Ganten, D., and Mann, J. F. (1978). *Klin. Wochenschr.* 56, Suppl. 1, 47–49.

Judy, W. V., Watanabe, A. M., Henry, D. P., Besch, H. R., Jr., Murphy, W. R., and Hockel, G. M. (1976). *Circ. Res.* 38, Suppl. II, 21–29.

Judy, W. V., Watanabe, A. M., Henry, D. P., Besch, H. R., Jr., and Aprison, B. (1978). *Circ. Res.* 43, 24–28.

Juskevich, J. C., Robinson, D. S., and Whitehorn, D. (1978). *Eur. J. Pharmacol.* 51, 429–439.

Kawamura, H., Gunn, C. G., and Frohlich, E. D. (1978). *Brain Res.* 140, 137–147.

Kezdi, P., and Geller, E. (1968). *Am. J. Physiol.* 214, 427–435.

Khairallah, P. A. (1972). *Fed. Proc., Fed. Am. Soc. Exp. Biol.* 31, 1351–1357.

Khökkar, A. M., Hough, C., and Slater, J. D. H. (1974). *Clin. Sci. Mol. Med.* 47, 9P.

Kirchheim, H. R. (1976). *Physiol. Rev.* 56, 100–176.

Kline, R. L., Kelton, P. M., and Mercer, P. F. (1978). *Can. J. Physiol. Pharmacol.* 56, 818–822.

Kobinger, W. (1978). *Ergeb. Physiol., Biol. Chem. Exp. Pharmakol.* 18, 40–100.

Koizumi, K., and Brooks, C. McC. (1972). *Ergeb. Physiol., Biol. Chem. Exp. Pharmakol.* 67, 1–68.

Koizumi, K., Sato, A., Kaufman, A., and Brooks, C. McC. (1968). *Brain Res.* 11, 212–224.

Koizumi, K., Seller, H., Kaufman, A., and Brooks, C. McC. (1971). *Brain Res.* 27, 281–294.

Korner, P. I. (1965). *J. Physiol. (London)* 180, 279–303.

Korner, P. I. (1971). *Physiol. Rev.* 51, 312–367.

Korner, P. I. (1979). *In* "Handbook of Physiology" (R. M. Berne and N. Sperelakis, eds.), Vol. 1, Sect. 2, pp. 691–739. Williams & Wilkins. Baltimore, Maryland.

Korner, P. I., Oliver, J. R., Reynoldson, J. A., Head, G. A., Carson, V. J., and Walker, M. M. (1978). *Eur. J. Pharmacol.* 53, 83–93.

Kubo, T. (1978). *Arch. Int. Pharmacodyn. Ther.* 234, 49–57.

Kubo, T. (1979). *Can. J. Physiol. Pharmacol.* 57, 59–64.

Kubo, T. and Hashimoto, M. (1978). *Arch. Int. Pharmacodyn. Ther.* 232, 166–176.

Kubo, T., and Tatsumi, M. (1979). *Naunyn-Schmiedeberg's Arch. Pharmacol.* 306, 81–83.

Kubo, T., Hashimoto, M., and Ohashi, T. (1978). *Arch. Int. Pharmacodyn. Ther.* 234, 270–278.

Kuhn, D., Wolf, B., and Lovenberg, W. (1980). *J. Pharmacol. Exp. Ther.* 214, 403–409.

Laffan, R. J., Goldberg, M. E., High, J. P., Schaeffer, T. R., Waugh, M. H., and Rubin, B. (1978). *J. Pharmacol. Exp. Ther.* 204, 281–288.

Lais, L. T., and Brody, M. J. (1978). *Eur. J. Pharmacol.* 47, 177–189.

Lais, L. T., Rios, L. L., Boutelle, S., DiBona, G. F., and Brody, M. J. (1977). *Blood Vessels* 14, 277–284.

Lambert, G. A., and Lang, W. J. (1970). *Eur. J. Pharmacol.* 9, 383–386.

Lambert, G. A., Friedman, E., Buchweitz, E., and Gershon, S. (1978). *Neuropharmacology* 17, 807–813.

Lang, I. M., Innes, D. L., and Tansy, M. F. (1979). *Experientia* 35, 57–59.

Lang, W. J., and Woodman, O. L. (1979). *Br. J. Pharmacol.* 66, 235–240.

Lewis, G. P., and Reit, E. (1966). *Br. J. Pharmacol* 26, 444–460.

Lewis, P. J., Rawlins, M. D., and Reid, J. L. (1974). *Br. J. Pharmacol.* 51, 207–212.

Liard, J. F. (1977). *Experientia* 33, 339–340.

Löfving, B. (1961). *Acta Physiol. Scand.* 53, Suppl. 184, 3–82.

Lokhandwala, M. F. (1978). *J. Pharmacol. Exp. Ther.* 206, 115–122.

Lokhandwala, M. F., and Buckley, J. P. (1977). *Life Sci.* 20, 507–516.

Lokhandwala, M. F., and Buckley, J. P. (1978). *J. Pharmacol. Exp. Ther.* 204, 362–371.

Lokhandwala, M. F., and Jandhyala, B. S. (1979). *J. Pharmacol. Exp. Ther.* 210, 120–126.

Louis, W. J., Jarrott, B., and Doyle, A. E. (1976). *Clin. Sci. Mol. Med.* 51, 427s–430s.

Louis, W. J., Jarrott, B., Burnstock, G., and Watanabe, H. (1977). *Contrib. Nephrol.* 8, 182–189.

Lovenberg, W., Yambe, H., de Jong, W., and Hansen, C. T. (1973). *In* "Frontiers in Catecholamine Research" (E. Usdin and S. H. Snyder, eds.), pp. 891–895. Pergamon, Oxford.

Lütold, B. E., Karoum, F., and Neff, N. H. (1979). *Circ. Res.* 44, 467–471.

McCall, R. B., Gebber, G. L., and Barman, S. M. (1977). *Am. J. Physiol.* 232, H657–H665.

McGrath, M. A. (1977). *Circ. Res.* 41, 428–435.

McGrath, M. A., and Shepherd, J. T. (1976). *Circ. Res.* 39, 566–573.

Malik, K. U., and Nasjletti, A. (1976). *Circ. Res.* 38, 26–30.

Mann, J. F. E., Phillips, M. I., Dietz, R., Haebara, H., and Ganten, D. (1978). *Am. J. Physiol.* 234, H629–H637.

Miura, M., and Reis, D. J. (1969). *Am. J. Physiol.* 217, 142–153.

Miura, M., and Reis, D. J. (1970). *Am. J. Physiol.* 219, 1330–1336.

Miura, M., and Reis, D. J. (1972). *J. Physiol. (London)* 223, 525–548.

Miura, Y., Kobayashi, K., Sakuma, H., Tomioka, H., Adachi, M., and Yoshinaga, K. (1978). *Jpn. Circ. J.* 42, 609–612.

Mogenson, G. J., and Calaresu, F. R. (1973). *Exp. Neurol.* 39, 166–180.

Morrison, S., and Whitehorn, D. (1978). *Neurosci. Abstr. (Soc. Neurosci.)* 4, 23.

Nagaoka, A., and Lovenberg, W. (1976). *Life Sci.* 19, 29–34.

Nagaoka, A., and Lovenberg, W. (1977). *Eur. J. Pharmacol.* 43, 297–306.

Nagatsu, T., Ikuta, K., Numata, Y., Kato, T., Sano, M., Nagatsu, I., and Takeuchi, T. (1976). *Science* 191, 290–291.

Nagatsu, T., Kato, T., Numata(Sudo), Y., Ikuta, K., and Sano, M. (1977). *Jpn. J. Pharmacol.* 27, 531–535.

Nakada, T., and Lovenberg, W. (1978). *Eur. J. Pharmacol.* 48, 87–96.

Nakamura, K., and Nakamura, K. (1977a). *Nature (London)* 266, 265–266.

Nakamura, K., and Nakamura, K. (1977b). *Naunyn-Schmiedeberg's Arch. Pharmacol.* 299, 143–148.

Nakamura, K., and Nakamura, K. (1978). *Naunyn-Schmiedelberg's Arch. Pharmacol.* 305, 127–133.

Nathan, M. A., and Reis, D. J. (1977). *Circ. Res.* 40, 72–81.

Nava-Félix, P., and Hong, E. (1979). *J. Cardiovasc. Pharmacol.* 1, 461–466.

Nicholas, T. E. (1970). *J. Pharm. Pharmacol.* 22, 37–41.

Ninomiya, I., and Irisawa, H. (1969). *Am. J. Physiol.* 216, 1330–1336.

Ninomiya, I., and Irisawa, H. (1975). *Brain Res.* 87, 313–322.

Ninomiya, I., Judy, W. V., and Wilson, M. F. (1970). *Am. J. Physiol.* 218, 453–462.

Ninomiya, I., Nisimaru, N., and Irisawa, H. (1971). *Am. J. Physiol.* 221, 1346–1351.

Nosaka, S. (1973). *Jpn. Circ. J.* 37, 607–618.

Nosaka, S., and Okamoto, K. (1970). *Jpn. Circ. J.* 34, 685–693.

Nosaka, S., and Wang, S. C. (1972). *Am. J. Physiol.* 222, 1079–1084.

Numao, Y., Suga, H., and Iriuchijima, J. (1975). *Jpn. Heart J.* 16, 719–730.

Ogawa, M. (1978) *Jpn. Circ. J.* 42, 581–597.

Ogawa, M., Fujita, Y., Niwa, M., Takami, N., and Ozaki, M. (1977). *Jpn. Heart J.* 18, 586–587.

Okada, H. (1964). *Am. J. Physiol.* 206, 918–922.

Okamoto, K., and Aoki, K. (1963). *Jpn. Circ. J.* 27, 282–293.

Okamoto, K., Nosaka, S., and Yamori, Y. (1965). *Jpn. Circ. J.* 29, 251–261.

Okamoto, K., Nosaka, S., Yamori, Y., and Matsumoto, M. (1967). *Jpn. Heart J.* 8, 168–180.

Owen, D. A. A. (1977). *Gen. Pharmacol.* 8, 141–156,

Padfield, P. L. (1977). *Am. Heart J.* 94, 531.

Palkovits, M., de Jong, W., Zandberg, P., Versteeg, D. H. G., Van Der Gugten, J., and Leranth, Cs. (1977). *Brain Res.* 127, 307–312.

Peach, M. (1977). *Physiol. Rev.* 57, 313–370.

Peach, M. J., Bumpus, F. M., and Khairallah, P. A. (1969). *J. Pharmacol. Exp. Ther.* 167, 291–299.

Petty, M. A., and Reid, J. L. (1977). *Brain Res.* 136, 376–380.

Phelan, E. L., (1968). *N.Z. Med. J.* 67, 334–344.

Philippu, A. (1975). *Clin. Sci. Mol. Med.* 48, 191s–194s.

Phillippu, A., Przuntek, H., Heyd, G., and Burger, A. (1971). *Eur. J. Pharmacol.* 15, 200–208.

Philippu, A., Roensberg, W., and Przuntek, H. (1973). *Naunyn-Schmiedeberg's Arch. Pharmacol.* 278, 373–386.

Phillips, M. I., (1978). *Neuroendocrinology* 25, 354–377.

Phillips, M. I., Mann, J. F., Haebara, H., Hoffman, W. E., Dietz, R., Schelling, P., and Ganten, D. (1977). *Nature (London)* 270, 445–447.

Polosa, C. (1968). *Can. J. Physiol. Pharmacol.* 46, 887–897.

Povolny, K. M., Jung, R. V., Kraft, E., and Zimmerman, B. G. (1977). *Blood Vessels* 14, 105–115.

Powell, J. R., (1979). *J. Pharmacol. Exp. Ther.* 208, 360–365.

Reid, I. A. (1977). *Circ. Res.* 41, 147–153.

Reid, I. A., and Moffat, B. (1978). *Endocrinology* 103, 1494–1498.

Reid, I. A., Day, R. P., Moffat, B., and Hughes, H. G. (1977). *J. Neurochem.* 28, 435–438.

Reis, D. J., and Cuénod, M. (1964). *Science* 145, 64–65.

Reis, D. J., Nathan, M. A., and Doba, N. (1975). *Clin. Exp. Pharmacol. Physiol.*, *Suppl.* 2, 179–183.

Reit, E. (1972). *Fed. Proc., Fed. Am. S. Exp. Biol.* 31, 1338–1343.

Renaud, B., Fourniere, S., Denoroy, L., Pujol, J. F., and Sassard, J. (1978). *Brain Res.* 159, 149–159.

Ricardo, J. A., and Koh, E. T. (1978). *Brain Res.* 153, 1–26.

Richter, D. W., Keck, W., and Seller, H. (1970). *Pfluegers Arch.* 317, 110–123.

Roth, R. H. (1972). *Fed. Proc., Fed. Am. Soc. Exp. Biol.* 31, 1358–1364.

Roth, R. H., and Hughes, J. (1972). *Biochem. Pharmacol.* 21, 3182–3187.

Saper, C. B., Loewy, A. D., Swanson, L. W., and Cowan, W. M. (1976). *Brain Res.* 117, 305–312.

Sapru, H. N., and Krieger, A. J. (1979). *Am. J. Physiol.* 236, H174–H182.

Schmid, P. G., and Abboud, F. M. (1974). *Arch. Intern. Med.* **133**, 935–945.

Schömig, A., Dietz, R., Rascher, W., Lüth, J. B., Mann, J. F., Schmidt, M., and Weber, J. (1978). *Klin. Wochenschr.* **56**, Suppl. 1, 131–138.

Schramm, L. P., and Barton, G. N. (1979). *Am. J. Physiol.* **236**, R147–R152.

Schümann, H. J., Starke, K., and Werner, U. (1970). *Br. J. Pharmacol.* **39**, 390–397.

Scriabne, A., Clineschmidt, B. V., and Sweet, C. S. (1976). *Annu. Rev. Pharmacol. Toxicol.* **16**, 113–123.

Seller, H., and Illert, M. (1969). *Pfluegers Arch.* **306**, 1–19.

Setler, P. E., Pendleton, R. G., and Finlay, E. (1975). *J. Pharmacol. Exp. Ther.* **192**, 702–712.

Severs, W. B., and Daniel-Severs, A. E. (1973). *Pharmacol. Rev.* **25**, 415–449.

Severs, W. B., Summy-Long, J., Taylor, J. S., and Connor, J. D. (1970). *J. Pharmacol. Exp. Ther.* **174**, 27–34.

Sharma, J. N., Sandrew, B. B., and Wang, S. C. (1979). *Neuropharmacology* **18**, 1–5.

Sherrer, H. (1963). *Exp. Neurol.* **7**, 343–354.

Shibota, M., Nagaoka, A., Shino, A., and Fujita, T. (1979). *Am. J. Physiol.* **236**, H409–H416.

Simon, E., and Riedel, W. (1975). *Brain Res.* **87**, 232–233.

Sirett, N. E., McLean, A. S., Bray, J. J., and Hubbard, J. I. (1977). *Brain Res.* **122**, 299–312.

Sirett, N. E., Thornton, S. N., and Hubbard, J. I. (1979). *Brain Res.* **166**, 139–148.

Smith, M. L., Browning, R. A., and Myers, J. H. (1979). *Eur. J. Pharmacol.* **53**, 301–305.

Smith, O. A. (1974). *Annu. Rev. Physiol.* **36**, 93–123.

Smits, J. F., and Struyker-Boudier, H. A. (1976). *Brain Res.* **111**, 422–427.

Smits, J. F. M., van Essen, H., and Struyker-Boudier, H. A. J. (1978). *Life Sci.* **23**, 173–178.

Snyder, D. W., and Gebber, G. L. (1973). *Am. J. Physiol.* **225**, 1129–1137.

Snyder, D. W., Nathan, M. A., and Reis, D. J. (1978). *Circ. Res.* **43**, 662–671.

Soffer, R. L., and Case, D. B. (1978). *Am. J. Med.* **64**, 147–160.

Spyer, K. M. (1975). *Brain Res.* **87**, 221–226.

Starke, K. (1970). *Naunyn-Schmiedeberg's Arch. Pharmacol.* **265**, 383–386.

Starke, K. (1971). *Eur. J. Pharmacol.* **14**, 112–123.

Starke, K., Werner, U., Hellerforth, R., and Schümann, H. J. (1970). *Eur. J. Pharmacol.* **9**, 136–140.

Starke, K., Taube, H. D., and Borowski, E. (1977). *Biochem. Pharmacol.* **26**, 259–268.

Struyker-Boudier, H. A. J., Smeets, G. W. M., Brouwer, G. M., and van Rossum, J. M. (1974). *Neuropharmacology* **13**, 837–846.

Struyker-Boudier, H., Smeets, G., Brouwer, G., and van Rossum, J. M. (1975). *Arch. Int. Pharmacodyn Ther.* **213**, 285–293.

Sved, A. F., Fernström, J. D., and Wurtman, R. J. (1979). *Proc. Natl. Acad. Sci. U.S.A.* **76**, 3511–3514.

Sweet, C. S., Columbo, J. M., and Gaul, S. L. (1976). *Am. J. Physiol.* **231**, 1794–1799.

Takeda, K., and Buñag, R. D. (1978). *J. Clin. Invest.* **62**, 642–648.

Taube, H. D., Starke, K., and Borowski, E. (1977). *Naunyn-Schmiedeberg's Arch. Pharmacol.* **299**, 123–141.

Thant, M., Yamori, Y., and Okamoto, K. (1969). *Jpn. Circ. J.* **33**, 501–507.

Thomas, M. R., and Calaresu, F. R. (1972). *Brain Res.* **44**, 49–62.

Torii, S., and Kawamura, H. (1960). *Jpn. J. Physiol.* **19**, 374–384.

Ward, D. G., and Gunn, C. G. (1976a). *Brain Res.* **107**, 401–406.

Ward, D. G., and Gunn, C. G. (1976b). *Brain Res.* **107**, 407–411.

Wijnen, H. J., De Kloet, E. R., Versteeg, D. H., and de Jong, W. (1978a). *Life Sci.* **23**, 2587–2591.

Wijnen, H. J., Palkovits, M., de Jong, W., and Versteeg, D. H. G. (1978b). *Brain Res.* **157**, 191–195.

Yambe, H., de Jong, W., and Lovenberg, W. (1973). *Eur. J. Pharmacol.* **22**, 91–98.

Yamori, Y., and Okamoto, K. (1969). *Jpn. Circ. J.* **33**, 509–519.

Yamori, Y., Yamabe, H., de Jong, W., Lovenberg, W., and Sjoerdsma, A. (1972a). *Eur. J. Pharmacol.* **17**, 135–140.

Yamori, Y., de Jong, W., Yamabe, H., Lovenberg, W., and Sjoerdsma, A. (1972b). *J. Pharm. Pharmacol.* **24**, 690–695.

Yamori, Y., Nakada, T., and Lovenberg, W. (1976). *Eur. J. Pharmacol.* **38**, 349–355.

Yu, R., and Dickinson, C. J. (1971). *Arch. Int. Pharmacodyn. Ther.* **191**, 24–36.

Zandberg, P., Palkovits, M., and de Jong, W. (1977). *Pfluegers. Arch.* **372**, 169–173.

Zandberg, P., de Jong, W., and de Wied, D. (1979). *Eur. J. Pharmacol.* **55**, 43–56.

Zimmerman, B. G. (1973). *J. Pharmacol. Exp. Ther.* **185**, 486–492.

Zimmerman, B. G. (1978). *Fed. Proc., Fed. Am. Soc. Exp. Biol.* **37**, 199–202.

Zimmerman, B. G., and Kraft, E. (1979). *J. Pharmacol. Exp. Ther.* **210**, 101–105.

Zimmerman, B. G., and Whitmore, L. (1967). *Int. J. Neuropharmacol.* **6**, 27–38.

Zimmerman, B. G., Gomer, S. K., and Liao, J. (1972). *Fed. Proc., Fed. Am. Soc. Exp. Biol.* **31**, 1344–1350.

CHAPTER 3

Regulation of Protein Synthesis by Phosphorylation

Jolinda A. Traugh

INTRODUCTION

The role of phosphorylation in protein synthesis is a complex topic due to the large number of components involved in protein synthesis, the number of phosphorylation events which have been shown to occur, the variety of enzymes involved in the phosphoryl transfer reactions, and the varied modes of regulation of the phosphotransferase activities. Phosphorylation of translational components was initially observed with ribosomes by Kabat (1970) and Loeb and Blat (1970). Recently, phosphorylation of initiation factors has also been described. The requirement for hemin to maintain globin synthesis in reticulocytes has been acknowledged for 15 years but only recently has the phosphorylation of initiation factor 2 (eIF-2) been shown to have a definitive role in this metabolic event. Phosphorylation of eIF-2 also appears to be involved in the interferon-mediated control of protein synthesis. In addition, recent data suggest regulation of aminoacylation of tRNA by phosphorylation. Many of the enzymes involved in these phosphorylation/dephosphorylation reactions have been identified and characterized and control of the protein kinases by such diverse compounds as hemin, cAMP, and dsRNA has been described. Thus, there is a multiplicity of phosphorylation events involving a large number of different components of the protein synthetic system and a diversity in the enzymes modifying these components.

In addition to recognizing and examining the phosphorylation events at a molecular level, it is crucial to put these studies into context with those of the whole cell or tissue. This is difficult, since few studies cover the entire range of experiments with a single tissue or cell type. In this review, attempts will be made to correlate biochemical and molecular biological observations on phosphorylation of translational components with the consequences of hormone action.

II. RIBOSOMES

A. PHOSPHORYLATION OF RIBOSOMAL PROTEIN S6

Mammalian ribosomes consist of approximately 70–80 different proteins; approximately 30 in the 40 S subunit and 45–50 in the 60 S subunit (for review, see Bielka and Stahl, 1978; Wool, 1979). The protein patterns from various tissues and species have been shown to be very similar and a uniform nomenclature for ribosomal proteins has been proposed recently (McConkey *et al.*, 1979) and will be used throughout this chapter.

Phosphorylation of 40 S ribosomal subunits was first observed in rabbit reticulocytes by Kabat (1970) and in rat liver by Loeb and Blat (1970). The major phosphorylated protein was identified as S6 by Gressner and Wool (1974a). This was accomplished with the two-dimensional polyacrylamide gel electrophoresis system described by Kaltschmidt and

Wittmann (1970). Ribosomal protein S6 is a basic protein with an approximate molecular weight between 30,000 and 35,000.

Phosphorylation of ribosomal protein S6 appears to be a universal phenomenon in mammalian cells and has been observed in all cell types examined. S6 is multiply phosphorylated; up to five phosphoryl groups are bound to the protein in ribosomes from rat liver (Gressner and Wool, 1974a,b; Treloar *et al.*, 1977), rabbit reticulocytes (Traugh and Porter, 1976), HeLa (Lastick *et al.*, 1977), rat cerebral cortex (Roberts and Ashby, 1978), and 3T3 fibroblasts (Thomas *et al.*, 1979). Exact quantitation of the number of phosphoryl groups associated with S6 has been hampered by the nature of the substrate, a ribonucleoprotein complex. The various phosphorylated derivatives have been identified by the rate of migration of S6 in the two-dimensional gel system mentioned above. In this electrophoretic system, the basic proteins isolated from ribosomes or ribosomal subunits migrate toward the cathode in the first dimension (urea, pH 8.6) while the acidic proteins migrate toward the anode. All of the proteins migrate toward the anode in the second dimension (urea, pH 4.5). When the protein is devoid of phosphate, migration toward the cathode at pH 8.6 is most rapid and addition of each phosphoryl group retards migration. Thus, upon inspection of a two-dimensional gel, the amount of phosphate and the amount of protein for each derivative can be approximated (Fig. 1). As an additional method of examining phosphate incorporation into S6, the first dimension of the two-dimensional gel system has been used. In this gel, each of the radioactive derivatives is distinctly separated from the others; thus the amount of radioactive phosphate incorporated into each can be quantitated directly by scintillation spectrometry or indirectly by autoradiography (Floyd-Smith, 1979).

The amount of phosphate associated with S6 varies depending upon the tissue and the state of the cell. Ribosomes from untreated rat liver (Gressner and Wool, 1974a) and confluent cells in culture (Leader *et al.*, 1976; Lastick *et al.*, 1977; Thomas *et al.*, 1979) have been shown to contain minimal amounts of phosphate. Stimulation of phosphorylation has been observed with compounds that increase the intracellular levels of adenosine 3':5'-monophosphate (cAMP), inhibit phosphoprotein phosphatase activity or stimulate cell division. It has been shown in reticulocytes (Cawthon *et al.*, 1974; Traugh *et al.*, 1981), liver (Gressner and Wool, 1976a), anterior pituitary (Barden and Labrie, 1973), pancreatic islet tumor cells (Schubart *et al.*, 1977), thymocytes (Wettenhall and Howlett, 1979), and confluent fibroblast cells (Leader and Coia, 1978a), that addition of cAMP or cAMP analogs increases phosphorylation of S6 (Table I). In rat liver (Blat and Loeb, 1971; Gressner and Wool, 1976a) and pancreatic islet tumor cells (Schubart *et al.*, 1977) the

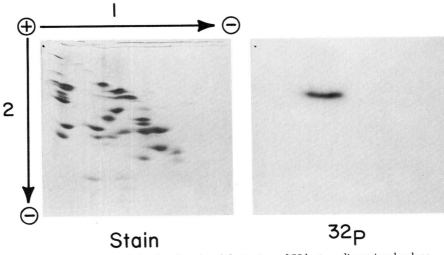

FIG. 1. Identification of the phosphorylated derivatives of S6 by two-dimensional polyacrylamide gel electrophoresis. 40 S ribosomal subunits were isolated from reticulocytes after incubation with $^{32}P_i$ and analyzed by two-dimensional electrophoresis as described by Traugh and Porter (1976). Left, stained protein pattern; right, autoradiogram.

peptide hormone, glucagon, has been shown to increase phosphorylation of S6, while prostaglandin E_1 (PGE_1) has similar effects with thymocytes (Wettenhall and Howlett, 1979). Both hormones elevate cAMP levels in the respective cells. However, increased phosphorylation of S6 is not always coincident with increased levels of cAMP. In hamster kidney fibroblasts (Leader *et al.*, 1976), maximum phosphorylation of S6 occurs in preconfluent cells, but no alterations in cAMP levels are detected between preconfluent and confluent cells. Infection of Erlich ascites tumor cells with Mengo virus (Rosnitschek *et al.*, 1978) stimulates phosphorylation of ribosomal protein S6, but again no increase in cAMP levels is observed. Additionally, isoproterenol treatment of 3T3-L1 (Smith *et al.*, 1979) and glioma cells (Horak and Koschel, 1977) increases significantly the cAMP levels in both cell types but a concomitant increase in phosphorylation is not observed.

To confound the issue further, hormones that stimulate mitotic growth have been shown to stimulate phosphorylation of S6 in cells in culture. Thus, serum, insulin and insulin-like growth factor increase phosphorylation of S6 in chick embryo fibroblasts (Haselbacher *et al.*, 1979). Serum and insulin have the same effect in 3T3 (Smith *et al.*, 1979; Thomas *et al.*, 1979) and HeLa cells (Lastick *et al.*, 1977; Lastick and McConkey, 1978) as does the lectin, concanavalin A in thymocytes (Wettenhall and

Howlett, 1979). Insulin has either no effect on cAMP levels or lowers them; the effect on cGMP levels is not clear at this time. In rat liver where streptozotocin-induced diabetes is accompanied by increased levels of cAMP and increased phosphorylation of S6, administration of insulin results in the concomitant decrease in cAMP and in phosphorylation of S6 (Gressner and Wool, 1976b). Thus it appears that different cell types in different states respond differently to hormones as far as phosphorylation of S6 is concerned.

Increased levels of phosphorylation of S6 have been observed during liver regeneration (Gressner and Wool, 1974a); upon addition of NaF (Kabat, 1970; Cawthon *et al.*, 1974; Floyd-Smith, 1979); upon viral infection (Kaerlein and Horak, 1976, 1978; Russell and Blair, 1977; Rosnitschek *et al.*, 1978); upon inhibition of protein synthesis by toxic compounds including cycloheximide (Gressner and Wool, 1974b; Kaerlein and Horak, 1978), puromycin (Gressner and Wool, 1974b), ethionine (Treolar *et al.*, 1977), D-galactosamine HCl (Gressner and Greiling, 1977), dimethylnitrosoamine (Gressner and Greiling, 1978a), and thioacetamide (Gressner and Greiling, 1978b). However, only in the case of rapid proliferation of cells such as serum or insulin stimulation of cells in culture (Lastick *et al.*, 1977; Thomas *et al.*, 1979) or addition of toxic compounds (Gressner and Wool, 1974b; Gressner and Greiling, 1978a,b) has the majority of S6 been shown to be maximally phosphorylated. In fact, in the presence of increased levels of cAMP, maximal phosphorylation of S6 may not be observed. For example, when rabbit reticulocytes are incubated with cAMP or a derivative of cAMP, the majority of the S6 contains only two phosphoryl groups and no increase in the more highly phosphorylated protein derivatives is observed (Traugh *et al.*, 1981).

S6 is phosphorylated *in vitro* by the cAMP-dependent protein kinases (Loeb and Blat, 1970; Barden and Labrie, 1973; Eil and Wool, 1973a; Traugh *et al.*, 1973; Walton and Gill, 1973; Traugh and Porter, 1976; Issinger *et al.*, 1980). Phosphate incorporation into S6 has been quantified with purifed 40 S ribosomal subunits and the cAMP-dependent protein kinases from reticulocytes. A maximum of 1.6 phosphoryl groups can be added per ribosomal subunit; the phosphate is incorporated specifically into S6 (DuVernay and Traugh, 1978). When the amount of unlabeled phosphate bound to S6 prior to isolation of the 40 S ribosomal subunits is considered (this has been estimated to be 0.5 or less per S6), the subunits phosphorylated *in vitro* contain a total of two phosphoryl groups (Traugh *et al.*, 1981). This has been substantiated by the position of S6 after one- and two-dimensional polyacrylamide gel electrophoresis. The data suggest not all of the phosphorylatable sites on S6 are modified by the cAMP-dependent protein kinases. However, it has not been resolved

TABLE I
Phosphorylation of S6

Source	Conditions stimulating phosphorylation	Conditions decreasing phosphorylation	Conditions not affecting phosphorylation	Total protein synthesis	Reference
Reticulocytes, rabbit	cAMP and derivatives			No change	Cawthon et al. (1974); Traugh et al. (1981); Kabat (1970); Cawthon et al. (1974); Floyd-Smith (1979)
	NaF			Inhibited	Floyd and Traugh (1980)
			Iron deficiency	Inhibited	Floyd-Smith (1979)
			Amino acid starvation	Inhibited	Blat and Loeb (1971); Gressner and Wool (1976a)
Liver, rat	Glucagon			No change	Gressner and Wool (1976a)
	cAMP		5′ AMP	No change	Gressner and Wool (1976b)
	Expt. diabetes	Expt. diabetes + insulin		Stimulated	Gressner and Wool (1974a); Anderson et al. (1975)
	Regeneration			Inhibited	Gressner and Wool (1974b)
	Cycloheximide			Inhibited	Gressner and Wool (1974b)
	Puromycin	Ethionine		Inhibited	Treloar et al. (1977); Treloar and Kisilevsky (1979)
	Ethionine + adenine			Stimulated	Treloar et al. (1977)
	D-Galactosamine HCl			Inhibited	Gressner and Greiling (1977)
	Dimethylnitrosoamine			Inhibited	Gressner and Greiling (1978a)
	Thioacetamide			Inhibited	Gressner and Greiling (1978b)
Cerebral cortex, rat	cAMP and derivatives		cGMP derivative		Roberts and Ashby (1978)
Anterior pituitary gland; bovine	cAMP derivative			Stimulation	Bardin and Labrie (1973)
Pancreatic islet, tumor cells, rat	Glucagon; cAMP derivative; Concanavalin A; Prostaglandin E₁; cAMP derivatives		Somatostatin	Stimulation	Schubart et al. (1977)
Thymocytes, rat				Stimulation	Wettenhall and Howlett (1979)

172

Cell type	Treatment		Resuspension + IBMX	Effect	Reference
HeLa		Confluency		Inhibited	Lastick et al. (1977); Lastick and McConkey (1978)
	Resuspension + serum			Stimulated	Lastick et al. (1977); Lastick and McConkey (1978)
	Resuspension + insulin		Resuspension + IBMX	Stimulated	Lastick and McConkey (1978)
	Cycloheximide			Inhibited	Kaerlein and Horak (1978)
	Vaccinia virus infection			Inhibited	Kaerlein and Horak (1976, 1978)
	Adenovirus infection				Russell and Blair (1977); Blair and Horak (1977)
Fibroblasts kidney, baby hamster	cAMP (confluent)				Leader and Coia (1978a)
embryo, chick	Serum; insulin; insulin-like growth factor			Stimulated	Haselbacher et al. (1979)
		Serum deprivation		Inhibited	Haselbacher et al. (1979)
3T3	Serum			Stimulated	Thomas et al. (1979)
		Serum deprivation		Inhibited	Thomas et al. (1979)
3T3-L1 preadipocytes	Insulin; serum			Stimulated	Smith et al. (1979)
Ascites tumor cells Krebs II		Serum deprivation		Inhibited	Leader et al. (1976)
Ehrlich		Resuspension		Stimulated	Leader et al. (1976)
Glioma C6, rat		Isoproterenol		Inhibited	Rosnitschek et al. (1978)
	Mengo virus infection			No change	Horak and Koschel (1977)
Myeloma, mouse		Hypertonic medium		Inhibited	Kruppa and Martini (1978)

whether the number of sites phosphorylated by these enzymes can be increased by addition of other translational components. In studies of this type, it is important that the structural integrity of the 40 S ribosomal subunit is maintained, otherwise additional ribosomal proteins will become phosphorylated (R. W. Del Grande and J. A. Traugh, unpublished results).

Recently it has been shown that other protein kinases phosphorylate 40 S ribosomal subunits and are specific for S6. These enzymes include the cGMP-dependent protein kinase (Issinger *et al.*, 1980; Traugh *et al.*, 1981) and protease activated kinase II (Del Grande and Traugh, 1979). With the knowledge that additional protein kinases are involved in the phosphorylation of S6, it becomes apparent how opposing types of hormones could appear to have the same result, i.e., increased phosphorylation of S6. Thus the cAMP-dependent protein kinases could phosphorylate a limited number of specific sites on S6. If the cGMP-dependent protein kinase has the same or a similar substrate specificity with S6, as observed with other protein substrates (Hashimoto *et al.*, 1976; Glass and Krebs, 1979), the same sites could also be modified by this enzyme under conditions where cAMP levels are unaltered or reduced and cGMP levels are elevated. Additional phosphorylation could be a result of protease-activated kinase II or an insulin activated protein kinase which has yet to be identified. Differential alterations in phosphoprotein phosphatase activities could give similar or enhanced effects.

Increased phosphorylation of S6 via two apparently independent mechanisms has been shown in thymocytes (Wettenhall and Howlett, 1979). PGE_1 stimulates phosphorylation of S6 by elevation of cAMP levels, whereas concanavalin A acts through a cyclic nucleotide-independent mechanism to achieve the same result. That these effects are related, but not identical, are shown when the two compounds are added simultaneously. In this case, stimulation of protein synthesis is not observed.

A correlation between phosphorylation of S6 and protein synthesis has not been clearly defined, primarily since sufficient definitive studies have not been completed. Phosphorylation of S6 has been shown to be accompanied by a stimulation of protein synthesis, by no alteration in protein synthesis and by an inhibition of protein synthesis following viral infection or upon administration of toxic compounds. Only in rapidly proliferating cells can a case be made for coincident elevation in the levels of phosphorylation of S6 and increased protein synthesis. In these studies (Gressner and Wool, 1974a; Lastick *et al.*, 1977; Lastick and McConkey, 1978; Smith *et al.*, 1979; Thomas *et al.*, 1979; Haselbacher *et al.*, 1979; Wettenhall and Howlett, 1979), a stimulation of protein synthesis is observed along with the stimulation of other metabolic functions.

However, it has not been shown whether this stimulation is due to an increased availability of total or specific mRNA or an increased rate of initiation or translation of existing mRNA. A correlation between stimulation of phosphorylation of S6 and protein synthesis by increased levels of cAMP has been observed in several cell types (Labrie *et al.*, 1971; Barden and Labrie, 1973; Wettenhall and Howlett, 1979). Although cAMP does not appear to affect total protein synthesis in liver cells, the rate of translation of tyrosine aminotransferase is altered when hepatoma cells are incubated with dibutyryl cAMP. The rate of elongation is accelerated as much as 10-fold and is directly proportional to the observed increase in enzyme synthesis (Roper and Wicks, 1978).

A correlation between inhibition of protein synthesis and increased phosphorylation has been observed with several toxic compounds (Gressner and Wool, 1974b; Gressner and Greiling, 1977, 1978a,b; Treloar *et al.*, 1977; Kaerlein and Horak, 1978). Increased phosphorylation is also observed following virus infection, resulting in decreased host cell protein synthesis with increased synthesis of viral directed proteins. This will be discussed below. The increased phosphorylation of S6 observed in these cases could be an effect of the inhibition of protein synthesis rather than the cause. Upon inhibition, the phosphorylation of S6 may be enhanced by alterations in the ribosome structure or in the interaction of the subunits with other translational components and/or by changes in the activity of the protein kinases and phosphoprotein phosphatases.

From the apparently conflicting data which has accumulated, a clear cause–effect relationship between phosphorylation of S6 and protein synthesis has not been established at the cellular level. The problem is compounded by the fact that although we can estimate the number of phosphoryl groups on S6, we cannot be assured that the sites modified under one condition are identical to the sites modified under other, very dissimilar conditions. Any definitive conclusions as to the role of these phosphorylation events in protein synthesis await identification of the sites phosphorylated under the various experimental conditions.

Few attempts have been made to examine the role of phosphorylation of S6 at a molecular level. Eil and Wool (1973b) examined a number of different partial reactions of protein synthesis using ribosomal subunits phosphorylated by the cAMP-dependent protein kinases. However, the studies were flawed by the fact that a number of ribosomal proteins, in addition to S6, were modified under the conditions of phosphorylation. Similar studies have not been completed since that time due to the numerous problems involved in examining the effects of phosphorylation in a reconstituted system. These difficulties include the lack of efficiency of the system, obtaining specific and stoichiometric incorporation of phosphate into S6, obtaining all of the components free of contaminating protein kinases and phosphoprotein phosphatases, identifying whether the other phosphorylated components of the system (initiation factors and 60 S ribosomal subunits) should be added in the phosphorylated or dephosphorylated form and lastly, which reactions are most likely to give positive results. Recent studies by Terao and Ogata (1979a,b) have identified S6 as the major poly (U) binding protein in 40 S ribosomal subunits from rat liver using four different procedural approaches. The data suggest that the partial reactions involving mRNA binding to 40 S ribosomal subunits and formation of the preinitiation complex could be affected by the degree of phosphorylation of S6.

B. Phosphorylation of Other Ribosomal Proteins

Due to the multiple sites on S6, phosphorylation of this protein is the major modification event observed on ribosomal proteins; however, in many cell types, phosphorylation of additional ribosomal proteins has been observed (Table II). In the 40 S ribosomal subunit, phosphorylation of S2 has been detected in Krebs II ascites cells (Rankine *et al.*, 1977; Leader and Coia, 1978c), and HeLa cells after infection with vaccinia virus (Kaerlein and Horak, 1976, 1978), and to a small extent in reticulocytes (Traugh and Porter, 1976) and cerebral cortex (Roberts and Ashby, 1978). Phosphorylation of S3 has been observed in confluent Krebs II ascites cells (Leader and Coia, 1978c) incubated with amino acids in the presence and absence of glucose (conditions resulting in a reduction of pH), in mouse L cells (Marvaldi and Lucas-Lenard, 1977) and to a minor extent in cerebral cortex (Roberts and Ashby, 1978). Occasionally phosphorylation of additional proteins has been observed, but these are isolated observations (see Table II).

In the large ribosomal subunit, the only basic protein which has been shown to be significantly phosphorylated in more than one tissue is L14. Phosphorylation of this protein has been observed in cerebral cortex (Roberts and Ashby, 1978), HeLa (Lastick *et al.*, 1977), confluent Krebs II ascites cells incubated with amino acids (Leader and Coia, 1978c) and mouse L cells (Marvaldi and Lucas-Lenard, 1977). However, in almost all tissues studied, acidic proteins associated with the 60 S ribosomal subunit are phosphorylated. Thus one or two phosphorylated proteins (MW 12,500 to 19,000) have been observed in reticulocytes (Kabat, 1970; Floyd-Smith, 1979), rat liver (Arpin *et al.*, 1978; Van Agthoven *et al.*, 1978; Tsurugi *et al.*, 1978), rat cerebral cortex (Roberts and Ashby, 1978), HeLa (Horak and Schiffmann, 1977), kidney fibroblasts (Leader and Coia, 1978b), myeloma cells (Kruppa and Martini, 1978), L cells

TABLE II
Phosphorylation of Other Ribosomal Proteins[a]

Source	Phosphorylated proteins		Conditions affecting phosphorylation	Reference
	40 S	60 S		
Reticulocytes, rabbit	(S2)	15,000, 16,000		Traugh and Porter (1976); Floyd-Smith (1979)
Liver, rat		18,200, 19,000 12,500 13,000, 13,500 15,200, 16,100	NaF	Kabat (1970); Cawthon et al. (1974) Arpin et al. (1978) Van Agthoven et al. (1978) Tsurugi et al. (1978)
Cerebral cortex, rat	(S2, S3)	(L6, L13) L14, 15,000, 36,000, 38,000		Roberts and Asbhy (1978)
HeLa	S2, S16 S32	37,000 13,700, 14,400 L14 14,500	Vaccinia virus	Kaerlein and Horak (1976, 1978) Schiffman and Horak (1978) Horak and Schiffmann (1977) Lastick et al. (1977) Leader and Coia (1978b)
Fibroblasts, hamster kidney				
Ascites tumor cells,	S2			Rankine et al. (1977); Leader and Coia (1978c)
Krebs II	S3	L14 (L6) 13,500, 14,500	Amino acids ± glucose	Leader and Coia (1978c) Rankine et al. (1977); Leader et al. (1978); Leader and Coia (1978c,d)
		(41,000) n.d.		Rankine et al. (1977) Kruppa and Martini (1978)
Myeloma cells, mouse				
L cells, mouse	(S3) (S12)	L22 (L14) n.d.	Ricin	Marvaldi and Lucas-Lenard (1977) Houston (1978)
Sarcoma 180 tumor cells, mouse		18,200; 19,500		Bitte and Kabat (1972)

[a] Phosphorylated acidic proteins in the 60 S ribosomal subunit are identified by molecular weight due to problems with positive identification between cell types. Numbers in parentheses indicate minor phosphorylation. Not determined, n.d.

(Houston 1978), and sarcoma cells (Bitte and Kabat, 1972). The identification of these proteins has been detailed recently by Leader (1980). Additional acidic proteins (MW 36,000 to 41,000) have been observed in cerebral cortex (Roberts and Ashby, 1978), HeLa (Schiffmann and Horak, 1978), and Krebs II ascites cells (Rankine *et al.*, 1977).

Studies on the role of phosphorylation of the acidic proteins in protein synthesis has been hampered by difficulties in detecting and positively identifying the proteins. Upon incubation of confluent Krebs II ascites cells with glucose and amino acids, phosphorylation of S3 and L14 and the decreased phosphorylation of the two smaller acidic proteins is observed (Leader and Coia, 1978c). No apparent correlation exists between phosphate incorporation into the acidic proteins and phosphorylation of S6. Phosphorylation of these proteins does not appear to be altered by cAMP and hormones that elevate cAMP levels (Kabat, 1970; Roberts and Ashby, 1978).

In the few cases where phosphorylation of these ribosomal proteins has been described *in vitro*, the protein kinase activity has been shown to be independent of cyclic nucleotides. Thus, an enzyme similar to casein kinase II (see Section III,C) has been shown to phosphorylate the acidic ribosomal proteins from HeLa (Horak and Schiffmann, 1977; Schiffmann and Horak, 1978) and from reticulocytes (Issinger, 1977). Recently we have isolated a protease activated protein kinase from reticulocytes which specifically phosphorylates ribosomal protein S10 (Del Grande and Traugh, 1979). Since this phosphorylation event has not been identified in studies with whole cells, the significance of this observation is not known.

C. Viral Infection and Phosphorylation of Ribosomal Proteins

Viral infection appears to affect phosphorylation of ribosomal proteins in several different ways. Increased phosphorylation of one ribosomal protein, S6, has been observed after adenovirus infection of HeLa cells (Blair and Horak, 1977) or Mengo virus infection of Ehrlich ascites tumor cells (Rosnitschek *et al.*, 1978). In the latter case, cAMP levels were monitored before and after infection and no change was observed. This suggests that phosphorylation of S6 was due either to inhibition of phosphoprotein phosphatase(s) or activation of a protein kinase other than the cAMP-dependent enzymes.

In HeLa cells, phosphorylation of S2 and S16 is observed after infection with vaccinia virus and is accompanied by an increase in the phosphorylation of S6 (Kaerlein and Horak, 1976, 1978). Phosphorylation of

S2 is observed almost immediately after infection; additional phosphorylation of S2 and phosphorylation of S16 is seen 60 minutes postinfection. The degree of phosphorylation of ribosomal proteins and the rate of inhibition of protein synthesis is dependent on the multiplicity of infection. It is possible that phosphorylation of S2 and S16 is due to a virus-associated protein kinase and/or a virus-coded enzyme as suggested by Kaerlein and Horak (1978). Vaccinia virions have been shown to contain a protein kinase (Paoletti and Moss, 1972; Kleiman and Moss, 1975). Isolated core proteins from the vaccinia virus inhibit protein synthesis in reticulocyte lysates and Ehrlich ascites tumor cell extracts when added in catalytic amounts (Ben-Hamida and Beaud, 1978). This is accompanied by disaggregation of polysomes with time, suggesting inhibition occurs at a step in initiation. Recently, a phosphorylated viral structural protein (MW 11,000) has been shown to be associated with ribosomes after infection and is removed from the ribosomes by high salt (Sagot and Beaud, 1979).

After infection of mouse L cells with vesicular stomatitis virus, a new basic protein has been shown to be associated with ribosomes. In addition, five basic phosphopeptides are associated with 40 S ribosomal subunits (Marvaldi and Lucas-Lenard, 1977). It is not known whether these proteins are phosphorylated forms of ribosomal proteins or other proteins. The amount of phosphorylation of the additional basic protein is dependent on the multiplicity of infection.

III. INITIATION FACTORS

A. STRUCTURE AND FUNCTION OF INITIATION FACTORS

Eight initiation factors have been obtained in highly purified form from rabbit reticulocytes in the laboratories of Merrick and Anderson, Staehelin, Hershey, and Voorma (see Methods in Enzymology Vol. 60, Part H, 1979) and from Krebs II ascites cells by Trachsel *et al.* (1979). The factors have been identified according to the uniform nomenclature proposed by Anderson *et al.* (1977) as eukaryotic initiation factors (eIF) 1, 2, 3, 4A, 4B, 4C, 4D, and 5. Considerable effort has been directed toward characterizing these factors and examining their role in protein synthesis. A summary of the research on the structure and function of the individual initiation factors is shown in Table III.

Although there is general agreement concerning the role of these eight

TABLE III
Structure and Function of Eukaryotic Initiation Factors

Initiation factor	Subunit molecular weight	Native molecular weight	Function	Reference
eIF-1	15,000	15,000	Stimulates globin synthesis and binding of met-tRNA$_f$ and mRNA to 80 S ribosomes	Merrick et al. (1975); Staehelin et al. (1975); Benne and Hershey (1978)
eIF-2 α β γ	38,000 53,000 57,000	125,000	Forms a ternary complex with met-tRNA$_f$ and GTP; binds complex to 40 S ribosomal subunits	Dettman and Stanley (1972); Schreier and Staehelin (1973a); Gupta et al. (1973); Levin et al. (1973); Safer et al. (1975); Smith and Henshaw (1975); Ranu and Wool (1976); Benne et al. (1976); Herrera et al. (1977)
eIF-3	10 subunits (35,000 to 130,000)	500,000 to 700,000	Enhances binding of the ternary complex to 40 S ribosomal subunits; dissociates 80 S ribosomes into subunits and prevents reassociation	Schreier and Staehelin (1973b); Staehelin et al. (1975); Freienstein and Blobel (1975); Benne and Hershey (1976); Safer et al. (1976); Thompson et al. (1977); Trachsel and Staehelin (1979)
eIF-4A	50,000	50,000	Promotes binding of mRNA to 40 S ribosomal subunits	Wigle and Smith (1973); Schreier and Staehelin (1975); Safer et al. (1976); Benne and Hershey (1978)
eIF-4B[a]	80,000	$(80,000)_n$	Promotes binding of mRNA to 40 S ribosomal subunits	Schreier and Staehelin (1973b); Prichard and Anderson (1974); Benne et al. (1977)
eIF-4C	18,000	18,000	Stimulates binding of met-tRNA$_f$ and mRNA to 40 S ribosomal subunits	Schreier and Staehelin (1973b); Kemper et al. (1976); Benne and Hershey (1978)
eIF-4D	16,000	16,000	Stimulates formation of first peptide bond when assayed by synthesis of methionyl-puromycin	Kemper et al. (1976); Benne and Hershey (1978)
eIF-5	155,000	155,000	Ribosome-dependent GTPase activity; required for binding of 60 S ribosomal subunits to 40 S initiation complex	Staehelin et al. (1975); Merrick et al. (1975); Benne and Hershey (1976)

[a] eIF-4B preparations have been contaminated with a protein (MW 24,000) which can be crosslinked to the 5' cap of mRNA and may be responsible for the activity attributed to the 80,000-dalton protein (Sonenberg et al., 1978).

initiation factors, several laboratories have obtained additional factors in a highly purified form which also may have a role in initiation. eIF-2A (MW 65,000) binds met-tRNA$_f$ to 40 S ribosomal subunits in the absence of GTP when AUG is used as template (Leader and Wool, 1972; Zasloff and Ochoa, 1973; Ilan and Ilan, 1973; Grummt, 1974; Merrick and Anderson, 1975; Cimadevilla and Hardesty, 1975a). Several initiation factors have been isolated in the laboratory of N. K. Gupta which do not appear to correspond to factors described in other laboratories. Co-EIF-1 (MW 20,000) stimulates met-tRNA$_f$ binding to eIF-2 apparently by formation of a stable quaternary complex (Dasgupta *et al.*, 1978a), while EIF-1* (MW 2500) promotes ternary complex formation (Dasgupta *et al.*, 1978b).

B. Phosphorylation of Initiation Factors

Phosphorylation of the eight initiation factors listed in Table III has been examined in reticulocytes and reticulocyte lysates. Phosphorylated factors were examined in reticulocytes after incubation with radioactive inorganic phosphate (Benne *et al.*, 1978; Floyd-Smith, 1979) and in reticulocyte lysates incubated with an ATP·GTP regenerating system and $^{32}P_i$ (Floyd *et al.*, 1979). The phosphorylated factors were either partially purified from the 0.5 M KCl wash fraction of ribosomes and identified by gel electrophoresis (Benne *et al.*, 1978) or by two-dimensional gel electrophoresis of the salt wash fraction (Floyd *et al.*, 1979). Subunits of eIF-2 (MW 53,000) and eIF-3 (MW 130,000 and 69,000) and eIF-4B were shown to be phosphorylated by both groups and minor phosphorylation of eIF-2α (MW 38,000) and eIF-3 (MW 35,000) was also observed in my laboratory (Table IV). Phosphate incorporation into initiation factors 1, 2A, 4A, 4C, and 4D was not observed. Due to the low concentration of eIF-5 in reticulocytes, this initiation factor was not detected in any of the studies. To my knowledge, Co-EIF-1 and EIF-1* have not been examined as possible phosphate acceptor proteins either in intact reticulocytes or with purified protein kinases.

C. Protein Kinases and Phosphorylation of Initiation Factors

The enzymes from reticulocytes that phosphorylate initiation factors have been identified and partially characterized. They include the type I and type II cAMP-dependent protein kinases, casein kinase I and II, the

TABLE IV
Phosphorylation of Eukaryotic Initiation Factors[a]

Phosphorylation conditions	eIF-2	eIF-3	eIF-4B	eIF-5	Reference
Reticulocytes	53,000 35,000	130,000 69,000 (35,000)	+	n.d.	Benne et al. (1978); Floyd-Smith (1979)
Reticulocyte lysates	53,000 38,000	130,000 69,000 35,000	+	n.d.	Floyd et al. (1979)
cAMP-dependent protein kinase	—	130,000	—	—	Traugh and Lundak (1978)
Casein kinase I	—	—	+	+	Hathaway et al. (1979)
Casein kinase II	53,000	130,000 69,000 (35,000)	+	+	Traugh et al. (1976); Issinger et al. (1976); Tahara et al. (1978); Hathaway et al. (1979)
Hemin controlled repressor	38,000	—	—	—	Levin et al. (1976); Kramer et al. (1976); Farrell et al. (1977); Gross and Mendelewski (1977); Tahara et al. (1978)
dsRNA-activated inhibitor	38,000	—	—	—	Kimchi et al. (1979b); Levin et al. (1980)
Protease-activated kinase I	—	130,000	+	n.d.	Tahara (1979); Tahara and Traugh (1979)
Protease activated kinase II	53,000	—	n.d.	n.d.	Tahara and Traugh (1979); Tuazon and Traugh (1980)

[a] The molecular weight of the phosphorylated components of the multisubunit factors is given. Phosphorylation of single subunit factors is designated as +, no phosphorylation as −, and not determined by n.d.

hemin controlled repressor (HCR), the dsRNA activated inhibitor, and protease activated kinase I and II. The type I and type II cAMP-dependent protein kinases in reticulocytes (Tao *et al.*, 1970; Traugh and Traut, 1974) appear to be similar to the highly studied enzymes from skeletal muscle and beef heart. These consist of complexes of two regulatory and two catalytic subunits which are dissociated and thereby activated by cAMP (for review, see Rubin and Rosen, 1975; Krebs and Beavo, 1979). The enzymes from reticulocytes have been partially purified using mixed histone as substrate and, like the enzymes from other tissues, use only ATP as a phosphoryl donor. In addition to 40 S ribosomal protein S6, the cAMP-dependent protein kinases phosphorylate the 130,000-dalton polypeptide of eIF-3 (Traugh and Lundak, 1978). Both types of the enzyme have been shown to be associated with ribosomes (Traugh and Sharp, 1977).

The remainder of the protein kinases which have been studied are all cyclic nucleotide-independent enzymes. Casein kinase I and II modify casein and it has been used as a substrate in the purification of these enzymes (Hathaway and Traugh, 1979; Hathaway *et al.*, 1979). Casein kinase I is a single subunit enzyme (MW 37,000) which is stimulated by monovalent cations and utilizes only ATP in the phosphotransferase reaction (Hathaway and Traugh, 1979; Tuazon *et al.*, 1979). The enzyme modifies seryl residues and the recognition sequence for casein kinase I in α_{sl} and β casein appears to be Glu-X-Ser (Tuazon *et al.*, 1979). Casein kinase I has been shown to phosphorylate eIF-4B and eIF-5 (Hathaway *et al.*, 1979). In addition, it is also self-phosphorylated (Hathaway and Traugh, 1979).

Casein kinase II has a molecular weight of approximately 130,000 as determined by analytical sedimentation (Hathaway and Traugh, 1979). Although it was reported initially to have three subunits, recent studies have shown that the enzyme has an $\alpha_2\beta_2$ structure (MW 42,000 and 24,000) (G. M. Hathaway and J. A. Traugh, unpublished results). The observed extra subunit was due to partial proteolysis which apparently occurred during purification. Monovalent cations have been shown to stimulate the activity (Tuazon *et al.*, 1979) while heparin effectively inhibits the protein kinase with an apparent K_i of 1.4 nM (Hathaway *et al.*, 1980). Casein kinase II is unique in that it effectively utilizes both ATP and GTP as phosphoryl donor molecules in the phosphotransferase reaction. Using α_{sl} and β caseins, the recognition sequence for casein kinase II has been determined to be Thr-Glu-Asp. A similar result was obtained by Deana *et al.* (1979) with the enzyme from rat liver. With partially dephosphorylated caseins the enzyme also modifies seryl residues with a requirement for an acidic amino acid two residues toward the C terminus

(Pinna *et al.*, 1979). Casein kinase II has the greatest diversity with regard to initiation factors and phosphorylates eIF-2β, two and possibly three subunits of eIF-3, eIF-4B, and eIF-5 (Traugh *et al.*, 1976; Issinger *et al.*, 1976; Tahara *et al.*, 1978; Hathaway *et al.*, 1979). In addition, the β subunit of the protein kinase is self-phosphorylated.

Casein kinase I and II have been shown to be associated with ribosomes (Traugh and Sharp, 1977) and an enzyme utilizing both ATP and GTP has been found on native 40 S ribosomal subunits of Krebs II ascites tumor cells (Issinger and Reichert, 1979). The chromatographic properties of casein kinase II are similar to several initiation factors, including eIF-2, making it difficult to exclude the enzyme from assays containing even highly purified initiation factors. This poses problems in examining the role of this enzyme in protein synthesis. Protein kinases similar to casein kinase I and II have been obtained in highly purified form from rat liver (Thornburg and Lindell, 1977; Thornberg *et al.*, 1978) and Novikoff ascites tumor cells (Dahmus and Natzle, 1977). The detection of these enzymes in three such diverse cell types suggests they may be found in most, if not all, mammalian cells.

HCR and the dsRNA activated inhibitor have been identified as protein kinases in reticulocytes and similar enzymes have been identified in a number of different cell types. As the names imply, HCR is activated in the absence of hemin and the inhibitor is activated by dsRNA. In reticulocyte lysates, under conditions of optimal protein synthesis, the repressor and the inhibitor are inactive. Activation coincides with an inhibition of protein synthesis and the phosphorylation of eIF-2α. The properties of these enzymes, and their role in protein synthesis will be detailed in Sections IV and V.

Protease-activated kinases have been described by Nishizuka and coworkers in a variety of different tissues (Takai *et al.*, 1977a,b; Inoue *et al.*, 1977). The enzymes are activated by trypsin or a Ca^{2+}-dependent protease. Takai *et al.* (1979) have shown that some of the enzymes are also activated by low concentrations of calcium ($10^{-5}M$) in the presence of membranes or phospholipids, suggesting that this may be the physiologically relevant mode of activation.

Two protease activated kinases, I and II, have recently been identified in reticulocytes. Both are proteolytically activated *in vitro* by trypsin and chymotrypsin (Tahara, 1979). An endogenous Ca^{2+}-activated protease from reticulocytes has been shown to activate protease activated kinase II but not I. Recently, we have shown both enzymes phosphorylate histone using ATP as the phosphoryl donor. These enzymes are not related to the cAMP-dependent enzymes since they are not inhibited by the heat stable inhibitor protein nor do they have the same substrate specificity with histone as do the cAMP-dependent enzymes. The two protease-activated kinases from reticulocytes have different substrate specificities with translational components to each other and to the other protein kinases from reticulocytes. Protease activated kinase I phosphorylates one subunit of eIF-3 (MW 130,000), eIF-4B, and ribosomal protein S10 (Tahara and Traugh, 1979). Protease activated kinase II modifies eIF-2β (Tuazon *et al.*, 1980) and ribosomal protein S6 (Del Grande and Traugh, 1979). These enzymes do not appear to be in an activated form in reticulocytes or fresh reticulocyte lysates. However, they are activated with time in the lysate by endogenous protease activities.

Thus it appears that the initiation factors are multiply phosphorylated and each factor is modified by two or more protein kinases (Table IV). The overall substrate specificity of the individual protein kinase is different (except for possibly HCR and the dsRNA activated inhibitor) and it would be expected that multiple enzymes which phosphorylate the same polypeptide modify different sites. This has been demonstrated with the β subunit of eIF-2. Upon analysis of the phosphopeptide by two-dimensional fingerprinting of tryptic and chymotryptic digests, different sites in eIF-2β are modified by casein kinase II and by protease activated kinase II (Tuazon *et al.*, 1980).

D. Phosphoprotein Phosphatases and Dephosphorylation of Initiation Factors

Although the protein kinases that modify translational components have been examined in detail, less work has been completed on the phosphoprotein phosphatases that dephosphorylate these proteins. In initial experiments, 40 S ribosomal subunits and 80 S ribosomes, phosphorylated either *in vitro* by the cAMP-dependent protein kinases or in reticulocytes incubated with $^{32}P_i$, were dephosphorylated by a phosphoprotein phosphatase (Lightfoot *et al.*, 1975). Using histone phosphorylated by the cAMP-dependent protein kinases and casein phosphorylated by casein kinase II, the major form of phosphoprotein phosphatase in reticulocytes has been isolated (Mumby and Traugh, 1979a,b, 1980). This B form (MW 270,000) comprises approximately 80% of the phosphatase activity with these substrates. The phosphatase activity is stimulated by limited tryptic digestion and by freezing and thawing in the presence of reducing agents. Phosphoprotein phosphatases similar to this enzyme have been described in several different tissues (Li, 1975; Kobayashi *et al.*, 1975; Lee *et al.*, 1976, 1978; Kobayashi and Kato, 1977). The B form dephosphorylates all of the translational components tested including 40 S ribosomal subunits phosphorylated by the cAMP-dependent protein kinases, eIF-2α phosphorylated by HCR, eIF-2β phosphorylated by casein kinase II and protease activated kinase II and eIF-3 phosphorylated by the cAMP-dependent protein kinases and casein kinase II (Mumby and Traugh, 1979a,b). Various small molecular weight compounds, which are involved in protein synthesis, differentially regulate dephosphorylation depending on the substrate. These compounds include ATP, GTP, glucose 6-phosphate, sodium fluoride, and hemin. GTP (4 μM) inhibits the phosphatase activity with all of the components tested and ATP (4 mM) and glucose 6-phosphate (4 mM) preferentially inhibit dephosphorylation of ribosomal protein S6 and eIF-2α. Hemin (25 mM) inhibits dephosphorylation of ribosomal protein S6, eIF-2α, and eIF-2β while high concentrations of cAMP (4 mM) stimulate dephosphorylation of eIF-2α. Thus the phosphatases, unlike the protein kinases, could be catholic in nature, regulation occurring by alterations in the rate of dephosphorylation of the different substrates by the various regulatory compounds. Alternatively, since phosphatase B is not homogenous, it is possible that more than one phosphatase is present in the preparations. Further purification and characterization of the regulatory properties of the enzyme are in progress.

Grankowski *et al.* (1980) have isolated a phosphatase from reticulocytes by ethanol precipitation at room temperature. This procedure activates phosphoprotein phosphatases with the concomitant conversion of the enzymes to a lower molecular form (Brandt *et al.*, 1975a,b; Killilea *et al.*, 1979). The enzyme has a molecular weight of approximately 76,000 and is inhibited by 0.1 mM ADP or GDP and 1 mM pyrophosphate. The enzyme dephosphorylates histone, casein, eIF-2α phosphorylated by HCR, eIF-2β phosphorylated by casein kinase II and HCR. Due to the harsh conditions used in the purification i.e., ethanol precipitation at room temperature, it is possible that the phosphatase is part of the 270,000 dalton enzyme observed by Mumby and Traugh (1979a,b, 1980).

IV. HEMIN REGULATION OF PROTEIN SYNTHESIS

Early studies with intact reticulocytes demonstrated a requirement for hemin and/or iron to maintain protein synthesis (Kruh and Borsook, 1956; Bruns and London, 1965; Waxman and Rabinovitz, 1965, 1966). In the absence of hemin, inhibition of protein synthesis occurs and this inhibition is accompanied by a conversion of polysomes to monosomes (Waxman and Rabinovitz, 1965, 1966; Grayzel *et al.*, 1966; Godchaux *et al.*, 1967). Since reticulocyte lysates are almost equally as efficient in protein synthesis as intact cells and easier to manipulate, experimentation quickly turned to an examination of the effects of hemin in reticulocyte lysates. During the past 10 years intense interest has centered around the requirement for hemin to maintain globin synthesis and recently, phosphorylation of one of the initiation factors, eIF-2, has been shown to be involved in this control.

In hemin-supplemented lysates, protein synthesis is linear for at least 30 minutes at 34°. In hemin-deprived lysates, protein synthesis is linear and comparable to heminated lysates for the first several minutes; however, a sharp inhibition of protein synthesis is observed at around 5 minutes in the hemin-deprived lysates and the level of protein synthesis drops to less than 10% of the heminated control (Zucker and Schulman, 1968; Adamson *et al.*, 1969; Hunt *et al.*, 1972; Gross and Rabinovitz, 1972, 1973a; Levin *et al.*, 1975). Disaggregation of polysomes accompanies the inhibition of protein synthesis and is complete at about 5 minutes (Zucker and Schulman, 1968; Mizuno *et al.*, 1972), which coincides with the point of alteration in the biphasic kinetics. These data suggest that protein synthesis is inhibited at a step in polypeptide chain initiation and are supported by experiments which show a concomitant decrease in binding of met-tRNA$_f$ to 40 S ribosomal subunits and the subsequent formation of the 80 S initiation complex (Balkow *et al.*, 1973a,b; Legon *et al.*, 1973). The cessation of protein synthesis is accompanied by the formation of a translational inhibitor (Maxwell and Rabinovitz, 1969; Howard *et al.*, 1970; Maxwell *et al.*, 1971) and the activation of a protein kinase which specifically phosphorylates the α subunit of eIF-2 (Levin *et al.*, 1976; Kramer *et al.*, 1976; Farrell *et al.*, 1977; Gross and Mendelewski, 1977; Tahara *et al.*, 1978).

The translational inhibitor, called the hemin controlled repressor or more commonly, HCR, is present in heminated lysates in a proinhibitor (inactive) form. In the absence of hemin, the proinhibitor is activated with a subsequent inhibition of protein synthesis (Adamson *et al.*, 1969; Gross and Rabinovitz, 1972, 1973a; Legon *et al.*, 1973). HCR acts catalytically to inhibit protein synthesis, one molecule reduces the activity of 1000 ribosomes by 50% (Gross and Rabinovitz, 1973a). The inhibitor activity is reversed by early addition of hemin to the lysate, whereupon protein synthesis returns to the initial rate (Adamson *et al.*, 1969; Gross and Rabinovitz, 1972, 1973a). Under prolonged incubation in the absence of hemin, or upon treatment of the lysate with sulfhydryl modifying reagents such as *N*-ethylmaleimide (NEM), an irreversible inhibitor is formed which is insensitive to hemin (Gross and Rabinovitz, 1972). The irreversible form has not been observed *in vivo*.

Both the reversible and the irreversible forms of HCR have been highly purified and the inhibitor activity and the protein kinase activity copurify and appear to reside in the same molecule (Gross and Rabinovitz, 1973b; Ranu and London, 1976; Farrell *et al.*, 1977; Trachsel *et al.*, 1978; Hunt, 1979; Lundak and Traugh, 1980). Antibody produced to HCR prevents the inhibition of protein synthesis and the phosphorylation of eIF-2 (Kramer *et al.*, 1976; Petryshyn *et al.*, 1979). The molecular weight of HCR has been estimated to be 300,000 to 400,000 by gel filtration when chromatographed either in the presence or absence of hemin although lower values have been observed. A sedimentation coefficient of 6 S has been determined. HCR appears to be composed of a single type of subunit with a molecular weight, as determined by gel electrophoresis, between 80,000 and 105,000. Using these data, Hunt (1979) has calculated that HCR is an elongated molecule with a molecular weight of approximately 160,000. Crosslinking studies with the enzyme have shown that HCR is a dimer (Hunt, 1979). When reversible HCR is incubated with NEM, hemin no longer has an effect on the protein kinase activity (Trachsel *et al.*, 1978). Like other protein kinases, purified HCR has been shown to be autophosphorylated (Farrell *et al.*, 1977; Trachsel *et al.*, 1978; Hunt, 1979; Lundak and Traugh, 1980).

Although complex theories have been constructed to describe the activation of HCR, hemin directly inhibits the protein kinase activity at concentrations less than those which stimulate protein synthesis. Fifty percent inhibition of the protein kinase activity is observed at around 5 μM hemin and the activity is completely inhibited at 10 μM (Trachsel *et al.*, 1978; Lundak and Traugh, 1980). Fifty percent stimulation of protein synthesis in the lysate is observed at 10–11 μM hemin. The extra hemin requirement for stimulation of protein synthesis is apparently due to nonspecific binding of the hemin to additional proteins in the lysate. Other porphyrin compounds including mesohemin IX, mesoporphyrin, deuterohemin IX, and protoporphyrin IX inhibit phosphorylation of eIF-2α at similar or lower concentrations than hemin (Lundak and Traugh, 1980). From the studies with protoporphyrin IX, it appears that addition of iron to the porphyrin ring is not essential for inhibition. Thus hemin and hemin-like compounds inhibit the reversible form of HCR presumably by binding directly to the enzyme. The irreversible inhibitor is not affected by hemin suggesting the protein is unable to complex with hemin. In this case, the hemin binding site could be altered by chemical modification, as suggested by the studies with NEM, or a limited proteolytic event could remove a small portion of the protein. In both cases, protein kinase activity could be irreversibly activated.

Under conditions of optimal protein synthesis, little phosphorylation of eIF-2α occurs in the lysate (Benne *et al.*, 1978; Farrell *et al.*, 1978a; Floyd *et al.*, 1979). Formation of the inhibitor in the lysate is accompanied by an increase in phosphorylation of the small subunit of eIF-2 as observed by two-dimensional electrophoresis in isoelectrofocusing SDS polyacrylamide gels (Farrell *et al.*, 1978a). An increased phosphorylation of eIF-2α in reticulocyte lysates occurs prior to inhibition of protein synthesis and has been shown using an ATP·GTP phosphate exchange system (Floyd and Traugh, 1980) or by addition of radioactive ATP (Ernst *et al.*, 1979). Additional evidence for the role of eIF-2 in the inhibition of protein synthesis is shown by the reinitiation of protein synthesis in hemin-deprived lysates upon addition of high concentrations of eIF-2 (Kaempfer, 1974; Clemens *et al.*, 1975; Ernst *et al.*, 1976; Gross, 1977). Recently an additional protein associated with crude ribosomes (MW 55,000) has also been shown to be phosphorylated in hemin-deprived lysates with similar kinetics to those observed with eIF-2α (Floyd and Traugh, 1980). The additional phosphorylated protein is not one of the eight initiation factors and the role of this protein is not currently known. Studies with intact reticulocytes incubated in the presence and absence of iron and transferrin have shown increased phosphorylation of the same two proteins with iron deprivation (Floyd and Traugh, 1980).

Dephosphorylation of eIF-2 modified in the α subunit by HCR and the β subunit by casein kinase II has been examined in reticulocyte lysates incubated in the presence and absence of hemin. eIF-2α is readily dephosphorylated; the rate is similar in both the hemin-deprived and hemin-supplemented lysates (Safer and Jagus, 1979). Little dephosphorylation of eIF-2β is observed in either case. In other studies it has been shown that the phosphoryl groups on eIF-2α are turning over even after inhibition has been observed (Ernst *et al.*, 1979; Levin *et al.*, 1979; Floyd and Traugh, 1980). This suggests an equilibrium exists between the phosphorylation and dephosphorylation of eIF-2. At optimal concentrations of hemin, HCR is repressed to a level where the rate of dephosphorylation is greater than the rate of phosphorylation, thus maintaining eIF-2α in a dephosphorylated state. Upon hemin deprivation, HCR is activated with a subsequent increase in the rate of phosphorylation, altering the equilibrium toward the phosphorylated state.

HCR is also activated in lysates by raising the pH (Hunt, 1979) and by high hydrostatic pressure (Hunt, 1979; Henderson *et al.*, 1979). After analysis of lysates containing pressure activated HCR, Henderson *et al.* (1979) have suggested an alternate mode of activation may include the proteolytic activation of a protein factor which subsequently activates HCR. Initial reports that cAMP activates the HCR (Datta *et al.*, 1977, 1978) appear to be without foundation since cAMP and the catalytic subunit of the cAMP-dependent protein kinase have no effect on protein synthesis in reticulocyte lysates or on the phosphorylation of eIF-2α (Grankowski *et al.*, 1979; Levin *et al.*, 1979; Hunt, 1979). In addition, no effect is observed in the lysate upon addition of the heat stable inhibitor protein specific for the cAMP-dependent protein kinase (Hunt, 1979). The cAMP-dependent protein kinase does not phosphorylate purified HCR, and HCR does not phosphorylate either the regulatory subunit of the type I and type II cAMP-dependent protein kinase or the catalytic subunit of the type II enzyme (Lundak and Traugh, 1980).

Although the appearance of the protein kinase, the phosphorylation of eIF-2α and the subsequent inhibition of globin synthesis are related, the exact mechanism by which the inhibition occurs remains elusive. It has been calculated that prior to inhibition of protein synthesis in a hemin-deprived lysate, 5–8 initiation events occur (Hunt *et al.*, 1972) and under these conditions, eIF-2 is used stoichiometrically instead of catalytically (Cherbas and London, 1976).

One of the problems encountered in examining the role of hemin in the regulation of protein synthesis has been to correlate the data obtained in lysates with studies at a molecular level. Conclusions reached with crude preparations of protein kinase and/or initiation factors have not been reproducible with highly purified components. With purified eIF-2, no inhibition of ternary complex formation with GTP and met-tRNA$_f$ is observed after phosphorylation with purified HCR (Farrell *et al.*, 1977; Trachsel and Staehelin, 1978; Merrick, 1979). In addition, there is no inhibition of the subsequent binding of this complex to 40 S ribosomal subunits or of methionyl-puromycin synthesis. When additional protein components are added, or when eIF-2 or HCR lack rigorous purification, inhibition of the binding of the ternary complex to 40 S ribosomal subunits is observed (Kramer *et al.*, 1977). Recent data suggest that at least one perhaps two additional protein components are required for the effects of phosphorylation to be expressed. The partially purified protein components stimulate formation of the ternary complex, thus enhancing formation of the preinitiation complex with 40 S ribosomal subunits (Ranu *et al.*, 1978; Ranu and London, 1979; DeHaro *et al.*, 1978; DeHaro and Ochoa, 1978, 1979; Das *et al.*, 1979). After phosphorylation of eIF-2α, stimulation of ternary complex formation by this factor is not observed. A secord partially purified component dissociates the ternary complex when eIF-2α is dephosphorylated but not when it is phosphorylated (Das *et al.*, 1979). Thus the inhibition appears to occur at the step of ternary complex formation. Dephosphorylation of eIF-2α by a phosphoprotein phosphatase appears to reverse the inhibitory effect of phosphorylation on formation of the 40 S preinitiation complex (Grankowski *et al.*, 1980). Recently inhibition of binding of AUG to the preinitiation complex has also been observed after phosphorylation of eIF-2α (Das *et al.*, 1979). Gross (1979) has observed a 48 S preinitiation complex upon hemin deprivation of the lysate system which contains deacylated met-tRNA$_f$ and increased levels of mRNA. He suggests that inhibition may involve the activation of met-tRNA$_f$ hydrolase activity. Further studies are required to elucidate the role of mRNA in inhibition and to determine the function of the met-tRNA$_f$ hydrolase.

Inhibition of protein synthesis by hemin deprivation is reversed by a protein isolated from the postribosomal supernate which is different from eIF-2 (Gross, 1975, 1976; Ralston *et al.*, 1978; Amesz *et al.*, 1979). The anti-inhibitor protein appears to reverse at the level of the inhibition and not by an interaction with HCR. The protein has been obtained in highly purified form and shown to stimulate ternary complex formation (Amesz *et al.*, 1979). When added to a hemin-deprived lysate, the protein restores 40 S complex formation.

Although phosphorylation of eIF-2 has been implicated in the inhibition of protein synthesis by hemin deprivation, recent evidence suggests that other events may be involved also. Benne *et al.* (1979) and Ralston *et al.* (1979) have shown that the anti-inhibitor protein reverses the inhibition of protein synthesis under conditions of hemin deprivation, while eIF-2α is highly phosphorylated. It is evident that further studies at a molecular level are required to resolve the role of hemin in translational control.

Although it has not been examined exhaustively, synthesis of all proteins in the reticulocyte lysate appear to be inhibited by hemin deprivation. This includes translation of endogenous RNA (Mizuno *et al.*, 1972; Lodish and Desalu, 1973; Beuzard *et al.*, 1973) as well as products of exogenous messages including calf lens crystalline (Mathews, 1972), reovirus (Lodish and Desalu, 1973), ovalbumin (Palmiter, 1973), and catalase (Sakamoto and Higashi, 1979).

The majority of the work with the HCR has been completed in reticulocyte lysates. However, the presence of a component similar to HCR has also been observed in human erythrocytes (Freedman *et al.*, 1974) and other cell types including Ehrlich ascites cells (Clemens *et al.*, 1976), Friend leukemia cells (Pinphanichakarn *et al.*, 1977), and liver (Delaunay *et al.*, 1977). The subsequent phosphorylation of eIF-2α by these enzymes has also been shown. However, the cell-free protein synthesizing sytems from these cells are not stimulated to the same degree as reticulocyte lysates upon addition of hemin, nor is the addition of HCR from reticulocytes equally inhibitory (Mathews, 1972: Beuzard *et al.*, 1973; Cimadevilla *et al.*, 1975; Cimadevilla and Hardesty, 1975a,b; Weber *et al.*, 1975; Dabney and Beaudett, 1978; Sakamoto and Higashi, 1979).

An inhibitor of protein synthesis similar to HCR is produced by incubating lysates with oxidized glutathione (GSSG). Since irreversible HCR can be produced by incubation with NEM, it suggests that the inhibitor produced with GSSG could be identical to HCR. Thus formation of irreversible HCR by prolonged incubation of lysates in the absence of hemin could be due to oxidation of the unprotected enzyme. The relationship between the two inhibitors has not been examined in detail; however, the properties of the GSSG-activated inhibitor in the lysate are similar to those of HCR. Biphasic kinetics are observed upon addition of $1 - 2 \times 10^{-4}$ *M* GSSG and the inhibition of protein synthesis is accompanied by a conversion of polysomes to monosomes (Kosower *et al.*, 1971, 1972) with a subsequent decrease in the amount of met-tRNA$_f$ bound to 40 S ribosomal subunits (Darnbrough *et al.*, 1973; Legon *et al.*, 1974). As with hemin deprivation, GSSG causes an increase in the phosphorylation of eIF-2α in the lysate (Farrell *et al.*, 1978a; Ernst *et al.*, 1978, 1979) and inhibition of protein synthesis is reversed by addition of eIF-2 (Clemens *et al.*, 1975). Early studies showed that addition of NADP and glucose prevented the inhibition of protein synthesis by GSSG suggesting a stimulation of glutathione disulfide reductase activity (Kowoser *et al.*, 1971). More detailed studies have shown that glucose and a number of other sugars completely protect the lysate against GSSG but only partially protect the hemin-deprived lysate (Ernst *et al.*, 1978b). These authors conclude the effectiveness of the sugars in restoring protein synthesis is unrelated to the regeneration of NADPH but may be involved in production of glucose 6-phosphate.

V. INTERFERON AND DOUBLE-STRANDED RNA ACTIVATED INHIBITION OF PROTEIN SYNTHESIS

Inhibition of protein synthesis by dsRNA was observed initially by Hunt and Ehrenfeld (1971) in reticulocyte lysates using preparations from polio virus-infected HeLa cells. Maximal inhibition of protein synthesis by dsRNA is observed between 10^{-6} and 10^{-9} g of dsRNA/ml (Legon *et al.*, 1974); at higher concentrations dsRNA is not inhibitory. Inhibition appears to be nonspecific for the type of dsRNA, although there is a minimum size requirement of 50 base pairs (Hunter *et al.*, 1975).

In the presence of ATP, dsRNA initiates the formation of a translational inhibitor (Farrell *et al.*, 1977) which inhibits formation of met-tRNA$_f$·40 S preinitiation complexes in reticulocyte lysates (Darnbrough *et al.*, 1972, 1973). At high concentrations of dsRNA, no inhibitor is formed, which coincides with the observation that protein synthesis is not inhibited at these concentrations. The proinhibitor is associated with the translational complex (Farrell *et al.*, 1977) and, upon activation by dsRNA and ATP, a protein kinase activity appears concomitant with the phosphorylation of two ribosomal-associated proteins (Farrell *et al.*, 1977; Levin and London, 1978; Lenz and Baglioni, 1978). The phospho-proteins have molecular weights of approximately 67,000 and 38,000; the latter corresponds to eIF-2α. The increase in phosphorylation of eIF-2α in inhibited lysates (Farrell *et al.*, 1978a; Ernst *et al.*, 1979) suggests, as in the case of hemin deprivation, that the phosphorylation of eIF-2 is correlated with the inhibition of protein synthesis. The inhibition of protein synthesis observed in reticulocyte lysates by dsRNA is prevented or reversed by addition of eIF-2 (Kaempfer, 1974; Clemens *et al.*, 1975; Levin and London, 1978).

Paralleling the studies on the dsRNA activated inhibitor in reticulocyte lysates has been an examination of the role of interferon during virus infection. In interferon induced cells and extracts from these cells, protein synthesis is inhibited in the presence of dsRNA; the RNA has little effect in extracts from noninduced cells (Gupta *et al.*, 1974; Kerr *et al.*, 1974, 1976; Celma and Ehrenfeld, 1974; Content *et al.*, 1975). Initiation factor activity in interferon-treated cells is impaired, specifically in the formation of ternary complexes (Ohtsuki *et al.*, 1977; Lewis *et al.*, 1978).

Recent advances in our understanding of the proceses by which the inhibition of protein synthesis occurs include the identification of the interferon-mediated activation of at least two pathways by dsRNA. The first begins with the dsRNA activation of an oligoadenylate 2'-5' synthetase in extracts from interferon-induced cells (Hovanessian *et al.*, 1977; Zilberstein *et al.*, 1978; Revel *et al.*, 1978; Ratner *et al.*, 1978; Ball and White, 1978). The resulting oligonucleotide product, pppA(2'p5'A)$_n$ (Kerr and Brown, 1978), activates an endonuclease (Farrell *et al.*, 1978b; Schmidt *et al.*, 1978; Baglioni *et al.*, 1978; Slattery *et al.*, 1979) which preferentially cleaves mRNA that is not associated with the protein-synthesizing complex (Farrell *et al.*, 1978b; Schmidt *et al.*, 1978). *In vivo*, degradation of mRNA has not been identified, but in SV40-infected monkey cells, specific cleavage of rRNA is observed (Revel *et al.*, 1979). The endonuclease appears to be present in both interferon treated and nontreated cells (Farrell *et al.*, 1978b; Williams *et al.*, 1978) but is activated only by the product of the interferon-induced oligoadenylate synthetase (Hovanessian and Kerr, 1978; Clemens and Williams, 1978; Clemens and Vaquero, 1978). The pppA(2'p5'A)$_n$ activates the endonuclease by binding to the enzyme and the activation is reversed by removal of the oligonucleotide (Slattery *et al.*, 1979). A phosphodiesterase activity which preferentially degrades 2'-5' phosphodiester linkages is activated four- to five-fold in L cells after interferon treatment and is probably responsible for destruction of the oligonucleotide (Schmidt *et al.*, 1979; Kimchi *et al.*, 1979a). The enzyme also attacks the CCA terminus of tRNA.

The second effect of dsRNA in interferon induced cells is the activation of a protein kinase with properties similar to those of the dsRNA activated inhibitor in reticulocyte lysates (Cooper and Farrell, 1977). In extracts from interferon induced mouse L cells (Zilberstein *et al.*, 1976; Roberts *et al.*, 1976), mouse fibroblasts (Samuel *et al.*, 1977; Samuel, 1979a), Ehrlich ascites tumor cells (Lebleu *et al.*, 1976), Hela (Shaila *et al.*, 1977; Lenz and Baglioni, 1978; Baglioni *et al.*, 1979), and human amnion U cells (Samuel, 1979b), increased phosphorylation of two proteins of approximately 67,000 and 38,000 molecular weight are observed in the presence of dsRNA. The proteins are associated with the salt wash fraction and the small protein corresponds to eIF-2α. Enhanced phosphorylation of these two proteins has also been observed in intact interferon treated L cells upon treatment with poly(rI)·poly(rC) (Gupta, 1979).

The protein kinase is activated by incubation with ATP and dsRNA and ATP hydrolysis is required for the activation (Sen *et al.*, 1978; Zilberstein *et al.*, 1978; Revel *et al.*, 1978). As observed with the dsRNA activated inhibitor in reticulocytes lysates, the protein kinase is activated at low concentrations of dsRNA but not at high concentrations (Kimchi *et al.*, 1979b). The protein kinase inhibits 40 S initiation complex formation and protein synthesis when added to reticulocyte lysates (Chernajovsky *et al.*, 1979). This inhibition is reversed by the addition of eIF-2 (Farrell *et al.*, 1978b).

The latent form of the protein kinase has been highly purified from interferon-treated Ehrlich ascites tumor cells (Sen *et al.*, 1978) and from interferon-treated L cells (Kimchi *et al.*, 1979b; Hovanessian and Kerr, 1979). Inhibitory activity and protein kinase activity for the endogenous 67,000 molecular weight protein and histone copurify (Kimchi *et al.*, 1979b). The L cell protein kinase has been shown to phosphorylate histones H3 and H4 (Zilberstein *et al.*, 1978) while the enzyme from Ehrlich ascites tumor cells has been purified with histone H1 from *Drosophilia* (Sen *et al.*, 1978). Preliminary evidence suggests that the highly purified preparations may contain two protein kinase activities, one of which phosphorylates the endogenous 67,000-dalton protein, a phosphorylation event which does not require dsRNA but is stimulated by it, and a second protein kinase activity, activated by dsRNA, which phosphorylates eIF-2 and histone. The latter protein kinase is activated concomitantly with the inhibitory activity (Kimchi *et al.*, 1979b). The protein kinase does not make $pppA(2'p5'A)_n$ and the oligonucleotide does not activate the protein kinase (Farrell *et al.*, 1978b). Recently, Epstein *et al.* (1980) have shown that dephosphorylation of the 67,000 dalton protein is inhibited by dsRNA in interferon-treated cell extracts.

Although both the dsRNA-activated inhibitor and HCR have been identified in reticulocyte lysates and modify the α subunit of eIF-2, they appear to be distinct since the enzymes are chromatographically different. In addition, antibody prepared to HCR does not interfere with the phosphorylation of eIF-2α or the inhibition of protein synthesis by the dsRNA activated inhibitor. Proteolytic digests of eIF-2α phosphorylated by HCR and the dsRNA activated inhibitor contain the same phosphopeptides (Farrell *et al.*, 1977; Samuel, 1979a; Ranu, 1979; Levin *et al.*, 1980); however, the fact that the purified dsRNA activated protein kinase from interferon-treated cells phosphorylates histones, whereas these proteins are not substrates for HCR, suggests that the enzymes do not have identical substrate specificity and thus may modify closely associated but nonidentical residues in eIF-2α.

VI. AMINOACYL-tRNA SYNTHETASES

Since aminoacylation is an initial step in protein synthesis, it is essential that this reaction be responsive to rapid stimulation or inhibition of translation. Thus the aminoacyl synthetases, the enzymes catalyzing the aminoacylation of tRNA, are likely to be highly regulated. Recently, data have been presented by Berg (1977, 1978) suggesting that the activity of many of the tRNA synthetases in uterus and liver may be regulated by phosphorylation and dephosphorylation. An examination of partially purified synthetase preparations shows that 12 of the activities tested from both liver and uterus are inhibited significantly by preincubation with ATP (class I enzymes), while five of the synthetase activities are either unaltered or increased under these conditions (class II enzymes), as shown in Table V. Preincubation with alkaline phosphatase results in increased activity of the class I synthetases and decreased activity of the class II enzymes. The synthetase preparations have been shown to contain both cAMP-dependent and cAMP-independent protein kinases as well as phosphoprotein phosphatase activity. The majority of the endogenous phosphorylation events are independent of cAMP while dephos-

TABLE V

EFFECTORS OF AMINOACYL tRNA SYNTHETASE ACTIVITY[a]

Aminoacyl-tRNA synthetases	Class	Synthetase activity in vivo				Synthetase activity in vitro	
		17 β-Estradiol		Dibutyryl cAMP		Preincubation with ATP	Preincubation with phosphatase
		Uterus	Liver	Uterus	Liver		
Ala, Arg, Glu, Gly, His, Iso, Leu, Lys, Met, Phe, Tyr, Val	I	Increase	Increase	Decrease	Increase	Decrease	Increase
Asn, Asp, Pro, Ser, Thr	II	Decrease	No change or decrease	Increase	Decrease	No change or decrease	Decrease

[a] Taken from Berg (1977, 1978).

phorylation is stimulated by preincubation of the preparations with cAMP and ATP.

The activities of the synthetases in uterus and liver have been examined after administration of 17β-estradiol or dibutyryl cAMP (Berg, 1978). In the uterus, a target organ of 17β-estradiol, both the hormone and dibutyryl cAMP increase the activity of the class I synthetases while the class II enzymes show no change or a decrease in activity (Table V). After hormonal stimulation, alterations in the synthetase activities are observed at 4 minutes and return to control levels by 30 minutes. Synthetases in liver show a similar pattern with dibutyryl cAMP, but an opposing effect with the estrogen hormone.

When the data obtained *in vivo* and *in vitro* are compared, they are consistent with the theory that the 17β-estradiol is acting by increasing the cAMP levels in uterus. The data suggest that when the class I enzymes are phosphorylated by cAMP-independent protein kinases, the activities are inhibited. With increased levels of cAMP, the phosphoprotein phosphatase(s) is activated resulting in a dephosphorylation of the class I enzymes. The class II enzymes may be regulated in the reverse manner. Thus it appears that 17β-estradiol and cAMP enhance the amount of aminoacylated tRNA under conditions where an increase in protein synthesis is observed. This is consistent with studies by Whelly and Barker (1974) showing that during the first hour after estradiol treatment of the uterus, protein synthesis appears to result from an increased rate of peptide elongation.

Definitive experiments are needed to substantiate these studies. There is a need to determine if the individual purified synthetases are directly phosphorylated and the effects of this phosphorylation on activity. In addition, the modification enzymes need to be identified to determine if more than one protein kinase and phosphoprotein phosphatase are involved and the mode of regulation of these enzymes. From the data it appears that regulation of synthetase activity by cAMP is not confined to a single tissue since both uterus and liver show the same effects upon administration of the dibutyryl compound. However, the effects of adenosine and butyric acid have not been examined.

VII. CONCLUSIONS

The ultimate goal, of course, is to establish whether specific phosphorylation events correlate with alterations in protein synthesis and whether the observed changes in protein synthesis are observed with all species of mRNA or whether phosphorylation invokes a specificity of translation. The simplest approach is to examine whether the entire protein synthetic machinery is activated or inhibited by the addition or removal of one or more phosphoryl groups. Although this may be true occasionally, as in the case of hemin deprivation or dsRNA-dependent inhibition, it is obviously not the case in the majority of circumstances. A more subtle role for phosphorylation, and thus more difficult to examine, would be to alter the rate of total protein synthesis; this could be dependent on the number and position of the added phosphoryl groups or upon the rate of turnover of these moieties. A still more complex and most attractive possibility is the control of the synthesis of specific proteins by phosphorylation. None of the accumulated evidence rules out this possibility, although there is also no supporting evidence.

An examination of the initiation scheme and the phosphorylated translational components and their role in the initiation process, as shown in Fig. 2, suggests that several steps in the initiation sequence could be subject to regulation by phosphorylation. The first step is formation of the ternary complex and binding of this complex to 40 S ribosomal subunits to form a preinitiation complex. Eukaryotic initiation factor 2 can be modified in the α subunit by HCR and the dsRNA activated inhibitor and at different sites in the β subunit by casein kinase II and protease activated kinase II. In addition, the potential exists for the transfer of approximately five phosphoryl groups to the 40 S ribosomal subunit protein, S6. Several of these sites are modified by cAMP-dependent protein kinases,

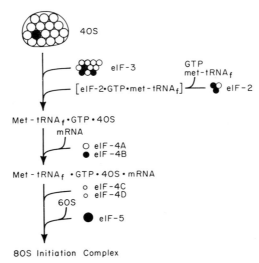

FIG. 2. Phosphorylated translational components in the initiation sequence.

the cGMP-dependent protein kinase, and/or protease activated kinase II. The preinitiation complex is stabilized by eIF-3 and this initiation factor is phosphorylated by the cAMP-dependent protein kinases, casein kinase II, and protease activated kinase I.

Thus, there are multiple phosphorylation events occurring with the translational components which form the preinitiation complex and these phosphorylation reactions are mediated by cAMP, dsRNA, hemin, heparin and proteolytic digestion. Dephosphorylation of these components could be regulated by nucleotides and glucose 6-phosphate. As has been described, regulation of protein synthesis by hemin and dsRNA has been shown to occur via phosphorylation of eIF-2 by altering the interaction of the phosphorylated factor with other translational components.

The second potential step for regulation by phosphorylation is binding of mRNA to the preinitiation complex containing eIF-2, eIF-3, met-tRNA$_f$, GTP, and 40 S ribosomal subunits to form the 40 S initiation complex. Eukaryotic initiation factors 4A and 4B are involved in this process and eIF-4B is multiply phosphorylated by casein kinase I and II and protease activated kinase I. Phosphorylation of eIF-4B or possibly the cap binding protein could be required for mRNA binding to occur since binding of mRNA has been shown to be dependent on ATP (Trachsel *et al.*, 1977).

Kozak (1978) has suggested that the 40 S initiation complex binds at the 5′ end of the mRNA and advances to the first AUG triplet. At this triplet, advance of the 40 S ribosomal subunit is halted, possibly by base pairing with the anticodon of met-tRNA$_f$, and the 60 S ribosomal subunit is added. Phosphorylation of the 40 S ribosomal subunit could produce conformational alterations which allow only mRNA with specific primary, secondary and/or tertiary structure to bind. The easiest interpretation would be that the additional phosphate groups block binding, although phosphorylation at sites other than the mRNA binding sites could also lead to structural alterations.

The third step in the initiation sequence which could be regulated by phosphorylation is the eIF-5 mediated association of 60 S subunits with the 40 S initiation complex. Phosphorylation of eIF-5 by multiple protein kinases has been observed *in vitro*. Phosphorylation of 60 S ribosomal proteins has also been identified. Thus the overall initiation process consists of interactions of components, many of which have the capacity to be multiply phosphorylated by a variety of different protein kinases.

Since phosphorylation is an ephemeral process, control by phosphorylation will always be the result of a dynamic equilibrium between phosphorylation and dephosphorylation. In reticulocytes, casein kinase I and II are in an active state which suggests their substrates could be fully phosphorylated. Other protein kinases are in a relatively inactive state in reticulocytes including the cAMP-dependent protein kinases, HCR, the dsRNA activated inhibitor, and the protease activated kinases. Thus activation of these enzymes would alter the equilibrium between the protein kinase and the phosphoprotein phosphatases, resulting in a temporal increase in phosphoproteins.

Considerable effort has gone into examining the hormonal control of adenylate cyclase, activation of the cAMP-dependent protein kinases and the ultimate control of various metabolic processes. However, the role of the cAMP-dependent phosphorylation of S6 and eIF-3 in protein synthesis has not been identified. On the other hand, little is known about regulation of the cyclic nucleotide-independent phosphorylation events. Altogether, six different cyclic nucleotide-independent protein kinases have been identified in reticulocytes. Since enzymes similar to these protein kinases have been identified in other cell types, they are not unique to the red cell system. The mode of regulation of the majority of the protein kinases *in vivo* is not known, although interferon is required for optimal production of the dsRNA activated inhibitor in most tissues. Hormonal control of at least some of the protein kinases and phosphoprotein phosphatases and thus of phosphorylation remains highly likely.

ACKNOWLEDGMENTS

I wish to thank Drs. Gary M. Hathaway, Stanley M. Tahara, and Robert W. Del Grande for critically reading the manuscript, Ms. Peggy Simons for expert typing and the many colleagues who graciously communicated results to me before publication. Research from my laboratory, cited in this chapter, was supported by grant GM 21424 from the U.S. Public Health Service and a grant from the American Cancer Society. A stay at the Rockefeller Foundation Study and Conference Center, Bellagio, Italy, during which the majority of this chapter was written, is gratefully acknowledged.

REFERENCES

Adamson, S. D., Herbert, E., and Kemp, S. F. (1969). *J. Mol. Biol.* **42**, 247–258.

Amesz, H., Goumans, H., Haubrich-Moree, T., Voorma, H. O., and Benne, R. (1979). *Eur. J. Biochem.* **98**, 513–520.

Anderson, W. F., Bosch, L., Cohn, W. E., Lodish, H., Merrick, W. C., Weissbach, H., Wittmann, H. G., and Wool, I. G. (1977). *FEBS Lett.* **76**, 1–10.

Anderson, W. M., Grundholm, A., and Sells, B. H. (1975). *Biochem. Biophys. Res. Commun.* **62**, 669–676.

Arpin, M., Madjar, J. J., and Reboud, J. P. (1978). *Biochim. Biophys. Acta* **519**, 537–541.

Baglioni, C., Minks, M. A., and Maroney, P. A. (1978). *Nature (London)* **273**, 684–687.

Baglioni, C., Maroney, P. A., and West, D. K. (1979). *Biochemistry* 18, 1765–1770.

Balkow, K., Mizumo, S., and Rabinovitz, M. (1973a). *Biochem. Biophys. Res. Commun.* 54, 315–323.

Balkow, K., Mizuno, S., Fisher, J. M., and Rabinovitz, M. (1973b). *Biochim. Biophys. Acta* 324, 397–409.

Ball, L. A., and White, C. N. (1978). *Proc. Natl. Acad. Sci. U.S.A.* 75, 1167–1171.

Barden, N., and Labrie, F. (1973). *Biochemistry* 12, 3096–3102.

Ben-Hamida, F., and Beaud, G. (1978). *Proc. Natl. Acad. Sci. U.S.A.* 75, 175–179.

Benne, R., and Hershey, J. W. B. (1976). *Proc. Natl. Acad. Sci. U.S.A.* 73, 3005–3009.

Benne, R., and Hershey, J. W. B. (1978). *J. Biol. Chem.* 253, 3078–3087.

Benne, R., Wong, C., Luedi, M., and Hershey, J. W. B. (1976). *J. Biol. Chem.* 251, 7675–7681.

Benne, R., Luedi, M., and Hershey, J. W. B. (1977). *J. Biol. Chem.* 252, 5798–5803.

Benne, R., Edman, J., Traut, R. R., and Hershey, J. W. B. (1978). *Proc. Natl. Acad. Sci. U.S.A.* 75, 108–112.

Benne, R., Salimans, M., Goumans, H., Amasz, H., and Voorma, H. (1980). *Eur. J. Biochem.* 104, 501–109.

Berg, B. H. (1977). *Biochim. Biophys. Acta* 479, 152–171.

Berg, B. H. (1978). *Biochim. Biophys. Acta* 521, 274–287.

Beuzard, Y., Rodvien, R., and London, I. M. (1973). *Proc. Natl. Acad. Sci. U.S.A.* 70, 1022–1026.

Biekla, H., and Stahl, J. (1978). *Int. Rev. Biochem.* 18, 79–168.

Bitte, L., and Kabat, D. (1972). *J. Biol. Chem.* 247, 5345–5350.

Blair, G. E., and Horak, I. (1977). *Biochem. Soc. Trans.* 5, 660–661.

Blat, C., and Loeb, J. E. (1971). *FEBS Lett.* 18, 124–126.

Brandt, H., Lee, E. Y. C., and Killilea, S. D. (1975a). *Biochem. Biophys. Res. Commun.* 63, 950–956.

Brandt, H., Capulong, Z. L., and Lee, E. Y. C. (1975b). *J. Biol. Chem.* 250, 8038–8044.

Bruns, G. P., and London, I. M. (1965). *Biochem. Biophys. Res. Commun.* 18, 236–242.

Cawthon, M. L., Bitte, L. F., Krystosek, A., and Kabat, D. (1974). *J. Biol. Chem.* 249, 275–278.

Celma, M. L., and Ehrenfeld, E. (1974). *Proc. Natl. Acad. Sci. U.S.A.* 71, 2440–2444.

Cherbas, L., and London, I. M. (1976). *Proc. Natl. Acad. Sci. U.S.A.* 73, 3506–3510.

Chernajovsky, Y., Kimchi, A., Schmidt, A., Zilberstein, A., and Revel, M. (1979). *Eur. J. Biochem.* 96, 35–41.

Cimadevilla, J. M., and Hardesty, B. (1975a). *J. Biol. Chem.* 250, 4389–4397.

Cimadevilla, J. M., and Hardesty, B. (1975b). *Biochem. Biophys. Res. Commun.* 63, 931–937.

Cimadevilla, J. M., Kramer, G., Pinphanichakarn, P., Konecki, D., and Hardesty, B. (1975). *Arch. Biophys. Biochem.* 171, 145–153.

Clemens, M. J., and Vaquero, C. M. (1978). *Biochem. Biophys. Res. Commun.* 83, 59–68.

Clemens, M. J., and Williams, B. R. G. (1978). *Cell* 13, 565–572.

Clemens, M. J., Safer, B., Merrick, W. C., Anderson, W. F., and London, I. M. (1975). *Proc. Natl. Acad. Sci. U.S.A.* 72, 1286–1290.

Clemens, M. J., Pain, V. M., Henshaw, E. C., and London, I. M. (1976). *Biochem. Biophys. Res. Commun.* 72, 768–775.

Content, J., Lebleu, B., Nudel, U., Zilberstein, A., Berissi, H., and Revel, M. (1975). *Eur. J. Biochem.* 54, 1–10.

Cooper, J. A., and Farrell, P. J. (1977). *Biochem. Biophys. Res. Commun.* 77, 124–131.

Dabney, G. J., and Beaudett, A. L. (1978). *J. Biol. Chem.* 253, 7124–7126.

Dahmus, M. E., and Natzle, J. (1977). *Biochemistry* **16**, 1901–1908.

Darnbrough, C., Hunt, T., and Jackson, R. J. (1972). *Biochem. Biophys. Res. Commun.* **48**, 1556–1564.

Darnbrough, C., Legon, S., Hunt, T., and Jackson, R. J. (1973). *J. Mol. Biol.* **76**, 379–403.

Das, A., Ralston, R. O., Grace, M., Roy, R., Ghosh-Dastidar, P., Das, H. K., Yaghmai, B., Palmieri, S., and Gupta, N. K. (1979). *Proc. Natl. Acad. Sci. U.S.A.* **76**, 5076–5079.

Dasgupta, A., Das, A., Roy, R., Ralson, R., Majumdar, A., and Gupta, N. K. (1978a). *J. Biol. Chem.* **253**, 6054–6059.

Dasgupta, A., Roy, R., Palmieri, S., Das, A., Ralston, R., and Gupta, N. K. (1978b). *Biochem. Biophys. Res. Commun.* **82**, 1019–1027.

Datta, A., DeHaro, C., Sierra, J. M., and Ochoa, S. (1977). *Proc. Natl. Acad. Sci. U.S.A.* **74**, 3326–3329.

Datta, A., DeHaro, C., and Ochoa, S. (1978). *Proc. Natl. Acad. Sci. U.S.A.* **75**, 1148–1152.

Deana, A. D., Meggio, F., and Pinna, L. A. (1979). *Biochem. J.* **179**, 693–696.

DeHaro, C., and Ochoa, S. (1978). *Proc. Natl. Acad. Sci. U.S.A.* **75**, 2713–2716.

DeHaro, C., and Ochoa, S. (1979). *Proc. Natl. Acad. Sci. U.S.A.* **76**, 1741–1745.

DeHaro, C., Datta, A., and Ochoa, S. (1978). *Proc. Natl. Acad. Sci. U.S.A.* **75**, 243–247.

Delaunay, J., Ranu, R. S., Levin, D. H., Ernst, V., and London, I. M. (1977). *Proc. Natl. Acad. Sci. U.S.A.* **74**, 2264–2268.

Del Grande, R. W., and Traugh, J. A. (1979). *J. Supramol Struct. Suppl.* **3**, 28.

Dettman, G. L., and Stanley, W. M. (1972). *Biochim. Biophys. Acta* **287**, 124–133.

DuVernay, V. H., and Traugh, J. A. (1978). *Biochemistry* **17**, 2045–2049.

Eil, C., and Wool, I. G. (1973a). *J. Biol. Chem.* **248**, 5122–5129.

Eil, C., and Wool., I. G. (1973b). *J. Biol. Chem.* **248**, 5130–5136.

Ernst, V., Levin, D. H., Ranu, R. S., and London, I. M. (1976). *Proc. Natl. Acad. Sci. U.S.A.* **73**, 1112–1116.

Ernst, V., Levin, D. H., and London, I. M. (1978a). *Proc. Natl. Acad. Sci. U.S.A.* **75**, 4110–4114.

Ernst, V., Levin, D. H., and London, I. M. (1978b). *J. Biol. Chem.* **253**, 7163–7172.

Ernst, V., Levin, D. H., and London, I. M. (1979). *Proc. Natl. Acad. Sci. U.S.A.* **76**, 2118–2122.

Epstein, D. A., Torrence, P. F., and Friedman, R. M. (1980). *Proc. Natl. Acad. Sci. U.S.A.* **77**, 107–111.

Farrell, P. J., Balkow, K., Hunt, T., Jackson, R. J., and Trachsel, H. (1977). *Cell* **11**, 187–200.

Farrell, P. J., Hunt, T., and Jackson, R. J. (1978a). *Eur. J. Biochem.* **89**, 517–521.

Farrell, P. J., Sen, G. C., Dubois, M. J., Ratner, L., Slattery, E., and Lengyel, P. (1978b). *Proc. Natl. Acad. Sci. U.S.A.* **75**, 5893–5897.

Floyd, G. A., and Traugh, J. A. (1980). *Eur. J. Biochem.* **106**, 269–277.

Floyd, G. A., Merrick, W. C., and Traugh, J. A. (1979). *Eur. J. Biochem.* **96**, 277–286.

Floyd-Smith, G. A. (1979). Ph. D. Thesis, University of California, Riverside.

Freedman, M. L., Geraghty, M., and Rosman, J. (1974). *J. Biol. Chem.* **249**, 7290–7294.

Freienstein, C., and Blobel, G. (1975). *Proc. Natl. Acad. Sci. U.S.A.* **72**, 3392–3396.

Glass, D. R., and Krebs, E. G. (1979). *J. Biol. Chem.* **254**, 9728–9738.

Godchaux, W., III, Adamson, S. D., and Herbert, E. (1967). *J. Mol. Biol.* **27**, 57–72.

Grankowski, N., Kramer, G., and Hardesty, B. (1979). *J. Biol. Chem.* **254**, 3145–3147.

Grankowski, N., Lehmusvirta, D., Kramer, G., and Hardesty, B. (1980). *J. Biol. Chem.* **255**, 310–317.

Grayzel, A. I., Hörchner, P., and London, I. M. (1966). *Proc. Natl. Acad. Sci. U.S.A.* **55**, 650–655.

Gressner, A. M., and Greiling, H. (1977). *FEBS Lett.* **74**, 77–81.

Gressner, A. M., and Greiling, H. (1978a). *Biochem. Pharmacol.* **27**, 2495–2498.

Gressner, A. M., and Greiling, H. (1978b). *Exp. Mol. Pathol.* **28**, 39–47.

Gressner, A. M., and Wool, I. G. (1974a). *J. Biol. Chem.* **249**, 6917–6925.

Gressner, A. M., and Wool, I. G. (1974b). *Biochem. Biophys. Res. Commun.* **60**, 1482–1490.

Gressner, A. M., and Wool, I. G. (1976a). *J. Biol. Chem.* **251**, 1500–1504.

Gressner, A. M., and Wool, I. G. (1976b). *Nature (London)* **259**, 148–150.

Gross, M. (1975). *Biochem. Biophys. Res. Commun.* **67**, 1507–1515.

Gross, M. (1976). *Biochim. Biophys. Acta* **447**, 445–459.

Gross, M. (1977). *Arch. Biochem. Biophys.* **180**, 121–129.

Gross, M. (1979). *J. Biol. Chem.* **254**, 2370–2377.

Gross, M., and Mendelewski, J. (1977). *Biochem. Biophys. Res. Commun.* **74**, 559–569.

Gross, M., and Rabinovitz, M. (1972). *Biochim. Biophys. Acta* **287**, 340–352.

Gross, M., and Rabinovitz, M. (1973a). *Biochim. Biophys. Acta* **299**, 472–479.

Gross, M., and Rabinovitz, M. (1973b). *Biochem. Biophys. Res. Commun.* **50**, 832–838.

Grummt, F. (1974). *Eur. J. Biochem.* **43**, 337–342.

Gupta, N. K., Woodley, C. L., Chen. Y. C., and Bose, K. K. (1973). *J. Biol. Chem.* **248**, 4500–4511.

Gupta, S. L. (1979). *J. Virol.* **29**, 301–311.

Gupta, S. L., Graziadei, W. D., III, Weideli, H., Sopori, M. L., and Lengyel, P. (1974). *Virology* **57**, 49–63.

Haselbacher, G. K., Humbel, R. E., and Thomas, G. (1979). *FEBS Lett.* **100**, 185–190.

Hashimoto, E., Takeda, M., Nishizuka, Y., Hamana, K., and Iwai, K. (1976). *J. Biol. Chem.* **251**, 6287–6293.

Hathaway, G. M., and Traugh, J. A. (1979). *J. Biol. Chem.* **254**, 762–768.

Hathaway, G. M., Lubben, T. H., and Traugh, J. A. (1980) *J. Biol. Chem.* **255**, 8038–8041.

Hathaway, G. M., Lundak, T. S., Tahara, S. M., and Traugh, J. A. (1979). *In* "Methods in Enzymology" (K. Moldave and L. Grossman, eds.), Vol. 60, pp. 495–511. Academic Press, New York.

Henderson, A. B., Miller, A. H., and Hardesty, B. (1979). *Proc. Natl. Acad. Sci. U.S.A.* **76**, 2605–2609.

Herrera, F., Sadnik, I., Gough, G., and Moldave, K. (1977). *Biochemistry* **16**, 4664–4672.

Horak, I., and Koschel, K. (1977). *FEBS Lett.* **83**, 68–70.

Horak, I., and Schiffmann, D. (1977). *Eur. J. Biochem.* **79**, 375–380.

Houston, L. L. (1978). *Biochem. Biophys. Res. Commun.* **85**, 131–139.

Hovanessian, A. G., and Kerr, I. M. (1978). *Eur. J. Biochem.* **84**, 149–159.

Hovanessian, A. G., and Kerr, I. M. (1979). *Eur. J. Biochem.* **93**, 515–526.

Hovanessian, A. G., Brown, R. E., and Kerr, I. M. (1977). *Nature (London)* **268**, 537–540.

Howard, G. A., Adamson, S. D., and Herbert, E. (1970). *Biochim. Biophys. Acta* **213**, 237–240.

Hunt, T. (1979). *Miami Winter Symp.* **16**, pp. 321–346.

Hunt, T., and Ehrenfeld, E. (1971). *Nature (London) New Biol.* **230**, 91–94.

Hunt, T., Vanderhoff, G., and London, I. M. (1972). *J. Mol. Biol.* **66**, 471–481.

Hunter, T., Hunt, T., Jackson, R. J., and Robertson, H. D. (1975). *J. Biol. Chem.* **250**, 409–417.

Ilan, J., and Ilan, J. (1973). *Nature (London) New Biol.* **241**, 176–180.

Inoue, M., Kishimoto, A., Takai, Y., and Nishizuka, Y. (1977). *J. Biol. Chem.* **252**, 7610–7616.

Issinger, O.-G. (1977). *Biochim. Biophys. Acta* **477**, 185–189.

Issinger, O.-G., and Reichert, G. (1979). *Biochem. Biophys. Res. Commun.* 88, 1275–1273.

Issinger, O.-G. Benne, R., Hershey, J. W. B., and Traut, R. R. (1976). *J. Biol. Chem.* 251, 6471–6474.

Issinger, O.-G., Beier, H., Speichermann, N., Flokerzi, V., and Hofmann, F. (1980). *Biochem. J.* 185, 89–99.

Kabat, D. (1970). *Biochemistry* 9, 4160–4175.

Kaempfer, R. (1974). *Biochem. Biophys. Res. Commun.* 61, 591–604.

Kaerlein, M., and Horak, I. (1976). *Nature (London)* 259, 150–151.

Kaerlein, M., and Horak, I. (1978). *Eur. J. Biochem.* 90, 463–469.

Kaltschmidt, E., and Wittmann, H. G. (1970). *Anal. Biochem.* 36, 401–412.

Kemper, W. M., Berry, K. W., and Merrick, W. C. (1976). *J. Biol. Chem.* 251, 5551–5557.

Kerr, I. M., and Brown, R. E. (1978). *Proc. Natl. Acad. Sci. U.S.A.* 75, 256–260.

Kerr, I. M., Brown, R. E., and Ball, L. A. (1974). *Nature (London)* 250, 57–59.

Kerr, I. M., Brown, R. E., Clemens, M. J., and Gilbert, C. S. (1976). *Eur. J. Biochem.* 69, 551–561.

Killilea, S. D., Mellgren, R. L., Aylward, J. H., Metieh, M. E., and Lee, E. Y. C. (1979). *Arch. Biochem. Biophys.* 193, 130–139.

Kimchi, A., Shulman, L., Schmidt, A., Chernajovsky, Y., Fradin, A., and Revel, M. (1979a). *Proc. Natl. Acad. Sci. U.S.A.* 76, 3208–3212.

Kimchi, A., Zilberstein, A., Schmidt, A., Shulman, L., and Revel, M. (1979b). *J. Biol. Chem.* 254, 9846–9853.

Kleiman, J. H., and Moss, B. (1975). *J. Biol. Chem.* 250, 2420–2429.

Kobayashi, M., and Kato, K. (1977). *J. Biochem. (Tokyo)* 81, 93–97.

Kobayashi, M., Kato, K., and Sato, S. (1975). *Biochim. Biophys. Acta* 377, 343–355.

Kosower, N. S., Vanderhoff, G. A., Benerofe, B., Hunt, T., and Kosower, E. M. (1971). *Biochem. Biophys. Res. Commun.* 45, 816–821.

Kosower, N. S., Vanderhoff, G. A., and Kosower, E. M. (1972). *Biochim. Biophys. Acta* 272, 623–637.

Kozak, M. (1978). *Cell* 15, 1109–1123.

Kramer, G., Cimadevilla, J. M., and Hardesty, B. (1976). *Proc. Natl. Acad. Sci. U.S.A.* 73, 3078–3082.

Kramer, G., Henderson, A. B., Pinphanichakarn, P., Wallis, M. H., and Hardesty, B. (1977). *Proc. Natl. Acad. Sci. U.S.A.* 74, 1445–1449.

Krebs, E. G., and Beavo, J. A. (1979). *Annu. Rev. Biochem.* 48, 923–959.

Kruh, J., and Borsook, H. (1956). *J. Biol. Chem.* 220, 905–915.

Kruppa, J., and Martini, O. S. W. (1978). *Biochem. Biophys. Res. Commun.* 85, 428–435

Labrie, F., Bereaud, G., Gauthier, M., and Lemay, A. (1971). *J. Biol. Chem.* 246, 1902–1908.

Lastick, S. M., and McConkey, E. H. (1978). *In* "Cell Reproduction" (E. R. Dirksen, D. M. Prescott, and C. F. Fox, eds.), Vol. 12, pp. 61–69. Academic Press, New York.

Lastick, S. M., Nielsen, P. J., and McConkey, E. H. (1977). *Mol. Gen. Genet.* 152, 223–230.

Leader, D. P. (1980). *In* "Molecular Aspects of Cellular Regulation," Vol. 1 (in press).

Leader, D. P., and Coia, A. A. (1978a). *FEBS Lett.* 90, 270–274.

Leader, D. P., and Coia, A. A. (1978b). *Biochim. Biophys. Acta* 519, 213–223.

Leader, D. P., and Coia, A. A. (1978c). *Biochim. Biophys. Acta* 519, 224–232.

Leader, D. P., and Coia, A. A. (1978d). *Biochem. J.* 176, 569–572.

Leader, D. P., and Wool, I. G. (1972). *Biochim. Biophys. Acta* 262, 360–370.

Leader, D. P., Rankine, A. D., and Coia, A. A. (1976). *Biochem. Biophys. Res. Commun.* 71, 966–974.

Leader, D. P., Coia, A. A., and Fahmy, L. H. (1978). *Biochem. Biophys. Res. Commun.* **83**, 50–58.

Lebleu, B., Sen, G. C., Shaila, S., Cabrer, B., and Lengyel, P. (1976). *Proc. Natl. Acad. Sci. U.S.A.* **73**, 3107–3111.

Lee, E. Y. C., Brandt, H., Capolong, Z. L., and Killilea, S. D. (1976). *Adv. Enzymol. Regul.* **14**, 467–490.

Lee, E. Y. C., Millgren, R. C., Killelea, S. D., and Aylward, J. H. (1978). *Proc. FEBS Meet.* Vol. 42, pp. 327–346.

Legon, S., Jackson, R. J., and Hunt, T. (1973). *Nature (London) New Biol.* **241**, 150–152.

Legon, S., Brayley, A., Hunt, T., and Jackson, R. J. (1974). *Biochem. Biophys. Res. Comm.* **56**, 745–752.

Lenz, J. R., and Baglioni, C. (1978). *J. Biol. Chem.* **253**, 4219–4223.

Levin, D. H., and London, I. M. (1978). *Proc. Natl. Acad. Sci. U.S.A.* **75**, 1121–1125.

Levin, D. H., Kyner, D., and Acs, G. (1973). *J. Biol. Chem.* **248**, 6416–6425.

Levin, D. H., Ranu, R. S., Ernst, V., Fifer, M. A., and London, I. M. (1975). *Proc. Natl. Acad. Sci. U.S.A.* **72**, 4849–4853.

Levin, D. H., Ranu, R. S., Ernst, V., and London, I. M. (1976). *Proc. Natl. Acad. Sci. U.S.A.* **73**, 3112–3116.

Levin, D. H., Ernst, V., and London, I. M. (1979). *J. Biol. Chem.* **254**, 7935–7941.

Levin, D., Petryshyn, R., and London, I. M. (1980). *Proc. Natl. Acad. Sci. U.S.A.* **77**, 832–836.

Lewis, J. A., Falcoff, E., and Falcoff, R. (1978). *Eur. J. Biochem.* **86**, 497–509.

Li, H.-C. (1975). *FEBS Lett.* **55**, 134–137.

Lightfoot, H. N., Mumby, M., and Traugh, J. A. (1975). *Biochem. Biophys. Res. Commun.* **66**, 1141–1146.

Lodish, H. F., and Desalu, O. (1973). *J. Biol. Chem.* **248**, 3520–3527.

Loeb, J. E., and Blat, C. (1970). *FEBS Lett.* **10**, 105–108.

Lundak, T. S., and Traugh, J. A. (1980). *In* "Protein Phosphorylation and Bio-Regulation" (G. Thomas, E. Podesta, and J. Gordon, eds.). S. Krager, Basel (in press).

McConkey, E. H., Bielka, H., Gordon, J., Lastick, S. M., Lin, A., Ogata, K., Reboud, J.-P., Traugh, J. A., Traut, R. R., Warner, J. R., Welfle, H., and Wool, I. G. (1979). *Mol. Gen. Genet.* **169**, 1–6.

Marvaldi, J., and Lucas-Lenard, J. (1977). *Biochemistry* **16**, 4320–4327.

Mathews, M. B. (1972). *Biochim. Biophys. Acta* **272**, 108–118.

Maxwell, C. R., and Rabinovitz, M. (1969). *Biochem. Biophys. Res. Commun.* **35**, 79–85.

Maxwell, C. R., Kemper, C. S., and Rabinovitz, M. (1971). *J. Mol. Biol.* **58**, 317–327.

Merrick, W. C. (1979). *ICN-UCLA Symp. Mol. Cell. Bio.* **13**, 391–405.

Merrick, W. C., and Anderson, W. F. (1975). *J. Biol. Chem.* **250**, 1197–1206.

Merrick, W. C., Kemper, W. M., and Anderson, W. F. (1975). *J. Biol. Chem.* **250**, 5556–5562.

Mizuno, S., Fisher, J. M., and Rabinovitz, M. (1972). *Biochim. Biophys. Acta* **272**, 638–650.

Mumby, M., and Traugh, J. A. (1979a). *Biochemistry* **18**, 4548–4556.

Mumby, M., and Traugh, J. A. (1979b). *In* "Methods in Enzymology," Vol. 60, pp. 522–534. Academic Press, New York.

Mumby, M., and Traugh, J. A. (1980). *Biochim. Biophys. Acta* **611**, 342–350.

Ohtsuki, K., Dianzani, F., and Baron, S. (1977). *Nature (London)* **269**, 536–538.

Palmiter, R. D. (1973). *J. Biol. Chem.* **248**, 2095–2106.

Paoletti, E., and Moss, B. (1972). *J. Virol.* **10**, 417–424.

Petryshyn, R., Trachsel, H., and London, I. M. (1979). *Proc. Natl. Acad. Sci. U.S.A.* **76,** 1575–1579.

Pinna, L. A., Donella-Deana, A., and Meggio, F. (1979). *Biochem. Biophys. Res. Commun.* **87,** 114–120.

Pinphanichakarn, P., Kramer, G., and Hardesty, B. (1977). *J. Biol. Chem.* **252,** 2106–2112.

Prichard, P. M., and Anderson, W. F. (1974). *In* "Methods in Enzymology" (L. Grossman and K. Moldave, eds.). Vol. 30, pp. 136–141.

Ralston, R. O., Das, A., Dasgupta, A., Roy, R., Palmieri, S., and Gupta, N.K. (1978). *Proc. Natl. Acad. Sci. U.S.A.* **75,** 4858–4862.

Ralston, R. O., Das, A., Grace, M., Das, H., and Gupta, N. K. (1979). *Proc. Natl. Acad. Sci. U.S.A.* **76,** 5490–5494.

Rankine, A. D., Leader, D. P., and Coia, A. A. (1977). *Biochim. Biophys. Acta* **474,** 293–307.

Ranu, R. S. (1979). *Biochem. Biophys. Res. Commun.* **91,** 1437–1444.

Ranu, R. S., and London, I. M. (1976). *Proc. Natl. Acad. Sci. U.S.A.* **73,** 4349–4353.

Ranu, R. S., and London, I. M. (1979). *Proc. Natl. Acad. Sci. U.S.A.* **76,** 1079–1983.

Ranu, R. S., and Wool, I. G. (1976). *J. Biol. Chem.* **251,** 1926–1935.

Ranu, R. S., London, I. M., Das, A., Dasgupta, A., Majumbar, A., Ralston, R., Roy, R., and Gupta, N. K. (1978). *Proc. Natl. Acad. Sci. U.S.A.* **75,** 745–749.

Ratner, L., Wiegand, R. C., Farrell, P. J., Sen, G. C., Cabrer, B., and Lengyel, P. (1978). *Biochem. Biophys. Res. Commun.* **81,** 947–954.

Revel, M., Schmidt, A., Shulman, L., Zilberstein, A., and Kronchi, A. (1978). *FEBS, Fed. Eur. Biochem. Soc., 12th Meet.* Vol. 51, pp. 415–426.

Revel, M., Kimchi, A., Schmidt, A., Shulman, L., Chernajovsky, Y., Rapoport S., and Lapidot, Y. (1979). *In* "Regulation of Macromolecular Synthesis by Low Molecular Weight Mediators" (G. Koch and D. Richter, eds.). Academic Press, New York. (in press).

Roberts, S., and Ashby, C. D. (1978). *J. Biol. Chem.* **253,** 288–296.

Roberts, W. K., Hovanessian, A., Brown, R. E., Clemens, M. J., and Kerr, I. M. (1976). *Nature (London)* **264,** 477–480.

Roper, M. D., and Wicks, W. D. (1978). *Proc. Natl. Acad. Sci. U.S.A.* **75,** 140–144.

Rosnitschek, I., Traub, U., and Traub, P. (1978). *Hoppe-Seyler's Z. Physiol. Chem.* **359,** 593–600.

Rubin, C. S., and Rosen, O. M. (1975). *Annu. Rev. Biochem.* **44,** 831–887.

Russell, W. C., and Blair, G. E. (1977). *J. Gen. Virol.* **34,** 19–35.

Safer, B., and Jagus, R. (1979). *Proc. Natl. Acad. Sci. U.S.A.* **76,** 1094–1098.

Safer, B., Anderson, W. F., and Merrick, W. C. (1975). *J. Biol. Chem.* **250,** 9067–9075.

Safer, B., Adams, S. L., Kemper, W. M., Berry, K. W., Lloyd, M., and Merrick, W. C. (1976). *Proc. Natl. Acad. Sci. U.S.A.* **73,** 2584–2588.

Sagot, J., and Beaud, G. (1979). *Eur. J. Biochem.* **98,** 131–140.

Sakamoto, T., and Higashi, T. (1979). *J. Biochem. (Tokyo)* **85,** 389–396.

Samuel, C. E. (1979a). *Virology* **93,** 281–285.

Samuel, C. E. (1979b). *Proc. Natl. Acad. Sci. U.S.A.* **76,** 600–604.

Samuel, C. E., Farris, D. A., and Eppstein, D. A. (1977). *Virology* **83,** 56–71.

Schiffmann, D., and Horak, I. (1978). *Eur. J. Biochem.* **82,** 91–95.

Schmidt, A., Zilberstein, A., Shulman, L., Federman, P., Berissi, H., and Revel, M. (1978). *FEBS Lett.* **95,** 257–264.

Schmidt, A., Chernajovsky, Y., Shulman, L., Federman, P., Berissi, H., and Revel, M. (1979). *Proc. Natl. Acad. Sci. U.S.A.* **76,** 4788–4792.

Schreier, M. H., and Staehelin, T. (1973a). *Nature (London) New Biol.* **242,** 35–38.

Schreier, M. H., and Staehelin, T. (1973b). *J. Mol. Biol.* **73,** 329–349.

Schreier, M. H., and Staehelin, T. (1975). In "24th Mosbach Colloquium" (E. K. F. Bautz, P. Karlson, and H. Kersten, eds.), pp. 335–348. Springer-Verlag, Berlin and New York.

Schubart, U. K., Shapiro, S., Fleischer, N., and Rosen, O. M. (1977). *J. Biol. Chem.* **252,** 92–101.

Sen, G. C., Taira, H., and Lengyel, P. (1978). *J. Biol. Chem.* **253,** 5915–5921.

Shaila, S., Lebleu, B., Brown, G. E., Sen, G. C., and Lengyel, P. (1977). *J. Gen. Virol.* **37,** 535–546.

Slattery, E., Ghosh, N., Samanta, H., and Lengyel, P. (1979). *Proc. Natl. Acad. Sci. U.S.A* **76,** 4778–4782.

Smith, C. J., Wejksnoza, P. J., Warner, J. R., Rubin, C. S., and Rosen, O. M. (1979). *Proc. Natl. Acad. Sci. U.S.A.* **76,** 2725–2729.

Smith, K. E., and Henshaw, E. C. (1975). *Biochemistry* **14,** 1060–1067.

Sonenberg, N., Morgan, M. A., Merrick, W. C., and Shatkin, A. J. (1978). *Proc. Natl. Acad. Sci. U.S.A.* **75,** 4843–4847.

Staehelin, T., Trachsel, H., Erni, B., Boschetti, A., and Schreier, M. H. (1975). *Proc. 10th FEBS Meet.* pp. 309–323.

Tahara, S. M. (1979). Ph.D. Thesis, University of California, Riverside.

Tahara, S. M., and Traugh, J. A. (1979). *J. Supramol. Struct. Suppl.* **3,** 29.

Tahara, S. M., Traugh, J. A., Sharp, S. B., Lundak, T. S., Safer, B., and Merick, W. C. (1978). *Proc. Natl. Acad. Sci. U.S.A.* **75,** 789–793.

Takai, Y., Kishimoto, A., Inoue, M., and Nishizuka, Y. (1977a). *J. Biol. Chem.* **252,** 7603–7609.

Takai, Y., Yamamoto, M., Inoue, M., Kishimoto, A., and Nishizuka, Y. (1977b). *Biochem. Biophys. Res. Commun.* **77,** 542–550.

Takai, Y., Kishimoto, A., Iwasa, Y., Kawahara, Y., Mori, T., and Nishizuka, Y. (1979). *J. Biol. Chem.* **254,** 3692–3695.

Tao, M., Salas, M. L., and Lipmann, F. (1970). *Proc. Natl. Acad. Sci. U.S.A.* **67,** 408–414.

Terao, K., and Ogata, K. (1979a). *J. Biochem. (Tokyo)* **86,** 579–603.

Terao, K., and Ogata, K. (1979b). *J. Biochem. (Tokyo)* **86,** 605–617.

Thomas, G., Siegmann, M., and Gordon, J. (1979). *Proc. Natl. Acad. Sci. U.S.A.* **76,** 3952–3956.

Thompson, H. A., Sadnik, I., Scheinbuks, J., and Moldave, K. (1977). *Biochemistry* **16,** 2221–2230.

Thornburg, W., and Lindell, T. J. (1977). *J. Biol. Chem.* **252,** 6660–6665.

Thornburg, W., O'Malley, A. F., and Lindell, T. J. (1978). *J. Biol. Chem.* **253,** 4638–4641.

Trachsel, H., and Staehelin, T. (1978). *Proc. Natl. Acad. Sci. U.S.A.* **75,** 204–208.

Trachsel, H., and Staehelin, T. (1979). *Biochem. Biophys. Acta* **565,** 305–314.

Trachsel, H., Erni, B., Schreier, M. H., and Staehelin, T. (1977). *J. Mol. Biol.* **116,** 755–767.

Trachsel, H., Ranu, R. S., and London, I. M. (1978). *Proc. Natl. Acad. Sci. U.S.A.* **75,** 3654–3658.

Trachsel, H., Erni, B., Schreier, M. H., Braun, L., and Staehelin, T. (1979). *Biochim. Biophys. Acta* **561,** 484–490.

Traugh, J. A., and Lundak, T. S. (1978). *Biochem. Biophys. Res. Commun.* **83,** 379–384.

Traugh, J. A., and Porter, G. G. (1976). *Biochemistry* **15,** 610–616.

Traugh, J. A., and Sharp, S. B. (1977). *J. Biol. Chem.* **252,** 3738–3744.

Traugh, J. A., and Traut, R. R. (1974). *J. Biol. Chem.* **249,** 1207–1212.

Traugh, J. A., Mumby, M., and Traut, R. R. (1973). *Proc. Natl. Acad. Sci. U.S.A.* **70,** 373–376.

Traugh, J. A., Tahara, S. M., Sharp, S. B., Safer, B., and Merrick, W. C. (1976). *Nature (London)* **263,** 163–165.

Traugh, J. A., Del Grande, R. W., and Tuazon, P. T. (1981). *In* "Cold Spring Harbor Conferences on Cell Proliferation–Protein Phosphorylation," Vol. 8 (in press).

Treloar, M. A., and Kisilevsky, R. (1979). *Can. J. Biochem.* **57**, 209–215.

Treloar, M. A., Treloar, M. E., and Kisilevsky, R. (1977). *J. Biol. Chem.* **252**, 6217–6221.

Tsurugi, K., Collatz, E., Todokoro, K., Ulbrich, N., Lightfoot, H. N., and Wool, I. G. (1978). *J. Biol. Chem.* **253**, 946–955.

Tuazon, P. T., Bingham, E. W., and Traugh, J. A. (1979). *Eur. J. Biochem.* **94**, 497–504.

Tuazon, P. T., Merrick, W. C., (1980). *J. Biol. Chem.* **255** (in press).

Van Agthoven, A., Kriek, J., Amons, R., and Möller, W. (1978). *Eur. J. Biochem.* **91**, 553–565.

Walton, G. M., and Gill, G. N. (1973). *Biochemistry* **12**, 2604–2611.

Waxman, H. S., and Rabinovitz, M. (1965). *Biochem. Biophys. Res. Commun.* **19**, 538–545.

Waxman, H. S., and Rabinovitz, M. (1966). *Biochim. Biophys. Acta* **129**, 369–379.

Weber, L. A., Feman, E. R., and Baglioni, C. (1975). *Biochemistry* **14**, 5315–5321.

Wettenhall, R. E. H., and Howlett, G. J. (1979). *J. Biol. Chem.* **254**, 9317–9323.

Whelly, S. M., and Barker, K. L. (1974). *Biochemistry* **13**, 341–346.

Wigle, D. T., and Smith, A. E. (1973). *Nature (London) New Biol.* **242**, 135–140.

Williams, B. R. G., Kerr, I. M., Gilbert, C. S., White, C. N., and Ball, L. A. (1978). *Eur. J. Biochem.* **92**, 455–462.

Wool, I. G. (1979). *Annu. Rev. Biochem.* **48**, 719–754.

Zasloff, M., and Ochoa, S. (1973). *J. Mol. Biol.* **73**, 65–76.

Zilberstein, A., Federman, P., Shulman, L., and Revel, M. (1976). *FEBS Lett.* **68**, 119–124.

Zilberstein, A., Kimchi, A., Schmidt, A., and Revel, M. (1978). *Proc. Natl. Acad. Sci. U.S.A.* **75**, 4734–4738

Zucker, W. V., and Schulman, H. M. (1968). *Proc. Natl. Acad. Sci. U.S.A.* **59**, 582–589.

CHAPTER 4

Hormonal Control of Hepatic Gluconeogenesis

T. H. Claus and S. J. Pilkis

INTRODUCTION

Gluconeogenesis is the process whereby lactate, pyruvate, glycerol, and certain amino acids are converted to glucose and glycogen. The liver is the major site of gluconeogenesis, although the kidney becomes important during prolonged starvation. The most important function of gluconeogenesis is the maintenance of blood glucose levels during times when food intake is restricted and/or glycogen stores are depleted. For example, the rate of gluconeogenesis is enhanced during starvation and in the diabetic state. It is also the means whereby the lactate that is produced by glycolysis in erythrocytes, and in exercising muscle is reconverted to

Copyright © 1981 by Academic Press, Inc.
All rights of reproduction in any form reserved.
ISBN 0–12–452808–2

glucose. Similarly, it conserves the glycerol that is released during lipolysis in adipose tissue and the alanine produced by amino acid metabolism and glycolysis in muscle. Gluconeogenesis also contributes significantly to the utilization of amino acids, which are either absorbed from the alimentary tract or released during protein breakdown in muscle and other tissues. The regulation of this process by hormones is complex, involving both rapid and long-term effects at multiple sites in the pathway. In order to clarify the nature of this regulation a review of some of the enzymatic reactions in the pathway will be briefly presented.

Figure 1 shows the sequence of reactions by which lactate, pyruvate, and various gluconeogenic amino acids are converted to glucose in the hepatocyte. Amino acids and probably lactate enter the cell by various carrier-mediated plasma membrane transport systems. Lactate and most amino acids are converted to pyruvate in the cytoplasm of the cell. Alanine may also be transaminated to pyruvate in the mitochondria (Swick *et al.*, 1965; DeRosa and Swick, 1975). It has been suggested that mitochondrial metabolism of alanine per se contributes significantly to glucose production from this amino acid (DeRosa and Swick, 1975;

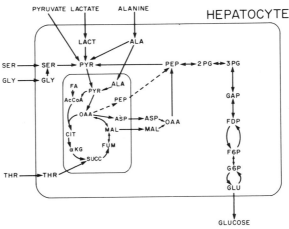

Fig. 1. Gluconeogenic pathway in the hepatocyte. The plasma membrane of the hepatocyte is represented by the large rectangle. The mitochondrion is depicted by the small rectangle. The dashed line represents the pathway for conversion of oxaloacetate to phosphoenolpyruvate in species that possess mitochondrial phosphoenolpyruvate carboxykinase. Abbreviations: LACT, lactate; PYR, pyruvate; ALA, alanine; SER, serine; GLY, glycine; FA, fatty acid; AcCoA, acetyl-CoA; CIT, citrate; αKG, α-ketoglutarate; SUCC, succinate; FUM, fumarate; MAL, malate; OAA, oxaloacetate; ASP, aspartate; THR, threonine; PEP, phosphoenolpyruvate; 2PG, 2-phosphoglycertate; 3PG, 3-phosphoglycerate; GAP, glyceraldehyde 3-phosphate; FDP, fructose 1,6-bisphosphate; F6P, fructose 6-phosphate; G6P, glucose 6-phosphate; GLU, glucose.

Mendes-Mourao *et al.*, 1975; Dieterle *et al.*, 1978). Pyruvate enters the mitochondria by a transport system and along with that generated in the mitochondria is converted to oxaloacetate by pyruvate carboxylase or to acetyl-CoA by pyruvate dehydrogenase. The fate of the mitochondrial oxaloacetate varies in different species, depending in large part on the distribution of the enzyme phosphoenolpyruvate carboxykinase between cytosol and mitochondria (Tilghman *et al.*, 1976). In the rat and mouse liver, it is converted to malate and/or aspartate, and these metabolites are transported to the cytosol, where they are reconverted to oxaloacetate. The oxaloacetate is then converted to phosphoenolpyruvate by phosphoenolpyruvate carboxykinase, which is predominantly a cytosolic enzyme in rat and mouse liver. This complicated series of interconversions is necessary because the mitochondrial membrane is presumably impermeable to oxaloacetate (however, see Gimpel *et al.*, 1973). In pigeon, chicken, and rabbit liver, phosphoenolpyruvate carboxykinase is located predominantly in the mitochondria and oxaloacetate is directly converted to phosphoenolpyruvate and then transported to the cytosol. In the human, guinea pig, sheep, and cow liver, the enzyme is distributed about equally between the mitochondria and the cytosol, but the fraction of total phosphoenolpyruvate synthesis at each site is as yet uncertain. Cytosolic phosphoenolpyruvate can be disposed of by two routes. First, a portion is converted to pyruvate because of the presence of pyruvate kinase. This creates a complicated substrate cycle between pyruvate and phosphoenolpyruvate. Second, the remaining phosphoenolpyruvate is converted to fructose biphosphate by the enzymes of the Embden-Meyerhof pathway. Fructose bisphosphate is then converted to fructose 6-phosphate by fructose bisphosphatase. However, the presence of phosphofructokinase also creates a second substrate cycle between fructose bisphosphate and fructose 6-phosphate. The fraction of fructose 6-phosphate not recycled to fructose bisphosphatase is converted to glucose 6-phosphate by glucose-6-phosphate isomerase. The final step in the pathway is the conversion of glucose 6-phosphate to glucose by glucose-6-phosphatase. However the presence of hexokinase and glucokinase in liver creates the potential for a third substrate cycle between glucose and glucose 6-phosphate.

Hormonal control of gluconeogenesis occurs on three levels. The first involves regulation of substrate supply. All gluconeogenic substrates reach the liver in subsaturating concentration. Thus, regulation of substrate release into the blood from the extrahepatic tissues will directly affect hepatic glucose formation. This type of regulation can be short term, as when large amounts of lactate reach the liver from exercising muscle, or long term as during the initial stages of starvation. This important aspect of gluconeogenic control has been reviewed by Scrutton and

Utter (1968), Exton *et al.* (1970), and Exton (1972, 1979b) and will not be discussed here. The second level deals with the very significant but relatively slow adaptive changes in enzyme activity due to regulation of protein synthesis and/or degradation. For example, during starvation and in the diabetic state the activity of a number of gluconeogenic enzymes is increased. In the case of glucose-6-phosphatase, fructose bisphosphatase, pyruvate carboxylase, and phosphoenolpyruvate carboxykinase the increase in activity reflects an increase in the amount of enzyme protein. Under these same conditions the activity and amount of glucokinase, phosphofructokinase, and pyruvate kinase are diminished. These topics will not be considered here in any detail. The third level is concerned with the minute-to-minute regulation of gluconeogenesis by glucagon, catecholamines, and insulin. These hormones are generally thought to play the most significant role in regulation in the pathway, although adrenal steroids (Exton and Park, 1965), thyroid hormone (Menahan and Wieland, 1969; Singh and Synder, 1978), growth hormone (Tolman *et al.*, 1973; Jefferson *et al.*, 1973) and angiotensin II, and vasopressin (Hems and Whitton, 1973; Whitton *et al.*, 1978) have all been shown to influence hepatic gluconeogenesis. The mechanism of the direct, immediate effect of hormones on the pathway will be the central topic of this chapter. The hypothesis will be put forth that these hormones act in the pathway by affecting the activity of enzymes which are involved in the substrate cycles between pyruvate and phosphoenolpyruvate and fructose bisphosphate and fructose 6-phosphate. While the emphasis will be on the minute-to-minute regulation of gluconeogensis, it is clear that regulation *in vivo* occurs on all three levels simultaneously and in an integrated fashion.

II. ROLE OF CYCLIC AMP IN HORMONAL CONTROL OF GLUCONEOGENESIS

The hormonal control of hepatic gluconeogenesis has been studied intensively since the early 1960s, during which time the isolated perfused liver system was fully developed. Schimassek and Mitzkat (1963), Garcia *et al.* (1964), Struck *et al.* (1965), and Exton and Park (1966) reported that glucagon stimulated gluconeogenesis in perfused rat liver, and Exton and Park (1966) demonstrated a similar effect of epinephrine. Using the isolated perfused liver system, Exton and Park (1966, 1968) postulated that the effect of these hormones was mediated by an elevation of cyclic AMP levels. The evidence for this was based on the following observations (1) both glucagon and epinephrine caused rapid elevations of hepatic cyclic AMP; (2) the concentration of hormone necessary to elicit elevation of cyclic AMP levels was the same as that needed to stimulate gluconeogenesis; and (3) addition of exogenous cyclic AMP mimicked the effect of the hormones. These observations are consistent with the concept of cyclic AMP as the second messenger (see Robison *et al.*, 1971). According to this concept, the hormone, or first messenger, carries the required information to the cell, where it binds to specific hormone receptors. This event in turn stimulates adenylate cyclase to convert ATP to cyclic AMP. This intracellular or second messenger then transfers the information to the cell's enzymatic machinery. In the case of gluconeogenesis, this information transfer is thought to be similar to that for glycogen metabolism. That is, cyclic AMP activates a protein kinase, which by catalyzing the phosphorylation of one or more enzymes alters their activity.

Regulation of the level of cyclic AMP could also explain the inhibitory effect of insulin on gluconeogenesis. Butcher *et al.* (1968) first showed that insulin lowered the level of cyclic AMP in adipocytes exposed to epinephrine, and Exton *et al.* (1971) observed a similar lowering of cyclic AMP by insulin in the isolated perfused liver exposed to glucagon and epinephrine. Similar data have been obtained in isolated hepatocyte preparations by Pilkis *et al.* (1975) and Claus and Pilkis (1976) who found that 10 nM insulin suppressed the response of gluconeogenesis to low concentrations of glucagon or cyclic AMP, and that the suppression was overcome as the concentration of agonist increased. Insulin also suppressed the small stimulation by a maximally effective concentration (1 μM) of epinephrine. Since insulin lowered cyclic AMP levels concomitantly, it was postulated that insulin affected gluconeogenesis by lowering cyclic AMP levels. The failure of insulin to suppress the effects of high concentrations of glucagon or cyclic AMP probably was due to the fact that the intracellular level of nucleotide had become so great that reduction in its level by insulin was insufficient to make it rate limiting for gluconeogenesis.

While it appears that all glucagon effects in liver are mediated by cyclic AMP, recent evidence indicates that other hormone effects may or may not be. Sherline *et al.* (1972) showed that the effects of catecholamines on glycogenolysis in the perfused rat liver were mediated by both β- and α-agonists. The α-adrenergic mechanism was not associated with changes in cyclic AMP levels. Tolbert *et al.* (1973) and Tolbert and Fain (1974) first showed that epinephrine could stimulate gluconeogenesis by an α-receptor-mediated mechanism. That is, the catecholamine stimulation of gluconeogensis was blocked by α-blocking agents such as phentolamine and dihydroergotamine, but not by the β blocker propranolol, which suppressed the increase in cyclic AMP. Furthermore, the catecholamine stimulation of glucose synthesis was suppressed by α blockers even though cyclic AMP levels remained elevated. In addition, isoproterenol, a pure β agonist, elevated cyclic AMP levels but had no effect on gluconeogenesis. Phenylephrine, a synthetic catecholamine and α agonist, also increased gluconeogenesis but did not elevate cyclic AMP. Many of these observations have been confirmed by others (Exton and Harper, 1975; Cherrington et al., 1976; Claus and Pilkis, 1976; Chan and Exton 1978; Hué et al., 1978; Kemp and Clark, 1978; Garrison and Borland, 1979). Garrison and Borland (1979) showed that norepinephrine also stimulated gluconeogenesis by an α-adrenergic mechanism. Chan and Exton (1978) also found that the stimulation of glucose synthesis by epinephrine or phenylephrine was potentiated by 1-methyl-3-isobutylxanthine, an inhibitor of cyclic nucleotide phosphodiesterase. These effects were accompanied by a rise in cyclic AMP levels. The effect of phenylephrine and 1-methyl-3-isobutylxanthine on glucose synthesis was preferentially blocked by α-adrenergic antagonists. In this instance, the methylxanthine appeared to potentiate an α-adrenergic effect of phenylephrine on glucose synthesis. Foster and Blair (1978) also observed that theophylline potentiated the epinephrine-induced stimulation of dihydroxyacetone gluconeogenesis. The stimulation of gluconeogenesis by vasopressin and angiotensin II (Hems and Whitton, 1973; Whitton et al., 1978) also was not associated with a rise in cyclic AMP levels (Hems et al., 1978a).

It has been suggested by several laboratories that the stimulation of liver glycogenolysis by vasopressin, angiotensin II, and the α-adrenergic component of catecholamines is mediated by alterations in Ca^{2+} flux (Van de Werve et al., 1977; Keppens et al., 1977; Assimacopoulos-Jeannet et al., 1977; Chan and Exton, 1977; Hems et al., 1978b). This proposal is supported by the observations that (1) the α-adrenergic agonist, phenylephrine, did not activate cyclic AMP-dependent protein kinase or elevate cyclic AMP levels (Keppens et al., 1977; Cherrington et al., 1976; Birnhaum and Fain, 1977); (2) in the absence of calcium, phenylephrine did not activate phosphorylase (Van de Werve et al., 1977; Keppens et al., 1977; Assimacopoulos-Jeannet et al., 1977); (3) the calcium ionophore A23127 mimicked the effect of phenylephrine (Keppens et al., 1977; Assimacopoulos-Jeannet et al., 1977); (4) phenylephrine altered $^{45}Ca^{2+}$ flux (Keppens et al., 1977; Assimacopoulos-Jeannet et al., 1977); (5) the effect of phenylephrine on Ca^{2+} flux was blocked by an α blocker (Keppens et al., 1977; Assimacopoulos-Jeannet et al., 1977); and (6) the effect of vasopressin and angiotensin II to enhance glycogenolysis and phosphorylase was dependent on extracellular Ca^{2+} (Stubbs et al., 1976;

Keppens *et al.*, 1977; Hems *et al.*, 1978b). Whether the α component of catecholamine action on gluconeogenesis is mediated by calcium is unclear, although a number of laboratories have implicated Ca^{2+} in the stimulation of gluconeogenesis by vasopressin and angiotensin II (Whitton *et al.*, 1978; Hué *et al.*, 1978; Garrison *et al.*, 1979).

The physiological significance of stimulation of gluconeogenesis by an α receptor-mediated cyclic AMP-independent mechanism is unclear and an important role for the cyclic AMP-mediated pathway of catecholmine action has not be excluded. It has been noted, for example, that maximal stimulation of gluconeogenesis by the α pathway in isolated rat hepatocytes from fed rats increased the rate by only about 60%, whereas glucagon in the same preparation stimulated three- to fourfold (Pilkis *et al.*, 1975). Furthermore, earlier studies by Exton and Park (1968), using a perfused liver preparation from fed rats, showed that epinephrine caused almost as large a stimulation (two- to threefold) as glucagon. The reason for the difference in behavior of these preparations is not clear, but the difference may be due to damage to isolated hepatocytes and their receptors by collagenase treatment and Ca^{2+} deprivation. Furthermore it is known from studies of lipolysis in fat tissue that the balance between α- and β-receptor effects shows striking species variability. It is therefore quite possible that catecholamines activate gluconeogenesis in some species by a predominantly β-receptor mechanism and in others by an α-receptor mechanism. The effects of vasopressin and angiotensin II on gluconeogenesis in isolated hepatocytes are also less than that of glucagon. Their role in physiological regulation of the pathway is uncertain, although they appear to be potent enough to be operative *in vivo* (Whitton *et al.*, 1978).

There is also evidence that insulin can suppress gluconeogenesis by a mechanism that is independent of changes in cyclic AMP (Claus and Pilkis, 1976). This is supported by three lines of evidence (1) glucagon (0.5 nM) stimulated glucose synthesis from 2 mM [U-^{14}C]lactate 40–50% in either the absence or the presence of extracellular Ca^{2+}. Insulin (10 nM) almost completely abolished the stimulation in both instances, even though it did not lower cyclic AMP levels in the absence of Ca^{2+}. (2) Insulin was able to suppress gluconeogenesis stimulated by 10 μM epinephrine plus a β-blocking agent. Under these conditions, insulin did not lower the tissue level of cyclic AMP, the rise of which had been largely or completely abolished by propranolol (10–100 μM). Neither insulin nor propranolol had any effect on cyclic AMP levels in the absence of epinephrine. Insulin also suppressed the stimulation of gluconeogenesis by phenylephrine, which has no measurable effect on cyclic AMP-dependent protein kinase activity (Hué *et al.*, 1978). (3) Insulin suppressed the epinephrine-induced stimulation of gluconeogenesis even when added 20 minutes after the catecholamine. At this time, cyclic AMP levels had already returned to near basal values and were not further reduced by insulin addition. When the two hormones were added together, insulin suppressed the rise of both cyclic AMP and gluconeogenesis. Thus insulin suppressed the stimulation of gluconeogenesis by either the α- or the β-component of catecholamines. It seems, therefore, that there are at least two mechanisms by which insulin can suppress gluconeogenesis, one dependent and the other independent of changes in tissue levels of cyclic AMP. Which mechanism is most important physiologically is unclear, but may depend on which gluconeogenic agonist is involved and in which species. Similar cyclic AMP-dependent and -independent effects of insulin on catecholamine activation of lipolysis in adipose tissue have been observed (Butcher *et al.*, 1968; Siddle and Hales, 1974). In muscle, all effects of insulin appear to be cyclic AMP independent (Larner, 1968).

III. SITES OF ACTION OF HORMONES ON HEPATIC GLUCONEOGENESIS

It was thought that the major rate-limiting step(s) were in the initial part of the gluconeogenic pathway, since maximal concentrations of lactate, pyruvate, or alanine produced rates of gluconeogenesis that were usually much less than those of substrates that entered at or above the triose phosphate level (Exton and Park, 1967; Ross *et al.*, 1967a). Analysis of intermediary metabolites from rat livers perfused with high concentrations of lactate, pyruvate, or alanine led to the hypothesis that glucagon, cyclic AMP, epinephrine, and insulin acted somewhere between pyruvate and phosphoenolpyruvate (Exton and Park, 1969; Williamson *et al.*, 1969b; Mallette *et al.*, 1969). However, glucagon also appeared to affect reactions between fructose bisphosphate and fructose 6-phosphate (Williamson *et al.*, 1969b; Blair *et al.*, 1973; Harris, 1975; Pilkis *et al.*, 1976a). In addition, the transport of alanine across the plasma membrane was found to be stimulated by glucagon (Mallette *et al.*, 1969). The region of the pathway between pyruvate and phosphoenolpyruvate involves many steps, both cytosolic and mitochondrial (Fig. 1). Attempts to localize the step affected by measurement of the total concentration of intermediary metabolites have been unsuccessful, since many of the metabolites exist in both the cytosol and mitochondria. However, a number of mitochondrial steps have been proposed as sites of glucagon action. They include the reactions catalyzed by pyruvate carboxylase and pyruvate dehydrogenase, as well as pyruvate transport into mitochondria and dicarboxylate transport from the mitochondria. Cytosolic sites that have been proposed for hormone action include the enzymes of the pyruvate–phosphoenolpyruvate substrate cycle (phosphoenolpyruvate carboxykinase and pyruvate kinase) and those of the fructose bisphosphate–fructose 6-phosphate cycle (fructose bisphosphatase and phosphofructokinase). These proposals will be discussed in detail in the following sections.

A. The Action of Hormones on Mitochondrial Sites

1. Pyruvate Carboxylase

Pyruvate carboxylase is an essential enzyme for gluconeogenesis since pyruvate must be converted to oxalacetate in order for net glucose synthesis to occur. This mitochondrial enzyme requires acetyl-CoA for activity (Keech and Utter, 1963), and this requirement was the basis for the hypothesis (Utter *et al.*, 1964) that glucagon stimulates gluconeogenesis by increasing the levels of this effector (Struck *et al.*, 1966; Williamson *et al.*, 1966a,b; Ross *et al.*, 1967b; Söling *et al.*, 1968). The elevation of acetyl-CoA levels could result from an increase in fatty acid oxidation triggered by the activation of lipolysis by a cyclic AMP-sensitive lipase (Bewsher and Ashmore, 1966). However, Debeer *et al.*, (1979) could not identify a hormone-sensitive cyclic AMP-dependent lipase in homogenates of isolated hepatocytes. They proposed that glucagon activated lipolysis by induction of autophagocytosis. In any case, it is clear now that fatty acids and glucagon affect gluconeogenesis by separate mechanisms (for reviews, see Exton *et al.*, 1970; Exton, 1972; Pilkis *et al.*, 1978c).

The activity of pyruvate carboxylase can be regulated by a number of other factors (for review, see Barritt *et al.*, 1976), and the level of several of these factors may be altered in the presence of hormones. Calcium ion can be a potent inhibitor of the enzyme by competing with Mg^{2+} (McClure and Lardy, 1971; Wimhurst and Manchester, 1970). Pyruvate carboxylation by isolated rat liver mitochondria also can be inhibited by calcium ion under some conditions (Kimmich and Rasmussen, 1969), but not under other conditions (Morikofer-Zwez *et al.*, 1973). Regulation of gluconeogenesis by changes in Ca^{2+} has been proposed by Friedmann and Rasmussen (1970) and by Rasmussen (1970). It has been shown that catecholamines, vasopressin, and angiotensin II are much more effective than glucagon in promoting the efflux of Ca^{2+} ions from mitochondria (Chen *et al.*, 1978; Salzmann *et al.*, 1978; Babcock *et al.*, 1979;

Blackmore *et al.*, 1979a). Thus, it is tempting to postulate that the small effect of these agents on gluconeogenesis relative to that of glucagon may be due to a decrease in mitochondrial Ca^{2+}, which removes some restraint on pyruvate carboxylation. However, as will be discussed later, these agents have been postulated to affect other reactions in the pathway as well.

Adenine nucleotides affect the activity of pyruvate carboxylase, but conclusions as to their importance have differed depending on whether the studies were done with the purified enzyme or with intact rat liver mitochondria. Purified pyruvate carboxylase showed product inhibition by Mg-ADP⁻, but only when saturating pyruvate concentrations were present (McClure and Lardy, 1971). The fact that no inhibition was observed when subsaturating pyruvate concentrations were used suggested that inhibition by Mg-ADP⁻ may not be important physiologically. However, experiments with intact rat liver mitochondria showed that increasing concentrations of intramitochondrial ADP produced decreasing rates of pyruvate carboxylation, and that the rate correlated with the ATP:ADP ratio whether high or low pyruvate concentrations were used as substrate (Stucki *et al.*, 1972; von Glutz and Walter, 1976). This suggested that changes in the intramitochondrial ATP:ADP ratio may be important for the regulation of pyruvate carboxylation. Siess *et al.* (1977) and Bryla *et al.* (1977) have shown that the addition of glucagon to intact hepatocytes produced an elevation in the intramitochondrial ATP:ADP ratio. This may provide a mechanism by which the hormone stimulates pyruvate carboxylation.

The intramitochondrial concentration of glutamate may also be a regulator of pyruvate caroboyxlase activity. The enzyme is inhibited by glutamate, but the high concentration required ($K_i > 5$ mM) was thought to preclude its physiological significance. Ui *et al.* (1973a,b) reported that glucagon dramatically lowered the intracellular level of glutamate and α-ketoglutarate. These effects were attributed to glucagon activation of either α-ketoglutarate dehydrogenase or succinic thiokinase. Siess *et al.* (1977) confirmed the glucagon-induced decrease in α-ketoglutarate and glutamate, and they reported that the intramitochondrial glutamate concentration dropped from approximately 15 mM to about 3 mM. Thus, it is possible that glutamate normally restrains the rate of pyruvate carboxylation and that the addition of glucagon removes that restraint. The effect of α-adrenergic agonists, vasopressin, and angiotensin II on intramitochondrial glutamate levels has not been reported.

The activity of pyruvate carboxylase in intact hepatocytes or mitochondria also may be limited by the rate of pyruvate entry into mitochrondria, and this carrier-mediated process (Papa *et al.*, 1969, 1971; Mowbray, 1974, 1975; Titheradge and Coore, 1975; Halestrap and Denton, 1975) has been postulated to be regulated by hormones. Adam and Haynes (1969) found that liver mitochondria isolated from rats injected with glucagon, epinephrine, or cortisol exhibited higher rates of pyruvate carboxylation and oxidation than mitochondria from control rats. None of the hormones altered the activity of pyruvate carboxylase assayed in sonicated extracts of mitochondria, but each one increased mitochondrial pyruvate uptake. When the mitochondria were suspended in a medium of low osmolarity, pyruvate uptake increased and the effect of hormones on pyruvate carboxylation and oxidation was reduced. These results suggested that the hormones increased a reaction common to both carboxylation and oxidation, i.e., pyruvate entry into the mitochondria. Garrison and Haynes (1975) obtained similar results with mitochondria from isolated hepatocytes that had been exposed to glucagon, epinephrine, or cyclic AMP. These results ruled out extrahepatic factors as being responsible for the effects. They also found that dose-response curves for enhancement of pyruvate carboxylation and gluconeogenesis were identical for each agonist. The glucagon-induced mitochondrial changes and the increase in the rate of gluconeogenesis were rapid effects, occurring with the same time course, and the increase in pyruvate carboxylation correlated with the hormone-induced changes in cyclic AMP levels. On the other hand, Garrison and Borland (1979) found that effects of catecholamines on mitochondrial CO_2 fixation correlated with the rate of gluconeogenesis but did not correlate with change in hepatocyte cyclic AMP levels. The effects were abolished by α antagonists such as ergotamine, phenoxybenzamine, and phentolamine, but not by the β antagonist propranolol. Thus, the catecholamine effects were mediated by an α-adrenergic cyclic AMP-independent mechanism. In contrast to the effects of glucagon and catecholamines on mitochondrial CO_2 fixation, which are evident within a few minutes after hormone addition, the effect of glucocorticoids appear to develop more slowly. Significant stimulation of mitochondrial CO_2 fixation was not observed until 60 minutes after injection of rats with cortisol and maximal stimulation required 2 to 4 hours (Wakat and Haynes, 1977). The glucocorticoid effect was additive with that of glucagon or triiodothyronine, which suggests that all of these hormones affect mitochondrial metabolism by separate mechanisms.

Titheradge and Coore (1976a,b) reported that glucagon treatment of rats had a direct effect on pyruvate transport in isolated mitochondria when transport was driven by the oxidation of ascorbate plus tetramethylphenylenediamine. Halestrap (1978a) was unable to repeat their observations. He found no differences in the time courses of pyruvate uptake into mitochondria from livers of control or glucagon-treated rats (Halestrap, 1975, 1978a). Most results suggest that glucagon does not affect pyruvate transport specifically. Yamazaki (1975) demonstrated that acute treatment of rats with glucagon caused a stimulation of hepatic mitochondrial respiration as measured by oxygen uptake. In the presence of phosphate and ADP (state 3) or in uncoupled mitochondria, the rates of oxygen uptake were increased using pyruvate-malate, malate-L-glutamate, α-ketoglutarate, or succinate as substrates. There was no effect of glucagon on the oxidation of ascorbate in the presence of tetraphenylenediamine or when the rate of respiration with NADH- and flavoprotein-linked substrates was measured in the absence of ADP (state 4). These results have been confirmed by Titheradge and Coore (1976b), Bryla *et al.* (1977), and Halestrap (1978a). Bryla *et al.* (1977) also observed that mitochondria from glucagon-treated rats showed an increased rate of respiration with β-hydroxybutyrate as substrate and an increased uptake of ADP. These hormone-induced effects on respiration have been found to persist even after the mitochondria were disrupted by sonication (Titheradge *et al.*, 1978). Significant increases in oxygen consumption under state 3 or uncoupled conditions were observed in submitochondrial particles prepared from glucagon-treated rats when either succinate or NADH were the respiratory substrates. No hormone effect was observed when ascorbate plus tetramethylphenylenediamine was used as the substrate. Together these results indicate that glucagon treatment stimulates mitochondrial function in a general manner rather than just affecting pyruvate transport. Consistent with this notion is the recent report that glucagon treatment of intact rats stimulated mitochondrial CO_2 fixation (pyruvate carboxylation) when alanine was used as substrate (Chan *et al.*, 1979). Under these conditions, pyruvate was generated inside the mitochondria and there was no need for pyruvate transport.

It now has been shown that mitochondria isolated from livers of rats treated with glucagon display a number of other differences from those of control rats. Haynes (1976) found that they contained a greater concentration of Mg^{2+} than controls. This was confirmed by Halestrap (1978a) who also found a greater concentration of K^+. Haynes (1976) found no difference in the K^+ concentration of control or glucagon-treated mitochondria, but he did observe a greater rate of K^+ uptake in glucagon-treated mitochondria. Yamazaki *et al.* (1977) have confirmed the latter observation. Yamazaki and Graetz (1977) found that glucagon treatment of rats stimulated the formation of citrulline by isolated liver mitochondria incubated with ornithine, ammonium ion, bicarbonate, phosphate, and an energy source such as succinate which generated intramitochondrial ATP via substrate oxidation. This finding was confirmed in mitocondria isolated from hepatocytes exposed to glucagon (Bryla *et al.*, 1977; Triebwasser and Freedland, 1977) and the increased rate correlated with an increase in ATP content (Bryla *et al.*, 1977). Chan *et al.* (1979) also observed a higher ATP content in mitochondria from glucagon-treated rats. Glucagon treatment also results in an enhanced mitochondrial ATPase activity in the presence of an uncoupler of oxidative phosphorylation (Yamazaki *et al.*, 1977) as well as in an increase in the membrane potential (Halestrap, 1978a).

Yamazaki (1975) suggested that the effects of glucagon to stimulate substrate-dependent respiration are consistent with either a general stimulation of mitochondrial transport systems or stimulation of the electron transport chain. Titheradge and Coore (1976b) found that glucagon treatment increased the pH of the mitochondrial matrix, a finding confirmed by Halestrap (1978a). He proposed that glucagon treatment enhanced electron transport chain activity and that this allowed enhanced proton ejection from the mitochondria thus increasing the pH of the mitochondrial matrix. The increase in hydroxyl ion concentration should stimulate mitochondrial anion transport since hydroxyl ions exchange either directly or indirectly with the various anions. The increase in electron transport chain activity also stimulated the rate of ATP formation within the mitochondria (Yamazaki and Graetz, 1977). Both pyruvate carboxylation and the initial step of citruilline formation (carbamyl phosphate synthesis) are mitochondrial reactions which require ATP as substrate. Thus, the stimulation of oxidative phosphorylation may be necessary to meet the increased demands for ATP during gluconeogenesis and ureagenesis.

The ability of glucagon to stimulate respiration from NADH- and flavoprotein-linked substrates, but not from ascorbate plus tetramethylphenylenediamine, suggested that the hormone activated the respiratory chain at point prior to the entry of electrons from tetramethylphenylenediamine into the system. This point appeared to be before phosphorylation site III, i.e., between cytochrome b and c (Yamazaki, 1975; Titheradge *et al.*, 1978; Halestrap, 1978b). Halestrap (1978b) measured the cytochrome spectra under uncoupled conditions in the presence of succinate and rotenone and found a crossover between cytochrome c and c_1 when mitochondria from glucagon-treated rats were compared to those of control rats. Cytochrome c was more reduced and cytochrome c_1 more oxidized in mitochondria from glucagon-treated rats and he concluded that glucagon stimulates electron flow between cytochrome c_1 and c.

The mechanism whereby glucagon stimulates the electron transport chain is uncertain. The fact that the effect persists throughout the time needed to isolate mitochondria and even after preparation of submito-chondrial particles, suggests that the hormone produces a stable, perhaps covalent, modification. Many of the glucagon-induced changes in mito-chondrial metabolism have been correlated with changes in cyclic AMP (Garrison and Haynes, 1975). If the effects of cyclic AMP are mediated through the phosphorylation of specific proteins by the cyclic AMP-dependent protein kinase, it would be predicted that glucagon should enhance the phosphorylation of mitochondrial protein(s). Zahlten *et al.* (1972) reported that rat liver inner mitochondrial membranes were phos-phoryled *in vivo* and that glucagon increased the phosphorylation. Using isolated hepatocytes, Halestrap (1978b,c) reported that he was able to phosphorylate inner mitochondrial membrane proteins and that one of the proteins had the same molecular weight as cytochrome c_1. However, no effect of glucagon on its phosphorylation was reported. If glucagon, via cyclic AMP, acts at the mitochondrial level, one would expect to find a cyclic AMP-dependent protein kinase associated with the mitochon-dria. However, no reports of the presence of a cyclic AMP-dependent protein kinase in mitochondria have appeared. Vardanis (1977) found a cyclic AMP-independent protein kinase on the inner membrane of mouse liver mitochondria. However, the enzyme was not characterized ex-tensively and it may represent the catalytic subunit of the cyclic AMP-dependent protein kinase. However, since cytochrome c_1 is on the outer surface of the inner mitochondrial membrane (Racker, 1970; Papa, 1976), its phosphorylation could be catalyzed by a cyclic AMP-dependent protein kinase located between the inner and outer mitochondrial mem-branes. The presence of a cyclic AMP-dependent protein kinase in mito-chondria is suggested by the recent claim that addition of cyclic AMP and ATP to isolated mitochondria can mimic the effects of glucagon (Hale-strap, 1978c), but this has not been reported in detail nor has it been con-firmed.

Epinephrine treatment of rats produced an increase in O_2 uptake by isolated mitochondria incubated under state 3 conditions when pyruvate plus malate was the substrate, but not when ascorbate plus tetramethy-lphenylenediamine was the substrate (Titheradge and Coore, 1976b). These results were identical to those obtained with glucagon treatment. However, epinephrine treatment did not alter the pH of the mitochon-dria matrix, but instead it reduced the matrix volume (Titheradge and Coore, 1976b). Different mechanisms for the two hormones are sup-ported by the observation that the catecholamine effects on pyruvate car-boxylation were not mediated by cyclic AMP (Garrison and Borland, 1979). There is no information on how catecholamines affect the matrix volume, but they may be related to the hormone-induced decrease in

Ca^{2+} ion content of the mitochondria (Chen *et al.*, 1978; Salzmann *et al.*, 1978; Babcock *et al.*, 1979; Blackmore *et al.*, 1979a). It is not known whether these effects of catecholamines or glucagon can be counteracted by insulin.

These studies suggest that glucagon and other hormones may affect the rate of pyruvate carboxylation in intact hepatocytes or isolated mitochondria by altering the level of various effectors of pyruvate carboxylase, particularly pyruvate, glutamate, ATP, and perhaps Ca^{2+}. While these changes may be associated with covalent modification of some mitochondrial protein(s), there is no evidence that pyruvate carboxylase itself undergoes phosphorylation (Leiter *et al.*, 1978). Measurement of pyruvate carboxylase activity in homogenates of livers treated with glucagon has not revealed any change.

2. Pyruvate Dehydrogenase

Pyruvate entering mitochondria either can be converted to oxalacetate by pyruvate carboxylase or oxidized to acetyl-CoA by pyruvate dehydrogenase (Fig. 1). Since the two enzymes compete for pyruvate, inactivation of pyruvate dehydrogenase would facilitate carboxylation and thus gluconeogenesis. The discovery that the activity of this enzyme complex could be regulated by a phosphorylation-dephosphorylation mechanism (Linn *et al.*, 1969a,b 1972) suggested that it might be a site of glucagon action. Zahlten *et al.* (1973) found that glucagon addition to hepatocytes from starved rats decreased [^{14}C]glucose and $^{14}CO_2$ production from 10 mM [1-^{14}C]pyruvate and they suggested that these effects were due to an inhibition of pyruvate dehydrogenase. On the other hand, Yamazaki and Haynes (1975) concluded that pyruvate dehydrogenase was not a primary site of glucagon action since the hormone still was able to stimulate pyruvate carboxylation under conditions where pyruvate dehydrogenase was inhibited. Also, Crabb *et al.* (1976) found the dichloroacetate, an activator of pyruvate dehydrogenase (Whitehouse and Randle, 1973; Whitehouse *et al.*, 1974), activated the enzyme but had minor effects on glucose synthesis from lactate and alanine. They concluded that the regulation of pyruvate dehydrogenase was only of marginal importance in the control of gluconeogenesis. Claus and Pilkis (1977) found that dichloroacetate did not prevent glucagon from inhibiting glucose synthesis from 10 mM pyruvate even though pyruvate dehydrogenase was completely activated. They concluded that the inhibition of pyruvate gluconeogenesis was not due to inhibition of pyruvate dehydrogenase. Mapes and Harris (1976), using a different approach, reached the same conclusion. Thus, it now appears that the glucagon-induced decrease in $^{14}CO_2$ production from 10 mM [1-^{14}C]pyruvate observed by Zahlten *et al.*

(1973) was due to the concomitant decrease in glucose synthesis. Claus and Pilkis (1977) also found that glucagon stimulated glucose synthesis from a variety of substrates regardless of whether pyruvate dehydrogenase was in the active or inactive state. Thus it appears that pyruvate dehydrogenase is not involved in the hormonal regulation of gluconeogenesis.

B. THE ACTION OF HORMONES ON EXTRAMITOCHONDRIAL SITES

Three enzymes specific for gluconeogenesis have been identified in cytosol of rat liver. They are phosphoenolpyruvate carboxykinase, which catalyzes the conversion of oxaloacetate to phosphoenolpyruvate; fructose-1,6-bisphosphatase, which converts fructose 1,6-bisphosphate to fructose 6-phosphate; and glucose-6-phosphatase, which hydrolyzes glucose 6-phosphate to free glucose and inorganic phosphate. These three gluconeogenic enzymes are opposed in the cell by three glycolytic enzymes, pyruvate kinase, phosphofructokinase, and hexokinase, respectively. The existence in the same cell of enzymes that catalyze opposing reactions raised the possibility of cycling between the substrates and products of the enzymes (Fig. 1). Since each of the reactions is in nonequilibrium, energy would be expended by such cycling. Newsholme and Gevers (1967) have speculated that the simultaneous operation of opposing reactions would make possible a very sensitive control system in which both the rate and direction of metabolism could be regulated by very small changes in the concentration of effectors of one or more of the enzymes involved in the cycle. Energy expended by such a substrate cycle would not be wasted, but would create a more efficient regulatory system than a simple "on–off" system.

1. The Phosphoenolpyruvate–Pyruvate Substrate Cycle and Its Enzymes

Recent studies have provided evidence that the phosphoenolpyruvate-pyruvate cycle is important in the regulation of gluconeogenesis. Earlier work employing crossover plots of metabolic intermediates had suggested that rate-limiting step(s) occur in this region of the pathway. The cycle is quite complex. The pyruvate produced by the action of pyruvate kinase must be carboxylated to oxaloacetate and then decarboxylated to phosphoenolpyruvate. The route of these conversions is dependent upon the location of phosphoenolpyruvate carboxykinase, which is distributed in various proportions between cytosol and mitochondria, depending on the species (Tilghman *et al.*, 1976). This cycle therefore may include both mitochondrial membrane transport systems and a number of enzymes. One mol of ATP and 1 mol of GTP are consumed, and 1 mol of ATP is generated. Thus, 1 mol of energy-rich phosphate is expended per cycle.

The first evidence that some phosphoenolpyruvate is recycled to pyruvate during gluconeogenesis was presented by Friedman *et al.* (1971a,b), using perfused rat liver, and by Rognstad and Katz (1972), using kidney cortex segments. Both groups used [2-¹⁴C]pyruvate as substrate and determined the flux through pyruvate kinase by measuring the distribution of radioactivity among carbon atoms of lactate and pyruvate. Both groups found that in the fasting state about one-half as much phosphoenolpyruvate was recycled to pyruvate as was converted to glucose. In the fed state, the situation was reversed, the rate of pyruvate kinase flux being four times that of glucose synthesis (Friedman *et al.*, 1971a,b). With [2-¹⁴C]lactate as substrate in kidney cortex segments, only 30% as much phosphoenolpyruvate was recycled to pyruvate as was converted to glucose (Rognstad and Katz, 1972).

A simpler approach to measuring flux through pyruvate kinase was devised by Rognstad (1975). Labeled $NaHCO_3$ was used instead of [2-¹⁴C] pyruvate or lactate, since it will incorporate radioactivity into phosphoenolpyruvate prior to pyruvate. The amount of label found in lactate and pyruvate, along with the estimated specific activity of phosphoenolpyruvate, was used to calculate pyruvate kinase flux. In hepatocytes from starved rats incubated with 20 mM pyruvate, the flux was estimated to be about 50% of the rate of gluconeogenesis (Rognstad, 1975). With 20 mM lactate as substrate, the flux through pyruvate kinase was estimated to be from 7 to 23% of the rate of gluconeogenesis in the starved case and about 50% in the fed case (Katz and Rognstad, 1976; Rognstad and Katz, 1977).

Various hormones have been found to affect flux through pyruvate kinase in intact hepatocytes. When 20 mM pyruvate was the substrate in hepatocytes from starved rats, glucagon and cyclic AMP inhibited pyruvate kinase flux by about 45% (Rognstad, 1975, 1976), whereas epinephrine was only marginally effective (Rognstad, 1976). In hepatocytes from fed rats, glucagon caused a dose-dependent decrease in flux, while epinephrine appeared to increase it (Rognstad and Katz, 1977). Other studies showed that pyruvate kinase flux was increased almost 10-fold during gluconeogenesis from 20 mM lactate in hepatocytes from fasted triiodothyronine-treated rats (Rognstad, 1977).

Flux through pyruvate kinase in isolated hepatocytes can also be measured from the rate of lactate and pyruvate production from dihydroxyacetone (Pilkis *et al.*, 1976a,b). This substrate is first converted to

dihydroxyacetone phosphate by glycerol kinase and then to either glucose
or to lactate and pyruvate. Pyruvate kinase flux was about equal to the
rate of gluconeogenesis in hepatocytes from fed or 24-hour starved rats,
but was depressed upon further starvation (Pilkis *et al.*, 1976a). In
hepatocytes from fed rats, glucagon caused a dose-dependent decrease in
lactate production from dihydroxyacetone and a concomitant, quantitatively equivalent increase in glucose synthesis (Fig. 2). Glucagon also
decreased flux through pyruvate kinase in hepatocytes from starved rats
(Pilkis *et al.*, 1976a, Rognstad, 1979). Insulin relieved the inhibition
when submaximal concentrations of glucagon were added to hepatocytes
from fed rats (Pilkis *et al.*, 1976b). Epinephrine produced only a small
decrease in pyruvate kinase flux in hepatocytes from fed or starved rats
(Pilkis *et al.*, 1976a; Rognstad, 1976), and the effect was α mediated
(Pilkis *et al.*, 1976a).

It is uncertain just how important changes in pyruvate kinase are as a
means of regulating gluconeogenesis. All the studies on pyruvate kinase
flux have been done with concentrations of physiological substrates that
produce maximum rates of gluconeogenesis or with nonphysiological substrates. While the glucagon-induced decrease in pyruvate kinase flux was
accompanied by an equivalent increase in glucose synthesis from dihydroxyacetone (Fig. 2; Pilkis *et al.*, 1976a; Claus *et al.*, 1979), that was
not the case when 20 m*M* lactate was the substrate. Rognstad and Katz

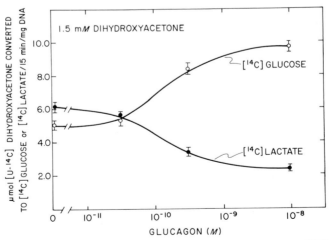

Fɪɢ. 2. Effect of glucagon on conversion of [¹⁴C]dihydroxyacetone to [¹⁴C]lactate and
[¹⁴C]glucose in hepatocytes from fed rats. Cells were incubated for 30 minutes with 1.5 mM
[¹⁴C]dihydroxyacetone, and labeled glucose and lactate were determined. The data are from
Pilkis *et al.* (1976a).

(1977) reported that neither glucagon nor epinephrine had any significant effect on pyruvate kinase flux in hepatocytes from starved rats, even though both hormones stimulated glucose synthesis from 20 mM lactate. In hepatocytes from fed rats, the glucagon-induced decrease in pyruvate kinase flux accounted for about 40% of the increase in glucose synthesis. Regulation of pyruvate kinase flux may be more (or less) important under conditions that mimic those found *in vivo*. This question can be resolved only by direct measurement of pyruvate kinase flux with physiological concentrations of lactate and pyruvate as substrate. However, studies on the regulation of the activity of pyruvate kinase provide strong evidence that the enzyme plays a central role in the hormonal regulation of gluconeogenesis.

a. *Hepatic Pyruvate Kinase.* There is approximately 10 times more pyruvate kinase activity in rat liver than phosphoenolpyruvate carboxykinase (Scrutton and Utter, 1968). This suggests that pyruvate kinase must be substantially inhibited in order for net gluconeogenesis to occur. This consideration, and the observation that hormones can affect flux through pyruvate kinase, has fostered a great deal of research on this enzyme. Many studies conducted in various species and tissues suggest that there are three isozymes of pyruvate kinase in mammalian tissues (Seubert and Schoner, 1971; Imamura *et al.*, 1972; Ibsen, 1977). Table I illustrates some of the differences and similarities between the three different classes of isozymes. The M-, K-, and the L-isozymes are homotetramers, with a subunit molecular weight of about 57,000. The L-isozyme, which is found predominately in liver, exhibits sigmoidal kinetics with regard to its substrate, phosphoenolpyruvate. When the allosteric activator fructose bisphosphate is added or the pH is lowered, the enzyme exhibits normal Michaelis-Menten kinetics (Bailey *et al.*, 1968; Jiménez de Asua *et al.*, 1970; Carminatti *et al.*, 1968; Llorente *et al.*, 1970; Rozengurt *et al.*, 1969; Schoner *et al.*, 1970; Seubert *et al.*, 1968; Susor and Rutter, 1968; Tanaka *et al.*, 1965; Taylor and Bailey, 1967; Gancedo *et al.*, 1967; Haeckel *et al.*, 1968; Hess *et al.*, 1966; Hunsley and Suelter, 1969; Koler and Vanbellinghen, 1968). The M-isozyme exhibits hyperbolic kinetics with phosphoenolpyruvate as substrate and is not activated by fructose bisphosphate (Imamura *et al.*, 1972). The K-isozyme has properties intermediate between those of the M- and L-types. There is some degree of sigmoidicity in the phosphoenolpyruvate concentration curve, and fructose bisphosphate does stimulate the activity of the K-isozyme, but not nearly as effectively as that of the L-isozyme (Imamura *et al.*, 1972). Differences between the isozymes also exist with regard to inhibition by ATP and alanine (see Table I). Further discussion of the properties of these isozymes can be found in a recent review (Pilkis *et al.*, 1978b).

TABLE I

COMPARISON OF THE PROPERTIES OF THE L-, K-, M- ISOZYMES OF PYRUVATE KINASE IN RAT TISSUES

Characteristic	L-type[a]	K-type[b]	M-type[c]
Tissue distribution	Liver, kidney, and erythrocytes	Kidney and many adult cells. Predominant in fetal tissues and tumors	Muscle and brain
Subunit structure	Tetramer	Tetramer	Tetramer
Molecular weight	228,000	216,000	250,000
Chronic adaptation			
Starvation	Decreased	Unchanged	Unchanged
High-carbohydrate diet	Increased	Unchanged	Unchanged
Diabetes	Decreased	Unchanged	Unchanged
Kinetics with regard to PEP ($S_{0.5}$)	Sigmoidal (0.6 mM)	Sigmoidal (0.4 mM)	Hyperbolic (0.07 mM)
Hill coefficient for PEP	2.0	1.4–1.5	1.0
Activation by FDP	Yes	Yes	No
Inhibition by alanine (K_i, app)	1mM	0.45 mM	—
Inhibition by ATP (K_i, app)	1 mM	3 mM	3 mM
Allosteric activation by hydrogen ions	Yes	?	No
Phosphorylation by protein kinase	Yes	Yes (chicken liver); No (pig kidney)	No
Acute hormonal regulation	Yes	?	No

[a] From Seubert and Schoner (1971); Imamura et al. (1972); Ibsen (1977); Riou et al. (1976); Pilkis et al. (1978a); Claus et al. (1979).

[b] Imamura et al. (1972).

[c] Kayne and Price (1972); Imamura et al. (1972); Berglund et al. (1977b); Eigenbrodt and Schoner (1977a,b).

The presence of ATP and alanine can have profound effects on the degree of cooperativity that L-type pyruvate kinase shows as well as on its $S_{0.5}$ for phosphoenolpyruvate. With physiological concentrations of alanine, ATP, and phosphoenolpyruvate, *in vitro* studies predict that the enzyme would be completely inhibited unless it were activated by fructose bisphosphate (Florey *et al.*, 1974; Van Berkel *et al.*, 1974). It is reasonable to postulate that the active form of pyruvate kinase *in vivo* is an enzyme–fructose bisphosphate complex. The amount of this complex depends on the concentration of free fructose bisphosphate in the cytosol. This in turn depends on the amount of fructose bisphosphate bound to other enzymes in liver, such as aldolase, fructose bisphosphatase, and perhaps phosphofructokinase. Marco and Sols (1970) have calculated that the concentration of free fructose bisphosphate is very small compared to that which is bound. Only 10% or less of the total fructose bisphosphate, at a concentration of 20–50 μM, is available to pyruvate kinase. Any change in the affinity of pyruvate kinase for fructose bisphosphate, or in the binding of the compound to other enzymes, would have a great influence on the activity of pyruvate kinase. Evidence for fructose bisphosphate was shown in hepatocytes incubated with dihydroxyacetone (Claus *et al.*, 1979). In this case, flux though pyruvate kinase (lactate and pyruvate production) was increased (Fig. 3). The increase in flux correlated with an elevation in fructose bisphosphate levels but not with phosphoenolpyruvate levels which were unchanged. Pyruvate kinase was activated and its affinity for phosphoenolpyruvate was increased sevenfold in hepatocyte extracts. Precipitation of the enzyme from extracts with ammonium sulfate removed fructose bisphosphate and activation was no longer observed. Thus, under these conditions, fructose bisphosphate controls the activity of and flux through pyruvate kinase (Claus *et al.*, 1979).

The activity of pyruvate kinase also can be regulated by a phosphorylation–dephosphorylation mechanism. Ljungström *et al.* (1974) first demonstrated that the purified rat L-isozyme could be phosphorylated by [γ-^{32}-P]ATP in a reaction catalyzed by cyclic AMP-dependent protein kinase. The activity of the enzyme was decreased by phosphorylation, especially at low phosphoenolpyruvate concentration. Riou *et al.* (1976) and Pilkis *et al.* (1978b) have confirmed the observation that phosphorylation of purified rat liver pyruvate kinase by cyclic AMP-dependent protein kinase resulted in inhibition of activity measured at low phosphoenolpyruvate concentrations. As shown in Fig. 4, phosphorylation results in an increase in the $S_{0.5}$ for phosphoenolpyruvate from 0.6 mM to 1.2 mM. No change in activity was obtained when the enzyme was assayed at high phosphoenolpyruvate concentrations or in the presence of optimal

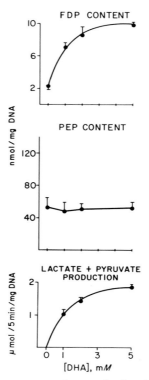

Fɪɢ. 3. Effects of dihydroxyacetone on fructose bisphosphate and phosphoenolpyruvate content and on lactate plus pyruvate production. Hepatocytes from 18 hours starved rats were incubated for 10 minutes with dihydroxyacetone. The reaction was stopped with HClO₄ and the various metabolites measured. Lactate plus pyruvate production is a measure of flux through pyruvate kinase. The data were adapted from those of Claus *et al.* (1979).

concentrations of fructose bisphosphate. Similar results have been obtained by Ljungström *et al.* (1974, 1976) with the pig liver enzyme. Thus, phosphorylation of the enzyme caused a shift of the phosphoenolpyruvate concentration curve to the right and resulted in an increase in the Hill coefficient (Table II). The effect of phosphorylation was overcome by saturating concentrations of phosphoenolpyruvate or by fructose bisphosphate (Ljungström *et al.*, 1974, 1976; Titanji *et al.*, 1976; Riou *et al.*, 1976) (Fig. 4). Hydrogen ions also overcame the inhibition due to phosphorylation (Ljungström *et al.*, 1976). This is consistent with the observation that fructose bisphosphate promoted binding of phosphoenolpyruvate only at high pH, indicating that dissociation of a proton is required for allosteric control (Rozengurt *et al.*, 1969). Thus, no deviation from Michaelis-Menten kinetics could be demonstrated at pH 6.9,

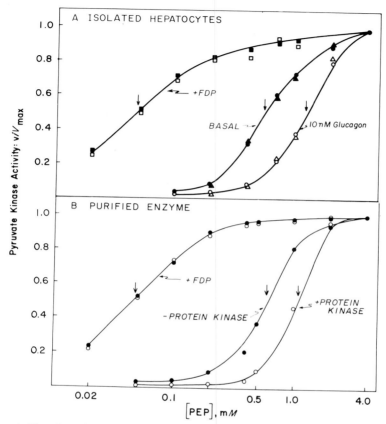

Fig. 4. Phosphoenolpyruvate (PEP) dependence of pyruvate kinase activity in ammonium sulfate-treated extracts of hepatocytes and of a homogeneous preparation of rat liver pyruvate kinase. Hepatocytes were incubated without (closed symbols) or with 10 nM glucagon (open symbols). The arrows represent the $S_{0.5}$ for PEP and the values were 0.55 mM in the absence of glucagon or protein kinase. When the samples were assayed in the presence of 50 μM fructose bisphosphate (FDP), the $S_{0.5}$ was 0.06 mM in the presence or absence of glucagon or portein kinase. The data were adapted from those of Claus *et al.* (1979).

using either the phosphorylated or nonphosphorylated enzyme in the presence or the absence of fructose bisphosphate (Ljungström *et al.*, 1976). In contrast to the above, ATP and alanine had greater effects on the phosphorylated than on the nonphosphorylated protein (Ljungström *et al.*, 1976; Riou *et al.*, 1976) (Table II). In fact, the inhibitory effect of phosphorylation was most clearly seen when the enzyme was assayed with low concentrations of phosphoenolpyruvate in the presence of millimolar concentrations of ATP and alanine (Riou *et al.*, 1976).

TABLE II

EFFECT OF PHOSPHORYLATION ON THE KINETIC PROPERTIES OF THE L-TYPE
PYRUVATE KINASE[a]

	L-type	Phospho-L-type
Kinetics with regard to PEP	Sigmoidal	Sigmoidal
$(S_{0.5})$	(0.6 mM)	1.2 mM)
Hill coefficient	2.0	2.7–2.9
Activation by FDP	Yes	Yes, but less sensitive than L-type
Inhibition by ATP (K_i, app)	1 mM	0.4 mM)
Inhibition by alanine (K_i, app)	1 mM	0.3

[a] From Ljungström et al. (1974, 1976); Riou et al. (1976); Berglund et al. (1977a); Pilkis et al. (1978a); Claus et al. (1979).

Phosphorylation of the pig or rat liver enzyme reduced activation by fructose bisphosphate (Ljungström et al., 1976; Riou et al., 1976; Van Berkel et al., 1977a). This also was seen best when the enzyme was assayed in the presence of physiological concentrations of alanine and ATP (Riou et al., 1976).

Phosphorylation appears to modify the ease with which the enzyme undergoes conformational changes in response to its effectors. The end result is to shift the equilibrium from the active to the inactive form of the enzyme. It can be postulated that increasing concentrations of phosphoenolpyruvate and fructose bisphosphate cause a conformational change in the enzyme perhaps by binding preferentially to the active form of the enzyme. Phosphorylation of the enzyme subunits tends to impede this conformational change, shifting the equilibrium between active and inactive forms of the enzyme subunit, and results in decreased enzyme activity. High concentrations of phosphoenolpyruvate and fructose bisphosphate can overcome this effect of phosphorylation. Such changes might be expected to result in changes in the quaternary structure of the enzyme. However, no evidence for an effect of phosphorylation on the association–dissociation properties of the L-isozyme has been reported, although such an effect has been claimed for the K-isozyme from chicken liver (Eigenbrodt and Schoner, 1977b).

There have been several reports that attempt to correlate the amount of phosphate incorporated into pyruvate kinase with changes in activity of the enzyme. Ljungström et al. (1974) found that the maximum amount of labeled phosphate that could be incorporated into the pig liver enzyme was 4 mol/mol of enzyme. Subsequently, they reported that incorporation of 1.5 mol of labeled phosphate per mol of enzyme produced only a 25% inhibition of enzyme activity (Ljungström et al., 1976). Titanji et

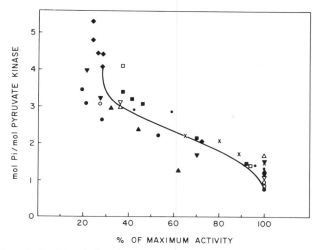

Fig. 5. The relationship of phosphate content of pyruvate kinase to enzymatic activity. Moles of phosphate per mole of pyruvate kinase are plotted versus the percent of maximum enzyme activity. The data are from El-Maghrabi *et al.* (1980).

al. (1976) found that the incorporation by the cyclic AMP-dependent protein kinase of 1.5–2 mol of labeled phosphate/mol of enzyme was sufficient to inhibit activity of the rat liver enzyme over 90%. When rat liver slices were incubated with 32 P_i and glucagon, the incorporation of 3 mol of labeled phosphate/mol of enzyme caused only a 50% reduction in enzyme activity (Ljungström and Ekman, 1977). Injection of $^{32}P_i$ and glucagon into a rat *in vivo* caused a 30% reduction in enzyme activity and the incorporation of 1.4 mol of labeled phosphate/mol of enzyme (Riou *et al.*, 1978). These different results may be due to the fact that only the amount of radioactive phosphate incorporation was determined while the amount of endogenous phosphate in these various preparations was unknown. Recently, El-Maghrabi *et al.* (1980) have attempted to correlate changes in activity of the rat liver enzyme with the actual amount of phosphate incorporated into the enzyme by the cyclic AMP-dependent protein kinase (Fig. 6). Changes from 90% to 40% of maximal activity occurred when the amount of phosphate increased from 1.5 mol to 3 mol/mol of enzyme. Since there was about 1 mol of phosphate/mol of enzyme in a site whose phosphorylation was not catalyzed by cyclic AMP-dependent protein kinase (for details, see El-Maghrabi *et al.*, 1980), the incorporation by the cyclic AMP-dependent protein kinase of 2 mol of phosphate/mol of enzyme resulted in essentially maximal inhibition of enzyme activity.

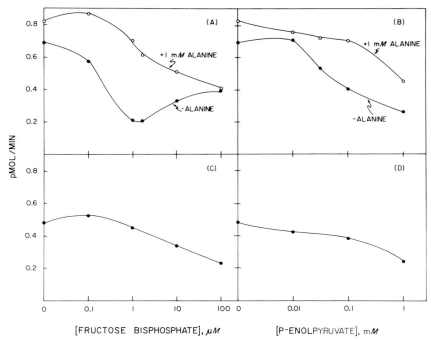

Fig. 6. The effect of fructose bisphosphate and phosphoenolpyruvate on the rate of phosphorylation of pyruvate kinase in the presence and absence of alanine. Purified pyruvate kinase containing either 1 mol of phosphate/mol of enzyme (panels A and B) or 3 mol/mol (panels C and D) was incubated for 5 minutes with $[\gamma\text{-}^{32}P]$ATP and cyclic AMP-dependent protein kinase in the presence of fructose bisphosphate (panels A and C or phosphoenolpyruvate (panels B and D) and either without (●) or with (○) 1 mM alanine. The data are from El-Maghrabi *et al.* (1980).

The site of phosphorylation on the enzyme has been determined. Humble *et al.* (1975) showed that alkali-inactivated pig liver pyruvate kinase and a cyanogen bromide peptide from the same enzyme could be phosphorylated by $[\gamma\text{-}^{32}P]$ATP in the presence of cyclic AMP-dependent protein kinase. They also isolated a peptide from rat liver pyruvate kinase and showed that the minimum structural requirements for phosphorylation were met by the pentapeptide Arg-Arg-Ala-Ser-Val (Hjelmqvist *et al.*, 1974). Evidence from other laboratories suggest that this or very closely related sequences are at the sites of phosphorylation in other proteins that serve as substrates for cyclic AMP-dependent protein kinases (Daile and Carnegie 1974; Kemp *et al.*, 1975; Daile *et al.*, 1975). The concentration of pentapeptide which gave half-maximal rates of phosphorylation was 0.08 mM while that of a heptapeptide (Leu-Arg-

Arg-Ser-Val-Ala) was 0.01 mM (Zetterqvist *et al.*, 1976). On the other hand, Pilkis *et al.* (1980) found that the concentration of native pyruvate kinase required for half-maximal rates of phosphorylation was about 17 μM or 68 μM in terms of its subunit concentration. Thus, the native enzyme was not as good a substrate for the cyclic AMP-dependent protein kinase as is the peptide analog, a conclusion which differed from that claimed by others (Zetterqvist *et al.*, 1976; Yeaman *et al.*, 1977). In the previous studies, an exact value could not be obtained since the rate of phosphorylation continued to increase even when micromolar concentrations of pyruvate kinase were used (Berglund *et al.*, 1977a). Pilkis *et al.* (1980) found that enzyme concentrations of up to 100 μM were required to determine the K_m value.

In studies to date, the rat and pig liver pyruvate kinases appear to be phosphorylated only by a cyclic AMP-dependent protein kinase (Titanji *et al.*, 1976; Berglund *et al.*, 1977a; Ljungström *et al.*, 1976; Riou *et al.*, 1976). Phosphorylation has been studied using a homogeneous preparation of bovine liver or heart catalytic subunit of the cyclic AMP-dependent protein kinase and homogenous rat liver pyruvate kinase (Pilkis *et al.*, 1978b). In many cases, however, crude preparations of protein kinase were used, and it is possible that they contained cyclic AMP-independent as well as cyclic AMP-dependent protein kinases. Pilkis *et al.* (1978a) have investigated the possibility that an independent kinase could be involved by studying phosphorylation in rat hepatocyte extracts that had been gel filtered on Sephadex G-25 in order to remove all low molecular weight compounds. The addition of cyclic AMP and Mg-ATP to these extracts produced a time-dependent inactivation of pyruvate kinase, whereas the addition of Mg-ATP alone had no effect. The cyclic AMP-induced inactivation was characterized by an increase in the $S_{0.5}$ for phosphoenolpyruvate and could be completely blocked by the addition of protein kinase inhibitor, a compound specific for the catalytic subunit of cyclic AMP-dependent protein kinase (Walsh *et al.*, 1971). These results demonstrated cyclic AMP-dependent phosphorylation but did not rule out the existence of an intermediate kinase that requires the cyclic AMP-dependent protein kinase for activation. This would be analogous to the cascade system that activates phosphorylase. If such an intermediate kinase existed, addition of protein kinase inhibitor to a Sephadex-treated extract after inactivation has been initiated by cyclic AMP should not stop further inactivation of pyruvate kinase. However, the inhibitor, added 6 minutes after cyclic AMP, completely suppressed any further inactivation of pyruvate kinase (Pilkis *et al.*, 1978a). The above results provide no evidence for cyclic AMP-independent phosphorylation of pyruvate kinase.

The inactivation of rat liver pyruvate kinase in hepatocyte extracts by submaximal concentrations of cyclic AMP can be suppressed by the addition of physiological concentrations of fructose bisphosphate or phosphoenolpyruvate (Feliu *et al.*, 1977; Pilkis *et al.*, 1978a). Alanine had no effect by itself (Feliu *et al.*, 1977; Pilkis *et al.*, 1978a), but it did relieve the inhibition by fructose bisphosphate or phosphoenolpyruvate (Feliu *et al.*, 1977). These studies suggested that the allosteric effectors influenced the phosphorylation of pyruvate kinase since they were done under conditions which should have inhibited the activity of phosphoprotein phosphatases. Berglund *et al.* (1977a) reported that alanine increased the rate of phosphorylation of purified pig liver pyruvate kinase by a partially purified preparation of cyclic AMP-dependent protein kinase. Fructose bisphosphate and phosphoenolpyruvate had no effect on the phosphorylation. Eigenbrodt and Schoner (1977b) found that fructose bisphosphate decreased and alanine increased the cyclic AMP-independent phosphorylation of the K-type pyruvate kinase from chicken liver by affecting the dimer-to-tetramer equilibrium of the enzyme. Alanine favored formation of the dimer whereas fructose bisphosphate favored tetramer formation. It is not known whether the L-isozyme from pig or rat liver undergoes any tetramer-to-dimer transitions under the influence of allosteric effectors. Recently, El-Maghrabi *et al.* (1980) studied the influence of allosteric effectors on the phosphorylation of purified rat liver pyruvate kinase by a homogeneous preparation of the catalytic subunit of cyclic AMP-dependent protein kinase (Fig. 6). When pyruvate kinase that contained less than 1 mol of phosphate/mol of enzyme was used as substrate, 1–3 μM fructose bisphosphate inhibited the initial rate of phosphorylation by more than 80% (panel A). Phosphoenolpyruvate also inhibited the initial rate of phosphorylation, but was not as effective as fructose bisphosphate (panel B). Alanine had only a slight stimulatory effect on the initial rate of phosphorylation, but it relieved the inhibition by physiological concentrations of fructose bisphosphate and phosphoenolpyruvate (panels A and B). When pyruvate kinase contained 3 mol of phosphate/mol of enzyme, the influence of allosteric effectors on the phosphorylation of the enzyme was less pronounced. Ten- and one-hundred-fold higher concentrations of phosphoenolpyruvate and fructose bisphosphate, respectively, were necessary to ellicit inhibition similar to those seen with the dephosphorylated enzyme (panels C and D). These results are in good agreement with those obtained using hepatocyte extracts (Feliu *et al.*, 1977; Pilkis *et al.*, 1978a). They suggest that pyruvate kinase is a better substrate for the cyclic AMP-dependent protein kinase when pyruvate kinase is in the inactive form than when it is in the active form.

The enzyme(s) responsible for the dephosphorylation of pyruvate kinase have received little attention. A histone phosphatase, which is capable of dephosphorylating [^{32}P]pyruvate kinase, has been purified from rat liver (Titanji *et al.*, 1976). The dephosphorylation produced an activation of the enzyme. Van Berkel *et al.* (1977a) reported that inactivated pyruvate kinase in crude homogenates from hepatocytes incubated with glucagon could be reactivated by incubation with divalent cations. A phosphoprotein phosphatase with a rather broad substrate specificity has also been isolated from chicken liver. It was able to dephosphorylate and reactivate the K-isozyme (Eigenbrodt and Schoner, 1977b).

Taunton *et al.* (1972) first reported that hormones could acutely affect the activity of pyruvate kinase. They showed that injection of glucagon or epinephrine into the portal vein of rats had a rapid decrease in activity and that insulin injection caused the opposite effect (Taunton *et al.*, 1974; Stifel *et al.*, 1974). A number of laboratories now have confirmed this observation by demonstrating that addition of glucagon to the isolated perfused rat liver (Blair *et al.*, 1976) or to isolated hepatocytes (Friedrichs, 1976; Ven Berkel *et al.*, 1976, 1977a,b; Riou *et al.*, 1976; Pilkis *et al.*, 1976a,b; Feliu *et al.*, 1976; Foster and Blair, 1976, 1978; Ishibashi and Cottam, 1978; Chan and Exton, 1978; Garrison *et al.*, 1979; Claus *et al.*, 1979) leads to an inhibition of pyruvate kinase activity. Riou *et al.* (1976) compared the kinetics of the enzyme in extracts of glucagon-treated cells with those of the purified enzyme that had been phosphorylated *in vitro*. They found several similarities. First, there was an apparent decrease in the affinity of the enzyme for phosphoenolpyruvate (Fig. 4). Second, both preparations were more sensitive to inhibition by ATP and alanine. Third, both enzymes were less sensitive to activation by fructose bisphosphate. Riou *et al.* (1978) have also obtained direct evidence to support the hypothesis that glucagon stimulates the phosphorylation of this enzyme by demonstrating that the hormone stimulates ^{32}P incorporation into the enzyme *in vivo*. Glucagon administration increased the moles of phosphate incorporated per mole of enzyme from 0.5 to 1.4. This increase in enzyme-bound phosphate was associated with an inhibition of pyruvate kinase activity and an increase in cyclic AMP (Riou *et al.*, 1978). Incubation of rat liver slices (Ljungström and Ekman, 1977) or isolated hepatocytes (Ishibashi and Cottam, 1978; Garrison *et al.*, 1979; Steiner *et al.*, 1980) with ^{32}P$_i$ and a high concentration of glucagon also stimulated the incorporation of labeled phosphate into the enzyme by three- to sixfold. Half-maximal stimulation of pyruvate kinase phosphorylation in liver slices was obtained with 7 nM glucagon (Ljungström and Ekman, 1977), while the value was 0.2 nM in isolated hepatocytes (Steiner *et al.*, 1980).

Catecholamines also inhibit hepatocyte pyruvate kinase activity, but the inhibition is quite small compared to that seen with glucagon (Feliu et al., 1976; Kemp and Clark, 1978; Foster and Blair, 1978; Chan and Exton, 1978; Garrison and Borland, 1979; Blackmore et al., 1979b; Garrison et al., 1979; Blair et al., 1979; Claus et al., 1979). The weak effect of catecholamines on pyruvate kinase activity in isolated hepatocytes correlated well with their small effect on gluconeogenesis (Pilkis et al., 1975; Claus and Pilkis, 1976). Chan and Exton (1978) used specific adrenergic antagonists to determine whether the effect of epinephrine was mediated by α- or β-adrenergic receptors. They found that both α- and β-antagonists partially reversed the inhibition of pyruvate kinase by 10 μM epinephrine or phenylephrine, a synthetic α-adrenergic agonist. The reversal of inhibition by β antagonists tended to correlate with changes in cyclic AMP levels whereas the reversal by α antagonists did not. The addition of 1-methyl-3-isobutylxanthine, a cyclic nucleotide phosphodiesterase inhibitor, along with epinephrine or phenylephrine enhanced the inhibitory effect of the catecholamines on pyruvate kinase. These inhibitions were largely abolished by α antagonists without significant changes in cyclic AMP levels. On the other hand, the β antagonist, propranolol, only partially blocked the inhibition of pyruvate kinase even though it decreased the rise in cyclic AMP levels. The authors concluded that epinephrine was affecting pyruvate kinase predominantly by an α-adrenergic cyclic AMP-independent mechanism and that 1-methyl-3-isobutylxanthine enhanced the effect of catecholamines mainly by potentiating this mechanism (Chan and Exton, 1977, 1978). The conclusion that catecholamines affect pyruvate kinase by an α-adrenergic mechanism is supported by results from other laboratories. Foster and Blair (1978) and Blair et al. (1979) reported that the inhibition of pyruvate kinase by 10 μM epinephrine with or without theophylline was reversed by phenoxybenzamine but unaffected by propranolol. Garrison and Borland (1979) reported that 10 μM norepinephrine caused a 25% inhibition of pyruvate kinase activity that was abolished by the α antagonist ergotamine but unaffected by propranolol. In the presence of propranolol, norepinephrine had no effect on cyclic AMP levels or on the activity of the cyclic AMP-dependent protein kinase (Garrison et al., 1979). Claus et al. (1979) reported that the small inhibition of pyruvate kinase activity induced by 1μM phenylephrine was not accompanied by any activation of the cyclic AMP-dependent protein kinase. On the other hand, Kemp and Clark (1978) reported that both α- and β-agonists and antagonists affected cyclic AMP-dependent protein kinase activity as well as pyruvate kinase activity. Activation of the cyclic AMP-dependent protein kinase by epinephrine or phenylephrine was partially blocked by either α antagonists or β antagonists whereas the inactivation of pyruvate kinase was blocked preferentially by the α antagonists. They suggested that the effects of catecholamines were mediated by activation of the cyclic AMP-dependent protein kinase. The difference between these results and those of Chan and Exton (1978) have been ascribed in part to the use of calcium-deficient hepatocytes by Kemp and Clark (Exton, 1979a). In calcium-depleted hepatocytes, the ability of epinephrine or phenylephrine to elevate cyclic AMP levels and to inhibit pyruvate kinase activity was enhanced in the presence or absence of 1-methyl-3-isobutyl-xanthine (Assimacopoulos-Jeannet *et al.*, 1977; Chan and Exton, 1977, 1978). Under these conditions, changes in pyruvate kinase activity elicited by α agonists correlated with changes in cyclic AMP levels, supporting the idea that in calcium-depleted cells cyclic AMP was the mediator of α-adrenergic effects on the enzyme (Chan and Exton, 1978). Garrison *et al.* (1979) reported similar effects of calcium depletion on the ability of norephinephrine to affect cyclic AMP levels, cyclic AMP-dependent protein kinase activity, and pyruvate kinase activity. In contrast to all of these reports, Hué *et al.* (1978) reported that phenylephrine had no effect on pyruvate kinase or cyclic AMP-dependent protein kinase activity unless calcium was removed from the medium. They argued that the inhibition of pyruvate kinase activity by α-adrenergic agonists is only observed in hepatocytes that are Ca^{2+}-deprived where these agents cause a paradoxical increase in cyclic AMP levels and in cyclic AMP-dependent protein kinase activity (Chan and Exton, 1977, 1978). Since preparation of hepatocytes usually involves some period of time when the cells are without Ca^{2+}, it is possible that the demonstration of variable but small inhibition of pyruvate kinase activity by α-adrenergic agonists is due to varying degrees of cellular Ca^{2+} depletion. Thus, it is not entirely clear whether the effects of α-adrenergic agonists on pyruvate kinase activity are mediated by a cyclic AMP-dependent or -independent mechanism, although most of the available evidence supports the latter mechanism.

As in the case of catecholamines, the effects of vasopressin and angiotensin II on pyruvate kinase activity also cannot be assigned clearly as yet to an activation of a cyclic AMP-independent pathway. These peptide hormones stimulated hepatic glycogenolysis and phosphorylase activity through a mechanism that does not involve changes in the level of cyclic AMP or the activity of cyclic AMP-dependent protein kinase (Hems and Whitton, 1973; Kirk and Hems, 1974; Keppens and DeWulf, 1975, 1977; Stubbs *et al.*, 1976; Van de Werve *et al.*, 1977; Hué *et al.*, 1978; Garrison *et al.*, 1979). Chan and Exton (1978) reported that vasopressin inhibited pyruvate kinase activity by 15%. Garrison *et al.* (1979) reported that vasopressin and angiotensin II inhibited the enzyme by 40%. However, Hué *et al.* (1978) reported that vasopressin had no effect on pyruvate kinase activity although it stimulated gluconeogenesis.

It has been proposed that the cyclic AMP-independent effects of catecholamines on hepatic glycogenolysis may be mediated by changes in the intracellular distribution of Ca^{2+} (Keppens *et al.*, 1977; Assimacopoulos-Jeannet *et al.*, 1977; Blackmore *et al.*, 1979a). However, the only evidence that Ca^{2+} is involved in the regulation of pyruvate kinase is that of Garrison *et al.* (1979). They reported that norepinephrine, vasopressin, and angiotensin II inhibited pyruvate kinase activity and stimulated phosphorylation of the enzyme in isolated hepatocytes. The effects of vasopressin and angiotensin II were completely abolished when the cells were incubated in a Ca^{2+}-free medium. These results strongly suggest that the effects of these two polypeptide hormones are mediated by a Ca^{2+}-requiring cyclic AMP-independent mechanism. However, the stimulation of pyruvate kinase phosphorylation by norepinephrine was unaffected by the absence of Ca^{2+}, perhaps because of the paradoxical elevation of cyclic AMP levels and activation of cyclic AMP-dependent protein kinse seen under these conditions. Furthermore, the addition of the Ca^{2+} ionophore A23187 to hepatocytes had little effect on pyruvate kinase or gluconeogenesis (Foster and Blair, 1978; Chan and Exton, 1978). Thus, there is little evidence for a role for Ca^{2+} in the regulation of pyruvate kinase by catecholamines. However, catecholamines do appear to act on pyruvate kinase by altering its phosphorylation state (Chan and Exton, 1978; Claus *et al.*, 1979; Garrison *et al.*, 1979). Further support for this hypothesis comes from the studies of Steiner *et al.* (1980) who showed that phenylephrine in the presence of 1-methyl-3-isobutylxanthine and propranolol also stimulated the phosphorylation of pyruvate kinase and the effect was largely abolished by the α antagonist dihydroergocryptine. The apparent cyclic AMP-independent effects of catecholamines, vasopressin, and angiotensin II may be due to activation of an as yet unidentified protein kinase(s) or inhibition of a phospho-protein phosphatase or both. Calcium ions do not play a role in the inhibition of pyruvate kinase by glucagon (Van Berkel *et al.*, 1977b).

Insulin has little effect on pyruvate kinase activity. It does prevent the inhibition induced by submaximal concentrations of glucagon (Feliu *et al.*, 1976; Blair *et al.*, 1976; Claus *et al.*, 1979). The concentration of glucagon that produced half-maximal inactivation of the enzyme was increased twofold in the presence of insulin (Feliu *et al.*, 1976; Claus *et al.*, 1979). Insulin suppressed both the activation of cyclic AMP-dependent protein kinase and the initial rate of pyruvate kinase inactivation by glucagon, suggesting that the effects were mediated by a fall in the level of cyclic AMP (Claus *et al.*, 1979). The effects of catecholamines on pyruvate kinase activity are small and insulin suppressed their effects at all concentrations (Feliu *et al.*, 1976). Insulin also suppressed the inhibition by phenylephrine (Claus *et al.*, 1979). Blackmore *et al.* (1979b) also reported such an effect, but only when Ca^{2+} was removed from the medium. The results by Claus *et al.* (1979) suggest that insulin can affect pyruvate kinase by a cyclic AMP-independent mechanism. There have been no direct demonstrations that insulin modulates the phosphorylation state of the enzyme in intact cells. However, the effect of insulin was associated with a decrease in the $S_{0.5}$ for phosphoenolpyruvate (Blair *et al.*, 1976; Claus *et al.*, 1979), which suggests that insulin alters the phosphorylation state. Further evidence was provided by the fact that the effect of insulin on activity of pyruvate kinase was observed in ammonium sulfate-treated extracts (Claus *et al.*, 1979), where allosteric effectors have been removed and only the effects of covalent modification (phosphorylation) are observed (Blair *et al.*, 1976; Foster and Blair, 1978; Claus *et al.*, 1979).

The phosphorylation state of pyruvate kinase in intact hepatocytes also may be influenced by the intracellular concentration of the allosteric effectors of the enzyme. Feliu *et al.* (1977) suggested an important role for phosphoenolpyruvate in regulating the phosphorylation state of pyruvate kinase since an inverse relationship existed between its concentration and the activation of pyruvate kinase in rat liver *in vivo*. Claus *et al.* (1979) found that elevated levels of fructose bisphospahte in isolated hepatocytes could influence the ability of glucagon to inactivate pyruvate kinase through a phosphorylation mechanism. When hepatocytes from fasted rats where incubated with 5 m*M* dihydroxyacetone, the intracellular level of fructose bisphosphate rose fourfold and the concentration of glucagon required for half-maximal inhibition increased from 0.3 n*M* to 0.8 n*M*. The elevated levels of fructose bisphosphate did not affect the activation of the cyclic AMP-dependent protein kinase by glucagon, but did not slow the initial rate of inactivation of pyruvate kinase by the hormone. Elevation of neither alanine nor phosphoenolpyruvate levels altered the ability of glucagon to inactivate pyruvate kinase. However, Foster and Blair (1978) reported that the inactivation of pyruvate kinase by physiological glucagon concentrations was enhanced in the presence of alanine. In these studies, the effect of alanine was observed in the presence of dihydroxyacetone which raises fructose bisphosphate levels, and their results may be related to the observation that alanine relieves the effect of fructose bisphosphate on the inactivation of the enzyme *in vitro* (Feliu *et al.*, 1977; El-Maghrabi *et al.*, 1980).

The various factors that can influence pyruvate kinase activity are summarized in Fig. 7. The addition of glucagon to hepatocytes leads to inactivation when the enzyme is assayed with low substrate concentrations, but not at high substrate concentrations or in the presence of micromolar concentrations of fructose bisphosphate. The effect of gluca-

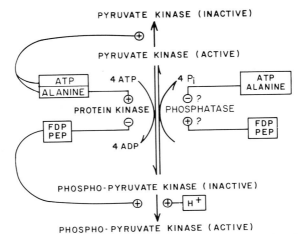

Fɪɢ. 7. Factors affecting the activity, phosphorylation, and dephosphorylation of hepatic pyruvate kinase.

gon is mediated by a cyclic AMP-induced increase in protein kinase activity and by a decrease in fructose bisphosphate levels (Blair *et al.*, 1973; Pilkis *et al.*, 1976a,b). The fall in the concentration of the latter reduces pyruvate kinase activity by affecting the equilbrium between active and inactive forms of the enzyme. This change presumably converts the protein to a more favorable substrate for inactivation by the protein kinase and perhaps to a less favorable substrate for activation by a phosphoprotein phosphatase. The inactivation of pyruvate kinase by these concerted changes brings about a rise in phosphoenolpyruvate, which may then act as a negative feedback inhibitor of further phosphorylation of pyruvate kinase. Thus, enzyme activity can be regulated by phosphorylation, changes in the level of allosteric effectors, and by the ability of allosteric effectors to modulate phosphorylation of the enzyme indirectly.

b. Phosphoenolpyruvate Carboxykinase. Phosphoenolpyruvate carboxykinase was first discovered in the chicken liver mitochondria by Utter and Kurahashi (1953). The enzyme has since been found to be present in high concentration in liver and kidney cortex in all species (Utter and Kolenbrander, 1972) where it plays an essential role in gluconeogenesis from three or four carbon precursors. Livers of all species studied to date contain both a mitochondrial and a cytosolic form of the enzyme (Tilghman *et al.*, 1976). Both forms of the enzyme appear to be a single polypeptide chain of molecular weight ranging from 71,000 for the avian liver enzyme (Chiao, 1976) to possibly 85,000 for the rat liver enzyme (Tilghman *et al.*, 1976). However, the two forms of phosphenolpyruvate carboxykinase have been shown to be distinct proteins on the basis of immunological and chemical studies (Ballard and Hanson, 1969; Ballard, 1971; Diesterhaft *et al.*, 1971).

While there is ample evidence for the dietary and hormonal regulation of phosphoenolpyruvate carboxykinase levels (see Tilghman *et al.*, 1976, for review) the evidence that the enzyme is acutely affected by hormones is only indirect. When rat livers were perfused with glucagon, cyclic AMP, or epinephrine and the amount of glycolytic intermediates were measured, a "crossover" was observed between pyruvate and phosphoenolpyruvate (Exton and Park, 1969; Ui *et al.*, 1973a,b). However, these changes appear to be adequately explained by inhibition of pyruvate kinase and activation of pyruvate carboxylation. Attempts to measure a change in the kinetic properties of phosphoenolpyruvate carboxykinase in homogenates of livers treated with glucagon have been unsuccessful. We also have been unable to phosphorylate the purified enzyme with the catalytic subunit of cyclic AMP-dependent protein kinase (T. H. Claus, unpublished results). Wicks *et al.* (1972) also reported that the enzyme was not subject to phosphorylation. However, the addition of ATP and Mg^{2+} to kidney cortex homogenates activated phosphoenolpyruvate carboxykinase (Graf *et al.*, 1976). Attempts to find metabolic effectors for the enzyme also appear to have been unsuccessful, although it can be postulated that variations in the concentration of oxaloacetate can regulate the activity of the enzyme. The $S_{0.5}$ for oxaloacetate was originally thought to be too high for the enzyme to participate in gluconeogenesis. But more recent studies have placed the value in the 1–10 μM range (Ballard, 1970; Walsh and Chen, 1971; Jomain-Baum *et al.*, 1976) which is about the same as the concentration of oxaloacetate (5–10 μM) in the cytosol of perfused rat liver (Williamson *et al.*, 1969a). On the other hand, the $S_{0.5}$ for $Mn-GTP^{2-}$ has been estimated to be 16 μM (Jomain-Baum *et al.*, 1976), whereas the GTP concentration in the whole liver is 100–600 μM (Chance *et al.*, 1965; Clifford *et al.*, 1972). If the nucleotide were evenly distributed in the liver, phosphoenolpyruvate carboxykinase would be nearly saturated with GTP. This would suggest that GTP does not have a regulatory role in phosphoenolpyruvate formation, as was suggested from studies with isolated guinea pig liver mitochondria Garber and Ballard, 1970; Ishihara and Kikuchi, 1968).

Another type of control of phosphoenolpyruvate carboxykinase appears to involve metal ions. The enzyme requires two metal ions in order to form phosphoenolpyruvate at maximum rates (Foster *et al.*, 1967; Holten and Nordlie, 1965; Utter and Kolenbrander, 1972). Magnesium is required in approximately stoichiometric amounts to the nucleotide (GTP or ITP), and micromolar concentrations of a divalent transition metal ion such as Fe^{2+}, Mn^{2+}, Co^{2+}, or Cd^{2+} activate the enzyme (Snoke *et al.*, 1971). When phosphoenolpyruvate carboxykinase was assayed in rat liver cytosol, the addition of the transition metal ions activated the enzyme two- to threefold (Snoke *et al.*, 1971; Bentle *et al.*, 1976). If the cytosol first was incubated with the transition metal ion, even greater effects were observed, and Fe^{2+} was the most effective activator. Evidence has been presented that Fe^{2+} is the natural activator in rat liver cytosol. When rat liver phosphoenolpyruvate carboxykinase was purified to homogeneity, the enzyme lost sensitivity to Fe^{2+} but not to Mn^{2+} stimulation (Bentle *et al.*, 1976). Addition of rat liver cytosol to the purified enzyme restored the response to Fe^{2+}. This observation prompted the search for and the discovery of a protein that permits Fe^{2+} to activate the purified enzyme three- to fourfold (Bentle and Lardy, 1977). This protein, called phosphoenolpyruvate carboxykinase ferroactivator, has a molecular weight of approximately 100,000. A subunit molecular weight of 23,600 was obtained by sodium dodecyl sulfate electrophoresis. The activity of phosphoenolpyruvate carboxykinase with Fe^{3+}, Mn^{2+}, Co^{2+}, Cd^{2+}, Mg^{2+}, or Ca^{2+} was not affected by the ferroactivator. These results suggest that the rate of phosphoenolpyruvate synthesis by gluconeogenic tissues may be regulated by the availability of intracellular Fe^{2+} to the ferroactivator and phosphoenolpyruvate carboxykinase. Support for this view comes from studies of the tissue distribution of the ferroactivator and the effects of diabetes and starvation on it (MacDonald *et al.*, 1978). The highest concentrations of ferroactivator were found in liver, kidney, and erythrocytes, and intermediate levels were found in the heart and pancreas. Except for erythrocytes and heart, the tissue distribution parallels that reported for phosphoenolpyruvate carboxykinase. Starvation and diabetes increased the amount of ferroactivator found in liver and kidney, and insulin treatment of diabetic rats returned the amount of ferroactivator to normal. Thus the ferroactivator showed adaptive behavior which paralleled that of phosphoenolpyruvate carboxykinase. Recently, MacDonald (1979) identified an enzymatic activity in rat liver microsomes which inactivated phosphoenolpyruvate carboxykinase rapidly. Since the addition of dithiothreitol restored activity to the enzyme, he proposed that this microsomal activity may inactivate phosphoenolpyruvate carboxykinase by oxidizing sulfhydryl groups. Whether or not these factors participate in an acute activation of the enzyme in response to a hormone such as glucagon is unknown.

2. The Fructose 6-Phosphate–Fructose Bisphosphate Substrate Cycle and Its Enzymes

The importance of the fructose bisphosphate cycle in the regulation of gluconeogenesis from physiological substrates is less certain than it is for the phosphoenolpyruvate–pyruvate cycle. The rate of gluconeogenesis from 3-carbon precursors is not limited directly by reactions in this region of the pathway. There is five times more fructose bisphosphatase than phosphofructokinase activity in liver (Scrutton and Utter, 1968), so that changes in the flux through phosphofructokinase may not have as large effects on gluconeogenesis as changes in flux through pyruvate kinase. Hué and Hers (1974) even have argued on the basis of the *in vivo* concentrations of inhibitors and activators of the enzymes that little substrate cycling would occur. Garfinkel *et al.* (1979) came to the same conclusion using computer modeling techniques. However, phosphofructokinase and fructose bisphosphatase activities may regulate gluconeogenesis indirectly by controlling the hepatic level of fructose bisphosphate, a potent activator of pyruvate kinase. The addition of glucagon or cyclic AMP to rat hepatocytes or perfused rat liver causes a decrease in the level of fructose biphosphate (Williamson *et al.*, 1969b; Blair *et al.*, 1973; Harris, 1975; Pilkis *et al.*, 1976a) and thus promotes inactivation of the enzyme, as discussed earlier. The mechanism whereby glucagon lowers fructose bisphosphate levels must involve a stimulation of fructose bisphosphatase and/or an inhibition of phosphofructokinase activity.

Evidence that both enzymes of this cycle are operative in liver *in vivo*, and in perfused liver or isolated hepatocytes has been reviewed by Katz and Rognstad (1976). Hormone effects on this substrate cycle have been studied by following the metabolism of glucose labeled in various positions with tritium and/or ^{14}C. Clark *et al.* (1974a) estimated the rate of substrate cycling in rat liver *in vivo* by following the metabolism of intraperitoneally injected [5-^3H, U-^{14}C]glucose. When the net flux of substrate was in the direction of glucose synthesis, phosphorylation of fructose 6-phosphate by phosphofructokinase was equal to the rate of substrate cycling. Fructose 6-phosphate phosphorylation was estimated by the amount of tritium found in the intrahepatic water. They found that the rate of phosphorylation of fructose 6-phosphate was about 60% greater than the *in vivo* rate of lactate gluconeogenesis in fed rats, but only about 40% of the rate of gluconeogenesis in starved rats. Clark *et al.* (1974b) also found that glucagon and cyclic AMP affected the substrate cycle in isolated hepatocytes by inhibiting flux through phosphofructokinase and stimulating flux through fructose bisphosphatase. Similar effects were reported by Katz *et al.* (1975). Kneer *et al.* (1974) found that epinephrine and cyclic GMP had the same effect on this substrate cycle as did glucagon. Since the effect of epinephrine was blocked by phenoxybenzamine but not by propranolol, they concluded that epinephrine expressed its activity through the α-receptor. However, Dunn *et al.* (1976), suggested that glucagon activated flux through fructose bisphosphatase with little change in phosphofructokinase flux.

The possibilities for serious quantitative errors in the [^{3}H,^{14}C]glucose method of measuring this substrate cycle in liver have been pointed out (Katz *et al.*, 1975; Katz and Rognstad, 1976). Hué and Hers (1974) have argued that this cycle does not exist in liver and have attributed the production of tritiated water from [5-^{3}H]glucose to a transaldolase exchange reaction and to the operation of the pentose cycle. In order to avoid these difficulties, Rognstad and Katz (1976) devised a method that uses [1-^{14}C] galactose instead of tritiated glucose as the tracer substrate. They found in isolated hepatocytes from starved rats that the estimated rate of flux through phosphofructokinase ranged from 15% to 40% of the net rate of gluconeogenesis from dihydroxyacetone. Glucagon depressed the rate of flux through phosphofructokinase by as much as 85%, but the decrease in flux accounted for only about 50% of the increase in glucose synthesis. Epinephrine (10–100 μM) also depressed flux but not as effectively as glucagon. The effect of epinephrine was reversed only partially by the addition of the β blocker propranolol suggesting that epinephrine affected flux at least in part by an α-adrenergic mechanism. Flux was also depressed by the addition of ethanol or glyoxylate, both of which may cause citrate, an inhibitor of phosphofructokinse, to accumulate. The addition of glycerol instead of dihydroxyacetone also depressed flux through phosphofructokinase. Thus the weight of evidence supports the existence in rat liver of a fructose 6-phosphate–fructose bisphosphate cycle that can be regulated by hormones and substrates. However, the amount of substrate cycling that occurs with physiological substrates at this step has not been determined by a reliable method.

a. Hepatic Fructose Bisphosphatase. The highest activities of fructose bisphosphatase are found in liver and kidney where high rates of gluconeogenesis occur (Scrutton and Utter, 1968). Most studies on the regulatory and kinetic properties of hepatic fructose bisphosphatase have been done with the rabbit and rat enzyme (for reviews, see Horecker *et al.*, 1975; Pilkis *et al.*, 1978c). This cytosolic enzyme is subject to a multiplicity of controls including allosteric inhibition by AMP (Taketa and Pogell, 1963, 1965; Mendicino and Vasarkely, 1963; Underwood and Newsholme, 1965a; Rosenberg *et al.*, 1973; Datta *et al.*, 1974; Nimmo and Tipton, 1975; Tejwani *et al.*, 1976a; Riou *et al.*, 1977), substrate inhibition by fructose bisphosphate (Taketa and Pogell, 1965, Nakashima *et al.*, 1970), and activation by histidine (Pogell *et al.*, 1968), fatty acids (Carlson *et al.*, 1973), and various chelators. Many of the early studies were done with enzyme that had a pH optimum of about 9. Traniello *et al.* (1971) showed that this was not the native enzyme, but that it arose from proteolytic cleavage of a small peptide (MW 6000) from the enzyme subunit during purification. The native enzyme had a pH optimum of less than 8, was more sensitive to AMP inhibition, and had a subunit molecular weight of 35,000 instead of 29,000. The nature of the proteolytic cleavage has been studied extensively and these studies have been reviewed recently (Pilkis *et al.*, 1978c).

It has been proposed that fructose bisphosphatase must exist in the cell as an activated form since the enzyme purified from rat or rabbit liver is inactive at neutral pH unless an activator is added. Many substances and mechanisms of activation have been advanced including sulfhydryl modification, chelation of metal ions, and activation by 3-phosphoglycerate, fatty acids, phospholipid, and protein factors. Pontremoli *et al.* (1965) showed that reaction of two sulfhydryl groups per mole of enzyme with *p*-hydroxymercuribenzoate increased the activity of the enzyme at pH 7.5. A similar effect could be obtained by forming mixed disulfides of the enzyme with acyl carrier protein, coenzyme A (Nakashima *et al.*, 1969, 1970), homocystine, and cystamine (Pontremoli *et al.*, 1967). However, it is unlikely that sulfhydryl modification is a relevant control mechanism *in vivo*. Fructose bisphosphatase is strongly activated by EDTA, which probably removes zinc ions that are tightly bound to the enzyme and which inhibit its activity. In general, EDTA lowers the pH optimum from about 8 to 7.2 (Pontremoli and Horecker, 1971). In the case of rat liver fructose bisphosphatase, EDTA stimulated enzyme activity 10- to 15-fold at pH 7.2 (Tejwani *et al.*, 1976a; J. P. Riou and S. J. Pilkis, unpublished results). Other chelators, such as histidine (Hers and Eggermont, 1961; McGilvery, 1961; Pogell *et al.*, 1968), 3-phosphoglycerate, and fatty acids (Carlson *et al.*, 1973), also activated the enzyme and shifted the pH optimum downward, probably by chelation of Zn^{2+} or other metals. It has been proposed that alterations in the intracellular levels of effectors such as those noted above could control the activity of fructose bisphosphate *in vivo* (Tejwani *et al.*, 1976b; Horecker *et al.*, 1975). However, the effects of most of these chelators, particularly free fatty acids, are probably not important physiologically, because their intracellular concentrations are not great enough. One possible exception is histidine (Horecker *et al.*, 1975).

Pogell *et al.* (1968) reported that rabbit liver fructose bisphosphatase could be specifically activated by phosphofructokinase. However, Söling and Kleineke (1976) showed that serum albumin was more effective in this regard than a homogeneous preparation of rat liver phosphofructokinase, and they concluded that the activation by proteins was a nonspecific effect. Thus, it does not appear likely that enzyme–enzyme interaction between fructose bisphosphatase and phosphofructokinase plays a significant role in the physiological regulation of fructose bisphosphatase activity.

Inhibition of fructose bisphosphatase by adenine nucleotides has been reported. AMP is a potent inhibitor of the liver enzyme with a K_i of about 20 μM (see Horecker et al., 1975). While the total hepatic concentration of AMP is nearly 500 μM, most of the nucleotide is located in the mitochondria (Siess et al., 1977) and the cytosolic concentration has been estimated to be about 20 μM. Thus, one might expect flux through fructose bisphosphatase to be regulated by changes in the cytosolic concentration of AMP. However, factors that altered flux through the enzyme in intact cells did not affect the AMP concentration (Start and Newsholme, 1968; Clark et al., 1974b; Siess et al., 1977). Using computer modeling techniques, Garfinkel et al. (1979) reported that flux through the enzyme was never very sensitive to change in AMP and that other factors must be involved. The inhibitory effect of AMP on the enzyme was potentiated by fructose bisphosphatase (Pontremoli et al., 1969), but potentiation was observed only with concentrations of fructose bisphosphatase in excess of in vivo levels of this metabolite. Inhibition by ATP and ADP was observed with purified as well as crude preparation of fructose bisphosphate if the enzyme was diluted after incubation with the nucleotides (Taketa and Pogell, 1963; Jones, 1972). The $S_{0.5}$ for fructose bisphosphate was not changed by ATP (Taketa et al., 1971). The inhibition by ATP of the rabbit and guinea pig enzyme could be prevented by 3-phosphoglycerate (Pogell et al., 1971; Jones, 1972). In addition, a large number of unrelated compounds all prevented to some degree the inhibition of the rabbit liver enzyme by ATP and ADP (Taketa et al., 1971). This lack of specificity casts some doubts on the physiological significance of the ATP and ADP inhibition. The purified rat liver enzyme did not appear to be affected by ATP (J. P. Riou and S. J. Pilkis, unpublished).

There have been only a few reports on the acute effect of hormones on the activity of hepatic fructose bisphosphatase. Taunton et al. (1972, 1974) and Stifel et al. (1974) reported that portal vein injection of glucagon or epinephrine in rats increased activity of the enzyme by 50–100% in liver homogenates. The effect of glucagon was observed within 2 minutes and was maximal 5–10 minutes after injection of the hormone. Infusion of cyclic AMP produced changes similar to those of glucagon. The effect of epinephrine was maximal within 2–5 minutes after injection. The injection of insulin produced an inactivation of fructose bisphosphatase that was detectable within 5 minutes following injection and was maximal (35% inhibition) by 10 minutes. Insulin injection also partially reversed the effects of glucagon or epinephrine. Recently, Chatterjee and Datta (1978) reported that the intravenous administration of glucagon to mice stimulated fructose bisphosphatase activity by about 100% within 15 minutes. Similar results were observed on administration of cyclic AMP. Adrenalectomy largely abolished the stimulation by glucagon but had no effect on the stimulation by cyclic AMP. The mechanism whereby these hormones affect fructose bisphosphatase is unknown, but the effects of glucagon were not accounted for by changes in allosteric effectors of the enzyme (Clark *et al.*, 1974b). It has been proposed that glucagon and catecholamines affect enzyme activity by a phosphorylation mechanism (Taunton *et al.*, 1974; Stifel *et al.*, 1974; Riou *et al.*, 1977; Chatterjee and Datta, 1978; Pilkis *et al.*, 1978c).

There also are several reports that indirectly point to an effect of hormones on fructose bisphosphatase. Hué *et al.* (1978) observed that phenylephrine stimulated pyruvate gluconeogenesis, but had no effect on pyruvate kinase or phosphofructokinase activity or on the level of phosphoenolpyruvate. They suggested that activation of fructose bisphosphatase may have been responsible for the stimulation of gluconeogenesis. Rognstad (1979) proposed a similar activation to explain the stimulation of dihydroxyacetone gluconeogenesis in isolated hepatocytes incubated at pH 7.0 where flux through pyruvate kinase and phosphofructokinase was almost negligible. Activation of fructose bisphosphatase may also explain the glucagon-induced fall in cytosolic phosphoenolpyruvate levels in biotin-deficient rats (Siess *et al.*, 1978).

Modification of fructose bisophosphatase activity by phosphorylation–dephosphorylation was first suggested by Mendicino *et al.* (1966). They reported that a crude preparation of kidney fructose bisphosphatase was inactivated when incubated with ATP and cyclic AMP. Riou *et al.* (1977) showed that ^{32}P was incorporated into the rat liver enzyme *in vivo*. They also showed that a homogeneous preparation of the catalytic subunit of cyclic AMP-dependent protein kinase from bovine liver or heart catalyzed the *in vitro* phosphorylation of a purified preparation of the enzyme. Phosphate was incorporated into seryl residues, and 4 mol of phosphate were incorporated/mol of enzyme. The rabbit skeletal muscle enzyme was not phosphorylated under the same conditions. A 40% increase in enzyme activity was associated with the phosphorylation, but only when the enzyme was assayed in the absence of EDTA. Phosphorylation had no effect on the K_i for AMP inhibition.

In summary, the evidence suggests that glucagon modifies fructose bisphosphatase activity, and an attractive hypothesis is that the hormone acts by a phosphorylation mechanism. However, glucagon has not yet been shown to affect phosphorylation of the enzyme *in vivo*. Studies on the hormonal control of the enzyme and on the possibility that activation of the enzyme in intact cells is related to its phosphorylation state deserve additional attention.

Recently, the *in vitro* phosphorylation of fructose bisphosphatase by the cyclic AMP-dependent protein kinase has been characterized and compared with pyruvate kinase (Pilkis *et al.*, 1980). The pH optimum for phosphorylation of fructose bisphosphatase was about pH 7 whereas the rate of phosphorylation of pyruvate kinase by the cyclic AMP-dependent protein kinase still was increasing at pH 9. Neither fructose bisphosphate nor AMP had any effect on the initial rate of phosphorylation of fructose bisphosphatase. In contrast, the allosteric effectors of pyruvate kinase, fructose bisphosphate and alanine, inhibited and stimulated, respectively, the rate of phosphorylation of that enzyme (El-Maghrabi *et al.*, 1980). Fructose bisphosphatase was not as good a substrate for the cyclic AMP-dependent protein kinase as pyruvate kinase. The K_m for fructose bisphosphatase was threefold greater (58 μM) than that for pyruvate kinase (17 μM) while the maximal rate of phosphorylation was about one-third that for pyruvate kinase. These results can be explained by the fact that pyruvate kinase contains two arginine residues on the N-terminal side of the phosphorylated serine (Hjelmqvist *et al.*, 1974; Edlund *et al.*, 1975) whereas fructose bisphosphatase contains only one. The sequence around the phosphorylated serine in rat liver fructose bisphosphatase has been reported to be either Ser-Arg-Pro-Ser(P)-Leu-Pro-Leu-Pro (Pilkis *et al.*, 1979b, 1980) or Ser-Arg-Tyr-Ser(P)-Leu-Pro-Leu-Pro (Humble *et al.*, 1979).

   b. Phosphofructokinase.   Phosphofructokinase is similar to pyruvate kinase in that there appear to be several isozymic forms (Tsai and Kemp, 1973). It has been postulated that rabbit heart and muscle contain predominantly a single isozyme (phosphofructokinase A) and the liver and red blood cell predominantly another (phosphofructokinase B). Brain contains a third type, designated phosphofructokinase C. Tissues other than liver, heart, and skeletal muscle contain isozymes A and B. These results were based on immunological and electrophoretic studies, and few comparisons of the kinetic and structural properties of these forms have been reported. Liver phosphofructokinase has been purified from pig (Massey and Deal, 1973, 1975), rat (Dunaway and Weber, 1974; Brand and Söling, 1974), sheep (Brock, 1969), chicken (Kono and Uyeda, 1971, 1973), and rabbit (Ramaiah and Tejwani, 1970; Kemp, 1971, 1975; Massey and Deal, 1975). The rat liver enzyme consists of four apparently identical subunits with a molecular weight of 82,000 (Brand and Söling, 1974). The liver enzyme, like that of heart (Mansour, 1965; Mansour *et al.*, 1966) and muscle (Paetkau *et al.*, 1968, Paetkau and Lardy, 1967), tends to form aggregates with molecular weights of the order of several million (Brand and Söling, 1974; Trujillo and Deal, 1977). This aggregation is an equilibrium process influenced by enzyme concentration, the presence of allosteric effectors, the oxidation–reduction state of the sulfhydryl groups, and temperature (Bloxham and Lardy, 1973; Mansour, 1972; Ramaiah, 1974). The aggregation state of phosphofructokinase may also influence its kinetic behavior. Reinhart (1977) observed that the rat liver enzyme gave nonlinear rates of activity when it was diluted whereas linear rates were obtained when high concentrations of enzyme were used. The sigmoidal kinetics with fructose 6-phosphate seen with the muscle enzyme have been postulated to be due to reassociation of the enzyme by the substrate (Bloxham and Lardy, 1973). Evidence that various ligands, including ATP, ADP, and fructose 6-phosphate, affect the quaternary structure of rat liver phosphofructokinase has been reported using enzyme labeled with the fluorescent probe pyrenebutyric acid (Reinhart and Lardy, 1979). It has also been shown that the purified rabbit muscle enzyme exhibits slow changes in specific activity that reflect the association of inactive dimers into active tetramers (Bock and Frieden, 1976a,b; Frieden *et al.*, 1976).

Phosphofructokinase from liver exhibits homotropic cooperativity with regard to its substrate fructose 6-phosphate (Brand and Söling, 1974; Massey and Deal, 1973, 1975). 5'-Adenosine monophosphate, ADP, and cyclic 5-AMP are allosteric activators of the liver enzyme, and ATP and citrate are allosteric inhibitors (Brand and Söling, 1974). Kemp (1971) reported that rabbit liver phosphofructokinase was more sensitive to inhibition by ATP and 2,3-diphosphoglycerate but less sensitive to inhibition by citrate than the skeletal muscle enzyme. The ATP inhibition of phosphofructokinase decreased markedly as the pH increased from 6.5 to 8.0. Citrate potentiated the inhibitory effect of ATP on hepatic phosphofructokinase from sheep (Passoneau and Lowry, 1964) and rats (Underwood and Newsholme, 1965b). Both 5'-AMP and fructose 6-phosphate overcame the increased sensitivity to ATP inhibition induced by the presence of citrate (Passoneau and Lowry, 1964; Underwood and Newsholme, 1965b).

Control of phosphofructokinase by enzyme–enzyme interactions has been suggested by Uyeda and Luby (1974), who reported that chicken liver fructose bisphosphatase potentiated ATP inhibition of phosphofructokinase from both rabbit muscle and chicken liver. Other proteins were without effect, but it was not possible to demonstrate that fructose bisphosphatase actually interacted with phosphofructokinase. Söling *et al.* (1977) since have shown that fructose bisphosphatase removed tightly bound fructose bisphosphate from phosphofructokinase. Thus, the inhibition of phosphofructokinase by fructose bisphosphatase did not represent enzyme–enzyme interaction, but resulted from removal of fructose bisphosphate.

It has been reported that the rat liver enzyme can be phosphorylated by a cyclic AMP-independent kinase, with a resulting increase in activity of the enzyme (Brand and Söling, 1975). Phosphate was incorporated into seryl residues, and 4 mol of phosphate were incorporated/mol of enzyme. It was postulated that phosphorylation affected the association–dissociation equilibrium between the enzyme subunits. The dephosphorylated phosphofructokinase dissociated into subunits, and phosphorylation of the enzyme caused association of the previously inactive subunits to form an active tetramer. In the presence of high concentrations of fructose bisphosphate, the inactive nonphosphorylated subunits also reassociated to form an active tetramer. When fructose bisphosphate was removed, the enzyme dissociated into inactive monomers again. Phosphorylation of the enzyme was more rapid in the presence of fructose bisphosphate than in its absence. It has been reported recently that rat liver phosphofructokinase activity can be reversibly affected by regulation of phosphofructokinase dephosphorylation. It has been claimed that the addition of glucose to the medium of perfused livers from starved rats changed phosphofructokinase from a dephosphorylated, inactive form to an active, phosphorylated one (Brand *et al.*, 1976). It has been postulated that this effect is brought about by a rapid decline in phosphofructokinase phosphatase activity through an increase in fructose bisphosphate levels and by the appearance of a phosphatase inhibitor (Luck *et al.*, 1979). The effect of glucose could be overcome by glucagon or dibutyryl cyclic AMP. The appearance of the phosphatase inhibitor appears to be mediated by a protease-like activity (Proud *et al.*, 1979). The phosphofructokinase phosphatase activity appears to be specific for phosphofructokinase since it will not dephosphorylate histones, protamine, or phosphorylated enzymes of glycogen metabolism (Brand and Söling, 1979). Most of these studies have been presented only in preliminary form and have not been confirmed yet.

No studies on the chemical phosphate content of hepatic phosphofructokinase have appeared, probably because of the difficulty in obtaining sufficient quantities of the enzyme from liver. However, there have been a number of reports on the phosphate content of the skeletal muscle enzyme. Skeletal muscle phosphofructokinase from rabbit (Hussey *et al.*, 1977) and mouse (Hofer and Furst, 1976; Riquelme *et al.*, 1978) has been found to contain 0.15–0.3 mol of phosphate/mol of enzyme subunit. Riquelme *et al.* (1978) demonstrated that phosphorylation of the purified skeletal muscle enzyme could be catalyzed by the cyclic AMP-dependent protein kinase with 1 mol of phosphate incorporated into seryl residues/mol of enzyme subunit. Hussey *et al.* (1977) partially fractionated rabbit muscle phosphofructokinase by gel filtration. They found that the fractions containing mostly 30 S polymers had a phosphate content of 0.6

mol/mol of tetramer while the lower molecular weight polymers (13 S and 18 S) contained 1.2 mol of phosphate/mol of enzyme. Uyeda *et al.* (1978) separated rabbit muscle phosphofructokinase by DEAE-cellulose chromatography into two fractions with 0.3 mol and 0.8 mol of phosphate/mol of tetramer. The low phosphate fraction showed a sedimentation velocity pattern of two major peaks (12 and 18 S), a minor peak (24 S), and no 30 S material. The higher phosphate fraction consisted mainly of 30 S material with some 24, 18, and 12 S polymers. Thus, it is unclear whether phosphorylation leads to an increase in the association of phosphofructokinase into higher molecular weight polymers. Recently, Hofer and Sorensen-Ziganke (1979) found that the phosphorylation state of mouse skeletal muscle changed with the functional state of the muscle. When the muscle was kept at rest, 4 mol of phosphate/mol of tetramer were found whereas 8 mol of phosphate/mol of tetramer were found after the muscle was stimulated to contract. When the mouse muscle enzyme was labeled *in vivo* by the injection of [^{32}P]phosphate or *in vitro* by incubation with cyclic AMP-dependent protein kinase and [^{32}P]ATP and then subjected to trypsin digestion, two labeled peptides were obtained (Sorensen-Ziganke and Hofer, 1979). This suggested that at least two sites were phosphorylated. Tryptic digestion of rat muscle phosphofructokinase, which was labeled *in vivo*, produced only a single radioactive peptide (Uyeda *et al.*, 1978), but it is possible that it contained more than one phosphoserine residue. In all the above studies no effect of the covalently bound phosphate on activity of the muscle enzyme was demonstrated.

Glucagon and catecholamines have been reported to depress the activity of hepatic phosphofructokinase within minutes after their administration to intact rats (Taunton *et al.*, 1972, 1974; Stifel *et al.*, 1974). Insulin reversed the effects of both hormones as well as activating phosphofructokinase by itself. The effects all hormones were dose dependent and were independent of changes in protein synthesis. Recently, it has been demonstrated that addition of glucagon to isolated hepatocytes produced an inhibition of phosphofructokinase activity (Pilkis *et al.*, 1979a; Castano *et al.*, 1979). This inhibition was characterized by a twofold increase in the $S_{0.5}$ for fructose 6-phosphate, but with no change in the activity of the enzyme when assayed under V_{max} conditions (Fig. 8.). Castano *et al.* (1979a) reported that the time course of inactivation by glucagon of phosphofructokinase was the same as that for pyruvate kinase, with maximal inactivation occurring in 10 minutes. Pilkis *et al.* (1979a) also found that maximal inactivation of phosphofructokinase occurred in 10 minutes, but that this was much slower than that for pyruvate kinase where maximal inactivation occurred within 20 sec (Claus *et al.*, 1979a). The

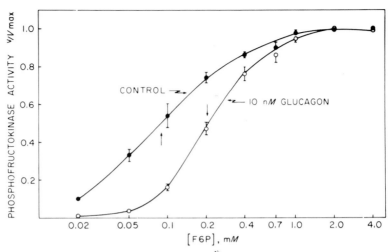

Fɪɢ. 8. Fructose 6-phosphate (F6P) dependence of phosphofructokinase activity in extracts of hepatocytes from fed rats. Hepatocytes were incubated for 10 minutes without ($\bullet$) and with ($\bigcirc$) 10 nM glucagon. The arrows represent the $S_{0.5}$ for F6P and the values were 0.09 mM in the absence of glucagon and 0.20 mM in the presence of glucagon. The data were adapted from those of Pilkis et al. (1979a).

inactivation of phosphofructokinase by glucagon persisted after partial purification of the enzyme on agarose-ATP (Castano et al., 1979) or after heat treatment (Pilkis et al., 1979a). Epinephrine was much less effective than glucagon in inactivating the enzyme and phenylephrine did not appear to affect it (Pilkis et al., 1979a). Insulin reversed the effect of subsaturating concentrations of glucagon on phosphofructokinase inactivation (Castano et al., 1979). Kagimoto and Uyeda (1979) demonstrated that glucagon stimulates the in vivo phosphorylation of hepatic phosphofructokinase. They also found that glucagon administration produced an increase in the sensitivity of the enzyme to ATP inhibition. This increase in sensitivity was observed in ammonium sulfate-treated extracts where the influence of low molecular weight effectors should be eliminated. All together these results suggest that glucagon acts by stimulating cyclic AMP-dependent phosphorylation of the enzyme which results in inactivation. They are not consistent with the observation that glucagon can prevent the activation of phosphofructokinase by a cyclic AMP-independent protein kinase (Luck et al., 1979). According to the hypothesis developed by Söling and co-workers, one would predict that glucagon stimulates the dephosphorylaion of phosphofructokinase. These differences might be resolved if phosphofructokinase were regulated by multisite phosphorylation, with cyclic AMP-dependent protein kinase catalyzing phosphorylation at one site and cyclic AMP-independent protein kinase catalyzing phosphorylation at another site.

IV. SUMMARY

The actions of glucagon, insulin, and catecholamines on gluconeogenesis were originally thought to be mediated by changes in the intracellular level of cyclic AMP (Exton *et al.*, 1970). It was assumed that changes in this nucleotide affected the ability of the cyclic AMP-dependent protein kinase to catalyze the phosphorylation of one or more than one rate-limiting enzyme in the pathway. In recent years, a number of discoveries have made it necessary to modify that hypothesis. Several laboratories have shown that in addition to a cyclic AMP-dependent mechanism, catecholamines, vasopressin, and angiotensin II can also promote hepatic gluconeogenesis in the rat by a mechanism independent of changes in the nucleotide (Tolbert *et al.*, 1973; Hems and Whitton, 1973; Whitton *et al.*, 1978). It also has been demonstrated that insulin can under certain conditions suppress gluconeogenesis that had been stimulated by either glucagon or catecholamines by a mechanism that does not involve changes in cyclic AMP. Thus it is clear that the second messenger hypothesis must be modified to include other intracellular messengers as well as cyclic AMP. The nature of the cyclic AMP-independent messengers of hormone action is uncertain, but changes in Ca^{2+} distribution have been suggested.

Since 1969, when it was postulated that the action of these hormones affected a site(s) in the gluconeogenic pathway somewhere between pyruvate and phosphoenlpyruvate (Exton and Park, 1969), the precise site has been sought by many investigators. This portion of the pathway involves both cytosolic and mitochondrial steps. Several discoveries have greatly aided the search for the affected reaction(s). First, it was discovered that glucagon and catecholamines produced changes in mitochondrial metabolism that persisted after isolation of the organelle (Adam and Haynes, 1969). Second, it was discovered that glucagon and catecholamines could stimulate glucose synthesis from substrates that entered the pathway beyond the mitochondrial steps (Veneziale and Nesheim, 1972). This stimulated the search for cytosolic enzymes that might be affected. It subsequently led to the observation that the hormones stimulate flux through fructose bisphosphatase and inhibit flux through phosphofructokinase and pyruvate kinase (Clark *et al.*, 1974b; Friedman *et al.*, 1971a,b; Blair *et al.*, 1973). Third, it was discovered that hepatic pyruvate kinase could be phosphorylated *in vitro* by a cyclic

AMP-dependent protein kinase with a concomitant inhibition of enzyme activity (Ljungström *et al.*, 1974). These observations provided a mechanism for glucagon stimulation of gluconeogenesis consistent with the role of cyclic AMP in affecting a reaction between pyruvate and phosphoenolpyruvate. Fourth, it was shown that both phosphofructokinase (Brand and Söling, 1975) and fructose bisphosphatase (Riou *et al.*, 1977) can be phosphorylated *in vitro* by protein kinase with associated alterations in the properties of the enzymes. These important observations provide a possible mechanism for the regulation of substrate cycling at the fructose 6-phosphate–fructose bisphosphate level.

The importance of pyruvate carboxylase to gluconeogensis is underscored by the observation that biotin deficiency reduced activity of this enzyme by 90% and gluconeogenesis by over 50% (Siess *et al.*, 1978). The finding that glucagon was unable to stimulate gluconeogenesis in biotin-deficient rats indicates that increased rates of flux through pyruvate carboxylase also are involved in hormonal regulation of gluconeogenesis. Indeed Garrison and Haynes (1975) showed a direct correlation between the rate of mitochondrial CO_2 fixation (pyruvate carboxylation) and the increase in gluconeogenesis caused by glucagon addition to isolated hepatocytes. Glucagon, as well as catecholamines, affect flux through pyruvate carboxylase indirectly. Glucagon, via cyclic AMP, appears to stimulate the respiratory chain (Yamazaki, 1975) by activating cytochrome c_1 (Halestrap, 1978a). This activation may involve an increase in the phosphorylation state of the cytochrome which is located on the outer surface of the inner mitochondrial membrane although this has not been demonstrated. This suggestion would be consistent with the reported stimulation of the phosphorylation of mitochondrial membrane protein (Zahlten *et al.*, 1972). Activation of the respiratory chain stimulates proton efflux from the mitochondrial and mitochondrial ATP production. The rise in intramitchondrial pH promotes anion transport by mitochondria. The increase in both pyruvate and ATP levels and perhaps the decrease in glutamate levels, stimulates pyruvate carboxylation and gluconeogenesis. The stimulation of pyruvate carboxylation by catecholamine also may be due to altered levels of substrates and effectors within the mitochondria. Epinephrine does not increase proton efflux but instead reduces the mitochondrial matrix volume (Titheradge and Coore, 1976b), thereby increasing the concentration of substrates and effectors. This effect appears to be mediated by a cyclic AMP-independent mechanism and it may involve movement of Ca^{2+} ions out of the mitochondria.

Since net glucose synthesis is enhanced by glucagon and catecholamines, these agents must also increase flux through phosphoenolpyruvate carboxykinase, but there is no evidence for any acute effects of these hormones on the activity of the enzyme. A ferroprotein activator of this enzyme has been identified (Bentle and Lardy, 1977), but no acute effects of hormones on its activity have been found either. Flux through phosphoenolpyruvate carboxykinase may be stimulated by increased levels of oxalacetate and/or GTP through the action of these hormones to stimulate mitochondrial metabolism.

Evidence supporting the hypothesis that pyruvate kinase is a site of hormone action comes from studies which show a direct correlation between hormonal stimulation of gluconeogenesis and inhibition of pyruvate kinase activity (e.g., Feliu *et al.*, 1976; Pilkis *et al.*, 1976a; Chan and Exton, 1978). Evidence for an important role for pyruvate kinase was also obtained by Garrison and Borland (1979) who found that catecholamines did not stimulate gluconeogenesis to the same extent as glucagon, but did stimulate mitochondrial CO_2 fixation to the same extent. The difference in the stimulation of gluconeogenesis by these hormones was ascribed to a smaller inhibition of pyruvate kinase activity by catecholamines. Both glucagon and catecholamines inhibit flux through pyruvate kinase in intact cells (Pilkis *et al.*, 1976a; Rognstad and Katz, 1977) as well as inhibit its activity in homogenates of hepatocytes treated with the hormones (Blair *et al.*, 1976; Feliu *et al.*, 1976; Pilkis *et al.*, 1976a,b; Riou *et al.*, 1976; Van Berkel *et al.*, 1976). The glucagon-induced changes in enzyme activity are identical to those induced by phosphorylation of the enzyme with the cyclic AMP-dependent protein kinase (Riou *et al.*, 1976). Also, glucagon stimulates phosphorylation of the enzyme *in vivo* (Riou *et al.*, 1978) and in isolated hepatocytes (Ishibashi and Cottam, 1978; Garrison *et al.*, 1979; Steiner *et al.*, 1980). Catecholamines also stimulate phosphorylation of the enzyme in isolated hepatocytes (Garrison *et al.*, 1979, Steiner *et al.*, 1980). The addition of glucagon to hepatocytes also lowers the level of fructose bisphosphate (Blair *et al.*, 1973; Pilkis *et al.*, 1976a). Although there is no direct evidence that lower levels of fructose bisphosphate contribute to the hormone-induced inhibition of pyruvate kinase, it is known that this metabolite can control the activity of the enzyme in the cell under certain circumstances, and that it can affect the ability of glucagon to phosphorylate pyruvate kinase in the intact hepatocyte (Claus *et al.*, 1979).

The catecholamine effects on pyruvate kinase appear to be mediated predominantly by a cyclic AMP-independent mechanism (Chan and Exton, 1978; Foster and Blair, 1978; Garrison *et al.*, 1979; Claus *et al.*, 1979; Exton, 1979a). In hepatocytes, catecholamines have smaller effects on pyruvate kinase activity than does glucagon, and these results correlate well with the smaller effects on gluconeogenesis. In perfused livers, the effects of glucagon and catecholamines on gluconeogenesis are more nearly equivalent (Exton and Park, 1968). The reason for this difference is not clear, but it may be due to some alteration of the catecholamine receptor during preparation of the hepatocytes. In any case, catecholamine effects on gluconeogenesis are elicited only with very high concentrations of the hormone in either isolated hepatocytes or the isolated perfused liver. Thus the physiological significance of their effects is uncertain, although it has been suggested that stimulation of the sympathetic nerves within the liver may produce such high concentrations at the nerve endings.

Insulin opposes the action of both maximal concentrations of catecholamine and submaximal concentrations of glucagon on pyruvate kinase activity (Feliu *et al.*, 1976; Blair *et al.*, 1976; Claus *et al.*, 1979). Since insulin has identical effects on glucose synthesis, it is reasonable to assume that an important site of insulin action on the gluconeogenic pathway is at the pyruvate kinase step. One action of insulin is to lower cyclic AMP levels leading to suppression of cyclic AMP-dependent protein kinase activation and to decreased phosphorylation of pyruvate kinase (Claus *et al.*, 1979). Insulin can also suppress inactivation of pyruvate kinase induced by cyclic AMP-independent mechanisms (Claus *et al.*, 1979). In this case insulin may act either by activating a specific phosphatase for pyruvate kinase and/or by suppressing a cyclic AMP-independent protein kinase activity.

There is no direct evidence that glucagon, catecholamines, or insulin affect the phosphorylation state of fructose bisphosphatase. However, the intravenous administration of glucagon or catecholamines increases enzyme activity and insulin administration decreases it (Taunton *et al.*, 1974; Stifel *et al.*, 1974). Since *in vitro* phosphorylation of fructose bisphosphatase by the cyclic AMP-dependent protein kinase leads to activation of the enzyme (Riou *et al.*, 1977), it seems reasonable to postulate that glucagon induces phosphorylation of the enzyme in intact cells. Hormonal stimulation of this enzyme may be the sole means of stimulating gluconeogenesis under certain conditions. Hué *et al.* (1978) found that the stimulation of gluconeogenesis by vasopressin or phenylephrine could not be accounted for by changes in pyruvate kinase or phosphofructokinase, and they suggested an activation of fructose bisphosphatase as a possible mechanism. Rognstad (1979) noted that glucagon stimulated dihydroxyacetone gluconeogenesis at pH 7.0 even though flux through pyruvate kinase and phosphofructokinase was almost negligible. He too proposed activation of fructose bisphosphatase.

Glucagon has been shown to stimulate the *in vivo* phosphorylation of phosphofructokinase (Kagemoto and Uyeda, 1979). Both glucagon and catecholamines also inhibit activity of the enzyme as well as decrease flux through the enzyme in intact hepatocytes (Pilkis *et al.*, 1979a; Castano *et al.*, 1979; Rognstad and Katz, 1976). Inactivation of phosphofructokinase or activation of fructose bisphosphatase or both would explain the glucagon-induced fall in fructose bisphosphate levels.

Some properties of pyruvate kinase, fructose bisphosphatase, and phosphofructokinase are summarized in Table III. They are tetrameric enzymes that behave allosterically with regard to substrates and/or effectors. They are inhibited by ATP and are affected by fructose bisphosphate. Their *in vitro* phosphorylation can be catalyzed by the cyclic AMP-dependent protein kinase. In the case of pyruvate kinase and fruc-

TABLE III

COMPARISON OF SOME PROPERTIES OF HEPATIC PYRUVATE KINASE, FRUCTOSE BISPHOSPHATASE, AND PHOSPHOFRUCTOKINASE

	Pyruvate kinase[a] (L-isozyme)	Fructose bisphosphatase[b]	Phospho-fructokinase[c]
Subunits	Tetramer	Tetramer	Tetramer
Phosphorylated by			
cAMP-dependent protein kinase	Yes	Yes	Yes
cAMP-independent protein kinase	No	?	Yes
Mol phosphate/mol subunit	1.0	1.0	1.0
Activity of the phosphoenzyme	Decreased	Increased	Decreased or increased
ATP	Inhibitor	Inhibitor	Inhibitor
FDP	Activator	Substrate (inhibitor)	Activator
Effect of phosphorylation + FDP	None	——	None
Acute effect of hormones on activity in liver			
Glucagon	Inhibition	Stimulation	Inhibition
Catecholamines	Inhibition	Stimulation	Inhibition
Insulin[d]	Stimulation	Inhibition	Stimulation

[a] From Ljungström *et al.* (1974); Riou *et al.* (1976) Pilkis *et al.* (1976a,b); Taunton *et al.* (1972, 1974); Stifel *et al.* (1974); Feliu *et al.* (1976); Blair *et al.* (1976).

[b] From Horecker *et al.* (1975); Riou *et al.* (1977); Taunton *et al.* (1972, 1974).

[c] From Brand and Söling (1974), 1975); Brand *et al.* (1976); Taunton *et al.* (1972, 1974); Stifel *et al.* (1974); Pilkis *et al.* (1979a); Castano *et al.* (1979); Kagemoto and Uyeda (1979).

[d] Insulin acts to suppress the effects of submaximal concentrations of glucagon and maximal concentrations of catecholamine on these enzyme activities. It has no effect when added alone.

tose bisphosphatase 4 mol of phosphate are incorporated/mol of enzyme. The details of the protein kinase catalyzed phosphorylation hepatic phosphofructokinase have not been worked out yet. Pyruvate kinase activity is inhibited by enzyme phosphorylation, whereas fructose bisphosphatase activity is enhanced. Recent evidence suggests that phosphofructokinase activity can be inhibited or stimulated depending upon the nature of the phosphorylation. It has been postulated that cyclic AMP-dependent phosphorylation leads to inactivation (Pilkis *et al.*, 1979a; Castano *et al.*, 1979; Kagimoto and Uyeda, 1979) while cyclic AMP-independent phosphorylation promotes activation of the enzyme (Brand and Söling, 1975). Phosphorylation of pyruvate kinase does not appear to be catalyzed by a cyclic AMP-independent kinase while it is unknown whether phosphorylation of fructose bisphosphatase can be.

V. OVERVIEW

It is the thesis of this review that glucagon stimulates gluconeogenesis by increasing the rate of phosphoenolpyruvate production and decreasing the rate of its disposal by pyruvate kinase. The hormone affects these processes by modulating flux through pyruvate carboxylase, pyruvate kinase, phosphoenolpyruvate carboxykinase, fructose bisphosphatase, and phosphofructokinase. Glucagon, via cyclic AMP and the cyclic AMP-dependent protein kinase, affects the activity of pyruvate kinase, phosphofructokinase, and perhaps fructose bisphosphatase by altering the phosphorylation state of each enzyme. Pyruvate carboxylase and phosphoenolpyruvate carboxykinase are not phosphorylated, but their activities are altered by changes in the level of various metabolites which affect the enzymes. Changes in intramitochondrial metabolite levels result from stimulation of the respiratory chain by the hormone. Catecholamines have similar, although usually smaller, effects on flux through the same enzymes. Catecholamines also act at the mitochondrial level and so appear to affect the phosphorylation state of the same enzymes as glucagon, but probably via a cyclic AMP-independent mechanism. Insulin opposes the effects of both glucagon and catecholamines on enzyme phosphorylation. However, it is not known whether insulin acts at the mitochondrial level. Alterations in flux through pyruvate carboxylase, pyruvate kinase, and phosphoenolpyruvate carboxykinase can lead directly to a crossover between phosphoenolpyruvate and pyruvate. Alterations in flux through fructose bisphosphatase and phosphofructokinase, enzymes which are not located in the rate-limiting portion of the pathway, can affect the activity of and flux through pyruvate kinase by altering the level of fructose bisphosphate, a potent activator of the enzyme. It appears that this metabolite not only affects pyruvate kinase activity directly, but also influences the phosphorylation state of the enzyme. Thus, fructose bisphosphate may serve as a link between the fructose 6-phosphate–fructose bisphosphate substrate cycle and the phosphoenolpyruvate–pyruvate substrate cycle.

As presented in Fig. 9, the regulation of hepatic gluconeogenesis by glucagon occurs at multiple sites and in several cellular compartments. These effects can be divided into two categories (1) covalent changes in cytosolic enzymes and (2) effects on mitochondrial energy production. The relative contribution of these two categories to the acute effects of glucagon on gluconeogenesis will depend on the nutritional and hormonal status of the animal. For example, in the well-fed case the levels of phosphofructokinase and pyruvate kinase and flux through these enzymes in intact cells are high. In this situation, pyruvate kinase is a major site of glucagon action since the hormone-induced decrease in flux through pyruvate kinase accounts for a large part of the increase in glucose synthesis (Rognstad and Katz, 1977). The effect of glucagon to inactivate

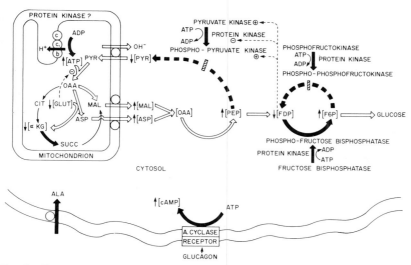

FIG. 9. Changes in the hepatic gluconeogenic pathway in response to glucagon. Wavy lines represent the plasma membrane. The rectangle represents the mitochondrion. Thickened, but unfilled, lines represent increased flow of substrates. Thickened, filled lines represent sites of glucagon action to accelerate a reaction, while thickened, filled, but broken lines represent sites of glucagon action to inhibit a reaction. The symbols b, c, and c_1 represent cytochromes; the other abbreviations are the same as in Fig. 1. For sake of simplicity, the activation by cyclic AMP of the protein kinase reaction has been omitted.

pyruvate kinase is potentiated by the ability of the hormone to lower fructose bisphosphate levels by influencing the amount of cycling at the fructose 6-phosphate–fructose bisphosphate level. Glucagon probably also acts to increase phosphoenolpyruvate production by influencing mitochondrial respiration. Thus, all the sites of action depicted in Fig. 9 are affected and glucagon has large effects on the rate of glucose synthesis (Claus et al., 1975; Claus and Pilkis, 1976). Insulin counteracts the effects of glucagon on pyruvate kinase, phosphofructokinase, and glucose synthesis in hepatocytes from fed rats (Claus and Pilkis, 1976; Feliu et al., 1976; Pilkis et al., 1979a; Castano et al., 1979; Claus et al., 1979). On the other hand, starvation results in an increase in the level of phosphoenolpyruvate carboxykinase and decreases in pyruvate kinase and phosphofructokinase activity. The level of fructose bisphosphate also is depressed during starvation (Claus et al., 1979). As a result of these changes, and perhaps others which are not defined yet, phosphoenolpyruvate production is enhanced, flux through pyruvate kinase and phosphofructokinase is very low, and the rate of glucose synthesis from physiological substrates is elevated two- to threefold (Claus and Pilkis, 1976). In this situation, the stimulation of glucose synthesis by glucagon is much smaller than in the fed situation (Claus and Pilkis, 1976) and the stimulation of mitochondrial metabolism probably makes a large contribution to it. However, even during starvation the inhibition of pyruvate kinase by glucagon contributes to the stimulation of glucose synthesis. Evidence for this comes from studies with hepatocytes from starved rats where the effect of glucagon and catecholamines on mitochondrial pyruvate carboxylation is of the same magnitude, but the effect of glucagon on both gluconeogenesis and pyruvate kinase activity is substantially greater than that of catecholamines (Garrison and Borland, 1979). In the diabetic state, the rate of hepatic gluconeogenesis is enhanced primarily as a result of alterations in the level of various gluconeogenic and glycolytic enzymes (Exton, 1972; Pilkis et al., 1978c) and acute hormone effects on rates of gluconeogenesis in isolated liver systems are not observed. It should also be noted that the accelerated rate of gluconeogenesis seen in vivo during starvation and in diabetes is influenced by an increased substrate supply.

Although our knowledge of how, and at what sites, hormones affect gluconeogenesis has greatly increased in the last few years, there are still many areas that merit further study. These include identification of the intracellular messengers for α-adrenergic agonists and insulin; elucidation of the mechanism of hormonal regulation at the level of the mitochondria; quantitation of substrate cycling at both the phosphoenolpyruvate–pyruvate and the fructose 6-phosphate–fructose bisphosphate cycles; further characterization of the phosphorylation and hormonal control of phosphofructokinase and fructose bisphosphatase; and identification, isolation, and characterization of the protein kinases and phosphatases involved in the phosphorylation and dephosphorylation of pyruvate kinase, phosphofructokinase, and fructose bisphosphatase. These studies should provide new insights into the mechanism of action of hormones on hepatic gluconeogenesis.

ACKNOWLEDGMENTS

The work of the author's laboratories described in the review was supported by a grant AM-18270 from the National Institutes of Health. We would like to thank Dr. Charles R. Park for his encouragement and critical reading of the manuscript and Mrs. Patsy Barrett for her skillful typing of the manuscript.

REFERENCES

Adam, P. A. J., and Haynes, R. C., Jr. (1969). *J. Biol. Chem.* **244**, 6444–6450.
Assimacopoulos-Jeannet, F. D., Blackmore, P. F., and Exton, J. H. (1977). *J. Biol. Chem.* **252**, 2662–2669.
Babcock, D. F., Chen, J.-L. J., Yip, B. P., and Lardy, H. A. (1979). *J. Biol. Chem.* **254**, 8117–8120.
Bailey, E., Stirpe, F., and Taylor, C. B. (1968). *Biochem.J.* **108**, 427.
Ballard, F. J. (1970). *Biochem. J.* **120**, 809–814.
Ballard, F. J. (1971). *Biochim. Biophys. Acta* **242**, 470–472.
Ballard, F. J., and Hanson, R. W. (1969). *J. Biol. Chem.* **244**, 5625–5630.
Barritt, G. J., Zander, G. L., and Utter, M. (1976). *In* "Gluconeogenesis: Its Regulation in Mammalian Species" (R. W. Hanson and M. A. Mehlman, eds.), pp. 3–46. Wiley, New York.
Bentle, L. A., and Lardy, H. A. (1977). *J. Biol. Chem.* **252**, 1431–1440.
Bentle, L. A., Snoke, R. E., and Lardy, H. A. (1976). *J. Biol. Chem.* **251**, 2922–2928.
Berglund, L., Ljungström, O., and Engström, L. (1977a). *J. Biol. Chem.* **252**, 613–619.
Berglund, L., Ljungström, O., and Engström, L. (1977b). *J. Biol. Chem.* **252**, 6108–6111.
Bewsher, P. D., and Ashmore, J. (1966). *Biochem. Biophys. Res. Commun.* **24**, 431–436.
Birnbaum, M. J., and Fain, J. N. (1977). *J. Biol. Chem.* **252**, 528–535.
Blackmore, P. F., Dehaye, J.-P., Strickland, W. G., and Exton, J. H. (1979a). *FEBS Lett.* **100**, 117–120.
Blackmore, P. F., Assimacopoulos-Jeannet, F., Chan, T. M., and Exton, J. H. (1979b). *J. Biol. Chem.* **254**, 2828–2834.
Blair, J. B., Cook, D. E., and Lardy, H. A. (1973). *J. Biol. Chem.* **248**, 3601–3607.
Blair, J. B., Cimbala, M. H., and Foster, J. L. (1976). *J. Biol. Chem.* **251**, 3756–3762.
Blair, J. B., James, M. E., and Foster, J. L. (1979). *J. Biol. Chem.* **254**, 7585–7590.
Bloxham, D., and Lardy, H. A. (1973). *In* "The Enzymes" (P. D. Boyer, ed.), 3rd ed., Vol. 8, pp. 229–278. Academic Press, New York.
Bock, P. E., and Frieden, C. (1976a). *J. Biol. Chem.* **251**, 5630–5636.

Bock, P. E., and Frieden, C. (1976b). J. Biol. Chem. 251, 5637–5643.

Brand, I., and Söling, H. D. (1974). J. Biol. Chem. 249, 7824–7831.

Brand, I., and Söling, H. D. (1975). FEBS Lett. 57, 163–168.

Brand, I., and Söling, H. D. (1979). Abst. Int. Congr. Biochem. 11th, 1979 Abstract No. 04-5-5128

Brand, I. A., Muller, M. K., Unger, C., and Söling, H. D. (1976). FEBS Lett. 68, 271–274.

Brock, D. J. H. (1969). Biochem. J. 113, 235–242.

Bryla, J., Harris, E. J., and Plumb, J. A. (1977). FEBS Lett. 80, 443–448.

Butcher, R. W., Baird, C. E., and Sutherland, E. A. (1968). J. Biol. Chem. 243, 1705–1712.

Carlson, C. W., Baxter, R. C., Ulm, E. F., and Pogell, B. M. (1973). J. Biol. Chem. 248, 5555–5561.

Carminatti, H., Jiménez de Asua, L., Recondo, E., Posserson, S., and Rozengurt, E. (1968). J. Biol. Chem. 243, 3051.

Castano, T. G., Nieto, A., and Feliu, J. E. (1979). J. Biol. Chem. 254, 5576–5579.

Chan, T. M., and Exton, J. H. (1977). J. Biol. Chem. 252, 8645–8651.

Chan, T. M., and Exton, J. H. (1978). J. Biol. Chem. 253, 6393–6400.

Chan, T. M., Bacon, C. B., and Hill, S. A. (1979) J. Biol. Chem. 254, 8730–8732.

Chance, B., Schoener, B., Krejci, K., Russmann, W., Wesemann, W., Schnitger, H., and Bucher, T. (1965). Biochem. J. 341, 325–333.

Chatterjee, T., and Datta, A. G. (1978). Biochem. Biophys. Res. Commun. 84, 950–956.

Chen, J.-L. J., Babcock, D. F., and Lardy, H. A. (1978). Proc. Natl. Acad. Sci. U.S.A. 75, 2234–2238.

Cherrington, A. D., Assimacopoulos, F. D., Harper, S. C., Corbin, J. D., Park, C. R., and Exton, J. H. (1976). J. Biol. Chem. 251, 5209–5218.

Chiao, Y.-B. (1976). Fed. Proc., Fed. Am. Soc. Exp. Biol. 35, Abstr. No. 1522.

Clark, M. G., Bloxham, D. P., Holland, P. C., and Lardy, H. A. (1974a). J. Biol. Chem. 249, 279–290.

Clark, M. G., Kneer, N. M., Bosch, A. L., and Lardy, H. A. (1974b). J. Biol. Chem. 249, 5695–5703.

Claus, T. H., and Pilkis, S. J. (1976). Biochim. Biophys. Acta 421, 246–262.

Claus, T. H., and Pilkis, S. J. (1977). Arch. Biochem. Biophys. 182, 52–63.

Claus, T. H., Pilkis, S. J., and Park, C. R. (1975). Biochim. Biophys. Acta 404, 110–123.

Claus, T. H., El-Maghrabi, M. R., and Pilkis, S. I. (1979). J. Biol. Chem. 254, 7855–7864.

Clifford, A. J., Riumallo, J. A., Baliga, B. S., Munro, H. N., and Brown, P. R. (1972). Biochim. Biophys. Acta 277, 433–458.

Crabb, D. W., Mapes, J. P., Boersma, R. W., and Harris, R. A. (1976). Arch. Biochem. Biophys. 173, 658–665.

Daile, P., and Carnegie, P. R. (1974). Biochem. Biophys. Res. Commun. 61, 852–858.

Daile, P., Carnegie, P. R., and Young, J. D. (1975). Nature (London) 257, 416–418.

Datta, A. G., Abrams, B., Sasaki, T., and Van den Berg, T. W. (1974). Arch. Biochem. Biophys. 165, 641–645.

Debeer, J. J., Thomas, J., DeSchepper, P. J., and Mannaerts, G. P. (1979). J. Biol. Chem. 254, 8841–8846.

DeRosa, G., and Swick, R. W. (1975). J. Biol. Chem. 240, 3334–3340.

Diesterhaft, M., Shrago, E., and Sallach, H. J. (1971). Biochem. Med. 5, 297–303.

Dieterle, P., Brawand, F., Moser, U. K., and Walter, P. (1978). Eur. J. Biochem. 88, 467–473.

Dunaway, G. A., and Weber, G. (1974). Arch. Biochem. Biophys. 162, 620–628.

Dunn, A., Chenoweth, M., and Beuer, K. (1976). Fed. Proc., Fed. Am. Soc. Exp. Biol. 35, 1427.

Edlund, B., Andersson, J., Titanji, V., Dahlqvist, U., Ekman, P., Zetterqvist, P., and Engström, L. (1975). *Biochem. Biophys. Res. Commun.* **67**, 1516–1526.

Eigenbrodt, E., and Schoner, W. (1977a). *Hoppe-Seyler's Z. Physiol. Chem.* **358**, 1047–1055.

Eigenbrodt, E., and Schoner, W. (1977b). *Hoppe-Seyler's Z. Physiol. Chem.* **358**, 1057–1066.

El-Maghrabi, M. F., Haston, W. S., Flockhart, D. A., Claus, T. H., and Pilkis, S. J. (1980). *J. Biol. Chem.* **255**, 668–675.

Exton, J. H. (1972). *Metab., Clin. Exp.* **21**, 945–990.

Exton, J. H. (1979a). *J. Cyclic Nucleotide Res.* **5**, 277–287.

Exton, J. H. (1979b). *In* "Hormones and Energy Metabolism" (D. M. Klachko, R. R. Anderson, and M. Heimberg, eds.), pp. 125–167. Plenum, New York.

Exton, J. H., and Harper, S. C. (1975). *Adv. Cyclic Nucleotide Res.* **5**, 519–532.

Exton, J. H., and Park, C. R. (1965). *J. Biol. Chem.* **240**, PC955–PC957.

Exton, J. H., and Park, C. R. (1966). *Pharmacol. Rev.* **18**, 181–188.

Exton, J. H., and Park, C. R. (1967). *J. Biol. Chem.* **242**, 2622–2636.

Exton, J. H., and Park, C. R. (1968). *J. Biol. Chem.* **243**, 4189–4196.

Exton, J. H., and Park, C. R. (1969). *J. Biol. Chem.* **244**, 1424–1433.

Exton, J. H., Mallette, L. E., Jefferson, L. S., Wong, E. H. A., Friedmann, N., Miller, T.B., Jr., and Park, C. R. (1970). *Recent Prog. Horm. Res.* **26**, 411–461.

Exton, J. H., Lewis, S. B., Ho., R. J., Robinson, G. A., and Park, C. R. (1971). *Ann. N.Y. Acad. Sci.* **185**, 85–100.

Feliu, J. E., Hué, L., and Hers, H. G. (1976). *Proc. Natl. Acad. Sci. U.S.A.* **73**, 2762–2766.

Feliu, J. E., Hué, L., and Hers, H. G. (1977). *Eur. J. Biochem.* **81**, 609–617.

Florey, W., Peczon, B. D., Koeppe, R. E., and Spivey, H. O. (1974). *Biochem. J.* **141**, 127–131.

Foster, D. O., Lardy, H. A., Ray, P. D., and Johnston, J. B. (1967). *Biochemistry* **6**, 2120–2128.

Foster, J. L., and Blair, J. (1976). *Fed. Proc., Fed. Am. Soc. Exp. Biol.* **35**, 1428.

Foster, J. L., and Blair, J. (1978). *Arch. Biochem. Biophys.* **189**, 263–276.

Frieden, C., Gilber, H. R., and Bock, P. (1976). *J. Biol. Chem.* **251**, 5644–5647.

Friedman, B., Goodman, E. H., Jr., Saunders, H. L., Kostos, V., and Weinhouse, S. (1971a). *Metab., Clin. Exp.* **20**, 2–12.

Friedman, B., Goodman, E. H., Jr., Saunders, H. L., Kostos, V., and Weinhouse, S. (1971b). *Arch. Biochem. Biophys.* **143**, 566–578.

Friedmann, N., and Rasmussen, H. (1970). *Biochim. Biophys. Acta* **222**, 241.

Friedrichs, D. (1976). *In* "Use of Isolated Liver Cells and Kidney Tubules in Metabolic Studies" (J. M. Tager, H. D. Soling, and J. R. Williamson, eds.), pp. 444–447. North-Holland Publ., Amsterdam.

Gancedo, T. M., Gancedo, C., and Sols, A. (1967). *Biochem. J.* **102**, 23c.

Garber, A. J., and Ballard, F. J. (1970). *J. Biol. Chem.* **245**, 2229–2240.

Garcia, A., Williamson, J. R., and Cahill, G. F., Jr. (1964). *Fed. Proc., Fed. Am. Soc. Exp. Biol.* **23**, 520.

Garfinkel, L., Kohn, M. C., and Garfinkel, D. (1979). *Eur. J. Biochem.* **96**, 183–192.

Garrison, J. C., and Borland, M. K. (1979). *J. Biol. Chem.* **254**, 1129–1133.

Garrison, J. C., and Haynes, R. C., Jr. (1975). *J. Biol. Chem.* **250**, 2769–2777.

Garrison, J. C., Borland, M. K., Florio, V. A., and Twible, D. A. (1979). *J. Biol. Chem.* **254**, 7147–7156.

Gimpel, J. A., de Haan, E. J., and Tager, J. M. (1973). *Biochim. Biophys. Acta* **292**, 582–591.

Graf, B., Peters, H. H., Bore-Nath, A., Steiller, G., and Weiss, G. (1976). *Abstr., Int. Congr. Biochem. 10th, 1976* p. 373.

Haeckel, R., Hess, B., Lauterborn, W., and Wuster, K. H. (1968). *Hoppe-Seyler's Z. Physiol. Chem.* **349**, 699.

Halestrap, A. P. (1975). *Biochem. J.* **148**, 85–96.

Halestrap, A. P. (1978a). *Biochem. J.* **172**, 389–398.

Halestrap, A. P. (1978b). *Biochem. J.* **172**, 399–405.

Halestrap, A. P. (1978c). *FEBS Symp.* **42**, 61–70.

Halestrap, A. P., and Denton, R. M. (1975). *Biochem. J.* **148**, 313–316.

Harris, R. A. (1975). *Arch. Biochem. Biophys.* **169**, 168–180.

Haynes, R. C., Jr. (1976). *Metab., Clin. Exp.* **25**, 1361–1363.

Hems, D. A., and Whitton, P. D. (1973). *Biochem. J.* **136**, 705–709.

Hems, D. A., Davies, C. J., and Siddle, K. (1978a). *FEBS Lett.* **87**, 196–198.

Hems, D. A., Rodrigues, L. M., and Whitton, P. D. (1978b). *Biochem. J.* **172**, 311–317.

Hers, H. G., and Eggermont, E. (1961). *In* "Fructose-1,6-Diphosphatase and Its Role in Gluconeogenesis" (R. W. McGilvery and B. M. Pogell, eds.), pp. 14–19. Am. Inst. Biol. Sci., Washington, D.C.

Hess, B., Hoeckel, R., and Brand, K. (1966). *Biochem. Biophys. Res. Commun.* **24**, 824.

Hjelmqvist, G., Andersson, J., Edlund, B., and Engström, L. (1974). *Biochem. Biophys. Res. Commun.* **6**, 559–563.

Hofer, H. W., and Furst, M. (1976). *FEBS Lett.* **62**, 118–122.

Hofer, H. W., and Sorensen-Ziganke, B. (1979). *Biochem. Biophys. Res. Commun.* **90**, 199–203.

Holten, D. D., and Nordlie, R. C. (1965). *Biochemistry* **4**, 723–731.

Horecker, B. L., Melloni, E., and Pontremoli, S. (1975). *Adv. Enzymol.* **42**, 193–226.

Hué, L., and Hers, H. G. (1974). *Biochem. Biophys. Res. Commun.* **58**, 532–539.

Hué, L., Feliu, J. M., and Hers, H. G. (1978). *Biochem. J.* **176**, 791–797.

Humble, E., Berglund, L., Titanji, V. P. K., Ljungström, O., Edlund, B., Zetterqvist, O., and Engström, L. (1975). *Biochem. Biophys. Res. Commun.* **66**, 614–621.

Humble, E., Dahlqvist-Edberg, U., Ekman, P., Netzel, E., Ragnaisson, U., and Engström, L. (1979). *Biochem. Biophys. Res. Commun.* **90**, 1064–1072.

Hunsley, T. R., and Suelter, C. H. (1969). *J. Biol. Chem.* **244**, 4819.

Hussey, C. R., Liddle, P. F., Ardron, D., and Kellett, G. L. (1977). *Eur. J. Biochem.* **80**, 497–506.

Ibsen, K. (1977). *Cancer Res.* **37**, 341–353.

Imamura, K., Taniuchi, K., and Tanaka, T. (1972). *J. Biochem. (Tokyo)* **32**, 1001–1015.

Ishibashi, H., and Cottam, G. L. (1978). *J. Biol. Chem.* **253**, 8767–8771.

Ishihara, N., and Kikuchi, G. (1968). *Biochim. Biophys. Acta* **153**, 733–748.

Jefferson, L. S., Robertson, J. W., and Tolman, E. L. (1973). *J. Biol. Chem.* **248**, 4561–4567.

Jiménez de Asua, L., Rozengurt, E., and Carminatti, H. (1970). *J. Biol. Chem.* **245**, 3901.

Jomain-Baum, M., Schramm, V. L., and Hanson, R. W. (1976). *J. Biol. Chem.* **251**, 37–44.

Jones, C. T. (1972). *Biochem. J.* **130**, 23P.

Kagimoto, T., and Uyeda, K. (1979). *J. Biol. Chem.* **254**, 5584–5587.

Katz, J., and Rognstad, R. (1976). *Curr. Top. Cell. Regul.* **10**, 237–289.

Katz, J., Wals, P. A., Golden, S., and Rognstad, R. (1975). *Eur. J. Biochem.* **60**, 91–101.

Kayne, F. J., and Price, N. C. (1972). *Biochemistry* **11**, 4415–4420.

Keech, D. B., and Utter, M. F. (1963). *J. Biol. Chem.* **238**, 2609–2614.

Kemp, B. E., and Clark, M. G. (1978). *J. Biol. Chem.* **253**, 5147–5154.

Kemp, B. E., Bylund, D. B., Huang, T.-S., and Krebs, E. G. (1975). *Proc. Natl. Acad. Sci. U.S.A.* **72**, 3448–3452.

Kemp, R. G. (1971). *J. Biol. Chem.* **246**, 245–252.

Kemp, R. G. (1975). *In* "Methods in Enzymology" (W. A. Wood, ed.), Vol. 42, p. 67. Academic Press, New York.

Keppens, S., and DeWulf, H. (1975). *FEBS Lett.* **51**, 29–32.

Keppens, S., and DeWulf, H. (1977). *Abstr., FEBS Meet., 11th* Abstract No. A1–9–107.

Keppens, S. S., Vandenheede, J. R., and DeWulf, H. (1977). *Biochim. Biophys. Acta* **496**, 448–457.

Kimmich, G. A., and Rasmussen, H. (1969). *J. Biol. Chem.* **244**, 190–199.

Kirk, C. J., and Hems, D. A. (1974). *FEBS Lett.* **47**, 128–131.

Kneer, N. M., Bosch, A. L., Clark, M. G., and Lardy, H. A. (1974). *Proc. Natl. Acad. Sci. U.S.A.* **71**, 4523–4527.

Koler, R. D., and Vanbellinghen, P. (1968). *Adv. Enzyme Regul.* **6**, 127.

Kono, N., and Uyeda, K. (1971). *Biochem. Biophys. Res. Commun.* **42**, 1095.

Kono, N., and Uyeda, K. (1973). *J. Biol. Chem.* **248**, 8592–8603.

Larner, J. (1968). *Adv. Enzyme Regul.* **6**, 409–423.

Leiter, A. B., Weinberg, M., Isohaslir, F., Utter, M. F., and Linn, T. (1978). *J. Biol. Chem.* **253**, 2716–2723.

Linn, T. C., Pettit, F. H., and Reed, L. J. (1969a). *Proc. Natl. Acad. Sci. U.S.A.* **64**, 221–234.

Linn, T. C., Pettit, F. H., Hucho, F., and Reed, L. J. (1969b). *Proc. Natl. Acad. Sci. U.S.A.* **64**, 234–241.

Linn, T. C., Pettey, J. W., Pettit, F. H., Hucho, F., Randall, D. D., and Reed, L. J. (1972). *Arch. Biochem. Biophys.* **148**, 327–342.

Ljungström, O., and Ekman, P. (1977). *Biochem. Biophys. Res. Commun.* **78**, 1147–1155.

Ljungström, O., Hjelmqvist, G., and Engström, L. (1974). *Biochim. Biophys. Acta* **358**, 289–298.

Ljungström, O., Berglund, L., and Engström, L. (1976). *Eur. J. Biochem.* **68**, 497–506.

Llorente, P., Marco, R., and Sols, A. (1970). *Eur. J. Biochem.* **13**, 45–52.

Luck, H. J., Brand, I., and Soling, H. D. (1979). *Abstr., Int. Congr. Biochem. 11th, 1979* Abstract No. 04–5–5129.

McClure, W. R., and Lardy, H. A. (1971). *J. Biol. Chem.* **246**, 3591–3596.

MacDonald, M. J. (1979). *Abstr. Congr. Int. Diabetes Fed. 10th, 1979* Abstract No. 382.

MacDonald, M. J., Bentle, L. A., and Lardy, H. A. (1978). *J. Biol. Chem.* **253**, 116–124.

McGilvery, R. W. (1961). *In* "Fructose-1,6-Diphosphatase and Its Role in Gluconeogenesis" (R. W. McGilvery and B. M. Pogell, eds.), pp. 3–13. Am. Inst. Biol. Sci., Washington, D. C.

Mallette, L. E., Exton, J. H., and Park, C. R. (1969). *J. Biol. Chem.* **244**, 5713–5723.

Mansour, T. E. (1965). *J. Biol. Chem.* **240**, 2165–2172.

Mansour, T. E. (1972). *Curr. Top. Cell. Regul.* **5**, 1–46.

Mansour, T. E., Wakid, N., and Sprouse, H. M. (1966). *J. Biol. Chem.* **241**, 1512.

Mapes, J. P., and Harris, R. A. (1976). *J. Biol. Chem.* **251**, 6189–6196.

Marco, R., and Sols, A. (1970). *In* "Metabolic Regulation and Enzyme Action" (A. Sols and S. Grisolia, eds.), p. 63. Academic Press, New York.

Massey, T. H., and Deal, W. C. (1973). *J. Biol. Chem.* **248**, 56.

Massey, T. H., and Deal, W. C. (1975). *In* "Methods in Enzymology" (W. A. Wood, ed.), Vol. 42, pp. 99. Academic Press, New York.

Menahan, L. A., and Wieland, O. (1969). *Eur. J. Biochem.* **10**, 188–196.

Mendes-Mourao, J., Halestrap, A. P., Crisp, D. M., and Pogson, C. I. (1975). *FEBS Lett.* **53**, 29–32.

Mendicino, T., and Vasarkely, F. (1963). *J. Biol. Chem.* **11**, 3528–3534.

Mendicino, T., Beaudreau, C., and Bhattacharyya, R. N. (1966). *Arch. Biochem. Biophys.* **116**, 436.

Morikofer-Zwez, S., Kinin, A. S., and Walter, P. (1973). *J. Biol. Chem.* **248**, 7588–7594.

Mowbray, J. (1974). *FEBS Lett.* **44**, 344–347.

Mowbray, J. (1975). *Biochem. J.* **148**, 41–47.

Nakashima, K., Pontremoli, S., and Horecker, B. L. (1969). *Proc. Natl. Acad. Sci. U.S.A.* **64**, 947–951.

Nakashima, K., Horecker, B. L., Traniello, S., and Pontremoli, S. (1970). *Arch. Biochem. Biophys.* **139**, 190.

Newsholme, E. A., and Gevers, W. (1967). *Vitam. Horm. (N.Y.)* **25**, 1–87.

Nimmo, H. G., and Tipton, K. F. (1975). *Biochem. J.* **145**, 323–334.

Paetkau, V., and Lardy, H. A. (1967). *J. Biol. Chem.* **252**, 2035.

Paetkau, V., Younathan, E. S., and Lardy, H. A. (1968). *J. Mol. Biol.* **33**, 731–736.

Papa, S. (1976). *Biochim. Biophys. Acta* **456**, 39–84.

Papa, S., Lofrumento, N. E., Loglisci, M., and Quagliarello, E. (1969). *Biochim. Biophys. Acta* **189**, 311–314.

Papa, S., Francavilla, A., Paradies, G., and Henduri, B. (1971). *FEBS Lett.* **12**, 285–288.

Passoneau, J. V., and Lowry, O. H. (1964). *Adv. Enzyme. Regul.* **2**, 265–274.

Pilkis, S. J., Claus, T. H., Johnson, R. A., and Park, C. R. (1975). *J. Biol. Chem.* **250**, 6238–6363.

Pilkis, S. J., Riou, J. P., and Claus, T. H. (1976a). *J. Biol. Chem.* **251**, 7841–7852.

Pilkis, S. J., Claus, T. H., Riou, J. P., and Park, C. R. (1976b). *Metab., Clin. Exp.* **25**, Suppl. 1, 1355–1341.

Pilkis, S. J., Pilkis, J., and Claus, T. H. (1978a). *Biochem. Biophys. Res. Commun.* **81**, 139–146.

Pilkis, S. J., Claus, T. H., Riou, J. P., Cherrington, A. D., Chaisson, J. E., Liljenquist, J. E., Lacy, W. W., and Park, C. R. (1978b). *FEBS Symp.* **42**, 13–29.

Pilkis, S. J., Park, C. R., and Claus, T. H. (1978c). *Vitam. Horm. (N.Y.)* **36**, 383–459.

Pilkis, S. J., Schlumpf, J., Pilkis, J., and Claus, T. H. (1979a). *Biochem. Biophys. Res. Commun.* **88**, 960–967.

Pilkis, S. J., Claus, T. H., Tager, H., Steiner, D., Keim, P., and Heinrikson, R. (1979b). *Abstr., Int. Congr. Biochem. 11th, 1979* Abstract No. 03–6–585.

Pilkis, S. J., El-Maghrabi, M. R., Claus, T. H., Tager, H., Steiner, D. F., Keim, P., and Heinrikson, R. L. (1980). *J. Biol. Chem.* **255**, 2770–2775.

Pogell, B. M., Tanaka, A., and Siddons, R. C. (1968). *J. Biol. Chem.* **243**, 1356–1367.

Pogell, B. M., Taketa, K., and Saingadharan, M. B. (1971). *J. Biol. Chem.* **246**, 1947–1948.

Pontremoli, S., and Horecker, B. L. (1971). *In* "The Enzymes" (P. D. Boyer, eds.), 3rd ed., Vol. 4, p. 611. Academic Press, New York.

Pontremoli, S., Luppis, B., Traniello, S., Rippa, M., and Horecker, B. L. (1965). *Arch. Biochem. Biophys.* **112**, 7.

Pontremoli, S., Traniello, S., Ensei, M., Shapiro, S., and Horecker, B. L. (1967). *Proc. Natl. Acad. Sci. U.S.A.* **58**, 286–293.

Pontremoli, S., Granzi, E., and Accorri, A. (1968). *Biochemistry* **7**, 3628.

Proud, C., Luck, H. J., Brand, I., and Söling, H. D. (1979). *Abstr., Int. Congr. Biochem. 11th, 1979* Abstract No. 04–5–5128.

Racker, E. (1970). *Essays Biochem.* **6**, 1–22.

Ramaiah, A. (1974). *Curr. Top. Cell. Regul.* **8**, 298–345.

Ramaiah, A., and Tejwani, G. A. (1970). *Biochem. Biophys. Res. Commun.* **39**, 1149.

Rasmussen, H. (1970). *Science* **170**, 404–412.

Reinhart, G. D. (1977). *Fed. Proc., Fed. Am. Soc. Exp. Biol.* **36**, 3095.

Reinhart, G. D., and Lardy, H. A. (1979). *Abstr., Int. Congr. Biochem. 11th, 1979* Abstract No. 04-3-5155.

Riou, J. P., Claus, T. H., and Pilkis, S. J. (1976). *Biochem. Biophys. Res. Commun.* **73**, 591–599.

Riou, J. P., Claus, T. H., Flockhart, D., Corbin, J., and Pilkis, S. J. (1977). *Proc. Natl. Acad. Sci. U.S.A.* **74**, 4615–4619.

Riou, J. P., Claus, T. H., and Pilkis, S. J. (1978). *J. Biol. Chem.* **253**, 656–659.

Riquelme, P. T., Hosey, M. M., Marcus, F., and Kemp, R. G. (1978). *Biochem. Biophys. Res. Commun.* **85**, 1480–1487.

Robison, G. A., Butcher, R. W., and Sutherland, E. W. (1971). "Cyclic AMP." Academic Press, New York.

Rognstad, R. (1975). *Biochem. Biophys. Res. Commun.* **63**, 900–905.

Rognstad, R. (1976). *Int. J. Biochem.* **7**, 403–408.

Rognstad, R. (1977). *Biochem. Biophys. Res. Commun.* **78**, 881–888.

Rognstad, R. (1979). *Int. J. Biochem.* **10**, 619–621.

Rognstad, R., and Katz, J. (1972). *J. Biol. Chem.* **247**, 6047–6054.

Rognstad, R., and Katz, J. (1976). *Arch. Biochem. Biophys.* **177**, 337–345.

Rognstad, R., and Katz, J. (1977). *J. Biol. Chem.* **252**, 1831–1833.

Rosenberg, J. S., Tashima, Y., and Horecker, B. L. (1973). *Arch. Biochem. Biophys.* **154**, 283–293.

Ross, B. D., Hems, R., and Krebs, H. A. (1967a). *Biochem. J.* **102**, 942–951.

Ross, B. D., Hems, R., Freedland, R. A., and Krebs, H. A. (1967b). *Biochem. J.* **105**, 869–875.

Rozengurt, E., Jiménez de Asua, L., and Carminatti, H. (1969). *J. Biol. Chem.* **244**, 3142–3147.

Salzmann, M., Carafoli, E., and Jakob, A. (1978). *Experientia* **34**, 917–

Schimassek, H., and Mitzkat, H. J. (1963). *Biochem. Z.* **337**, 510–518.

Schoner, W., Haag, U., and Seubert, W. (1970). *Hoppe-Seyler's Z. Physiol. Chem.* **351**, 1071–1088.

Scrutton, M. C., and Utter, M. F. (1968). *Annu. Rev. Biochem.* **37**, 249–302.

Seubert, W., and Schoner, W. (1971). *Curr. Top. Cell. Regul.* **3**, 237–267.

Seubert, W., Henning, H. V., Schoner, W., and L'Age, M. (1968). *Adv. Enzyme Regul.* **6**, 153–187.

Sherline, P., Lynch, A., and Glinsmann, W. H. (1972). *Endocrinology* **91**, 680–690.

Siddle, K., and Hales, C. N. (1974). *Biochem. J.* **142**, 97–103.

Siess, E. A., Brocks, D. G., Lattke, H. K., and Wieland, O. H. (1977). *Biochem. J.* **166**, 225–235.

Siess, E. A., Brocks, D. G., and Wieland, O. H. (1978). *Biochem. J.* **172**, 517–521.

Singh, S. P., and Synder, A. K. (1978). *Endocrinology* **102**, 182–187.

Snoke, R. E., Johnston, J. B., and Lardy, H. A. (1971). *Eur. J. Biochem.* **24**, 342–346.

Söling, H. D., Bernard, G., Kuhn, A., and Lück, H.-J. (1977). *Arch. Biochem. Biophys.* **182**, 563–572.

Söling, H. D., and Kleineke, J. (1976). *In* "Gluconeogenesis: Its Regulation in Mammalian Species" (R. W. Hanson and M. A. Mehlman, eds.), pp. 369–462. Wiley, New York.

Söling, H. D., Willams, B., Friedrichs, D., and Kleineke, J (1968). **Eur. J. Biochem. 4**, 364–372.

Sorensen-Ziganke, B., and Hofer, H. W. (1979). *Biochem. Biophys. Res. Commun.* **90**, 204–208.

Start, C., and Newsholme, E. A. (1968). *Biochem. J.* **107**, 411.

Steiner, K., Chan, T. M., Claus, T. H., Exton, J. H., and Pilkis, S. J. (1980). *Biochim. Biophys. Acta* (in press).

Stifel, F. B., Taunton, O. D., Greene, H. L., and Herman, R. H. (1974). *J. Biol. Chem.* **249**, 7239–7244.

Struck, E., Ashmore, J., and Wieland, O. (1965). *Biochem. Z.* **343**, 107–110.

Struck, E., Ashmore, J., and Wieland, O. H. (1966). *Adv. Enzyme Regul.* **4**, 219–224.

Stubbs, M., Kirk, C. J., and Hems, D. A. (1976). *FEBS Lett.* **69**, 199–202.

Stucki, J. W., Brawand, F., and Walter, P. (1972). *Eur. J. Biochem.* **27**, 181–191.

Susor, W. A., and Rutter, W. J. (1968). *Biochem. Biophys. Res. Commun.* **30**, 14.

Swick, R. W., Barnstein, P. L., and Stange, J. L. (1965). *J. Biol. Chem.* **240**, 3334–3340.

Taketa, K., and Pogell, B. M. (1963). *Biochem. Biophys. Res. Commun.* **12**, 229–235.

Taketa, K., and Pogell, B. M. (1965). *J. Biol. Chem.* **240**, 651–662.

Taketa, K., Sarngadharon, M. G., Watanabe, A., Aoe, H., and Pogell, B. M. (1971). *J. Biol. Chem.* **236**, 5676–5683.

Tanaka, T., Sue, F., and Marimura, H. J. (1965). *Biochem. Biophys. Res. Commun.* **29**, 444.

Taunton, O. D., Stifel, F. B., Greene, H. L., and Herman, R. H. (1972). *Biochem. Biophys. Res. Commun.* **48**, 1663–1670.

Taunton, O. D., Stifel, F. B., Greene, H. L., and Herman, R. H. (1974). *J. Biol. Chem.* **249**, 7228–7239.

Taylor, C. B., and Bailey, E. (1967). *Biochem. J.* **102**, 32c.

Tejwani, G. A., Pedrosa, F. O., Pontremoli, S., and Horecker, B. L. (1976a). *Arch. Biochem. Biophys.* **177**, 253–264.

Tejwani, G. A., Pedrosa, F. O., Pontremoli, S., and Horecker, B. L. (1976b). *Proc. Natl. Acad. Sci. U.S.A.* **73**, 2692–2695.

Tilghman, S. M., Hanson, R. W., and Ballard, F. J. (1976). *In* "Gluconeogenesis: Its Regulation in Mammalian Species" (R. W. Hanson and M. A. Mehlman, eds.), pp. 47–91. Wiley, New York.

Titanji, V. P. K., Zetterqvist, O., and Engström, L. (1976). *Biochim. Biophys. Acta* **22**, 98–108.

Titheradge, M., and Coore, H. G. (1975). *Biochem. J.* **150**, 553–556.

Titheradge, M., and Coore, H. G. (1976a). *FEBS Lett.* **63**, 45–50.

Titheradge, M., and Coore, H. G. (1976b). *FEBS Lett.* **71**, 73–78.

Titheradge, M., Binder, S. B., Yamazaki, R. K., and Haynes, R. C., Jr. (1978). *J. Biol. Chem.* **253**, 3357–3360.

Tolbert, M. E. M., and Fain, J. N. (1974). *J. Biol. Chem.* **249**, 1162–1166.

Tolbert, M. E. M., Butcher, F. R., and Fain, J. N. (1973). *J. Biol. Chem.* **248**, 5886–5692.

Tolman, E. L., Schworer, C. M., and Jefferson, L. S. (1973). *J. Biol. Chem.* **248**, 4552–4560.

Traniello, S., Pontremoli, S., Tashima, Y., and Horecker, B. L. (1971). *Arch. Biochem. Biophys.* **146**, 161–166.

Triebwasser, K. C., and Freedland, R. A. (1977). *Biochem. Biophys. Res. Commun.* **76**, 1159–1165.

Trujillo, J. L., and Deal, W. C. (1977). *Biochemistry* **16**, 3098–3104.

Tsai, M. Y., and Kemp, R. (1973). *J. Biol. Chem.* **248**, 785.

Ui, M., Claus, T. H., Exton, J. H., and Park, C. R. (1973a). *J. Biol. Chem.* **248**, 5344–5349.

Ui, M., Exton, J. H., and Park, C. R. (1973b). *J. Biol. Chem.* **248**, 5350–5359.

Underwood, A. H., and Newsholme, E. A. (1965a). *Biochem. J.* **95**, 767–774.

Underwood, A. H., and Newsholme, E. A. (1965b). *Biochem. J.* 95, 868–875.

Utter, M. F., and Kolenbrander, H. M. (1972). In "The Enzymes" (P. D. Boyer, ed.), 3rd Vol. 6, pp. 117–168. Academic Press, New York.

Utter, M. F., and Kurahashi, K. (1953). *J. Am. Chem. Soc.* 75, 758.

Utter, M. F., Keech, D. B., and Scrutton, M. C. (1964). *Adv. Enzyme. Regul.* 2, 44–68.

Uyeda, K., and Luby, L. J. (1974). *J. Biol. Chem.* 14, 4562–4570.

Uyeda, K., Miyatake, A., Luby, L. J., and Richards, E. G. (1978). *J. Biol. Chem.* 253, 8319–8327.

Van Berkel, T. J. C., De Jonge, R., Koster, J. F., and Hulsmann, W. C. (1974). *Biochem. Biophys. Res. Commun.* 60, 398–405.

Van Berkel, T. J. C., Kruijt, T. K., Koster, J. F., and Hulsmann, W. C. (1976). *Biochem. Biophys. Res. Commun.* 72, 917–925.

Van Berkel, T. J. C., Kruijt, T. K., and Koster, J. F. (1977a). *Eur. J. Biochem.* 81, 423–432.

Van Berkel, T. J. C., Kruijt, T. K., and Koster, J. F. (1977b). *Biochim. Biophys. Acta* 500, 267–276.

Van de Werve, G., Hué, L., and Hers, H. G. (1977). *Biochem. J.* 162, 135–142.

Vardanis, A. (1977). *J. Biol. Chem.* 252, 807–813.

Veneziale, C. M., and Nesheim, M. E. (1972). *Biochemistry* 11, 3286–3289.

von Glutz, G., and Walter, P. (1976). *FEBS Lett.* 72, 299–303.

Wakat, D., and Haynes, R. C., Jr. (1977). *Arch. Biochem. Biophys.* 184, 561–571.

Walsh, D. A., and Chen, L.-J. (1971). *Biochem. Biophys. Res. Commun.* 45, 669–675.

Walsh, D. A., Ashby, C. D., Gonzalez, C., Calkins, D., Fisher, E. G., and Krebs, E. G. (1971). *J. Biol. Chem.* 246, 1977–1985.

Whitehouse, S., and Randle, P. J. (1973). *Biochem. J.* 134, 651–653.

Whitehouse, S., Cooper, R. G., and Randle, P. J. (1974). *Biochem. J.* 141, 761–774.

Whitton, P. D., Rodrigues, L. M., and Hems, D. A. (1978). *Biochem. J.* 176, 893–898.

Wicks, W. D., Lewis W., and McKibbin, T. B. (1972). *Biochim. Biophys. Acta* 264, 177–185.

Williamson, J. R., Garcia, A., Renold, A. E., and Cahill, G. F., Jr. (1966a). *Diabetes* 15, 183–187.

Williamson, J. R., Herczeg, B., Coles, H., and Danish, R. (1966b). *Biochem. Biophys. Res. Commun.* 24, 437–442.

Williamson, J. R., Scholz, R., and Browning, E. T. (1969a). *J. Biol. Chem.* 244, 4617–4627.

Williamson, J. R., Browning, E. T., Thurman, R. G., and Scholz, R. (1969b). *J. Biol. Chem.* 244, 5055–5064.

Wimhurst, J. M., and Manchester, K. L. (1970). *Biochem. J.* 120, 79–93.

Yamazaki, R. K. (1975). *J. Biol. Chem.* 250, 7924–7930.

Yamazaki, R. K., and Graetz, G. S. (1977). *Arch. Biochem. Biophys.* 178, 19–25.

Yamazaki, R. K., and Haynes, R. C., Jr. (1975). *Arch. Biochem. Biophys.* 166, 575–583.

Yamazaki, R. K., Sax, R. D., and Hauser, M. A. (1977). *Arch. Biochem. Biophys.* 178, 19–25.

Yeaman, S. J., Cohen, P., Watson, D. C., and Dixon, G. H. (1977). *Biochem. J.* 162, 411–421.

Zahlten, R. N., Hochberg, A. A., Stratman, F. W., and Lardy, H. A. (1972). *Proc. Natl. Acad. Sci. U.S.A.* 69, 800–804.

Zahlten, R. N., Stratman, F. W., and Lardy, H. A. (1973). *Proc. Natl. Acad. Sci. U.S.A.* 70, 3213–3218.

Zetterqvist, O., Rognaisson, U., Humble, E., Berglund, L., and Engström, L. (1976). *Biochem. Biophys. Res. Commun.* 70, 696–703.

CHAPTER 5

Effects of Insulin
on Intracellular Functions

Ira D. Goldfine

I. INTRODUCTION

Insulin is a major anabolic hormone that regulates the metabolism of most cells. The potency of insulin is derived from its having short, intermediate, and long-term effects on cellular functions. The short-term effects of insulin (occurring within seconds) are the rapid regulation of plasma membrane activities including membrane potential and the transport of sugars, amino acids, and ions (Krahl, 1974; Pilkis and Park, 1974; Fain, 1974; Czech, 1977; Goldfine, 1977, 1978a). The intermediate effects of insulin (occurring within minutes) are the activation and inactivation of enzymes, stimulation of protein synthesis, and the inhibition of protein degradation (Krahl, 1974; Pilkis and Park, 1974; Fain, 1974; Czech, 1977; Goldfine, 1977, 1978a). The long-term effects of insulin (occurring within hours) are the stimulation of RNA and DNA synthesis (Krahl, 1974; Pilkis and Park, 1974; Fain, 1974; Czech, 1977; Goldfine 1977, 1978a). In addition to regulating cellular effects that have varying temporal sequences, insulin also regulates functions on a variety of cellular components including plasma membranes, nuclei, endoplasmic reticulum, lysosomes, mitochondria, and cytoplasm.

The short-term effects of insulin on cell surface transport are quite dramatic, are seen within seconds after the addition of insulin, and have been studied intensively. It is likely that they are the direct result of the interaction of insulin with its plasma membrane receptor. The effects of insulin on transport have been recently reviewed (Czech, 1977; Gliemann and Sonne, 1977) and will not be discussed herein. In contrast to the control of plasma membrane activities, less is known about how insulin regulates intermediate and long-term intracellular events. A major effect of insulin is the regulation of a number of intracellular enzymes (Table I). This review will first classify several of the major intracellular actions of insulin, and then review recent data suggesting that insulin enters cells and then may have one or more direct intracellular effects.

II. INTRACELLULAR EFFECTS OF INSULIN

A. Effects of Insulin on the Nucleus

1. DNA Synthesis

Insulin regulates the synthesis of both DNA and RNA. *In vitro* insulin has been used for a number of decades to stimulate the growth of cells in tissue culture (Gey and Thalhimer, 1924). Usually, however, higher than

TABLE I

GLUCOSE METABOLISM
A. *Glycolysis and glycogenesis (stimulation)*
   Hexokinase II (Borrebaek, 1966; Hansen *et al.*, 1967, 1970)
   Glucokinase (DiPietro and Weinhouse, 1960; Niemeyer *et al.*, 1965; Sols, 1965; Walker and Rao, 1964; Weber, 1972; Pilkis, 1970)
   Phosphofructokinase (Weber, 1972; Taunton *et al.*, 1974; Dunaway *et al.*, 1978; Saggerson and Greenbaum, 1969)
   Glycogen synthase (Larner, 1972; Hers, 1976; Steiner and King, 1964; Craig *et al.*, 1969; Jungas and Ball, 1963)
   Pyruvate kinase (Weber, 1972; Taunton *et al.*, 1974; Gerschenson and Andersson, 1971; Denton *et al.*, 1979; Feliu *et al.*, 1976; Blair *et al.*, 1976; Claus *et al.*, 1979; Saggerson and Greenbaum, 1969)
   Glucose-6-P-dehydrogenase (Steiner and King, 1964; Geisler *et al.*, 1978; Saggerson and Greenbaum, 1969)
   Lactate dehydrogenase (Suleiman and Vestling, 1979)
B. *Gluconeogenesis (inhibition)*
   Pyruvate carboxylase (Weber *et al.*, 1968)
   Phosphoenolpyruvate carboxykinase (Weber *et al.*, 1968; Seitz *et al.*, 1977; Peret and Chanez, 1976; Wicks *et al.*, 1974)
   Fructose-1,6-diphosphatase (Weber *et al.*, 1968; Pontremoli *et al.*, 1975)
   Glucose-6-phosphatase (Ashmore *et al.*, 1954; Weber *et al.*, 1965)
FAT METABOLISM
A. *Lipogenesis (stimulation)*
   Acetyl-CoA ligase (Jason *et al.*, 1976; Nakanishi *et al.*, 1976)
   Acetyl-CoA carboxylase (Nakanishi *et al.*, 1976; Witters *et al.*, 1979)
   Fatty acid synthase (Lakshmanan *et al.*, 1972; Joshi and Wakil, 1978; Speake *et al.*, 1976)
   Pyruvate dehydrogenase (Denton *et al.*, 1971; Hutson *et al.*, 1978; Baxter and Coore, 1978; Mukherjee and Jungas, 1975; Paetzke-Brunner *et al.*, 1979; Sakamoto and Kuzuya, 1979)
   Malic enzyme (Shrago *et al.*, 1963; Goodridge, 1975)
   ATP-citrate lyase (Söling *et al.*, 1969)
   Lipoprotein lipase (Garfinkel *et al.*, 1976; Eckel *et al.*, 1978; Spooner *et al.*, 1979)
   Hydroxymethylglutaryl-CoA reductase (Paetzke-Brunner *et al.*, 1979; Sakamoto and Kuzuya, 1979; Shrago *et al.*, 1963; Goodridge, 1975; Söling *et al.*, 1969; Garfinkel *et al.*, 1976; Eckel *et al.*, 1978; Spooner *et al.*, 1979; Bhathena *et al.*, 1974; Lakshmanan *et al.*, 1973; Ingebritsen *et al.*, 1979)
   Hydroxymethylglutaryl-CoA reductase kinase (Ingebritsen *et al.*, 1979)
B. *Lipolysis (inhibition)*
   Hormone-sensitive lipase (Jungas and Ball, 1963; Steinberg and Khoo, 1977; Fain *et al.*, 1966)
PROTEIN METABOLISM
A. *Protein synthesis (stimulation)*
   Tyrosine aminotransferase (Gelehrter and Tomkins, 1970; Reel *et al.*, 1970)
   Ribosomal enzymes (Wool *et al.*, 1968, 1972)
B. *Protein degradation (inhibition)*
   Serine dehydratase (Söling *et al.*, 1969; Grillo and Sisini, 1977)
   Cathepsin D (Kanter, 1976)
   Acid phosphatase (Kanter, 1976)
RNA AND DNA METABOLISM
   RNA polymerase (Steiner, 1966)
   Enzymes favoring t-RNA synthesis (Davey and Manchester, 1969)
CYCLIC AMP (inhibition)
   Cyclic AMP phosphodiesterase (Krahl, 1974; Pilkis and Park, 1974; Fain, 1974; Loten and Sneyd, 1970)
   Cyclic AMP protein kinase (Larner, 1975)
MISCELLANEOUS
   δ-Aminolevulinate synthetase (Granick *et al.*, 1975)

physiologic concentrations of insulin are necessary for this effect (Smith and Temin, 1974; Rechler *et al.*, 1974) and it is likely that in many instances insulin is interacting with receptors for the various insulin-like growth peptides such as somatotomedin, MSA, or nonsuppressible insulin-like activity (NSILA-s) (Smith and Temin, 1974; Rechler *et al.*, 1974; Chochinov and Daughaday, 1976). In a few instances physiological concentrations of insulin increase cell division. In the regrowth of liver that follows partial hepatectomy in rats and other animals, it has been shown *in vivo* that insulin is necessary for this process to occur (Bucher and Weir, 1976; Bucher and Swaffield, 1975a,b; Bucher *et al.*, 1969; Higgins and Anderson, 1931; Price, 1976). In cultured cells from regenerating rat liver there is also *in vitro* evidence indicating that insulin stimulates DNA synthesis (Richman *et al.*, 1976). In the mammary gland, insulin *in vitro* increases DNA synthesis, cell proliferation, and cell differentiation (Stockdale and Topper, 1966; Topper *et al.*, 1970; Turkington, 1968). Effects of insulin on DNA synthesis in various tissues may take a day or longer to be fully expressed.

2. RNA Synthesis

Effects of insulin on transcription have been reported in liver, adipose tissue, and mammary gland. *In vivo*, insulin has been shown to increase both RNA polymerase activity and template activity of liver (Steiner, 1966; Morgan and Bonner, 1970). Inhibition of RNA synthesis by actinomycin has been reported to block the insulin-stimulated synthesis of several enzymes in diabetic rats including fatty acid synthetase, glycogen synthetase, hexokinase, phosphofructose kinase, and pyruvate kinase (Krahl, 1974; Weber, 1972; Steiner and King, 1964; Steiner, 1966). In liver, insulin administration inhibits the activities of glucose-6-phosphatase, fructose-1, 6-diphosphatase, pyruvate carboxylase, and phosphoenolpyruvate carboxykinase (Krahl, 1974; Weber, 1972; Steiner and King, 1964; Steiner, 1966); actinomycin D pretreatment of animals also blocks this inhibition (Krahl, 1974; Weber, 1972; Steiner and King, 1964; Steiner, 1966). More recent studies have indicated that the production of messenger RNA for albumin is decreased in the liver of diabetic rats and that this diminished level of messenger RNA can be restored by insulin administration *in vivo* (Peavy *et al.*, 1978). Administration of insulin to diabetic rats both restores diminished pancreatic amylase levels and reduces increased trypsinogen levels; actinomycin treatment blocks this effect (Söling and Unger, 1972).

In adipose tissue, insulin *in vivo* has been shown to stimulate the synthesis of hexokinase II via the formation of new RNA (Krahl, 1974; Hansen *et al.*, 1967, 1970). In addition insulin stimulates the activity of glucose-6-p-dehydrogenase, phosphofructose kinase, and pyruvate kinase (Krahl, 1974; Hansen *et al.*, 1967, 1970); these effects are blocked by the administration of actinomycin D. It has recently been reported that insulin *in vitro* increases lipoprotein lipase activity in 3T3-L1 fibroblasts (Spooner *et al.*, 1979) in part by nuclear regulation.

In mammary glands, insulin *in vitro* activates RNA synthesis, stimulates RNA polymerase activity, and stimulates the phosphorylation of histone and nonhistone proteins (Stockdale and Topper, 1966; Topper *et al.*, 1970; Turkington, 1968; Terry *et al.*, 1977; Turkington and Riddle, 1969).

B. Effects of Insulin on the Endoplasmic Reticulum

In many tissues, insulin stimulates protein synthesis. It does so via at least two mechanisms. First, insulin increases the membrane transport of several (but not all) amino acids (Kipnis and Cori, 1959; Manchester and Young, 1960; Morgan and Neely, 1972). Second, insulin (independently of its transport effects) also stimulates ribosomes to translate messenger RNA (Krahl, 1974; Pilkis and Park, 1974; Fain, 1974; Wool *et al.*, 1972; Manchester, 1970). In muscle and liver from diabetic animals, insulin *in vivo* increases the assembly of polysomes (Wool *et al.*, 1972). Wool and co-workers (1972) and others (Rannels *et al.*, 1978) have reported a defect in the 60 S ribosomal subunit of muscle from diabetic animals, and in diabetes there is a decrease in the initiation of endogenous protein synthesis. Recently Gressner and Wool (1976) have reported that phosphorylation of liver ribosomal factor 6 is increased in diabetic rats and this phosphorylation can be reduced by insulin administration. This finding suggests the possibility of a specific enzymatic defect in protein synthesis during the diabetic state.

In muscle, insulin stimulates the synthesis of all cellular proteins (Krahl, 1974; Pilkis and Park, 1974; Fain, 1974; Manchester, 1970). The effects of insulin in muscle can be detected as early as 5 minutes after its injection into diabetic animals (Krahl, 1974; Pilkis and Park, 1974; Fain, 1974; Wool *et al.*, 1972).

In liver of diabetic animals there is also diminished protein synthesis and this decreased synthesis is corrected by insulin administration (Krahl, 1974; Pilkis and Park, 1974; Fain, 1974). In addition, in liver, several specific proteins are regulated. Tyrosine aminotransferase is perhaps the most extensively studied enzyme where insulin exerts translational control (Table I) (Krahl, 1974; Pilkis and Park, 1974; Fain, 1974; Reel *et al.*, 1970; Gelehrter and Tomkins, 1970). Also in hepatocytes, insulin *in vitro* has been reported to increase the synthesis of albumin (Dich and Gluud, 1975) and the enzymes δ-aminolevulinic acid synthetase, acetyl-CoA-ligase and carboxylase, and malic enzyme (Table I). The activity of hydroxymethylglutaryl CoA reductase (an enzyme located in the rough and smooth endoplasmic reticulum) is stimulated by insulin but this effect of insulin appears to be mediated by dephosphorylation of the enzyme (Ingebritsen *et al.*, 1979).

In adipose tissue and mammary gland insulin stimulates both general protein synthesis and the specific synthesis of several proteins (Terry *et al.*, 1977) including casein (Terry *et al.*, 1977) and glucose-6-phosphate dehydrogenase (Krahl, 1974). In isolated pancreatic acini prepared from diabetic rats, insulin increases protein synthesis (Korc *et al.*, 1980).

C. Effects of Insulin on Lysosomes

The catabolism of proteins by cells serves several important functions. First, this process removes abnormal proteins that are formed by aging, mutation, or chemicals. Second, protein catabolism provides cells with needed amino acids. Third, it allows for the regulation of the cellular content of both exogenous and endogenous proteins. In several tissues, insulin inhibits protein degradation. This effect can be seen in muscle *in vivo* (Krahl, 1974; Pilkis and Park, 1974; Fain, 1974; Kanter, 1976; Jefferson *et al.*, 1977), in the perfused rat liver (Krahl, 1974; Pilkis and Park, 1974; Fain, 1974; Kanter, 1976; Mortimore and Mondon, 1977) and in hepatoma cells and fibroblasts *in vitro* (Krahl, 1974; Pilkis and Park, 1974; Fain, 1974; Kanter, 1976; Hershko *et al.*, 1971; Gelehrter and Tomkins, 1970). A considerable portion of the protein degradative activity of cells takes place in lysosomes. In rat heart muscle, it has been postulated that insulin reduces protein degradation by both inhibiting autophagic lysosomal vacule formation and the inactivation of lysosomal enzymes (Kanter, 1976). There is evidence that insulin, under certain conditions, reduces the activities of acid phosphatase and cathepsin D (Kanter, 1976). Recent studies by Spencer and co-workers (1978), studying HTC rat hepatoma cells, have suggested that the major effect of insulin on tyrosine aminotransferase activity is to inhibit the degradation of this protein.

D. Effects of Insulin on Mitochondria

Insulin regulates the pyruvate dehydrogenase enzyme complex that produces acetyl-CoA necessary for lipid synthesis (Krahl, 1974; Denton *et al.*, 1971; Hutson *et al.*, 1978; Baxter and Coore, 1978; Mukherjee and

Jungas, 1975; Paetzke-Brunner *et al.*, 1979; Sakamoto and Kuzuya, 1979). Insulin activates this enzyme complex by dephosphorylation (Krahl, 1974; Denton *et al.*, 1971; Hutson *et al.*, 1978; Baxter and Coore, 1978; Mukherjee and Jungas, 1975; Paetzke-Brunner *et al.*, 1979; Sakamoto and Kuzuya, 1979). Recently Seals *et al.* (1979) have suggested that this enzyme in adipocytes can be regulated by insulin in broken cell preparations.

E. Effects of Insulin on Cytoplasmic Enzymes

In addition to enzymes in the endoplasmic reticulum, lysosomes, and mitochondria, insulin increases the activity of a number of soluble enzymes involved in glucose metabolism including glycogen synthetase, phosphofructose kinase, and pyruvate kinase. These effects can occur after several minutes and appear to be independent of new protein or RNA synthesis (Krahl, 1972, 1974). The enzyme studied most extensively has been glycogen synthetase and this enzyme is activated by insulin via a dephosphorylation mechanism (Larner, 1972; Hers, 1976). In addition, there is evidence that insulin also activates pyruvate kinase by dephosphorylation mechanisms (Blair *et al.*, 1976; Claus *et al.*, 1979).

Insulin rapidly inhibits the activity of hormone-sensitive lipase in adipose tissue via dephosphorylation of the enzyme (Steinberg and Khoo, 1977). Insulin also has rapid effects on inhibition of the activities of several other enzymes including phosphoenolpyruvate carboxykinase and fructose-1, 6-diphosphatase (Taunton *et al.*, 1974). The mechanism whereby insulin regulates these enzymes is unknown but a dephosphorylation process may also be involved.

F. Effects of Insulin on Phosphorylation

Insulin activates and inactivates enzymes in the cytoplasm, endoplasmic reticulum, and mitochondria by a dephosphorylation mechanism. In addition, it is likely that insulin stimulation of protein synthesis may involve dephosphorylation of one or more enzymes. Several investigators, therefore, have investigated the effects of insulin on phosphorylation in fat cells (Fain, 1974; Benjamin and Singer, 1974, 1975; Avruch *et al.*, 1976a,b). Insulin increases the phosphorylation of several proteins in the endoplasmic reticulum of fat cells (Avruch *et al.*, 1976a,b,c) but does antagonize the phosphorylation of several proteins induced by epinephrine (Avruch *et al.*, 1976a,b,c). Insulin may either inactivate the activity of a protein kinase or activate the activity of a phosphoprotein phosphatase (Krahl, 1974; Pilkis and Park, 1974; Fain, 1974; Larner, 1972; Hers, 1976).

III. MECHANISM OF INSULIN ACTION

A comprehensive theory of insulin action must explain very rapid stimulation of membrane transport, rapid activation of intracellular enzymes (both in intracellular organelles and in the cytoplasm) and protein synthesis, and more delayed effects on protein degradation and RNA and DNA synthesis. Since the discovery of cyclic AMP as the intracellular messenger of many, if not all, of the activities of hormones such as glucagon, a similar type of intracellular mediator has been searched for that could explain all of these diverse effects of insulin. No such messenger, however, has yet been found for insulin (Goldfine, 1977).

Over the past few decades, there have been several candidates for an intracellular mediator of insulin action. Since insulin can antagonize certain of the actions of hormones that act through cyclic AMP (Krahl, 1974; Pilkis and Park, 1974; Fain, 1974) (such as glucagon or epinephrine), it was hypothesized that insulin acts in part by lowering cyclic AMP levels. In several tissues, insulin does lower either basal and/or hormone-stimulated cyclic AMP levels (Krahl, 1974; Pilkis and Park, 1974; Fain, 1974). Further, insulin activates the enzyme cyclic AMP phosphodiesterase in liver and fat (Krahl, 1974; Pilkis and Park, 1974; Fain, 1974). As reviewed by Fain and Steinberg, however, there are a number of instances where the actions of insulin can be divorced from the regulation of cyclic AMP levels (Fain, 1974; Steinberg *et al.*, 1975). Furthermore, in certain instances both insulin and cyclic AMP have the same effect on cells. For instance, in thymocytes (Goldfine and Sherline, 1972) and bone cells (Phang and Downing, 1973), both insulin and cyclic AMP increase amino acid transport. Also in liver, both increase the activity of tyrosine aminotransferase (Gelehrter and Tomkins, 1970; Reel *et al.*, 1970). While it is likely that insulin exerts some of its effects on target cells via decreasing cyclic AMP levels, it is unlikely that lowering of cyclic AMP leads to all the effects of insulin. There have been other candidates for an insulin second messenger including the nucleotide cyclic GMP; ions such as Ca^{2+}, Mg^{2+}, K^+, and H_2O_2 (Krahl, 1974; Pilkis and Park, 1974; Fain, 1974; Goldfine, 1977; Livingston *et al.*, 1977; Cascieri *et al.*, 1979; May and de Haën, 1979). However the regulation of these compounds by insulin can not explain all of the diverse effects of insulin.

In view of the facts that insulin has multiple effects on target cells and that insulin has no known second messenger, the possibility must be considered that insulin has multiple sites (and mechanisms) of action. It is now well established that many proteins larger than insulin enter the interior of intact cells (Neville and Chang, 1978; Goldstein *et al.*, 1979). Recent data will be reviewed demonstrating both the presence of intracellular binding sites for insulin and that insulin enters cells and interacts with these sites.

IV. CELLULAR BINDING SITES FOR INSULIN

To date, specific binding sites for insulin have been described on five intracellular organelles from liver.

A. PLASMA MEMBRANES

Specific binding sites for insulin on purified liver plasma membranes were first unequivocally demonstrated by Freychet *et al.* (1971) and have now been described in a number of cell types including fat, muscle, lymphocytes, placenta, and fibroblasts (Freychet, 1976; Roth, 1973; Kahn, 1975; Goldfine, 1978b; Desbuquois and Cuatrecasas, 1973). The characteristics of these binding sites have been the subject of a number of reviews (Freychet, 1976; Roth, 1973; Kahn, 1975; Goldfine, 1978b) and will not be discussed in detail here. The major characteristics of binding are listed in Table II. In addition to these cell surface binding sites, other insulin binding sites have also been described on intracellular structures including nuclear membranes, smooth and rough endoplasmic reticulum, and Golgi.

TABLE II

MAJOR CHARACTERISTICS OF INSULIN BINDING TO CELLULAR MEMBRANES

Characteristic	Cellular membrane		
	Plasma	Golgi	Nuclear
1. Regulated by extracellular insulin	yes	yes	yes
2. Two orders of binding sites	yes	yes	yes
3. Negative cooperativity	yes	yes	no
4. Alkaline pH optimum	yes	yes	no
5. High NaCl optimum	yes	yes	no
6. Low temperature stability	yes	yes	no
7. Concomitant insulin degradation	yes	no	no
8. Binding inhibited by antibody	yes	?	no

B. NUCLEUS AND NUCLEAR ENVELOPE

Horvat and co-workers first described specific binding sites for insulin on highly purified liver nuclei free of other cellular components (Horvat *et al.*, 1975). This finding has been confirmed both in our laboratory (Goldfine and Smith, 1976), and in the laboratory of Goidl (1979). In addition Brisson-Lougarre and Blum (1979) have found specific binding sites for insulin on isolated nuclei purified from thyroid cells. Several lines of evidence indicate that the major site of insulin binding to the nucleus is the nuclear envelope (Vigneri *et al.*, 1978a; Horvat, 1978). When whole nuclei are incubated with native insulin followed by an immunofluorescence procedure, fluorescence is detected only on the nuclear surface (Horvat, 1978). Also when nuclei are first incubated with radiolabeled [^{125}I]insulin and then subfractionated, most of the specific hormone binding is seen with the nuclear membrane fractions (Vigneri *et al.*, 1978a). In addition, when nuclei are incubated with very high concentrations of detergent to remove both layers of the nuclear envelope, binding is either reduced or eliminated (Vigneri *et al.*, 1978a). Finally, insulin does not bind directly to DNA or histones, but does bind directly to purified nuclear membranes (Vigneri *et al.*, 1978a) (Fig. 1).

The binding of insulin to nuclear membranes, like binding to plasma membranes, fulfills the requirements of a hormone receptor. It is rapid, reversible, high affinity, and hormone specific. The characteristics of insulin binding to the nuclear membrane differ, however, in a number of

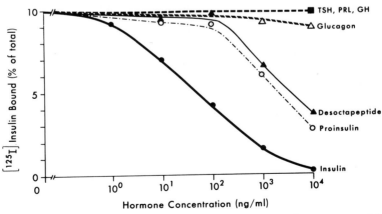

FIG. 1. Direct binding of [^{125}I]insulin to purified nuclear membranes prepared by the method of Kashnig and Kasper (1969) and competitive inhibition of labeled hormone binding by native insulin, proinsulin, desoctapeptide insulin and nonrelated hormones. (From Vigneri *et al.*, 1978a.)

respects from the characteristics of insulin binding to plasma membranes (Table II). Studies of insulin binding to liver plasma membranes have revealed two classes of binding sites (Roth, 1973; Kahn, 1975; Goldfine, 1978b). In our studies of insulin binding sites to nuclear membranes, prepared by the method of Kashnig and Kasper (1969), two orders of binding sites were seen but with lower affinities (K_d 5.6 nM, 65 nM) than that seen on the plasma membranes (K_d 0.5 nM, 10 nM) (Fig. 2a,b). Both plasma membranes and nuclear membranes, however, have similar total insulin binding capacities (approximately 1–2 nmol/mg protein). Horvat, studying nuclear membranes prepared by the method of Kay (Kay and

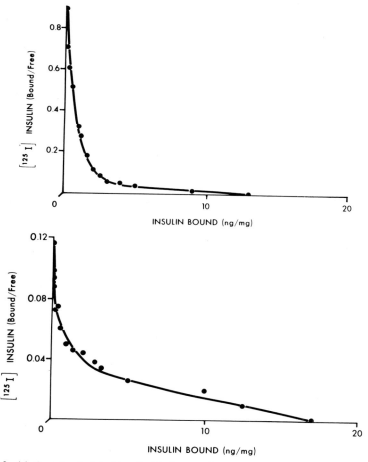

Fig. 2. (a). Scatchard plot of insulin binding to plasma membranes. (b). Scatchard plot of insulin binding to nuclear membranes. (From Vigneri *et al.*, 1978a.)

Johnston, 1973), reported only one class of binding sites for insulin on nuclear membranes with a K_d 3 nM (Horvat, 1978). In liver and other tissues the binding of insulin to plasma membrane has three major characteristics: a sharp pH optimum of 8.0 (Roth, 1973; Kahn, 1975; Goldfine, 1978b), enhanced binding in the presence of high concentrations of sodium chloride (Roth, 1973; Kahn, 1975; Goldfine, 1978b), and negative cooperativity (Roth, 1973; Kahn, 1975; Goldfine, 1978b) that can be demonstrated by the enhanced dissociation of labeled insulin in the presence of unlabeled insulin (Fig. 3 a–c). When the characteristics of insulin binding in these nuclear membranes were examined, we found that the pH optimum was between 7.0 and 7.5, there was no enhanced binding with sodium chloride, and there was no evidence of negative cooperativity. Horvat (1978) also did not find negative cooperativity in studies of insulin binding to nuclear membranes.

In the serum of patients with severe insulin resistance and acanthosis nigricans, there are antibodies to the plasma membrane insulin receptor, and preincubation of plasma membranes with these antibodies blocks the subsequent binding of insulin (Fig. 4) (Flier *et al.*, 1975; Kahn *et al.*, 1976; Jarrett *et al.*, 1976; Goldfine *et al.*, 1977a). This phenomenon can be demonstrated in a variety of species and in a variety of tissues (Flier *et al.*, 1975; Kahn *et al.*, 1976; Jarrett *et al.*, 1976). These antibodies do not, however, interact with receptors for other hormones such as glucagon, growth hormone, and nonsuppressible insulin-like activity (Flier *et al.*, 1975; Kahn *et al.*, 1976; Jarrett *et al.*, 1976). When we preincubated this antiserum with nuclei, there was very little inhibition of the subsequent binding of labeled hormone (Goldfine *et al.*, 1977a) (Fig. 4). Similar results were seen with purified nuclear membranes. This finding raises the possibility that the insulin binding sites in the nuclear envelope are separate proteins from the insulin binding sites on the plasma membrane. A second possibility is that they are the same protein, but the different milieu of the nuclear membrane significantly alters the characteristics of insulin binding. For instance, the lipid composition of nuclear membranes, especially the cholesterol content, is markedly different from plasma membranes (Kay and Johnston, 1973). Since changes in the lipid environment of the plasma membrane can cause changes in insulin binding to plasma membrane receptors (Sun *et al.*, 1977; Lavau *et al.*, 1979), there is evidence for this hypothesis.

The concentration of insulin binding sites on the plasma membrane is regulated both *in vitro* and *in vivo* by the concentration of extracellular insulin. For example, in the hypoinsulinemic states of fasting, hypophysectomy, and both spontaneous and streptozotocin-induced diabetes, there are increased binding sites on plasma membranes (Freychet, 1976;

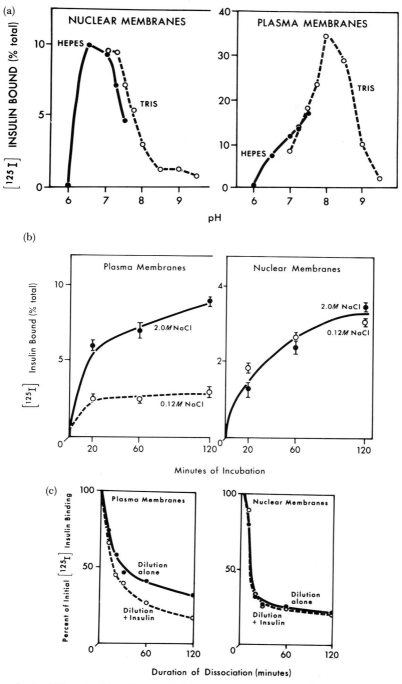

Fig. 3. (a). Effect of pH on the specific binding of [^{125}I]insulin to plasma membranes and nuclear membranes. (b) Effect of high concentrations of NaCl on the binding of insulin to plasma membranes and nuclear membranes. (c) Lack of effect of unlabeled insulin to enhance the dissociation of [^{125}I]insulin from nuclear membranes (absence of negative cooperativity) as compared to plasma membranes. (From Vigneri *et al.*, 1978a.)

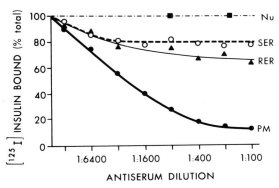

Fig. 4. The effect of preincubation with an antiserum to the plasma membrane insulin receptor on the subsequent specific binding of [^{125}I]insulin to isolated nuclei (Nu), rough and smooth endoplasmic reticulum (RER,SER), and plasma membranes (PM). (From Goldfine et al., 1977a.)

Kahn, 1975; Goldfine, 1978b). Conversely, in hyperinsulinemic states such as obesity and insulinoma, there is a decreased number of binding sites (Freychet, 1976; Kahn, 1975; Goldfine, 1978b). We have also found that the binding of insulin to intracellular structures is regulated by the extracellular insulin concentration (Vigneri et al., 1978b) (Fig. 5). In streptozotocin-induced diabetes, the binding of insulin to nuclei is increased and, conversely, in hyperinsulinemia produced by exogenous insulin injection, the binding of insulin is decreased. Studying the hyperinsulinemic ob/ob mouse, Goidl (1979) has reported that the binding of insulin to liver nuclei is markedly reduced when compared with liver nuclei from thin litter mates.

C. Smooth and Rough Endoplasmic Reticulum

Horvat and co-workers (1975), Kahn and Neville (Kahn, 1976), and our laboratory (Vigneri et al., 1978b) have reported specific binding sites for insulin on the smooth and rough endoplasmic reticulum. The characteristics of insulin binding to the endoplasmic reticulum, however, have not been studied as extensively as the characteristics of insulin binding to either the plasma membrane or nuclear envelope. It appears, however, that like the nuclear envelope there are two classes of binding sites for insulin on both smooth and rough endoplasmic reticulum (Kahn, 1976; Vigneri et al., 1978b) and that the affinity of these two classes of sites is lower than that for plasma membranes (Kahn, 1976; Vigneri et al.,

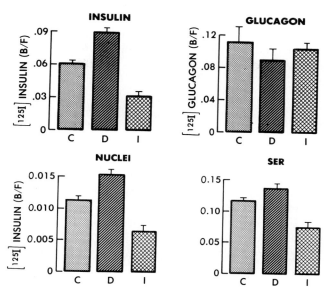

FIG. 5. Regulation of cell surface and intracellular insulin binding sites by extracellular insulin. Rats were either untreated (C), made diabetic with streptozotocin (D), were given insulin injections (I). (a) Specific binding of [125I]insulin and [125I]glucagon to plasma membranes. (b) Specific binding of [125I]insulin to nuclei and smooth endoplasmic reticulum (SER). (From Vigneri *et al.*, 1978b.)

1978b). The aforementioned antibodies to plasma membrane insulin receptors inhibit only weakly the binding of insulin to the smooth and rough endoplasmic reticulum (Fig. 4).

D. GOLGI

Bergeron and co-workers (1973, 1978) have studied the binding of insulin to Golgi fractions (including light and heavy Golgi membranes and Golgi vesicles) from livers of starved ethanol-fed immature rats. In contrast to the nuclear membrane and endoplasmic reticulum, Golgi fractions bind insulin in a manner very similar to that seen with plasma membranes; this similarity includes the affinity and capacity of the binding sites, negative cooperativity effects, and pH optimum (Bergeron *et al.*, 1973, 1978). These authors have speculated that certain of the Golgi binding sites may be precursors of the plasma membrane binding site. Schilling *et al.* (1979) have confirmed that Golgi membranes have insulin binding sites. Insulin binding to both light and heavy Golgi membranes is de-

creased in the hyperinsulinemic *ob/ob* mouse suggesting that these fractions are also regulated by extracellular insulin (Posner *et al.*, 1978). In
contrast, insulin binding to liver Golgi vesicles is unchanged or elevated in
this animal (Posner *et al.*, 1978).

E. Other Subcellular Fractions

The studies of Horvat and co-workers (1975) and Kahn and Neville
(Kahn, 1976) suggest that mitochondria do not contain high concentrations of insulin binding sites. Intracellular organelles in liver and other
tissues, such as lysosomes, vesicles, and secretory granules, have not been
studied in a systematic fashion.

V. THE ENTRY OF INSULIN INTO TARGET CELLS

In addition to the studies demonstrating the presence of specific binding sites for insulin on intracellular membranes in target cells, there are
other studies indicating that insulin can enter target cells and interact
with these sites. In general, three types of experiments have been performed; cell fractionation studies, fluorescent-labeled insulin studies, and
autoradiographic analysis.

A. Cell Fractionation Studies

The first study to demonstrate that insulin enters the interior of cells
was carried out by Lee and Williams (1954) who injected radiolabeled insulin intravenously into the portal vein of rats and then prepared subcellular fractions of liver. These investigators detected insulin uptake into
nuclear, mitochondrial, and microsomal pellets. They further demonstrated that this insulin remained intact and was not degraded. More
recently Izzo and colleagues (1979) have injected [^{125}I] insulin into the
portal vein of rats and then, after various times, subfractionated the
liver. These investigators detected intact insulin in several intracellular
organelles. Brush and Kitabchi (1970) incubated radiolabeled insulin
with rat diaphragm and then subfractionated the tissue. They found
radiolabeled insulin in several intracellular fractions that were not
associated with the cell surface membranes. Studies from our laboratory
(Goldfine *et al.*, 1977b), employing human cultured lymphocytes, have

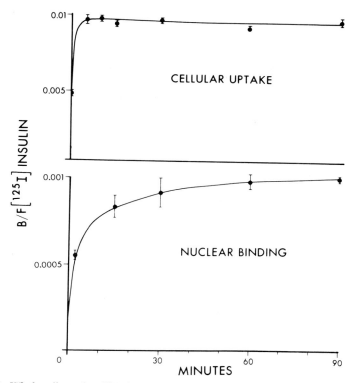

FIG. 6. Whole cell uptake of [^{125}I]insulin and its subsequent translocation into the nucleus. IM-9 lymphocytes (10^6/ml) were incubated with 0.1 nM [^{125}I]insulin and whole cell uptake measured. Cells were then subfractionated and specific hormone binding to nuclei measured. (From Goldfine *et al.*, 1977b.)

demonstrated that insulin initially binds to the surface of the cells and then is translocated into the cell interior. When whole lymphocytes were incubated with [^{125}I]insulin, binding was rapid, being one half-maximal within 1 minute and maximal within 5 minutes (Fig. 6). Subsequently, if the cells were subfractionated and purified nuclei obtained, specific insulin binding to this organelle was detected. Nuclear binding, however, was slower than whole cell uptake and was one half-maximal within 5 minutes and maximal within 15 minutes (Goldfine *et al.*, 1977b). The extraction of the nuclear radioactivity revealed that it was intact insulin (Goldfine *et al.*, 1977b). Both Kahn and Baird (1978) and Suzuki and Kono (1979) have reported data indicating that insulin is internalized into rat fat cells.

B. Fluorescent-Labeled Insulin

Pastan and co-workers have covalently attached insulin to β-lactalbumin and then introduced rodamine into this hybrid molecule. This material has approximately 1% the biological activity of native insulin but approximately 10% of its receptor binding activity (Shechter *et al.*, 1978). These investigators have used this ligand to monitor the internalization of insulin into living 3T3 mouse fibroblasts with a television camera coupled to an image intensifier (Schlessinger *et al.*, 1978). Initially, the ligand binds diffusely to the cell surface. Within a few minutes the hormone receptor complexes then become aggregated into patches. After 30 minutes the hormone then enters the cell in endocytotic vesicles. These investigators have also studied isolated rat hepatocytes with this technique. They find that insulin enters the interior of these cells in the same manner and then has a perinuclear location (Le Cam *et al.*, 1979).

C. Autoradiographic Analysis

Stein and Gross employed radiolabeled insulin and were the first to demonstrate morphologically by light microscope autoradiographs that insulin localizes in the cell interior. These investigators (1959) injected the [^{131}I]insulin into rats and found intracellular hormone distributed in muscle, heart, liver, and lung. We have performed both light and electron microscopic autoradiographs of insulin in IM-9 human cultured lymphocytes (Goldfine *et al.*, 1977b, 1978, 1980). After 30 seconds of incubation with radiolabeled insulin, silver grains representing the label are distributed mainly on the cell surface (Fig. 7). In contrast, after progressive periods of incubation, the hormone is internalized and is concentrated in the endoplasmic reticulum and nuclear membrane (Fig. 8). In lymphocytes, insulin is not seen in either vesicular structures or Golgi.

In addition, we have studied the uptake of insulin into rat liver *in vivo*. One minute after the injection of radiolabeled insulin into the portal vein, grains of insulin are seen predominantly on the cell surface of hepatocytes (Fig. 9). In contrast, 10 minutes after injection, grains are predominantly located in the cell interior (Table III). As with the lymphocytes, grains are concentrated in the rough and smooth endoplasmic reticulum and nuclear membrane (Fig. 9). In addition (and not seen in lymphocytes), approximately 30% of the cellular grains were also detected in the Golgi apparatus, small vesicles, and multivesicular bodies.

Carpentier and co-workers (1978) have confirmed our findings that in-

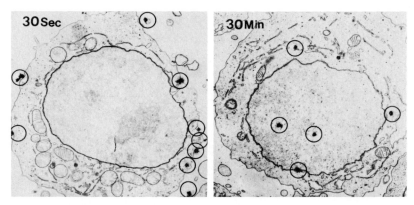

Fig. 7. EM autoradiograph of IM-9 lymphocytes incubated with 1 nm [^{125}I]insulin for 30 seconds and 30 minutes. (From Goldfine *et al.*, 1978.)

sulin can enter the interior of human cultured lymphocytes and have extended this observation to isolated hepatocytes (Gorden *et al.*, 1978; Carpentier *et al.*, 1979b). For unexplained reasons in both of their studies with isolated cells, they found that insulin is incompletely internalized to

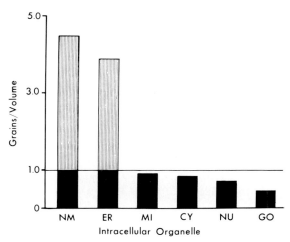

Fig. 8. Ratio of the percentage of grains on intracellular organelles to organelle volume density in autoradiographs of IM-9 lymphocytes incubated 30 minutes with 1 nM [^{125}I]insulin. Grain concentration occurs in organelles that have a ratio > 1.0. Nuclear membrane, NM; endosplasmic reticulum, ER; mitochondria, MI; cytoplasm, CY; nucleus, NU; Golgi, GO. (From Goldfine *et al.*, 1978.)

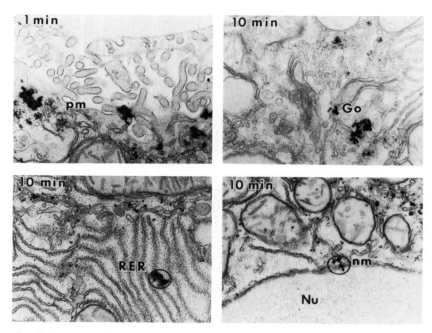

FIG. 9. EM autoradiographs of [^{125}I]insulin associated with liver organelles after the injection of 0.75 μg of [^{125}I]insulin into the portal vein followed by perfusion-fixation at 1 and 10 minutes. Golgi, GO; nucleus, Nu; rough endoplasmic reticulum, RER; plasma membrane, pm; nuclear membrane, nm. (From Renston *et al.*, 1980.)

TABLE III

ORGANELLE DISTRIBUTION OF [^{125}I]INSULIN GRAINS IN LIVER OF FASTED RATS

Cellular structure	Time after injection (min)	
	(1)	(10)
Plasma membrane	41.2	12.7
Smooth endoplasmic reticulum	27.8	33.4
Rough endoplasmic reticulum	3.9	14.2
Mitochondria	5.1	11.0
Nuclear membrane	0.4	3.7
Golgi	0	4.1
Vesicles (< 0.1 μm)	10.3	9.0
Multivesicular bodies	7.1	10.2
Other	3.8	2.7

only a distance of 1 μm or less. These investigators however have also injected radiolabeled insulin into the portal vein of rats, detected complete internalization, and found an intracellular distribution pattern for insulin in liver similar to that which we find (Carpentier *et al.*, 1979c). Bergeron and co-workers (1979) have also performed similar experiments with rats *in vivo* and have reported similar results.

Both our studies and those in the literature suggest the possibility that there may be at least two mechanisms of insulin distribution in certain tissues. In liver, we have reported the cellular uptake and distribution of horseradish peroxidase (HR) (Renston *et al.*, 1980). This protein can be measured in tissue sections with electron microscopy because after fixation it retains enzymatic activity (and thus can be localized histochemically). After injection into the portal vein, HRP is taken up into liver cells via small vesicles, transported through the liver cell in these vesicles, and then the vesicles fuse with the bile cannaliculus, depositing the horseradish peroxidase into the bile (Fig. 10a–c). We have speculated

(a)

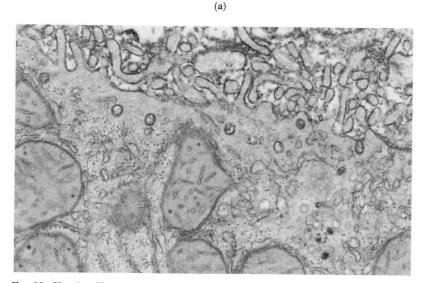

Fig. 10. Uptake of horseradish peroxidase into rat liver *in vivo*. Rats were injected with 10 mg of horseradish peroxidase into the portal vein and the liver perfused-fixed with glutaraldehyde after 1 and 10 minutes (Renston *et al.*, 1980). Horseradish peroxidase was in the sections stained with diaminobenzidine. (From Renston *et al.*, 1980.) (a) Uptake of horseradish peroxidase into 0.1 μm vesicles at the plasma membrane. (b) Vesicles with horseradish peroxidase approaching the bile cannaliculus. (c) Vesicles with horseradish peroxidase fusing with the bile cannalicular membrane (*continued*).

(b)

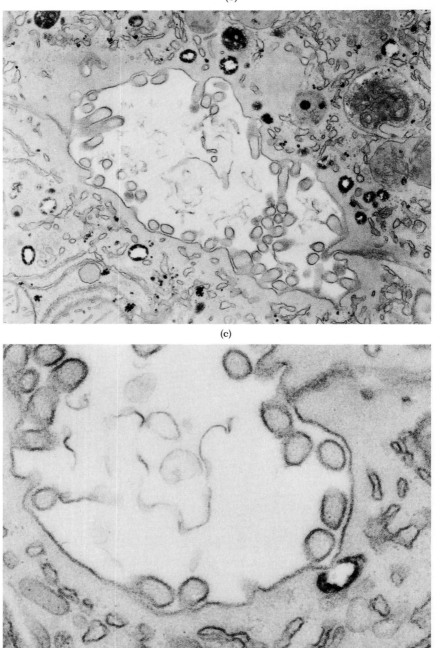

(c)

FIG. 10. (*Continued*)

that this uptake mechanism represents the pathway whereby numerous serum proteins are transported from extracellular fluid into bile. When [^{125}I]insulin is injected with the horseradish peroxidase and then combined electron microscopic localization of insulin and histochemical localization of peroxidase is carried out, it can be shown that a portion of the insulin enters the cell via the vesicular transport mechanism for horseradish peroxidase (Figure 11 a–c). Inside the liver cell this insulin is degraded in the vesicles and degraded insulin is deposited into bile (Renston *et al.*, 1980). In addition to insulin in vesicles, we also find insulin not in vesicles but rather localized over intracellular membranes including the endoplasmic reticulum and the nuclear envelope (Table III). One possibility is that insulin enters the cell via vesicles, escapes from vesicles, and then binds to intracellular structures (Fig. 12). Another possibility is that insulin enters cells via nonvesicular uptake system and then interacts with membranous structures (Fig. 12). In contrast, in lymphocytes there appears not to be a vesicular uptake of insulin, but rather insulin enters the cell via a nonvesicular uptake system.

(a)

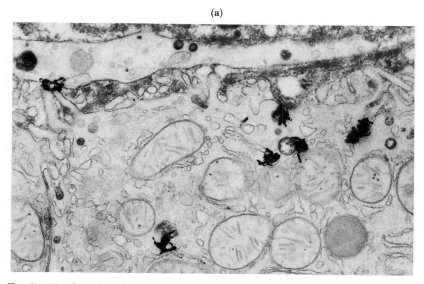

FIG. 11. Uptake of both [^{125}I]insulin and horseradish peroxidase into rat liver *in vivo*. Rats were injected with both 0.75 μg of [^{125}I]insulin and 10 mg of horseradish peroxidase into the portal vein and the liver perfused-fixed with glutaraldehyde after 1 and 10 minutes and both proteins measured. (a) Uptake of [^{125}I]insulin into 0.1 μm vesicles filled with horseradish peroxidase at the plasma membrane. (b) Vesicles with both [^{125}I]insulin and horseradish peroxidase approaching the bile cannaliculus. (c) Vesicles with both [^{125}I]insulin and horseradish peroxidase about to fuse with the bile cannalicular membrane *(continued)*.

(b)

(c)

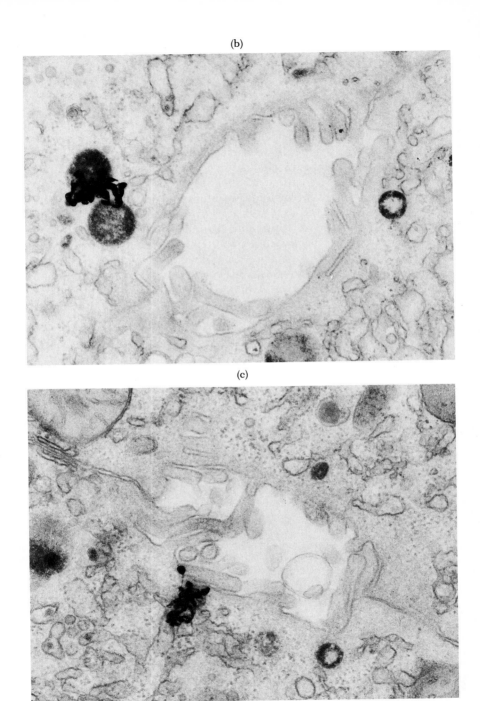

Fig. 11. (*Continued*)

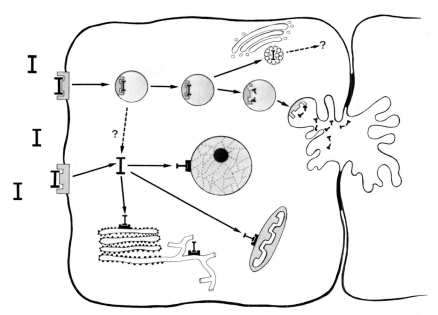

Fig. 12. Uptake of insulin into liver via vesicular (top) and nonvesicular mechanisms (bottom).

D. Is Internalization Necessary for the Biological Actions of Insulin?

As mentioned earlier, insulin has rapid effects on the cell surface and delayed effects in the cell interior. The rapid effects of insulin at the plasma membrane are due most likely to a perturbation of cell surface proteins that are a direct consequence of the binding of insulin to its cell surface receptor. For instance, insulin could regulate membrane transport by either altering the conformation of transport proteins or by influencing phosphorylation and dephosphorylation of these structures. How insulin regulates intracellular events such as protein, RNA, and DNA synthesis or the activation and inactivation of enzymes is unclear. Since insulin enters cells and interacts with intracellular structures, the possibility exists, therefore, that insulin could directly regulate intracellular events. In general, three types of experiments have been attempted to determine whether insulin needs to enter cells in order to exert these biological activities.

1. Insulin Coupled to Large Molecules

Cuatrecasas (1969) was the first to couple insulin to large molecules of agarose via the cyanogen bromide reaction, and reported that this coupled insulin had full biological activity in isolated rat adipocytes both in stimulating glucose oxidation and inhibiting lipolysis. Since the molecules of agarose are much larger than the cells, it was believed these studies indicated that insulin did not need to enter cells in order to exert its biological effects. It is now known, however, that the insulin–agarose complex is unstable in the presence of biological fluids; the insulin leaks off the agarose and the free insulin has biological activity (Garwin and Gelehrter, 1974; Kolb *et al.*, 1975; Davidson *et al.*, 1973; Oka and Topper, 1974). Insulin has been coupled to other large polymers such as dextrans via cyanogen bromide or has been coupled to agarose via the avidin– biotin reaction (Sakamoto *et al.*, 1977; May *et al.*, 1978). Both of these coupled insulins have markedly reduced, but detectable, biological activities. Finally, insulin has been coupled to ferritin, and in fat cells it has been reported that ferritin insulin has full biological activity in promoting protein synthesis (Jarett and Smith, 1974). However, the question that still remains unanswered in these studies is whether a small amount of insulin is leaking off and being internalized, and thus is accounting for the biological activity observed.

2. Antireceptor Antibodies

As mentioned previously, there exists in the serum of certain patients with severe insulin resistance and acanthosis nigricans specific antibodies directed toward the insulin receptor. Further, these antibodies *in vitro* behave as partial or full agonists of insulin (Kahn, 1979). These antibodies can mimic not only the effects of insulin on glucose transport but also other intracellular effects of insulin such as the activation of glycogen synthetase or the synthesis of lipoprotein lipase (Kahn, 1979). On the basis of these observations, it has been concluded that insulin need not enter cells to exert its biological effects (Roth, 1979). This hypothesis is based on the assumptions that antibodies to insulin receptors neither enter cells nor bind to intracellular structures. It is known, however, that antibodies to cell surface proteins on lymphocytes can enter cells and become associated with intracellular structures such as the nucleus (Lewis *et al.*, 1974). Also, Gorden and co-workers reported that radiolabeled anti-insulin receptor antibodies enter cells via a mechanism similar to that employed by insulin (Carpentier *et al.*, 1979a).

3. Inhibition of Internalization

Pastan and co-workers have reported that polyamines block insulin internalization in both fibroblasts and hepatocytes. In isolated hepatocytes, insulin has a delayed effect on stimulating amino acid transport and this effect requires new protein synthesis (Le Cam *et al.*, 1979). It was reported that by carefully adjusting the dose of polyamines, the effect of insulin on protein synthesis can be partially blocked, whereas the internalization of insulin is almost completely blocked. Internalization was monitored by using the aforementioned fluorescent-insulin ligand that has markedly reduced biological activity. No data were presented, however, to distinguish between inhibition of insulin uptake via vesicular and nonvesicular uptake systems (Le Cam *et al.*, 1979).

While these three types of experiments have provided interesting data concerning the effects of insulin on target cells, they have not provided definitive data concerning the mechanisms whereby insulin carries out its cellular actions. Thus, at the present time, it is unknown whether the internalization of insulin is necessary for insulin action.

VI. HYPOTHESIS, SPECULATION, AND CONCLUSION

Insulin has a diverse number of effects in target cells but the mechanism of action of insulin is still unknown. Although it is possible that insulin carries out *all* its actions via the generation of a second messenger formed at the plasma membrane, no such messenger has yet been identified. It is equally possible, therefore, that insulin does not have a unified mechanism of action on target cells and that insulin acts at one or more sites on both the cell surface and in the cell interior. The recent findings of both the internalization of insulin into target cells and the presence of specific binding for insulin on intracellular organelles allows for the following speculation as to how insulin may act.

Since the effects of insulin on plasma membrane functions occur within seconds after the hormone binds to its surface receptor (Häring *et al.*, 1978), it is possible that the insulin–receptor complex may either open ion channels in the plasma membrane such as those described for acetylcholine in nerve terminals, directly activate plasma membrane enzymes such as Na^+/K^+ ATPase, or directly interact with various other plasma membrane components to regulate their functions. In addition, several effects of insulin in the cell interior can be explained by a direct interaction of insulin with intracellular organelles. For instance, the long-term regulation of DNA and RNA synthesis at the nuclear level could be explained by the binding of insulin to the nuclear membrane followed by changes in the influx and efflux of substances from the nucleus. Likewise, the effects of insulin on protein degradation in the lysosome, protein synthesis in the endoplasmic reticulum, and enzyme activation in both the endoplasmic reticulum and mitochondria could be explained by the binding of insulin to receptors in these structures followed by specific alterations in organelle function.

It is more difficult, however, to explain how insulin, via dephosphorylation, activates a variety of enzymes that are located in the cell cytoplasm and are not associated with specific intracellular organelles. One distinct possibility is that part of this effect of insulin is through its activation of membrane bound cyclic AMP phosphodiesterase (Krahl, 1974; Pilkis and Park, 1974; Fain, 1974; Loten and Sneyd, 1970), which is then followed by decreased cyclic AMP levels and changes in enzyme phosphorylation. Another possibility is that insulin, after entering the cell interior, interacts with an intracellular organelle, such as the endoplasmic reticulum, to generate a unique second messenger. In the cell interior this substance would in turn carry out insulin's intermediate actions by either the activation of a phosphoprotein phosphatase or the inactivation of a phosphoprotein kinase. The presence of this hypothetical messenger would provide an explanation for the activation of soluble enzymes by insulin via protein dephosphorylation. The activation of membrane-bound enzymes by a dephosphorylation process, such as hydroxymethylglutaryl-CoA reductase in the endoplasmic reticulum and pyruvate dehydrogenase in the mitochondria, could also be explained by this type of messenger. Furthermore, stimulation of protein synthesis by insulin via this messenger could also occur by dephosphorylation of one or more enzymes necessary for the initiation of protein synthesis. In this regard (Larner *et al.*, 1979) have recently reported the isolation of a factor from insulin-stimulated muscle that has activity both in muscle on inhibiting cyclic AMP protein kinase activity and in fat cells on activating pyruvate dehydrogenase activity (Jarett and Seals, 1979; Larner *et al.*, 1979). It will be of major interest therefore to determine whether this substance is a mediator of other intracellular effects of insulin.

In summary the understanding of the mechanisms of insulin action on target cells still presents a major challenge to investigators in the fields of endocrinology, biochemistry, physiology, and cell biology. At present there has been no major conceptual breakthrough for insulin that is analogous to the discovery of cyclic AMP for glucagon and epinephrine. It is likely, however, that in the coming decade much new information will come forth to clarify some of the problems that have been presented in this chapter.

ACKNOWLEDGMENTS

This work has been supported by the Elise Stern Haas Research Fund, Harold Brunn Institute, Mount Zion Hospital and Medical Center, and National Institutes of Health grant #AM-26667. The author wishes to thank Ms. Dixie B. Shipp for providing library services, and Mr. R. Renston and Dr. B. Kriz for preparing the electron microscope autoradiographs.

REFERENCES

Ashmore, J., Hastings, A. B., and Nesbett, F. B. (1954). *Proc. Natl. Acad. Sci. U.S.A.* **40**, 673.

Avruch, J., Leone, G. R., and Martin, D. B. (1976a). *J. Biol. Chem.* **251**, 1505–1510.

Avruch, J., Leone, G. R., and Martin, D. B. (1976b). *J. Biol. Chem.* **251**, 1511–1515.

Avruch, J., Fairbanks, G., and Crapo, L. M. (1976c). *J. Cell. Physiol.* **89**, 815–826.

Baxter, M. A., and Coore, H. G. (1978). *Biochem. J.* **174**, 553–561.

Benjamin, W. B., and Singer, I. (1974). *Biochim. Biophys. Acta* **351**, 28–41.

Benjamin, W. B., and Singer, I. (1975). *Biochemistry* **14**, 3301–3309.

Bergeron, J. J. M., Evans, W. H., and Geschwind, I. I. (1973). *J. Cell Biol.* **59**, 771–776.

Bergeron, J. J. M., Posner, B. I., Josefsberg, Z., and Sikstrom, R. (1978). *J. Biol. Chem.* **253**, 4058–4066.

Bergeron, J., Sikstrom, R., Hand, A., and Posner, B. (1979). *J. Cell Biol.* **80**, 427–443.

Bhathena, S. J., Avigan, J., and Schreiner, M. E. (1974). *Proc. Natl. Acad. Sci. U.S.A.* **71**, 2174–2178.

Blair, J. B., Cimbala, M. A., Foster, J. L., and Morgan, R. A. (1976). *J. Biol. Chem.* **251**, 3756–3762.

Borrebaek, B. (1966). *Biochim. Biophys. Acta* **128**, 209.

Brisson-Lougarre, A., and Blum, C. J. (1979). *C. R. Hebd. Seances Acad Sci., Ser. D* **289**, 129–132.

Brush, J. S., and Kitabchi, A. E. (1970). *Biochim. Biophys. Acta* **215**, 134–144.

Bucher, N. L. R., and Swaffield, M. N. (1975a). *Adv. Enzyme Regul.* **13**, 281–293.

Bucher, N. L. R., and Swaffield, M. N. (1975b). *Proc. Natl. Acad. Sci. U.S.A.* **72**, 1157–1160.

Bucher, N. L. R., and Weir, G. C. (1976). *Metab. Clin. Exp.* **25**, 1423–1425.

Bucher, N. L. R., Schrock, T. R., and Moolten, F. L. (1969). *Johns Hopkins Med. J.* **125**, 250–257.

Carpentier, J.-L., Gorden, P., Amherdt, M., Obberghen, E., Kahn, C., and Orci, L. (1978). *J. Clin. Invest.* **61**, 1057–1070.

Carpentier, J.-L., Van Obberghen, E., Gorden, P., and Orci, L. (1979a). *Diabetes* **28**, 345.

Carpentier, J.-L., Gorden, P., Freychet, P., Le Cam, A., and Orci, L. (1979b). *J. Clin. Invest.* **63**, 1249–1261.

Carpentier, J.-L., Gorden, P., Barazzone, P., Freychet, P., Le Cam, A., and Orci, L. (1979c). *Proc. Natl. Acad. Sci. U.S.A.* **76**, 2803–2807.

Cascieri, M. A., Mumford, R. A., and Katzen, H. M. (1979). *Arch. Biochem. Biophys.* **195**, 30–44.

Chochinov, R. H., and Daughaday, W. H. (1976). *Diabetes* **25**, 994–1007.

Claus, T. H., El-Maghrabi, M. R., and Pilkis, S. J. (1979). *J. Biol. Chem.* **254**, 7855–7864.

Craig, J. W., Rall, T. W., and Larner, J. (1969). *Biochim. Biophys. Acta* **177**, 213.

Cuatrecasas, P. (1969). *Proc. Natl. Acad. Sci. U.S.A.* **63**, 450–457.

Czech, M. P. (1977). *Annu. Rev. Biochem.* **46**, 359–384.

Davey, P. J., and Manchester, K. L. (1969). *Biochim. Biophys. Acta* **182**, 85.

Davidson, M. B., Van Herle, A. J., and Gerschenson, L.E . (1973). *Endocrinology* **92**, 1442–1446.

Denton, R. M., Coore, H. G., Martin, B. R., and Randle, P. J. (1971). *Nature (London) New Biol.* **231** 115.

Denton, R. M., Edgell, N. J., Bridges, B. J., and Poole, G. P. (1979). *Biochem. J.* **180**, 523–531.

Desbuquois, B., and Cuatrecasas, P. (1973). *Annu. Rev. Med.* **24**, 233–240.

Dich, J., and Gluud, C. N. (1975). *Acta Physiol. Scand.* **94**, 236–243.

DiPietro, D. L., and Weinhouse, S. (1960). *J. Biol. Chem.* **235**, 2542.

Dunaway, G. A., Leung, G. L.-Y., Thrasher, J. R. and Cooper, M. D. (1978). *J. Biol. Chem.* **253**, 7460–7463.

Eckel, R. H., Fujimoto, W. Y., and Brunzell, J. D. (1978). *Biochem. Biophys. Res. Commun.* **84**, 1069–1075.

Fain, J. N. (1974). *Biochem., Ser. One* **8**, 1–23.

Fain, J. N., Kovacev, V. P., and Scow, R. O. (1966). *Endocrinology* **78**, 773.

Feliu, J. E., Hue, L., and Hers, H.-G. (1976). *Proc. Natl. Acad. Sci. U.S.A.* **73**, 2762–2766.

Flier, J. S., Kahn, C. R., Roth, J., and Bar, R. S. (1975). *Science* **190**, 63–65.

Freychet, P. (1976). *Diabetologia* **12**, 83–100.

Freychet, P., Roth, J., and Neville, D. M., Jr. (1971). *Proc. Natl. Acad. Sci. U.S.A.* **68**, 1833–1837.

Garfinkel, A. S., Nilsson-Ehle, P., and Schotz, M. C. (1976). *Biochim. Biophys. Acta* **424**, 264–273.

Garwin, J. L., and Gelehrter, T. D. (1974). *Arch. Biochem. Biophys.* **164**, 52–59.

Geisler, R. W., Roggeveen, A. E., and Hansen, R. J. (1978). *Biochim. Biophys. Acta* **544**, 284–293.

Gelehrter, T. D., and Tomkins, G. M. (1970). *Proc. Natl. Acad. Sci. U.S.A.* **66**, 390–397.

Gerschenson, L. E., and Andersson, M. (1971). *Biochem. Biophys. Res. Commun.* **43**, 1211.

Gey, G. O., and Thalhimer, W. (1924). *J. Am. Med. Assoc.* **82**, 1609.

Gliemann, J., and Sonne, O. (1977). *Clin. Endocrinol. (Oxford)* **7**, 405–415.

Goidl, J. A. (1979). *Biochemistry* **18**, 3674–3679.

Goldfine, I. D. (1977). *Diabetes* **26**, 148–155.

Goldfine, I. D. (1978a). *Life Sci.* **23**, 2639–2648.

Goldfine, I. D. (1978b). *In* "Receptors in Pharmacology" (J. R. Smythies and R. J. Bradley, eds.), pp. 335–377. Dekker, New York.

Goldfine, I. D., and Sherline, P. (1972). *J. Biol. Chem.* **247**, 6927.

Goldfine, I. D., and Smith, G. J. (1976). *Proc. Natl. Acad. Sci. U.S.A.* **73**, 1427–1431.

Goldfine, I. D., Vigneri, R., Cohen, D., and Pliam, N. B. (1977a). *Nature (London)* **269**, 698–700.

Goldfine, I. D., Smith, G. J., Wong, K. Y., and Jones, A. L. (1977b). *Proc. Natl. Acad. Sci. U.S.A.* **74**, 1368–1372.

Goldfine, I. D., Wong, K. Y., Korc, M., Hradek, G., and Jones, A. L. (1978). *J. Cell Biol.* **79**, 194a.

Goldfine, I. D., Jones, A. L., Kriz, B. M., Wong, K. Y., and Hradek, G. (1981). *In* "Hormones in Normal and Abnormal Human Tissues" (K. Fotherby and S. B. Pal, eds.). de Gruyter, Berlin (in press).

Goldstein, J. L., Anderson, R. G. W., and Brown, M. S. (1979). *Nature (London)* **279**, 679–685.

Goodridge, A. G. (1975). *Fed. Proc., Fed. Am. Soc. Exp. Biol.* **34**, 117–123.

Gorden, P., Carpentier, J., Freychet, P., Le Cam, A., and Orci, L. (1978). *Science* **200**, 782–785.

Granick, S., Sinclair, P., Sassa, S., and Grieninger, G. (1975). *J. Biol. Chem.* **250**, 9215–9225.

Gressner, A. M., and Wool, I. G. (1976). *Nature (London)* **259**, 148–150.

Grillo, M. A., and Sisini, A. (1977). *Int. J. Biochem.* **8**, 131–134.

Hansen, R. J., Pilkis, S. J., and Krahl, M. E. (1967). *Endocrinology,* **81**, 1397.

Hansen, R. J., Pilkis, S. J., and Krahl, M. E. (1970). *Endocrinology* **86**, 57.

Häring, H. U., Kemmler, W., Renner, R., and Hepp, K. D. (1978). *FEBS Lett.* **95**, 177–180.

Hers, H. G. (1976). *Annu. Rev. Biochem.* **45**, 167–188.

Hershko, A., Mamont, P., Shields, R., and Tomkins, G. M. (1971). *Nature (London) New Biol.* **232**, 206–211.

Higgins, G. M., and Anderson, R. M. (1931). *Arch. Pathol. Lab. Med.* **12**, 186–202.

Horvat, A. (1978). *J. Cell. Physiol.* **97**, 37–48.

Horvat, A., Li, E., and Katsoyannis, P. G. (1975). *Biochim. Biophys. Acta* **382**, 609–620.

Hutson, N. J., Kerbey, A. L., Randle, P. J., and Sugden, P. H. (1978). *Biochem. J.* **173**, 669–680.

Ingebritsen, T. S., Geelen, M. J. H., Parker, R. A., Evenson, K. J., and Gibson, D. M. (1979). *J. Biol. Chem.* **254**, 9986–9989.

Izzo, J. L., Roncone, A. M., Helton, D. L., and Izzo, M. J. (1979). *Arch. Biochem. Biophys.* **198**, 97–109.

Jarett, L., and Smith, R. M. (1974). *J. Biol. Chem.* **249**, 7024–7031.

Jarett, L., and Seals, J. R. (1979). *Science* **206**, 1407–1408.

Jarrett, D. B., Roth, J., Kahn, C. R., and Flier, J. S. (1976). *Proc. Natl. Acad. Sci. U.S.A.* **73**, 4115–4119.

Jason, C. J., Polokoff, M. A., and Bell, R. M. (1976). *J. Biol. Chem.* **251**, 1488–1492.

Jefferson, L. S., Li, J. B., and Rannels, S. R. (1977). *J. Biol. Chem.* **252**, 1476–1483.

Joshi, V. C., and Wakil, S. J. (1978). *J. Biol. Chem.* **253**, 2120–2125.

Jungas, R. L., and Ball, E. G. (1963). *Biochemistry* **2**, 383.

Kahn, C. R. (1975). *Methods Membr. Biol.* **3**, 81–146.

Kahn, C. R. (1976). *J. Cell Biol.* **70**, 261–286.

Kahn, C. R. (1979). *Proc. Soc. Exp. Biol. Med.* **162**, 13–21.

Kahn, C. R., and Baird, K. (1978). *J. Biol. Chem.* **253**, 4900–4906.

Kahn, C. R., Flier, J. S., Bar, R. S., Archer, J. A., Gorden, P., Martin, M. M., and Roth, J. (1976). *N. Engl. J. Med.* **294**, 739–745.

Kanter, Y. (1976). *Int. J. Biochem.* **7**, 253–257.

Kashnig, D. M., and Kasper, C. B. (1969). *J. Biol. Chem.* **244**, 3786–3792.

Kay, R. R., and Johnston, I. R. (1973). *Sub-Cell Biochem.* **2**, 127–167.

Kipnis, D. M., and Cori, C. F. (1959). *J. Biol. Chem.* **234**, 171.

Kolb, H. J., Renner, R., Hepp, K. D., Weiss, L., and Wieland, O. H. (1975). *Proc. Natl. Acad. Sci. U.S.A.* **72**, 248–252.

Korc, M., Sankaran, H., Williams, J. A., and Goldfine, I. D. (1981). *Am J. Physiol.* (in press).

Krahl, M. E., (1972). *In* "Insulin Action" (J. B. Fritz, ed.), p. 461. Academic Press, New York.

Krahl, M. E. (1974). *Annu. Rev. Physiol.* **36**, 331–360.

Lakshmanan, M. R., Nepokroeff, C. M., and Porter, J. W. (1972). *Proc. Natl. Acad. Sci. U.S.A.* **69**, 3516–3519.

Lakshmanan, M. R., Nepokroeff, C. M., Ness, G. C., Dugan, R. E., and Porter, J. W. (1973). *Biochem. Biophys. Res. Commun.* **50**, 704–710.

Larner, J. (1972). *Diabetes* **21**, 428–438.

Larner, J. (1975). *Metab. Clin. Exp.* **24**, 249–256.

Larner, J., Galasko, G., Cheng, K., DePaoli-Roach, A. A., Huang, L., Daggy, P., and Kellog, J. (1979). *Science* **206**, 1408–1410.

Lavau, M., Fried, S. K., Susini, C., and Freychet, P. (1979). *J. Lipid Res.* **20**, 8–16.

Le Cam, A., Maxfield, F., Willingham, M., and Pastan, I. (1979). *Biochem. Biophys. Res. Commun.* **88**, 873–881.

Lee, N. D., and Williams, R. H. (1954). *Endocrinology* **54**, 5–19.

Lewis, C. M., Pegrum, G. D., and Evans, C. A. (1974). *Nature (London)* **247**, 463–465.

Livingston, J. M., Gurny, P. A., and Lockwood, D. H. (1977). *J. Biol. Chem.* **252**, 560–562.

Loten, E. G., and Sneyd, J. T. G. (1970). *Biochem. J.* **120**, 187–193.
Manchester, K. L. (1970). *In* "Biochemical Actions of Hormones" (G. Litwack ed.), Vol. 1, p. 267. Academic Press, New York.
Manchester, K. L., and Young, F. G. (1960). *Biochem. J.* **75**, 487.
May, J. M., and de Haën, C. (1979). *J. Biol. Chem.* **254**, 9017–9021.
May, J. M., Williams, R. H., and de Haën, C. (1978). *J. Biol. Chem.* **253**, 686–690.
Morgan, C. R., and Bonner, J. (1970). *Proc. Natl. Acad. Sci. U.S.A.* **65**, 1077–80.
Morgan, H. E., and Neely, J. R. (1972). *In* "Handbook of Physiology" (R. O. Greep and E. B. Astwood, eds.), Vol. 1, pp. 323–331. Williams and Wilkins, Baltimore, Maryland.
Mortimore, G. E., and Mondon, C. E. (1979). *J. Biol. Chem.* **245**, 2375.
Mukherjee, C., and Jungas, R. L. (1975). *Biochem. J.* **148**, 229–235.
Nakanishi, S., Tanabe, T., Horikawa, S., and Numa, S. (1976). *Proc. Natl. Acad. Sci. U.S.A.* **73**, 2304–2307.
Neville, D. M., Jr., and Chang, T.-M. (1978). *Curr. Top. Membr. Trans.* **10**, 65–150.
Niemeyer, H., Clark-Turri, L., Perez, N., and Rabajille, E. (1965). *Arch. Biochem. Biophys.* **109**, 634,
Oka, T., and Topper, Y. J. (1974). *Proc. Natl. Acad. Sci. U.S.A.* **71**, 1630–1633.
Paetzke-Brunner, I., Löffler, G., and Wieland, O. H. (1979). *Horm. Metab. Res.* **11**, 285–288.
Peavy, D. E., Taylor, J. M., and Jefferson, L. S. (1978). *Proc. Natl. Acad. Sci. U.S.A.* **75**, 5879–5883.
Peret, J., and Chanez, M. (1976). *J. Nutr.* **106**, 103–110.
Phang, J. M., and Downing, S. K. (1973). *Am. J. Physiol.* **224**, 191.
Pilkis, S. J. (1970). *Biochim. Biophys. Acta* **215**, 461.
Pilkis, S. J., and Park, C. R. (1974). *Annu. Rev. Pharmacol.* **14**, 365–388.
Pontremoli, S., De Flora, A., Salamino, F., Melloni, E., and Horecker, B. L. (1975). *Proc. Natl. Acad. Sci. U.S.A.* **72**, 2969–2973.
Posner, B. I., Raquidan, D., Josefsberg, Z., and Bergeron, J. J. M. (1978). *Proc. Natl. Acad. Sci. U.S.A.* **75**, 8302–8306.
Price, J. B., Jr. (1976). *Metab. Clin. Exp.* **25**, 1427–1428.
Rannels, D. E., Pegg, A. E., Rannels, S. R., and Jefferson, L. S. (1978). *Am. J. Physiol.* **235**, E126–E133.
Rechler, M. M., Podskalny, J. M., Goldfine, I. D., and Wells, C. A. (1974). *J. Clin. Endocrinol. Metab.* **39**, 512–521.
Reel, J. R., Lee, K.-L., and Kenney, F. T. (1970). *J. Biol. Chem.* **245**, 5800–5805.
Renston, R., Jones, A. L., Hradek, G., Wong, K. Y., and Goldfine, I. D. (1980). *Gastroenterology* **78**, 1373–1388.
Richman, R. A., Claus, T. H., Pilkis, S. J., and Friedman, D. L. (1976). *Proc. Natl. Acad. Sci. U.S.A.* **73**, 3589–3593.
Roth, J. (1973). *Metab. Clin. Exp.* **22**, 1059–1073.
Roth, J. (1979). *Proc. Soc. Exp. Biol. Med.* **162**, 1–12.
Saggerson, E. D., and Greenbaum, A. L. (1969). *Biochem. J.* **115**, 405–418.
Sakamoto, Y., and Kuzuya, T. (1979). *Biochem. Biophys. Res. Commun.* **88**, 37–43.
Sakamoto, Y., Akanuma, Y., Kosaka, K., and Jeanrenaud, B. (1977). *Biochim. Biophys. Acta* **498**, 102–113.
Schilling, E. E., Goldenberg, H., Morré, D. J., and Crane, F. L. (1979). *Biochim. Biophys. Acta* **555**, 504–511.
Schlessinger, J., Shechter, Y., Willingham, M., and Pastan, I. (1978). *Proc. Natl. Acad. Sci. U.S.A.* **75**, 2659–2663.
Seals, J. R., McDonald, J. M., and Jarett, L. (1979). *J. Biol. Chem.* **254**, 6997–7001.
Seitz, H. J., Krone, W., and Tarnowski, W. (1977). *Acta Endocrinol. (Copenhagen)* **85**, 389–397.

Shechter, Y., Schlessinger, J., Jacobs, S., Chang, K.-J., and Cuatrecasas, P. (1978). *Proc. Natl. Acad. Sci. U.S.A.* **75**, 2135–2139.

Shrago, E., Lardy, H. A., Nordlie, R. C., and Foster, D. O. (1963). *J. Biol. Chem.* **238**, 3188.

Smith, G. L., and Temin, H. M. (1974). *J. Cell. Physiol.* **84**, 181–192.

Söling, H. D., and Unger, K. O. (1972). *Eur. J. Clin. Invest.* **2**, 199–212.

Söling, H. D., Kaplan, J., Erbstoeszer, M., and Pitot, H. C. (1969). *Adv. Enzyme Regul.* **7**, 171.

Sols, A. (1965). *In* "On the Nature and Treatment of Diabetes" (B. S. Leibel and G. A. Wrenshall, eds.), pp. 118–128. Excerpta Med. Found., Amsterdam.

Speake, B. K., Dils, R., and Mayer, R. J. (1976). *Biochem. J.* **154**, 359–370.

Spencer, C. J., Heaton, J. H., Gelehrter, T. D., Richardson, K. I., and Garwin, J. L. (1978). *J. Biol. Chem.* **253**, 7677–7682.

Spooner, P. M., Chernick, S. S., Garrison, M. M., and Scow, R. O. (1979). *J. Biol. Chem.* **254**, 10021–10029.

Stein, O., and Gross, J. (1959). *Endocrinology* **65**, 707–716.

Steinberg, D., and Khoo, J. C. (1977). *Fed. Proc., Fed. Am. Soc. Exp. Biol.* **36**, 1986–1990.

Steinberg, D., Mayer, S. E., Khoo, J. C., Miller, E. A., Miller, R. E., Fredholm, B., and Eichner, R. E. (1975). *Adv. Cyclic Nucleotide Res.* p. 549.

Steiner, D. F. (1966). *Vitam. Horm. (N.Y.)* **24**, 1–61.

Steiner, D. F., and King, J. (1964). *J. Biol. Chem.* **239**, 1292–1298.

Stockdale, F. E., and Topper, Y. J. (1966). *Proc. Natl. Acad. Sci. U.S.A.* **56**, 1283–1289.

Suleiman, S. A., and Vestling, C. S. (1979). *J. Biol. Chem.* **254**, 10621–10628.

Sun, J. V., Tepperman, H. M., and Tepperman, J. (1977). *J. Lipid Res.* **18**, 533–539.

Suzuki, K., and Kono, T. (1979). *J. Biol. Chem.* **254**, 9786–9794.

Taunton, O. D., Stifel, F. B., Greene, H. L., and Herman, R. H. (1974). *J. Biol. Chem.* **249**, 7228–7239.

Terry, P. M., Banerjee, M. R., and Lui, R. M. (1977). *Proc. Natl. Acad. Sci. U.S.A.* **74**, 2441–2445.

Topper, Y. J., Friedberg, S. H., and Oka, T. (1970). *Dev. Biol. Suppl.* **4**, 101–113.

Turkington, R. W. (1968). *Endocrinology* **82**, 540–546.

Turkington, R. W., and Riddle, M. (1969). *J. Biol. Chem.* **244**, 6040–6046.

Vigneri, R., Goldfine, I. D., Wong, K. Y., Smith, G. J., and Pezzino, V. (1978a). *J. Biol. Chem.* **253**, 2098–2103.

Vigneri, R., Pliam, N. B., Cohen, D. C., Pezzino, V., Wong, K. Y., and Goldfine, I. D. (1978b). *J. Biol. Chem.* **253**, 8192–8197.

Walker, D. G., and Rao, S. (1964). *Biochem. J.* **90**, 360.

Weber, G. (1972). *Isr. J. Med. Sci.* **8**, 325–343.

Weber, G., Singhal, R. L., and Srivastava, S. K. (1965). *Adv. Enzyme Regul.* **3**, 43.

Weber, G., Morgan, C. R., Wright, P. H., Ashmore, J., Lea, M. A., and Convery, H. J. H. (1968). *Prog. Endocrinol., Proc. Int. Congr. Endocrinol., 3rd, 1968 Excerpta Med. Found., Int. Congr. Ser. No. 184*, p. 52.

Wicks, W. D., Barnett, C. A., and McKibbin, J. B. (1974). *Fed. Proc., Fed Am. Soc. Exp. Biol.* **33**, 1105–1111.

Witters, L. A., Moriarity, D., and Martin, D. B. (1979). *J. Biol. Chem.* **254**, 6644–6649.

Wool, I. G., Stirewalt, W. S., Kurihara, K., Low, R. B., Bailey, P., and Oyer, D. (1968). *Recent Prog. Horm. Res.* **24**, 139.

Wool, I. G., Castles, J. J., Leader, D. P., and Fox, A. (1972). *Handb. Physiol. Sec. 7: Endocrinol.* **1**, 385–394.

CHAPTER 6

Membrane Recognition and Effector Sites in Steroid Hormone Action

Clara M. Szego
and Richard J. Pietras

I. INTRODUCTION

A. GENERAL CONSIDERATIONS AND PERSPECTIVE

The encounter between a cell and its specific tropic hormone would be only fleeting and thus ineffective as a regulatory device were it not for capture of the potential ligand and its retention for time sufficiently prolonged to perturb the prior state. And no more effective and economical means of discrimination among the myriads of molecules in the extracellular fluid can be envisioned than that which would occur were the mutual recognition to take place at the cell surface—the very interface between the inner cell domain and its immediate environment. Indeed, such is the precise condition proposed by Paul Ehrlich in his Croonian lecture at The Royal Society (1900), to our knowledge the first formal postulation of the receptor concept: specific ligands modify that cell, which is equipped with surface recognition sites capable of intercepting the signal molecules. Implicit in his quaint but visionary diagram (Fig. 1) are several hallmarks of such interactions: complementarity, noncovalent nature and reversibility, and even replenishment, but above all: specificity based upon structural features inherent in both molecular species.

B. DOGMA AND DICHOTOMY

These views are now well ingrained in the body scientific. Indeed, central to any modern account of peptide hormone action are analyses in intimate detail of the physicochemical nature of such hormone–receptor encounters, the secondary repercussions of these encounters in altered membrane function, and tentative proposals of the means by which resultant signals are communicated to the intracellular machinery, including the genetic apparatus. For, until very recently (reviewed in Szego, 1975, 1978), such hormones, by virtue of charge and mass, were believed to be prevented from cellular ingress by an absolute barrier—the plasmalemma (Sutherland, 1972; Kahn, 1976; Catt and Dufau, 1977).

Quite a converse view has generally prevailed in the localization of receptor macromolecules for the steroid hormones. Thus, despite certain evidence to the contrary, it has been widely held that steroid hormones freely and indiscriminately enter all cells (Peck et al., 1973; Müller and Wotiz, 1979; Giorgi and Stein, 1980). It is believed that such hormones selectively affect only those cellular "targets" that possess "cytoplasmic" receptors capable of preventing or delaying their otherwise unopposed egress (cf. Gorski and Gannon, 1976). Once bound to hormone, the

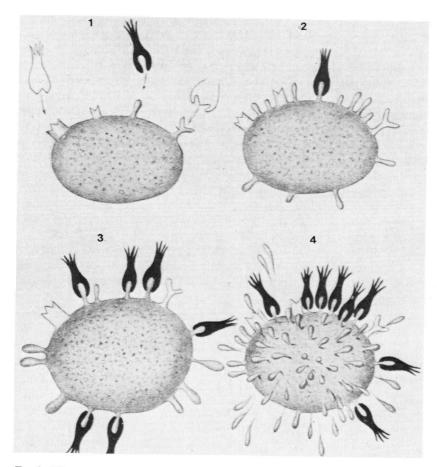

FIG. 1. Diagrammatic representation of the "side-chain" theory to illustrate Ehrlich's concept of specific recognition sites at the cell surface. 1. Complementarity of agonist and receptor. 2. Specific and reversible binding of agonist only to its own receptor. 3. The bound form of the receptor is unavailable for providing negative-feedback toward its own biosynthesis. 4. This results in overcorrection by regeneration. (Reprinted by permission, with minor paraphrasing of the text, from the Croonian Lecture, *On Immunity with Special Reference to Cell Life*, delivered to the Royal Society by Paul Ehrlich, 22 March, 1900, *Collected Papers*, 1957.)

cytosol receptor may undergo "transformation" or "activation," rendering it capable of "migration" to the nucleus, by a process incompletely defined (Gorski *et al.*, 1968; Jensen *et al.*, 1968; Puca *et al.*, 1977; Greene *et al.*, 1977). Interaction of the steroid-receptor complex with chromatin is generally believed to elicit expression of all phenotypic effects (Hamilton, 1968; Katzenellenbogen and Gorski, 1975; Buller and O'Malley, 1976; Thrall *et al.*, 1978).

These dichotomous views (cf. Friedberg, 1977; Sterling, 1979; Greengard, 1979) are currently in a state of flux. In the case of peptide hormones, evidence for selective cellular entry is now overwhelming (Petrusz, 1978; Gorden *et al.*, 1978; Schlessinger *et al.*, 1978; Neville and Chang, 1978; Szego, 1974, 1975, 1978; Catt *et al.*, 1979; cf. also Chapter 5, this volume). On the other hand, there is being forged a chain of evidence for the occurrence of recognition sites for steroid hormones on the external surfaces of their responsive cells—and, conversely, the paucity of such membrane receptors in so-called nontarget cells. Thus, it is becoming increasingly evident that parallels exist for the modes of action of both major classes of hormone—indeed, for all ligands potentially capable of being intercepted by specialized high-affinity binding sites at cell surfaces and, thereby, of exerting regulatory influences upon them. It would be difficult to envision otherwise the evolution of regulatory mechanisms because of the enormous variety of agonists and the indications already available of the universality of biologic processes: nature seems to have rung many changes upon limited means.

C. Prospectus and Scope

This concept of a parallel mechanism of action for effectors that is independent of their chemical configuration (*except at the crucial point of their interception by specific receptors integral to cell membranes*) seems to be at variance with established "central dogma." However, as will be developed in following sections, this view is fully capable of integration into existing interpretations when new experimental evidence is fully explored in context with that previously available. It is one purpose of the present essay to carry out just such an integrative effort, focusing upon proximate steps in steroid hormone action with particular emphasis upon that of estrogen.

In accord with this aim, this chapter will be concerned with the following major aspects of this subject:

1. recognition of agonist at the blood/cell interface
2. acute repercussions of this interaction in membrane functions and potential means of transduction and amplification of the recognition signal
3. proposed mechanism(s) of ligand access to the intracellular compartment

In course of this analysis, new evidence of interactions of steroid hormones with membranes of their cellular targets will be evaluated in some detail. Because certain related topics, such as limited cascade in the cytoplasm (Szego, 1974, 1975), accompanied by controlled delivery of cytoplasmic components to the nuclear compartment (Szego, 1975; Yamamoto and Alberts, 1976; Gorski and Gannon, 1976; Buller and O'Malley, 1976; Katzenellenbogen *et al.*, 1979), have been covered at great length in recent reviews, these secondary phases of steroid hormone action, deeply significant as they are, will be treated only tangentially in the present analysis.

Some definition of terminology used in this review is appropriate. It should be noted that the terms *specific* and *nonspecific* binding have been widely applied. It will be assumed that these terms are synonymous with *high-* and *low-affinity* binding, respectively, of a given ligand to its receptor (cf. King and Mainwaring, 1974). Methodologic approaches for the estimation of specific and nonspecific binding of steroids to macromolecular receptors and for the assessment of their relative degrees of saturability with agonist have been reviewed in detail by King and Mainwaring (1974), O'Malley and Hardman (1975), and Chamness and McGuire (1975). Although noncovalent (cf. Szego, 1976), the specific binding of estradiol-17β ($E_2\beta$) to biological receptors is very intense, with association constants ranging from 10^9 to $10^{12}\,M^{-1}$ (cf. Jensen and DeSombre, 1973). While binding to high-affinity low-capacity receptors is usually specific with respect to the character of ligands bound (see, however, Appel and Vincenzi, 1973; Zava and McGuire, 1978), it cannot yet be excluded that some of the observed low-affinity high-capacity sites are nonspecific (Erdos *et al.*, 1969; Sanborn *et al.*, 1971). King and Mainwaring (1974) suggest that the apparent absence of ligand specificity of some low-affinity sites may simply reflect a lack of saturation at either physiological levels of given steroids or at the limits of their solubilities. Although each high-affinity receptor generally functions by binding only those ligands that possess a particular class of structural characteristics, competitive binding of non-steroidal antihormones (cf. Liao *et al.*, 1974; Katzenellenbogen *et al.*, 1979), the chlorinated hydrocarbon kepone (Palmiter and Mulvihill, 1978), and certain anti-inflammatory drugs (Feldman and Couropmitree, 1976; Feldman, 1978) to steroid hormone receptors are examples of exceptions to this generalization. There is general concensus, but little proof, that the high-affinity sites mediate the biological actions of steroid hormones, and thereby qualify as true "receptors" (cf. Hechter, 1978). However, some investigators contend that the low-affinity sites may also be related to some aspect of steroid hormone binding or action in responsive cells (Eriksson *et al.*, 1978;

Smith *et al.*, 1979). Finally, the distinction between *target* and *nontarget* cells, with the former being defined as those cells possessing high-affinity receptors for a given steroid, appears to be less absolute than had previously been assumed. With newer refinements in experimental methods (and sometimes only renewed curiosity), many tissues which were once used as nontarget controls in the investigation of steroid receptors have since been found to possess specific steroid binding sites. For example, a short list of *new* target tissues for $E_2\beta$ includes lung (Morishige and Uetake, 1978), skin (Uzuka *et al.*, 1978), adrenal gland (van Beurden-Lamers *et al.*, 1974; Calandra *et al.*, 1978), preputial gland (Hirsch and Szego, 1974; Szego *et al.*, 1977), pancreas (Rosenthal and Sandberg, 1978), heart (Stumpf *et al.*, 1977), liver (cf. Eisenfeld *et al.*, 1976; Pietras and Szego, 1979a), thymus (Reichman and Villee, 1978), skeletal muscle (Dionne *et al.*, 1979), endothelial cells (Colburn and Buonassisi, 1978), and kidney (cf. Wu, 1979; Murono *et al.*, 1979). It is thus likely that the true distinction between "responsive" and "unresponsive" cells will eventually prove to be the *relative concentration* of specific receptors in a given cell (cf. Lee, 1978; Pietras and Szego, 1980a).

II. COMPARTMENTATION IN THE CELLULAR ECONOMY

A. Where Teleology Leaves Off

As recognized by an earlier generation of cell biologists, separation of potential reactants by structural barriers is a most efficient means of maintaining a poised system with minimum energy expenditure. Such a system can respond without undue delay to environmental signals intercepted by surface receptors. Reorientation of cytostructural barriers or alterations, even most minute ones, in their physicochemical conformation on ligand capture can promote *or* inhibit the propagation of perturbations with the ease and rapidity of the phase changes in the child's game of cat's cradle. For swift transmission of signals is requisite to the early stages in hormone action. By the same token, the integrity of the membrane interfaces of the cellular interior—the cytoskeleton (cf. J. Needham, cited by Peters, 1956)— is essential "if the organized system is not to become a chaos of biochemical processes" (Hill, 1928). Instead of such disorder in an unstructured cytoplasmic soup (cf. also Mollenhauer and Morré, 1978), one would visualize signal processing by controlled and strictly limited cascade. But all this must start at the beginning.

III. CELL SURFACE SPECIALIZATION AND THE OCCURRENCE OF RECOGNITION SYSTEMS

A. EVIDENCE FOR INTEGRAL LOCALIZATION OF NATIVE FORMS OF RECOGNITION MOLECULES FOR STEROID HORMONES

1. Circumstantial

Were hard evidence unavailable—which it is not—a priori rationale tells us that there must exist multiple cellular sites of concentration of molecules capable of recognizing given ligands. Such receptor molecules for steroids, long acknowledged to be, at least in part, proteins with relatively hydrophobic properties (see review on the initial development of this concept by Szego, 1976), are apparently synthesized within the very target cells themselves. Clearly, one must visualize such biosynthesis occurring in the orderly fashion common to all cellular proteins: at the ribosomal assembly-line. Subsequent intracellular redistribution, by processes largely unknown, would then likely proceed. Moreover, by analogy to the occurrence of high-affinity low-capacity interactions of membranes of responsive cells with low-molecular weight, non-steroid lipids, potential binding of steroids with hormonal function to membrane proteins of their target cells must be considered on theoretical grounds alone. Examples include high-affinity receptors with specificities for interaction with prostaglandins (Rao, 1974; Smigel and Fleischer, 1977; Wright *et al.*, 1979; Rao and Mitra, 1979) and retinol (Maraini *et al.*, 1977). Moreover, specific high-affinity low-capacity binding sites for thyroid hormone, a relatively low-molecular-weight agonist with limited water solubility, have also been identified in purified plasma membranes from rat liver (Pliam and Goldfine, 1977). Such analogies leave sufficient room for skepticism regarding the prevalent view that steroidal interactions with recognition sites are localized exclusively in the cell sap of their target structures.

The influence of steroids, hormonal and other, on cellular permeability (for reviews, see Roberts and Szego, 1953; Spaziani, 1975), and even, in pharmacologic concentrations, on the membrane phase transitions associated with their elicitation of narcosis (Selye, 1941; Das and Arora, 1957), are further circumstantial indications that cell surface membranes are integral to the registry of initial impact if not, indeed, subsequent effects of these agonists. Additional thought-provoking observations linking proximate steroid hormone actions to primary events at the cell membrane are considered in Sections IV,A–C.

2. Experimental

a. Early Indications. All indirect data aside, even more cogent evidence has long been available in support of the general premise that particulate sites apart from the nucleus of target cells function in recognition of the steroid hormones. Assembly of these data and their evaluation as guideposts for the more recent investigations to be presented below have required the perspective of intervening time. These early indications are summarized in Table I. In retrospect, many of these studies as well as some recent investigations, are subject to criticism for failure to account for various experimental artifacts (see below, and also Williams and Gorski, 1973). For example, Williams and Gorski (1971) have found that many of the earlier determinations of specifically bound estradiol in the cytosol extracted from whole uterus were overestimated by as much as 10-fold because hormone trapped in the organ during incubation becomes bound to macromolecules in the cytosol during homogenization. Nevertheless, selected studies in this early period are often cited as definitive evidence for the current dogma on steroid hormone action, and renewed consideration of these findings can be instructive. The pioneering investigations of Gorski and associates (1968) were largely interpreted as evidence that the bulk of specific estradiol binding that occurred when uterine segments that had been incubated with hormone at $0°-4°$ were homogenized was to macromolecular components in the 105,000 g supernatant fractions (i.e., cytosol). However, a passing comment in the paper of Noteboom and Gorski (1965) offers additional insight:

> The inhibition [of binding of [^{3}H]estradiol] observed in the mitochondria and microsomes [in the presence of excess "cold" estradiol] indicates that there may be sites specific for estradiol in these fractions. Inhibition also occurs in the soluble fraction. From the data available, one can only conclude that either the binding molecules are distributed throughout the cell, including the cell membrane, or that the fractionation procedures have released some of the binding molecules or the estradiol or both. [Insertions ours].

In similar vein, we have the statement by Gorski *et al.* (1968):

> The data from the density gradient centrifugations repeatedly indicate that some of the bound estrogen sediments faster than the 9.5 S receptor. Whether this is simply aggregated 9.5 S receptor or receptor bound to membrane fragments is open to question. Receptor binding to membrane fragments might facilitate the transfer of the steroid-receptor complex through the cell membrane or the nuclear membrane.

In consideration of more recent findings to be reviewed in the following sections, it is unfortunate that these investigators did not further pursue the intriguing questions raised by their experimental findings.

TABLE I

EARLY INDICATIONS FOR ASSOCIATION OF STEROIDS OR RELATED AGONISTS WITH EXTRANUCLEAR PARTICULATE FRACTIONS OF TARGET CELLS[a]

Tissue	Observations	Reference
A. ESTROGENS		
Uterus	Cell fractionation 3 days after *in vivo* injection of [^{3}H]E$_2\beta$: radioactivity in CN (28%), Mt (6–7%), Ms (10–14%), and S (51–56%) fractions.	Talwar *et al.* (1964)
Anterior pituitary	Cell fractionation 1 hour after *in vivo* injection of [^{3}H]E$_2\beta$ into ovariectomized rats: radioactivity in CN (56.9%), Mt (3.1%), Ms (4.2%), and S (23.2%) fractions. [^{3}H]E$_2\beta$ bound in Mt, Ms, and S maximal by 15 minutes, and in CN by 1 hour.	King *et al.* (1965)
Uterus	Cell fractionation 2 hours after [^{3}H]E$_2\beta$ *in vivo* to immature rats: radioactivity in CN (56.5%), Mt (9.9%), Ms (6.0%), and S (27.6%) fractions. Prior treatment with DES inhibited [^{3}H]E$_2\beta$ binding in all fractions.	Noteboom and Gorski (1965)
Endometrium	Cell fractionation 2–3 minutes after [^{3}H]E$_2\beta$ *in vivo*: radioactivity in CN (37%), Mt and Ms (20%), and S (42%).	King and Gordon (1966)
Uterus	Incubation with *p*-chloromercuribenzoate (10^{-4} M) for 15 minutes blocked subsequent uptake of E$_2\beta$ in organ segments *in vitro*; uptake by nontarget diaphragm not affected.	Terenius (1967)

(continued)

TABLE I (*continued*)

Tissue	Observations	Reference
Uterus, vagina, anterior pituitary	Cell fractionation 5 hours after [³H]DES *in vivo*: radioactivity in CN (44–61%), Mt (5–13%), Ms (4–10%), and S (31–48%) fractions.	Laumas *et al.* (1970)
Endometrium	Slices of untreated calf endometrium homogenized in Tris-EDTA buffer or buffer with 0.25 M sucrose–1mM CaCl₂. S fractions had identical protein levels but binding of [³H]E₂β to 9 S component of 0.25 M sucrose-S was only 30% that of Tris-EDTA cytosol extract.	Jungblut *et al.* (1970)
Liver	Prepared smooth Ms membranes from livers of *intact* male and female rats. Specific binding of E₂β to male membranes, and of testosterone to female membranes, saturable, with $K_d \approx 9$–10 nM. Displaceable binding, not saturable up to 10^{-6} M free steroid, believed to represent nonspecific partition into nonpolar phase of membrane.	Blyth *et al.* (1971)
B. ANDROGENS		
Ventral prostate	Cell fractionation 20 minutes after [¹⁴C]testosterone *in vivo*: radioactivity predominantly in S and Ms fractions (85%); remainder in Mt and CN.	Harding and Samuels (1962)
Ventral prostate	Cell fractionation 2 hours after [³H]testosterone *in vivo*: radioactivity in Ms > CN ≥ Mt > S.	Kowarski *et al.* (1969)

Ventral prostate	Cell fractionation 1 hour after [^{3}H]testosterone *in vivo* to castrated rats: radioactivity in CN (55%), Mt (12%), Ms (3%), and S (30%) fractions.	Tveter (1969)
Ventral prostate	Specific binding of androstanolone, testosterone, and 3β-androstanediol to Mt, Ms, and S *in vitro*. At 10^{-10} M, specific activity of bound androstanolone in particulate fractions > S. For androstanolone binding to Ms, $K_a = 3 \times 10^{10}$ M^{-1}.	Baulieu *et al.* (1971)
Ventral prostate	Cell fractionation after [^{3}H]testosterone *in vivo* to castrated rats: within 15 minutes, radioactivity maximal in Ms and S, and later (30 minutes) in CN; negligible binding in Mt fraction.	Mainwaring and Peterken (1971)

C. MINERALOCORTICOIDS

Kidney	Cell fractionation 15 minutes to 2 hours after [^{3}H]-aldosterone *in vivo* to adrenalectomized rats: radioactivity in CN > S > Mt > Ms. Only CN binding saturable and reduced by 100-fold molar excess of 9α-fluorocortisol; 10,000-fold molar excess of spirolactone reduced binding in all fractions, but to statistical significance only in CN and S fractions.	Fanestil and Edelman (1966); Fanestil (1968)
Renal tubular cells	Localization of [^{3}H]aldosterone by electron microscope autoradiography in proximal and distal convoluted tubule cells of rat kidney. After 10 to 20 min, 60% of label associated with plasma membrane and mitochondria; remainder in nuclei, lysosomes, ribosomes, and smooth endoplasmic recticulum. After 40 minutes, label in nuclei increased significantly, to 22% of total radioactivity.	Williams and Baba (1967)

TABLE I (*continued*)

Tissue	Observations	Reference
D. GLUCOCORTICOIDS		
Liver	Cell fractionation after *in vitro* incubation of [¹⁴C]cortisol for 1 minute to 1 hour at 0°: radioactivity at 1 minute in CN (2.8%), Mt (3.0%), Ms (18.1%), and S (76.1%) fractions. Redistribution of label from particulate to S fractions appeared to occur with more prolonged incubations.	Ulrich (1959)
Liver	Cell fractionation 5 minutes after [¹⁴C]cortisol or [¹⁴C]corticosterone *in vivo* to adrenalectomized rats: radioactivity in CN (8–13%), Mt (15–27%), Ms (7–8%), and S (51–61%) fractions. Of cortisol bound in Mt and Ms, 80–85% remained as native hormone. Using multiple equilibrium dialysis, binding by Mt and Ms was specific. Provided evidence that particulate-bound steroid is redistributed to the final S fraction in standard fractionation schemes.	De Venuto *et al.* (1962)
Liver	Cell fractionation after [¹⁴C]cortisol *in vitro* at 4°: radioactivity in S (58%), with remainder in CN, Mt, and Ms. Binding in particulate fractions not displaced by molar excess of unlabeled corticosterone at 4° and was substantially greater in liver as compared to particulate fractions of non-target organs.	Bellamy (1963)

Liver	Cell fractionation after 30 to 240 minutes of [^{14}C] cortisol *in vivo*: bulk of radioactivity concentrated in S and Ms from 30 to 45 minutes; peak in CN after 60 minutes; negligible binding in Mt.	Litwack *et al.* (1963)
Thymus	In equilibrium dialysis, Ms and ribosomal fractions bound [^{14}C]cortisol, and binding was not displaced by unlabeled progesterone or testosterone.	Brunkhorst and Hess (1964)
Liver	Cell fractionation after 1 hour of [^{3}H]cortisol *in vivo*: radioactivity in CN (3–4%), Mt (7–9%), Ms (4%), and S (85–87%).	Dingman and Sporn (1965)
Thymus	In multiple equilibrium dialysis, binding of [^{14}C]cortisol or [^{14}C]corticosterone *in vitro* at 4° was distributed equally among CN, Mt, Ms, and S fractions.	De Venuto and Chader (1966)
Liver	Cell fractionation after 30 minutes of [^{3}H]corticosterone *in vivo*: radioactivity in CN (24%), Mt (7%), Ms (14%), and S (48%).	Bottoms and Goetsch (1967)
Liver	Cell fractionation after 30 seconds of [^{14}C]cortisol *in vivo*: radioactivity in S > Ms > Mt. In pulse-label experiments, radioactivity appeared to pass from Ms to S fractions.	Morris and Barnes (1967)
Liver, Kidney	Localization of [^{3}H]cortisol by electron microscope autoradiography in liver and renal tubular cells: after 10 minutes, 50–60% of label in kidney associated with plasma membranes and mitochondria, 8–13% with nuclei and remainder in lyso-	Williams and Baba (1967)

(continued)

TABLE I (*continued*)

Tissue	Observations	Reference
	somes and endoplasmic recticulum. In liver, label found to be associated with mitochondria, endoplasmic recticulum and nuclei.	
Liver	Cell fractionation 5 to 15 minutes after [^{3}H]cortisol *in vivo*: Ms accumulated radioactivity parallel to that by whole homogenate. Label bound predominantly to smooth membrane fraction (1.5% of total dose), poorly to rough membranes (0.3% dose), and not to ribosomes.	Mayewski and Litwack (1969)
Liver	Cell fractionation 20 minutes after [^{3}H]cortisol in *vivo*: radioactivity in S (53.9%), Mt (13.7%), and Ms (11.4%).	Beato *et al.* (1971)
E. CARDIAC GLYCOSIDES AND AGLYCONES		
Giant axon	Ouabain-inhibited efflux of Na$^+$ from squid axon only when present in external medium; no effect observed at 100-fold higher concentration of steroid inside axon.	Caldwell and Keynes (1959)

320

Erythrocyte	Cells lysed in presence of strophanthidin and resealed with aglycone inside showed no inhibition of active Na^+ efflux, but drug-containing lysate did inhibit Na^+ transport by intact cells.	Hoffman (1966)
Heart	Organ perfusion for 1 hour followed by washout period. [^{3}H]ouabain uptake saturable and inhibited by iodoacetic acid, phloretin, phlorizin, and unlabeled digitoxin. After cell fraction: radioactivity in particulate (80%), with Ms > Mt > CN; and in S (18–23%).	Dutta et al. (1968, 1972); Dutta and Marks (1969)

[a] Abbreviations used in Table I include: CN (crude nuclear fraction), Mt (mitochondrial: lysosomal fraction), Ms (microsomal fraction), and S (high-speed supernatant or cytosol fraction).

The impact of these data, when assembled as above (Table I) is considerable. Nevertheless, only rarely has this material been considered collectively in relation to the need to account ultimately for *all* aspects of steroid hormone action. Because of the long preoccupation of our laboratory with the problem of membrane-bounded compartments in hormone action (cf. Szego and Roberts, 1953; Szego, 1957) we have not lost sight of these straws in the wind. Moreover, with advancing sophistication in all areas of cellular biochemistry in the intervening decades, there have appeared additional observations, based on methods of greater precision than were available to the investigators whose primary observations are compiled in Table I. These investigations, which provide further evidence for the occurrence of specific binding sites for steroid hormones in surface membranes of their selective targets, are summarized in Table II.

b. Current Observations.   Table II in its entirety (parts A–E) provides impressive documentation of what appears to be a general phenomenon. The broad representation of steroidal agonists and the extensive range of phylogenetic and tissue origins of their cellular targets clearly suggest biological relevance. Just as meaningful as the evidence for criteria satisfied with respect to stereospecificity, high affinity, saturability, and target-cell selectivity of the comprehensive series of binding interactions surveyed, is the paucity of such associations in "nontarget" cells. In many cases there is further indication of physiologic relevance, in correlation of the distribution of binding sites with regional or other subfraction of membrane. The absolute number of observations listed in Table II constitutes, in reality, a minimum, for there are also a substantial series of abrupt effects of certain steroidal agonists that can only be ascribed to virtually instantaneous interactions at the cell surface. For elicitation of such effects (see Section IV,A–C), a priori rationale requires that binding *in situ* occur first.

However, certain data, to be discussed below, fail to validate these overall findings of specific binding sites for steroid hormones in surface membranes of their cellular targets (i.e., Davidson *et al.*, 1963; Blyth *et al.*, 1973; Müller *et al.*, 1979). Unfortunately, as will be developed in detail in the following section, which seeks to provide a comprehensive evaluation of the specific conditions required for the demonstration of native binding components for steroid hormones in plasma membranes and their subfractions, there are serious problems with methodologies that can account for these deficits. The need to preserve such components throughout the necessary cell disruption and fractionation procedures constitutes a formidable problem in cell biology generally, to which the solutions are at best, incomplete (DePierre and Karnovsky, 1973).

TABLE II

Direct Evidence for Specific Interactions of Steroid Agonists with Surface Membranes of Their Cellular Targets

Steroid	Tissue	Observations	Reference
A. ESTROGENS			
$E_2\beta$	Isolated endometrial cells and hepatocytes of ovariectomized rats	Cells bound to nylon fibers derivatized covalently with 17β-estradiol-17α-hemisuccinate; binding stereospecific and related in extent to the degree of uptake of $E_2\beta$ by similar cells in independent experiments. Intestinal cells, with negligible uptake of free steroid, did not bind to the immobilized $E_2\beta$.	Pietras and Szego (1977a, 1979a)
$E_2\beta$	Purified plasma membrane subfractions of uterine cells from ovariectomized rats	Plasma membrane subfractions (ϱ = 1.13–1.16) were purified from crude nuclear fractions and showed enrichment of 5'-nucleotidase to 12-times homogenate and concentration of stereospecific $E_2\beta$ binding sites to 23-times homogenate. $E_2\beta$ binding was saturable (K_a = 4.3 × 10^{10} M^{-1}) and represented ~27% of total cell binding. Specific $E_2\beta$ binding to membranes not reduced by extraction with hypotonic or high-salt buffers.	Pietras and Szego (1979c)
$E_2\beta$	Purified plasma membrane subfractions of hepatocytes from ovariectomized rats.	Plasma membrane subfractions with densities of 1.13–1.16 were purified from crude nuclear and microsomal fractions and showed ~50-fold enrichment of WGA[a] binding sites over homogenate. Stereospecific $E_2\beta$ binding sites enriched ~56-fold and concentrated at blood-front of cell surface. $E_2\beta$ binding was saturable (K_a = 3.5 × 10^9 M^{-1}) and represented ~44% of total cell	Pietras et al. (1978); Pietras and Szego (1980a)

(continued)

TABLE II (continued)

Steroid	Tissue	Observations	Reference
		binding. Membrane E$_2\beta$-binding component extracted with Triton X-100 at 4° and purified 1560-fold on low-salt sucrose density gradients as 7.4 S macromolecule.	
E$_2\beta$	Crude plasma membrane fraction of human spermatozoa	Binding sites of high affinity ($K_d = 6.6 \times 10^{-10}\ M$) detected. In related experiments carried out under saturating conditions, 75–84% of the [^{3}H] E$_2\beta$ binding was to sperm membranes. Binding specific, as judged by effective competition with E$_2\beta$; E$_2\alpha$, progesterone ineffective; slight competition with testosterone.	Hernández-Pérez et al. (1979)
E$_2\beta$	Human breast cancer cells	Cells treated at 4° with a fluorescent analog of E$_2\beta$ covalently linked to BSA ($4 \times 10^{-8}\ M$) showed homogeneous distribution of fluorescence over the surface. Warming to 37° promoted aggregation of the bound complex into a polar "cap". Similar observations were made with polyestradiol phosphate coupled to rabbit IgG when distribution was probed with horseradish peroxidase-labeled second antibody and the resultant preparations visualized by light microscopy, SEM, or electron probe X-ray microanalysis. Binding at surface was abolished by polyestradiol phosphate and E$_2\beta$, but not by testosterone or DES.	Nenci et al. (1980)

324

B. ANDROGENS

Testosterone	*Pseudomonas testosteroni*	Saturable, NAD⁺-dependent uptake against conc. gradient by membrane vesicles isolated from testosterone-induced cultures. In related work from the same laboratory, the steroid "receptor" was released by osmotic shock; it was sensitive to pronase and heat denaturation, while being resistant to RNAase and DNAase treatment (Watanabe *et al.*, 1973).	Watanabe and Po (1974)
Testosterone	*Pseudomonas testosteroni*	Uptake of testosterone by membrane vesicles required functional integrity of 3β- and 17β-hydroxy steroid dehydrogenases, a viable electron transport chain, and intact disulfide bonds.	Lefebvre *et al.* (1976)

C. ADRENOCORTICAL STEROIDS

Aldosterone	Plasma membranes from kidney of adrenalecto-mized rat	[³H]aldosterone binding *in vivo* (1 hour) and *in vitro* (30 minutes, 5×10^{-9} M) antagonized by mineralocorticoids, DOC and 9α-fluorocortisol, and by spironolactone and progesterone; $E_2\beta$ ineffective. Binding was resistant to extensive washing. Extraction of the membranes with Lubrol-WX, followed by gel filtration chromatography revealed DOC-suppressible isotopic aldosterone associated with the solubilized proteins in addition to a free steroid peak retarded by the gel.	Forte (1972)
Glucocorticoids	Purified plasma membranes isolated from normal rat liver and hepatoma	Cortisol exhibited specific, high-affinity binding to subfractions: $\varrho = 1.13–1.16$, $K_d = 1.5–1.9 \times 10^{-9}M$; $\varrho = 1.16–1.18$, $K_d = 1.5–1.9 \times 10^{-9}$ M and $K_d = 3.1–4.6 \times 10^{-9}$ M. Affinity corticoster-	Suyemitsu and Terayama (1975); Terayama *et al.* (1976)

(continued)

TABLE II (continued)

Steroid	Tissue	Observations	Reference
		one > cortisol > cortisone. No specific binding or competition seen with dexamethasone. Plasma membranes prepared from rat ascites hepatoma showed sharp reduction in numbers of binding sites.	
Aldosterone	Isolated plasma membranes of rat kidney	Specific, saturable, high-affinity binding ($K_d = 1.3 \times 10^{-8}\,M$) to a membrane component of protein characteristics; $n_{max} \cong 1.69 \times 10^{-13}$ mol/mg of membrane protein. Aldosterone in vivo or in vitro diminished binding of the [³H]hormone.	Ožegović et al. (1977)
Corticosterone; dexamethasone	Partially purified plasma membranes of pituitary glands of adrenalectomized rats	High-affinity, low-capacity binding, specific for natural corticosteroid in cell membrane fraction. However, binding component solubilized from the crude plasma membranes had properties similar to transcortin (K_d, sedimentation profile in sucrose density gradients, and number of binding sites).	Koch et al. (1977, 1978)
Corticosterone	Membrane vesicles prepared from mouse pituitary AtT-20 tumor cells and semipurified by flotation	Specific and saturable binding. In contrast to results with whole cells, removal of sialic acid with neuraminidase enhanced binding, possibly by unmasking sites. The order of binding affinities tested in competition experiments was corticosterone > 11-dehydrocorticosterone > 11-ketoprogesterone > cortisol; triamcinolone acetonide, dexamethasone, $E_2\beta$, and testosterone	Harrison et al. (1979)

		were ineffective competitors. The glucocorticoid affinities differed from those of corresponding cytosol.	Fant *et al.* (1979)
Corticosterone	Human placental membrane vesicles	Saturable, hormone-specific uptake by "cytosol-receptor-free" vesicles, with a K_m of 7 mM. The order of specificities was corticosterone > cortisol > dexamethasone > testosterone > progesterone; unlike the case with corresponding cytosol, triamcinalone acetonide an ineffective competitor. Uptake stimulated by NAD⁺ and inhibited by sulfhydryl group blockade.	
Corticosterone	Purified rat liver plasma membrane vesicles	Specific, high-affinity ($K_d = 7.2 \pm 2.0$ nM), saturable within 5 seconds at 23°. At physiological concs. of corticosterone (B), uptake was inhibited essentially completely by B, strongly by a series of corticosteroid analogs, and partially by sex hormones; the 5 α-dihydrosteroids were potent inhibitors.	Alléra *et al.* (1980)
Triamcinolone acetonide	Cultured AtT-20	Glucocorticoid uptake reversibly inhibited by *p*-chloromercuriphenylsulfonate under conditions which do not significantly affect the cytosol receptor. Entry thus a membrane-mediated process requiring SH-integrity.	Harrison and Yeakley (1979)

D. CARDIAC GLYCOSIDES AND AGLYCONES

Ouabain and digoxin	Cardiac muscle and erythrocytes	Glycosides bound covalently to albumin or myoglobin and found to be 100–1000 times less active biologically than free agonists; activity may	Smith *et al.* (1972)

(continued)

TABLE II (continued)

Steroid	Tissue	Observations	Reference
		have been due to 0.1–1.0% contamination of conjugates with free glycosides. Conjugates with long flexible polyamide chains as "spacers" between the glycoside and albumin (or myoglobin) still showed negligible effects on contractility of cardiac muscle, Rb⁺ uptake by erythrocytes, or Na⁺/K⁺-ATPase activity of cardiac microsomes. The latter conjugates did reduce the activity of solubilized Na⁺/K⁺-ATPase. Authors concluded that plasma membrane receptor for cardiac glycosides must be localized deep within membrane (cf. also Fortes, 1977).	
Ouabain	Amphibian urinary bladder	Specific [³H]ouabain binding to the lateral plasma membranes of the granular cells on exposure *in vitro* of whole mounts.	Mills *et al.* (1974)
Ouabain and other cardiac glycosides	Membranes of canine heart	High-affinity, saturable binding, specific for the cardiac glycosides and their aglycones; antagonized by certain steroids related to hydroxy-progesterone and by K⁺.	Kim *et al.* (1978)
Ouabain	Membranes of canine ventricle	Specific, high-affinity saturable binding of ouabain. Chlormadinone acetate (CMA; 3,5-diene-3-one-17α-ol-6-chloro-pregn-17-acetate) was *ca.* 50% as potent as ouabain in displacing specifically bound ouabain; CMA significantly suppressed Na⁺/K⁺-ATPase in broken cells and	LaBella *et al.* (1979; cf. also Akera (1977)

Ouabain	Rectal gland of dogfish, *Squalus acanthias*	inhibited Na⁺ pumping in beating atria, however without inotropic effect.

Specific, high-affinity binding of [³H]ouabain in slices of rectal gland tissue at sites which correlated with Na⁺/K⁺-ATPase inhibition. Autoradiographs demonstrated localization of ~ 85% of the bound ouabain within 1-μm wide boundary region of the basal-lateral cell membranes, with higher densities in regions close to underlying mitochondria. | Eveloff *et al.* (1979) |

E. OOCYTE MATURATION-INDUCING COMPOUNDS

Progesterone	Oocytes of *Rana pipiens*	Resumption of meiotic maturation with germinal vesicle breakdown (GVBD) and/or polar body extrusion as indicators when progesterone was present in the *external* medium of oocytes denuded of follicular cells. Maturation failed to occur when progesterone was injected into oocytes in concentrations more than enough to elicit maturation if applied to external surfaces.	Smith and Ecker (1971)
Progesterone	Oocytes of *R. pipiens*	Externally applied progesterone led to production of cytoplasmic "maturation promoting factor," while injected progesterone did not.	Masui and Markert (1971)
Progesterone; 11α-hydroxy progesterone; cortisol; aldosterone; testosterone	Oocytes of *Xenopus laevis*	In contrast to the actions of progesterone, 11α-hydroxyprogesterone, and aldosterone, only at external surfaces of follicle-denuded oocytes, cortisol and testosterone were effective in inducing meiotic maturation after either incubation or injection.[b]	Jacobelli *et al.* (1974)

(continued)

329

TABLE II (continued)

Steroid	Tissue	Observations	Reference
Progesterone; cortisol	Oocytes of X. *laevis*	Confirms Jacobelli *et al.* and predecessors on effectiveness of progesterone in inducing GVBD only when externally applied. Efficacy of injected cortisol attributed to "leakage" of the relatively hydrophilic steroid into the external medium.[c]	Drury and Schorderet-Slatkine (1975)
Deoxycorticosterone	Oocytes of X. *laevis*	Deoxycorticosterone (DOC) bound to agarose beads induced GVBD only when in contact with the oocyte surface. GVBD did not occur when the follicle cells were left *in situ* during treatment or when a nylon net barrier was present between the agarose-bound DOC and the oocyte.	Ishikawa *et al.* (1977)
Progesterone analog	Oocytes of X. *laevis*	Incubation with the polymer-linked synthetic steroid, α, ω-bis-3-oxo-4-androsten-17β-amido-polyethylene oxide, led to GVBD, while injection into the oocyte was ineffective. Hydrolytic release of free steroid was excluded in control experiments. A corresponding derivative of E$_2\beta$ failed to induce maturation when exposed to external oocyte surfaces.	Godeau *et al.* (1978)

330

| Progesterone, C-21 analogs, and a series of natural and synthetic steroids | Oocytes of *X. laevis* | Polymer-linked agonists effective in promoting meiotic maturation (GVBD); $E_2\beta$ not an agonist. Certain amphipathic cationic drugs known to penetrate membrane phospholipids and increase surface pressure could mimic progesterone action in triggering meiosis. Data discussed in context with literature on membrane-related Ca^{2+} alterations. | Baulieu *et al.* (1978) |

[a] WGA, wheat germ agglutinin.
[b] See also Table III and Ozon and Bellé (1973) for specific localization of steroids in subcortical melanosomes of the oocyte[']
[c] This paper resolves the apparent discrepant results with injected cortisol (Schorderet-Slatkine, 1972; Schorderet-Slatkine and Drury, 1973; Jacobelli *et al.*, 1974).

Similar problems occur in the context of experimental analysis of the occurrence of specific *intra*cellular binding sites for steroidal agonists: inadvertent stripping, fortuitous adsorption, and various degrees of cross-contamination of one particulate fraction with another (see below). Awareness of these potential artifacts is by no means universal, and the experimental procedures are not uniformly rigorous in their exclusion. Nevertheless, once again there is substantial evidence that macromolecules capable of specific high-affinity interaction with given steroids are distributed in several extranuclear compartments of certain target cells (Table III).

Among the more pressing unsolved problems in steroid hormone biology is the significance of compartmentalization of macromolecules for agonal recognition and the interrelations, if any, among such sites in the orderly transfer of hormone to those subcellular regions in which vital information processing takes place. Critical to understanding of these interrelations is timing in the ebb and flow of steroid among the several compartments. In this context, many observers have presented evidence suggesting that steroid hormones and their analogs bind to target-cell plasma membranes (Williams and Baba, 1967), mitochondria and/or lysosomes (King *et al.*, 1965; Williams and Baba, 1967; Voigt *et al.*, 1978), and microsomal fractions (i.e., microsomes with plasma membrane vesicles; Litwack *et al.*, 1963; King *et al.*, 1965; Morris and Barnes, 1967; Mainwaring and Peterken, 1971), either simultaneously with, or prior to association with cytosol components, and thus well in advance of nuclear accumulation. Similarly, the relative specific activities of the lysosomal–mitochondrial fraction of preputial glands of ovariectomized rats from 30 seconds to 2 minutes after intravenous administration of $[^3H]E_2\beta$ was enriched to 2.7 times that of the corresponding nuclear preparations (Table IV; cf. also Hirsch and Szego in Table III). The possibility thus appears plausible that sequential subcellular recompartmentation plays a role in the vectorial translocation of hormone from the cell surface to the nucleus (Szego, 1975). This problem remains to be investigated in depth, with due consideration to technical pitfalls.

In experiments conducted in our laboratory, we have adopted an affinity-binding approach (cf. Cuatrecasas, 1969; Edelman *et al.*, 1971; Inman and Hornby, 1972) to probe for plasma membrane binding sites for estradiol. Significant numbers of hormone-responsive endometrial and liver parenchymal cells were found to adhere to 17β-estradiol-17α-hemisuccinyl–albumin–nylon fibers (Fig. 2), but cells conventionally deemed nontarget, such as those from intestinal epithelium (cf. Toft and Gorski, 1966), showed negligible binding (Pietras and Szego, 1977a).

TABLE III

DIRECT EVIDENCE FOR SPECIFIC INTERACTIONS OF STEROID AGONISTS WITH INTRACELLULAR[a] MEMBRANES OF THEIR TARGET CELLS

Steroid	Tissue	Observations	Reference
A. ESTROGEN AND ANDROGEN			
Testosterone, DHT and other androgens	Minced tissue and "microsomal" fractions from human prostate	High correlation between displaceable binding of a series of androgens and their effects on ATPase activity (see text, Section IV,A).	Farnsworth (1972)
$E_2\beta$	"Microsomal" fraction of uteri from near-pubertal (6 months old) pigs	Homogenates prepared in isotonic buffer yielded macromolecular pronase-sensitive "receptors" in the "microsomal" fraction. When subsequently extracted with hypotonic buffer, high-affinity binding sites (saturated at $5 \times 10^{-9}\,M\,E_2\beta$), sedimenting at 3.5 S, 4.5 S, and 6–10 S in sucrose density gradients, were obtained. The 4.5 S peak was distinct from albumin and highly sensitive to SH-reagents. Although not covalently bound (as indicated by extractibility with organic solvents), the $E_2\beta$ interaction with 4.5 S components was resistant to exchange with cold hormone. TEM revealed complex membranous and microfibrilar components of the "microsomal" pellet. The combined data supported a membrane origin of a portion of the "cytosolic" receptors as usually prepared in hypotonic buffer.	Little et al. (1972)
$E_2\beta$	"Microsomal" fraction, as above	Interrelations of the two forms of receptor, 3.5 S, $K_a = 1.2 \times 10^9\,M^{-1}$; 4.5 S, $K_a = 9 \times 10^8$	Little et al. (1973)

(continued)

TABLE III (continued)

Steroid	Tissue	Observations	Reference
		M^{-1}, suggested that the latter was a dimer of the 3.5 S moiety, with addition of an anionic component.	
$E_2\beta$	"Nuclear" and "microsomal" fractions from mature bovine endometrium	After incubation of endometrial tissue with 5×10^{-10} M [^{3}H]E$_2\beta$, 37°, 45 minutes, subcellular distribution of isotope was determined, with cell disruption in isotonic buffer. Approx. 37% was "nuclear," 10% "mitochondrial/heavy microsomal," 10% light microsomal," 20% "cytosolic," and the remainder, free. Partially purified nuclei and microsomes exposed after isolation to [^{3}H]E$_2\beta$ exhibited almost instantaneous binding which was nonsaturable up to 2.5×10^{-5} mol/mg of protein. A second, higher affinity saturable binding site was observed in nuclear fractions, with 507 ± 47 sites/nucleus. This was specific for estrogen, varied with stage of estrous cycle, appeared restricted to the nuclear membrane and associated "cytoplasmic membrane" contaminants, but was not extractable by 0.4 M KCl (cf. also Berezny and Coffey, 1976, 1977; Barrack *et al.*, 1977).	Jackson and Chalkley (1974a)
$E_2\beta$	"Nuclear" and "microsomal" fractions from bovine uteri, as above	Presented evidence that 70% of 4 S receptors in *intact* cells restricted from interaction with hormone; tissue disruption artifacts may lead to erroneous estimates of cytosol binding. Due	Jackson and Chalkley (1974b)

$E_2\beta$	Highly purified lysosome-enriched fractions from preputial glands of ovariectomized rats	to affinity of 4 S cytosol receptor for binding to "microsomal" membrane, it was suggested that receptor may be associated with plasma membranes prior to homogenization.	Hirsch and Szego (1974)
		"Specific" high affinity ($K_a = 1.60 \pm 0.75 \times 10^{10}\ M^{-1}$) saturable binding which could be suppressed by proteolytic enzymes and $E_2\beta$. $E_2\alpha$ ineffective as a competitor. The combined data were consistent with possible lysosomal origin of a portion of the "cytosol" receptors when extracted on hyposmotic shock.	
$E_2\beta$	Highly purified lysosome-enriched fractions from preputial glands of ovariectomized rats	Preferential and rapid uptake of [³H]$E_2\beta$ in lysosomal fraction 30 seconds to 2 minutes after i.v. administration. Relative enrichment over whole homogenate $2.7 \times$ that of crude nuclear pellet at these early times after injection.	Szego (1974)
$E_2\beta$ and/or metabolites	Liver slices from 10 to 20-day-old Leghorn roosters	Incubation conducted for 15 minutes, 37° with [³H]$E_2\beta$, $1 \times 10^{-8}\ M$. Autoradiography showed grains from $E_2\beta$ or its metabolites associated with organelles, including mitochondria, ER, as well as the nucleus. Grains especially prominent at latter membrane, (cf. also Inman et al., 1965). Conspicuous lack of grains in the cytoplasmic matrix. Radioactivity could be displaced with cold $E_2\beta$. Repeated priming with $E_2\beta$ before incubation promoted increased numbers of Ag grains in the sections, with no visible differences in localization.	Sen et al. (1975)

(continued)

335

TABLE III (continued)

Steroid	Tissue	Observations	Reference
B. PROGESTERONE			
Progesterone	"Melanosome" fraction from ovaries of *Pleurodeles waltlii*	Binding sites of high affinity ($K_d \sim 3.6 \times 10^{-8}\ M$), saturability ($\sim 2 \times 10^{-7}$ mol/mg of protein), and specificity (displaceable by excess progesterone and DOC).	Ozon and Bellé (1973)
Progesterone	"Melanosome" fraction from ovaries of *Xenopus laevis*	Binding sites of high affinity ($K_d \sim 4.6 \times 10^{-8}\ M$), low capacity ($\sim 16 \times 10^{-8}$ mol/mg of protein). Competing steroids included progesterone, corticosterone, and 17α-progesterone $\gg$ aldosterone, 11α-OH-progesterone $\gg$ cortisol, cortisone, and estrogens.	Jacobelli *et al.* (1974)
Progesterone	"Microsomes" from myometrium of pregnant and postpartum rats	Specific binding sites of high affinity ($K_a \sim 5 \times 10^7\ M^{-1}$), low capacity (1 pmol/mg of protein). Synthetic progestins not bound. Similar findings with "microsomes" from liver, whereas those from heart and skeletal muscle failed to exhibit binding.	Haukkamaa and Luukkainen (1974)
Progesterone	Particulate fractions from uterus of estrogen-primed rats	Subcellular fractions prepared from uteri at various times after intracardiac injection of [³H]-steroid. Specific binding sites were found in "mitochondria" and "microsomes."	Egert *et al.* (1977)

C. MISCELLANEOUS STEROIDS

1,25-(OH)$_2$D$_3$	Intestinal mucosa of White Leghorn cockerels	Incubations conducted for 40–70 minutes at 25° with tissues or their homogenates from vitamin D-deficient birds. Radioactivity from 1,25-(OH)$_2$cholecalciferol was distributed in intestinal homogenates as follows: "Mt" 20%; "Ms" 13%; "cytosol" 22%; CN 45%. Only the chromatin fraction prepared from CN exhibited saturability. When whole intestines were pre-incubated 15 minutes with hormone at 0°, washed and further incubated at 37°, ^{3}H was translocated to chromatin at expense of "cytosol," with little or no change in distribution to "Mt" or "Ms."	Brumbaugh and Haussler (1973)
Gibberellins	Chloroplasts from *Triticum aestivum* seedlings	Gibberellins A$_9$ and A$_4$ were extractable from chloroplast preparations with Triton X-100 in quantities much higher than had been obtained from vegetative tissues of any plant with methanol extraction.	Browning and Saunders (1977)
Ouabain	"Microsomal" fraction of electric organ of *Electrophorus electricus*	Photosensitive derivative of ouabain inhibited binding of [^{3}H]ouabain by association with large MW subunit of Na$^+$/K$^+$-ATPase (cf. also Ruoho and Kyte, 1974).	Rogers and Lazdunski (1979)

ᵃ Except as noted, membranes of nuclei and their components are excluded. It should be noted, however, that nuclei as generally prepared, are often heavily contaminated with plasma and microsomal membranes (DePierre and Karnovsky, 1973) and/or lysosomes; the latter especially after hormone treatment (Szego et al., 1974, 1976; Szego and Seeler, 1973). Microsomes as generally prepared may likewise be cross-contaminated with plasmalemmal vesicles.

TABLE IV

SUBCELLULAR DISTRIBUTION OF [³H]ESTRADIOL-17β IN PREPUTIAL GLAND AT EARLY INTERVALS AFTER INTRAVENOUS ADMINISTRATION[a]

Specific activity $10^{-2} \times$ dpm/mg protein			Relative specific activity		Enrichment ratio
WH	NP	LP	NP/WH	LP/WH	LP/NP
8.35	3.73	11.15	0.447	1.335	2.987
14.33	6.70	19.78	0.468	1.380	2.949
14.80	4.27	10.10	0.289	0.682	2.360
13.30	4.44	10.20	0.334	0.767	2.296
8.58	5.12	18.30	0.600	2.150	3.584
9.13	5.61	12.29	0.615	1.410	2.290
M ± SEM			0.459 ± 0.054	1.287 ± 0.217	2.744 ± 0.213
t				3.7135	
P				<0.01	

[a] Estradiol-17β was injected i.v. in the amount of 0.1 μg and 5 μCi/100 gm body weight to adult rats of an inbred Sprague-Dawley strain that had been maintained in a low steroid environment for 3 weeks after ovariectomy. Preputial glands were excised within 30 seconds to 2 minutes after injection and immediately frozen in liquid nitrogen. After cellular disruption in groups of three paired organs, without thawing (Szego, 1972a), they were processed for preparation of subcellular fractions as outlined in Szego et al. (1971); the lysosomal pellet isolated was the equivalent of LP1. Aliquots of the unfractionated homogenate (WH), crude nuclear pellet (NP), and lysosomal pellet (LP), each suspended in an appropriate volume, were analyzed for protein by the method of Lowry et al. (1951) and for radioactivity by scintillation counting in Aquasol® (New England Nuclear Co.). Corrections were made for counting efficiency (ca. 58%) and also for quenching (approximately 20%) by addition of internal standard.

From Szego (1974), reproduced with permission.

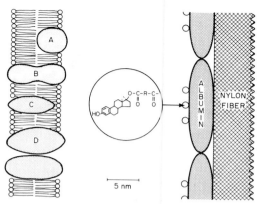

FIG. 2. Schematic representation of 17β-estradiol-17-α-hemisuccinyl: albumin: nylon fiber and the plasma membrane of a target cell. Hormone-derivatized fibers were prepared as described by Pietras and Szego (1977a). The plasma membrane model is adapted from that of Singer (1977). It is proposed that immobilized estradiol may interact specifically with one of at least four classes of protein integral to the membrane (see text for details).

Target-cell binding to the covalently immobilized hormone was temperature-dependent and proportional to the extent of the cellular accumulation of free $[^3H]E_2\beta$, as determined in independent experiments (Fig. 3). There was no association of cells when unmodified nylon fibers, or fibers derivatized only with albumin, were used. Moreover, prior incubation with free estradiol-17β diminished the binding of washed endometrial cells to the estrogen-derivatized fiber whereas incubation with the 17α-congener failed to influence their subsequent binding behavior (Pietras and Szego, 1977a). Similarly, of the two stereoisomers, only the free 17β-steroid was capable of effective competition in eliciting release from the fiber of cells bound by the immobilized hormone. The association constant for binding of 17β-estradiol-17α-hemisuccinyl–albumin to receptors from calf uterus is approximately 100-times less than that for free 17β-estradiol (cf. Sica *et al.*, 1976). On this basis, we have estimated that the K_a for specific binding of the estradiol–fiber complex to rat uterine membrane receptor *in situ* is approximately 10^9 M^{-1} (cf. Pietras and Szego, 1980b).

Others have suggested an alternative interpretation of these data. Müller *et al.* (1979) argue that a portion of the estradiol–albumin linked to the nylon fibers may become internalized by target cells, with consequent binding to cytoplasmic receptors and retention within the cells. However, these workers have also acknowledged elsewhere (Müller and Wotiz, 1979) that estradiol covalently bound to albumin constitutes a macromolecular complex, which does not penetrate the target cell.

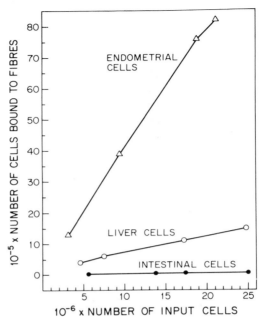

F IG. 3. Extent of cell binding to estrogen immobilized on nylon fibers. Cells isolated from intestinal mucosa (●), liver (○), and endometrium (△) were incubated with the fibers by the addition of 3 to 25 × 10^6 cells per 4 ml of medium, using standard conditions of mixing and shaking. After removal of unbound cells, cells attached to the derivatized fibers were dislodged by incubation for 1 hour in divalent cation-free Ringer solution containing 2 × $10^{-7} M$ $E_2\beta$, followed by 1 minute of incubation in hypotonic (150 mOsm) saline with excess $E_2\beta$. ($E_2\alpha$ was ineffective in displacing cells from their association with fibers.) Cells recovered by these procedures were disrupted by sonication at 4°, and samples of the sonicate were taken for determination of cellular DNA contents. Cell numbers reported here were derived from measurements of DNA content per cell. Each data point represents the mean of two or three independent experiments. The relation of the number of fiber-bound cells to total cells present in the incubation medium is defined by the slope, 0.003 for intestinal cells (r = .098), 0.054 for liver cells (r = .99), and 0.386 for endometrial cells (r = .99). (From Pietras and Szego, 1977a, reproduced by permission.)

Although some free [^{131}I]albumin is known to become associated with uterine cells after several hours' exposure to estrogen *in vivo* (Peterson and Spaziani, 1969), the uptake of the macromolecule by a wide variety of mammalian cells is known to proceed at an extremely low rate (cf. Ryser, 1968). We consider it more probable that hydrolysis of the estradiol–albumin–nylon complex will occur after exposure to intact cells, thereby reducing the number of cells capable of specific association with the fiber support. It is also important to emphasize that the steroid stereospecificity of cell binding to immobilized hormone (cf. Pietras and Szego, 1979a,b) indicates that estrogen, not albumin, governs these interactions with target cell membranes.

    c. Detailed Account of Properties of Surface Recognition Sites Identified by Affinity Chromatography. More recently, these primary findings have been extended in the detailed analysis of surface receptor sites in hepatocytes (Pietras and Szego, 1979a), cells now known to possess moderate numbers of high-affinity binding sites for estrogenic hormones (Smirovna *et al.*, 1974; Eisenfeld *et al.*, 1976; Beers and Rosner, 1977). Figure 4 demonstrates some characteristic microscopic views of hepatocytes bound to the estrogen-derivatized fibers. As seen in Fig. 4, some of the fiber-bound cells appear fairly rounded, while others tend to flatten out at the fiber surface with prolonged incubation. The variable conformations exhibited may be a function of numbers of receptor sites and their distribution on the individual cells. Not yet studied in detail, however, is the possibility that contractile elements in the immediately subcortical cytoplasm may influence cell shape through differential degree of coupling to plasmalemmal components (see Section IV,E).

    i. Specificity of binding sites for estradiol at outer surfaces of responsive cells. Specificity of cell binding to the immobilized estrogen was assured by several criteria. No binding was observed to underivatized fibers, or to fibers coupled only to the intermediary reagent, albumin. Moreover, in each experiment, the prevailing concentration of immobilized $E_2\beta$ was approximately 5×10^{-10} *M*, thus favoring interactions primarily of high affinity. Finally, quantitative determination of the influence of free ligands on the extent of hepatocyte binding to the hormone covalently linked to the fibers was evaluated. The degree of retention of bound cells, as determined by standarized procedures (cf. Pietras and Szego, 1979a) in the presence of 200-fold molar excess of other steroids, according to the notation of Williams and Gorski (1973), was essentially uninfluenced by estradiol-17α ($E_2\alpha$), cortisol, progesterone, or testosterone (Table V). In contrast, physiologically active estrogens elicited either profound (e.g., $E_2\beta$, diethylstilbestrol) or moderate (e.g., estriol) suppression of cell binding to the fibers. The lack of competition by testosterone in these investigations as well as in parallel studies with isolated endometrial cells (Pietras and Szego, 1979c) militates strongly against the reservation that the occurrence of binding sites for $E_2\beta$ at the surfaces of these estrogenic target cells could be merely a reflection of possible adsorption, however remote under the conditions of preparation specified, of typical steroid transport proteins to the cell surfaces. Moreover, since steroidal interactions with the latter molecules are characterized by much higher dissociation rates than those of the hor-

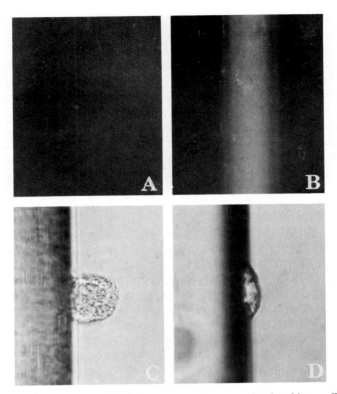

FIG. 4. Binding of fluorescein-labeled estrogen antiserum and isolated liver cells to estradiol immobilized by covalent linkage to albumin-derivatized nylon fibers. Mounted fibers were prepared as described in the text and incubated at 22° with FITC-labeled normal sheep serum (4680 μg of protein; Fig. 4A; × 100) or estrogen antiserum (23 μg of protein; Fig. 4B; × 100) in 5 ml of 0.01 M phosphate buffer (pH 7.0). After 40 minutes, the fibers were washed free of unbound material by five successive 5-minute incubations at 22° with fresh, serum-free buffer (5 ml), with shaking. Darkfield-ultraviolet fluorescence micrographs were then obtained. In independent experiments, cells derived from liver were incubated at 22° with the derivatized fibers by the addition of 1×10^7 cells/4 ml Ca-$^{2+}$, Mg^{2+}-free Ringer solution. The washed fibers with bound cells were then transferred to 4 ml of fresh incubation medium for photomicrography using an immersion lens and Kodak Tri-X Panatomic film (ASA 400). Some fiber-bound cells appear fairly rounded (Fig. 4C; × 850) but others tend to flatten out at the fiber surface (Fig. 4D; × 850). (From Pietras and Szego 1979a, reproduced by permission.)

monal complexes with cellular receptors (Szego, 1957, 1976; Ellis and Ringold, 1971; U. Westphal, *et al.*, 1978), cell surface recognition sites are highly favored for effective competitive capture of the ligands

The above indications for the occurrence of specific binding sites for estrogen in macromolecules intrinsic to the plasmalemma of hepatocytes

TABLE V
SPECIFICITY OF ESTROGEN BINDING IN LIVER CELLS AT 22°

Competing compound[a]	A. Specific [³H]estradiol-17β[b] binding to liver cells $10^{-2} \times$ (dpm/2 $\times$ 10^7 cells)	B. Cell retention by estrogen-derivatized fibers (percent of input cells)[c]
None	187 ± 2 (5)	6.5 ± 0.2 (5)
Estradiol-17β	0. ± 0 (3)[d]	0 ± 0 (3)[d]
Estradiol-17α	179 ± 6 (3)	6.4 ± 0.2 (3)
Estriol	114 ± 7 (3)[d]	4.7 ± 0.2 (3)[e]
Diethylstilbestrol	34 ± 4 (3)[d]	1.6 ± 0.3 (3)[d]
Cortisol	177 ± 2 (3)	6.0 ± 0.4 (3)
Progesterone	190 (2)	6.4 (2)
Testosterone	188 (2)	6.3 (2)

[a] $2 \times 10^{-7} M$.

[b] $1 \times 10^{-9} M$.

[c] Percent of input cells calculated on the basis of DNA ratios; for example, the values in five independent vehicle control experiments were 18.9 ± 0.6 μg DNA of bound cells ($\cong$ 1.3 $\times$ 10^6 cells)/291.4 ± 8.4 μg DNA of input cells ($\cong$ 2.0 $\times$ 10^7 cells).

[d] Value significantly different from paired control at $P < .001$.

[e] Value significantly different from paired control at $P < .01$.

From Pietras and Szego (1979a), reproduced with permission.

have now been extended to endometrial cells (Pietras and Szego, 1979c). The results closely parallel those obtained for hepatocytes, with, however, a characteristically higher number of specific binding sites per isolated uterine cell, as would be anticipated from the higher order of their sensitivity to the hormone. Accordingly, data to illustrate in some depth the properties of these recognition sites for the hormone, *in situ* as well as in solubilized form, will be adduced from both cell types. In course of this presentation, evidence will be provided to reconcile these findings, limited precedents for which have already been given (see Tables I–III), with the more generally prevailing view of occurrence of such macromolecules strictly within the amorphous cytosol of responsive cells.

d. *Specific Binding Sites in Plasmalemmal Subfraction.*

i. *Establishment of appropriate conditions of cell disruption and fractionation.* If cells responsive to specific steroid hormones are indeed poised to intercept these at their surfaces, it should be possible to prepare membrane subfractions, enriched in such binding sites over the respective concentrations in whole homogenates as well as in certain "marker-enzymes" characteristic of the plasmalemma. For this prime criterion to be achieved, as it has now been (Pietras and Szego, 1979b,c, 1978a), it has been essential to utilize methods of cell disruption and media for their resolution that promote the maintenance of cellular constituents in their native state. Closely monitored standardized homogenization of isolated cells (rather than organ segments that require more extensive mechanical shearing) was one means of achieving these aims, while the use of isotonic media and avoidance of chelating agents were likewise calculated to promote retention of membrane integrity. Previous workers have cautioned that the drastic homogenization necessary to disrupt intact uterine organs in conventional schemes for extraction of cytosol results in very small fragments of plasma membrane, most of which are lost in the postnuclear supernatant at the first low-speed centrifugation (Kidwai *et al.*, 1971). Stringent precautions were also taken to maintain the rats that served as the sources of responsive cells free of estrogen- and other steroid hormone exposure during the 3-week period between ovariectomy and experiment (cf. Szego, 1974), in order to avoid failure to account for binding sites occupied by endogenous hormone. By obviating influence of ligand on receptor transformation and subcellular redistribution, these further precautions also served to enhance membrane integrity and retention of native forms of the recognition sites therein. Estrogen was, therefore, *excluded* from these protocols until the binding assays were carried out on isolated cellular fractions.

To facilitate comparison of the resultant data for distribution of extranuclear binding sites with findings obtained from disruption of organ segments by conventional procedures, a series of readily reproduced protocols was tested to evaluate the degrees of damage to cellular structures. Moreover, because data adequate to permit evaluation of the relative homogeneity of the resulting cell fractions and the integrity of cellular organelles have been seriously lacking in essentially all biochemical investigations of the cellular localization of binding sites for steroid hormones, we sought to furnish the relevant information. Likewise, we have adopted the valuable recommendations of others (de Duve, 1967; DePierre and Karnovsky, 1973) to provide the vital balance-sheet for distribution of the relevant activities, as these are related to the levels of the corresponding components in the homogenate.

In Table VI are presented the results of such analyses in two sets of paired experiments in which isolated uterine cells from ovariectomized rats were disrupted and fractionated by one of the five individual protocols specified (Pietras and Szego, 1979c). Protocol 1 will be readily recognized as the procedure common to virtually all reports in which extranuclear macromolecules interacting specifically with steroid hormones are confined largely to cytosol extracts. Inspection of protocols 1–5 reveals that they have been organized into a standardized sequence of

TABLE VI
Effects of Various Conditions of Disruption of Isolated Uterine Cells on Distribution of Protein, 5′-Nucleotidase and Specific Binding of [³H]Estradiol-17β among the Cell Fractions[a]

Determination	No.	Medium	Homogenizer (no. of strokes)[b]	Homogenate (units)	Subcellular fraction (% homogenate) N	M+L	P	S	Recovery (%)	Subcellular fraction (relative specific activity) N	M+L	P	S
Protein	1	5 mM Tris-HCl (pH 7.4) 1.5 mM EDTA	Glass–glass (13)	26.6[c]	36.6	8.6	12.4	38.7	96.3				
	2	5 mM Tris-HCl (pH 7.4) 1.5 mM EDTA	Teflon–glass (26)	23.7	40.0	9.8	10.9	36.4	97.1				
	3	5 mM Tris-HCl (pH 7.4) 1.5 mM EDTA 0.25 M sucrose	Teflon–glass (33)	24.8	37.9	10.9	12.1	34.4	95.3				
	4	5 mM Tris-HCl (pH 7.4) 0.5 mM CaCl₂ 0.25 M sucrose	Glass–glass (17)	25.5	40.0	11.4	14.3	31.4	97.1				
	5	5 mM Tris-HCl (pH 7.4) 0.5 mM CaCl₂ 0.25 M sucrose	Teflon–glass (35)	26.8	40.5	9.3	12.4	37.5	99.7				
5′-Nucleotidase	1			55.8[d]	22.9	6.6	10.3	59.8	99.6	0.63	0.77	0.82	1.54
	2			67.1	33.6	8.5	15.0	38.2	95.3	0.84	0.87	1.37	1.05
	3			65.2	38.9	10.2	15.1	30.8	95.0	1.01	0.94	1.33	0.89
	4			60.2	40.5	14.7	20.3	25.1	100.6	1.01	1.28	1.42	0.80
	5			66.5	47.3	13.8	29.1	9.1	99.3	1.17	1.48	2.35	0.13
E₂β binding	1			32.2[e]	15.2	0.5	6.2	78.1	100.0	0.42	0.06	0.49	2.02
	2			32.5	25.0	4.2	7.0	62.9	99.1	0.62	0.43	0.64	1.73
	3			34.0	32.2	9.0	13.4	47.2	101.8	0.85	0.82	1.19	1.37
	4			34.7	41.2	12.1	19.4	27.2	99.9	1.03	1.05	1.36	0.86
	5			36.8	44.5	12.2	22.1	20.4	99.2	1.10	1.31	1.80	0.54

[a] Isolated uterine cells were suspended in 4 volumes of the indicated homogenization media at 4°. Subsequent preparation of N, M + L, P, and S fractions was carried out using the corresponding homogenization medium at that temperature. However, in protocols 4 and 5, the media used after homogenization contained no additional CaCl₂. The mean values of data from two sets of paired experiments are shown.

[b] Mean number of manual strokes required to disrupt ~100% of cells, as monitored by phase-contrast microscopy.

[c] mg/10⁸ cells.

[d] nmol/min/mg protein.

[e] Specific binding of 2 × 10⁻⁹ M [³H]E₂β, expressed as 10⁻³ × (dpm/mg protein).

From Pietras and Szego (1979c), reproduced with permission.

decreasing severity, based on the anticipated recovery of 5'-nucleotidase in particulate fractions of uterus (Kidwai *et al.*, 1971; Soloff, 1976; Matlib *et al.*, 1979). Procedure 5 is thus inferred to be the mildest.

As is readily evident from the results depicted in Table VI, distribution of protein among the crude nuclear (N), mitochondrial–lysosomal (M + L), microsome-rich (P), and cytosol (S) fractions showed little variation among the major cell fractions prepared by protocols 1–5. In contrast, activity of the plasmalemmal marker-enzyme, 5'-nucleotidase, exhibited marked variation in distribution, with aberrant, cytosolic activity in protocol $1 > 2 > 3 > 4 > 5$. Its appearance in the cell sap to the extent of 78% of the values in the homogenate is particularly striking in protocol 1, calculated to be the most rigorous. Concomitantly, relative specific activity of 5'-nucleotidase in the crude nuclear and microsome-rich fractions, where the bulk of plasma membrane is known to cosediment (Berman *et al.*, 1969; DePierre and Karnovsky, 1973), followed an inverse sequence, with activity of protocol $5 > > 1$ (Table VI).

It is particularly instructive to analyze the occurrence of specific estradiol binding in light of these data that demonstrate redistribution of a plasma membrane marker-enzyme from particulate to soluble fractions in protocol $1 > > 5$. Indeed, the bulk of specific binding of the hormone is associated with particulate fractions in protocol 5, while $E_2\beta$ binding is minimal in cytosol prepared by this protocol. In contrast, specific $E_2\beta$ binding occurs predominantly in cytosol extracts obtained by protocol 1, in accord with expectations from the literature (cf. Raspé, 1971; Birnbaumer and O'Malley, 1978). Thus, homogenization conditions less conservative of membrane integrity, as judged by distribution of 5'-nucleotidase among cell fractions, lead to appearance of augmented levels of specific $E_2\beta$-binding activities in the cytosol extracts.

It should be noted that the extent of cell disruption in the standardized protocols of Table VI was carefully adjusted to essentially 100%, as monitored by phase contrast microscopy within each sample, in the paired series shown. Now, in order to minimize still further the aberrant redistribution of macromolecules due to excessive homogenization (cf. Plagemann, 1969; Kidwai *et al.*, 1971), the degree of cell disruption, likewise monitored, was limited, by appropriate reduction of homogenizer strokes, to no more than 98% of the total cell population (see flow-diagram in Fig. 5) in the further paired experiments shown in Fig. 6. The two homogenization procedures leading to the data depicted in Fig. 6 (protocols 6 and 7) correspond otherwise to protocols 1 and 5 of Table VI, respectively. Unbroken cells were removed by filtration as indicated in Fig. 5. The resultant data (Fig. 6) reveal the more characteristic proportion of 5'-nucleotidase in particulate fractions with reduction of number

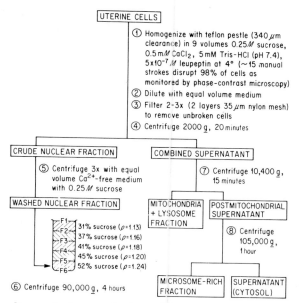

FIG. 5. Flow diagram for homogenization and fractionation of isolated uterine cells (protocol 7). See text and Fig. 6 for additional details. (From Pietras and Szego, 1979c, reproduced by permission.)

of homogenizer-strokes used for cell shearing. However, and despite the diminished extent of force required in protocol 6 vs. its counterpart in Table VI, the atypical appearance of a substantial portion of 5'-nucleotidase in cytosol remains characteristic of samples prepared in hypotonic buffer ($P < .001$), protocol 6 vs. protocol 7). The distribution of specific binding sites for $E_2\beta$ is, likewise, overwhelmingly greater in the cell sap in the absence of osmotic protection ($P < .001$).

These data, together with the results of more extensive analyses for cellular distribution of marker-enzymes (Pietras and Szego, 1979c, 1980a), dictated the overall method of choice for disruption and fractionation of isolated estrogen-sensitive cells. Accordingly, protocol 7 was utilized in the initial steps of the experiments depicted in the following series.

ii. Enrichment of binding sites for $E_2\beta$ in membrane subfractions isolated by conservative procedures from responsive cells. A logical extension of the above observations is the isolation of more highly purified cellular subfractions in which plasmalemmal components predominate, as identified by characteristic biochemical, morphologic, and enzyme

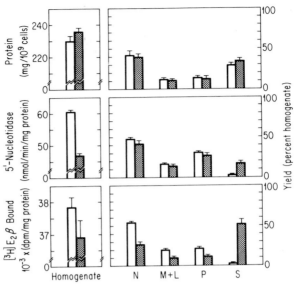

Fɪɢ. 6. Effect of homogenization conditions on yield of protein, 5'-nucleotidase activity, and specific binding of [^{3}H]estradiol-17β (E$_2\beta$) in major fractions of disrupted uterine cells. In protocol 6 (shaded bars), cells were suspended in 4 volumes of hypotonic medium consisting of 5 mM Tris-HCl (pH 7.4) with 1.5 mM EDTA. In accord with the recommendation of Plagemann (1969), about 98% of the cells were disrupted at 4° with a glass–glass homogenizer (Kontes), using 7–10 manual strokes. The same homogenization medium was utilized throughout subsequent steps in the otherwise standard fractionation procedure (Fig. 5). In protocol 7 (clear bars), isolated uterine cells were homogenized and fractionated according to the scheme presented in Fig. 5. The mean ± SEM of data from 3 paired experiments is shown. Total recoveries of protein, 5'-nucleotidase activity and specific E$_2\beta$ binding in crude nuclear (N), mitochondrial–lysosomal (M + L), microsome-rich (P), and cytosol (S) fractions ranged from 97 to 101% of that in the initial homogenates. (From Pietras and Szego, 1979c, reproduced by permission.)

properties, and determination of specific association of E$_2\beta$ with these. This aim was forwarded by isopyknic centrifugation in discontinuous sucrose-density gradients of the crude nuclear sediment, which is known to be contaminated with plasmalemmal as well as microsomal membrane components liberated during cell disruption (Fig. 5). In course of these experiments, bands sedimenting at $\varrho < 1.13$ (F1), $\varrho = 1.13$–1.16 (F2), $\varrho = 1.16$–1.18 (F3), $\varrho = 1.18$–1.20 (F4), and $\varrho = 1.20$–1.24 (F5), as well as the resultant semipurified nuclear sediment (F6) were collected, washed at the centrifuge, and analyzed for E$_2\beta$-binding and enzymatic activities.

The residual nuclear material, which accounted for 96% of the DNA content of the initial homogenate, exhibited no specific binding sites for $E_2\beta$ and little or no activity of the enzymes characteristic of extranuclear organelles. Nor were $E_2\beta$-binding activities evident in fractions F4 and F5, which represented a mixture of particulate material with no enrichment of plasma membrane marker enzymes. On the other hand, F2 and F3, which were characterized by the highest specific activities of the plasmalemmal markers, 5′-nucleotidase and alkaline phosphatase, exhibited striking enrichment in specific $E_2\beta$ binding sites (Pietras and Szego 1979c). F2 was enriched in the latter to the extent of 23 times the homogenate when prepared by the indicated methods from isolated uterine cells.

The morphologic character of an electron micrograph from a representative preparation of F2 is consistent with its composition and demonstrates structural integrity (Fig. 7).

Even more striking was the selective enrichment in specific $E_2\beta$ binding, to greater than 50-fold over the homogenate, of similar membrane fractions from hepatic parenchymal cells that had been further purified by flotation through a second sucrose-gradient, a procedure made feasible by the relatively greater amount of liver tissue available as starting material (Pietras and Szego, 1980a). These plasma membrane subfractions were isolated from both the crude nuclear and microsomal preparations (see Table II). Several biochemical and enzymatic properties of the resultant membranes indicated their probable origin from cell surfaces bordering upon blood sinusoids and bile canaliculi (Evans, 1978). The potential functional significance of concentration of binding sites for $E_2\beta$—to an extent accounting for ~ 44% of that of isolated hepatocytes— at the blood front, as well as the canalicular interface (cf. Cantarow *et al.*, 1942), is indeed provocative and requires intensive further investigation.

The ligand specificity of $[^3H]E_2\beta$ binding to a partially purified plasma membrane fraction from hepatocytes (Pietras and Szego, 1980a) and uterine cells (Pietras and Szego, 1979c) was established by effective suppression with a 200-fold molar excess of unlabeled $E_2\beta$ or DES. In contrast, the extent of binding of these fractions was essentially uninfluenced by equivalent concentrations of $E_2\alpha$, progesterone, testosterone, or cortisol.

Integral to the minimum criteria for receptor functions, and thus, beyond the specificity and selectivity already revealed for putative recognition sites for $E_2\beta$ at the surfaces of its target cells, is saturability: the built-in limitation to indiscriminate reactivity. This criterion—the occurrence of limited numbers of high-affinity binding sites—is met for the plasma membrane subfractions purified from isolated hepatocytes

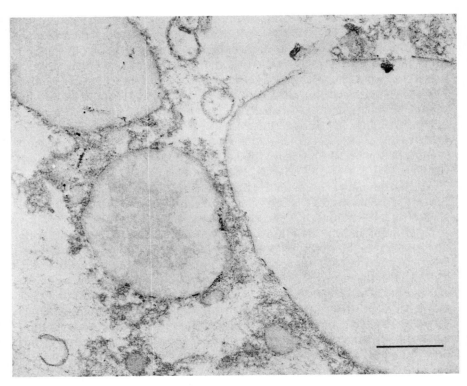

Fig. 7. Electron micrograph of plasma membrane preparation F2 from isolated uterine cells. It is evident that F2 consists primarily of smooth membrane vesicles and large "ghosts." Cross-sectional views of trilaminar membrane and apparent planar surfaces of membrane are observed. Stained material, possibly myofibrillar elements, is associated with some membranes. Occasional electron-dense vesicles are also present, but mitochondria and nuclei are not detected. (Micrographs were prepared through the courtesy of Dr. W. Jann Brown. Magnification 35,000; bar represents 0.5 μm. From Pietras and Szego, 1979c, reproduced by permission.)

(Pietras and Szego, 1980a) and uterine cells (Pietras and Szego, 1979c). A typical set of the relevant data for fraction F2 of the latter cells is shown in Fig. 8.

iii. Evaluation of potential artifacts. Potentially applicable to the above data is the possibility that the $E_2\beta$ binding sites concentrated in plasmalemmal fractions of target cells for the hormone could represent mere adsorption of circulating proteins, however unlikely such a mechanism might be in light of the high affinity, saturability, and stereospecificity already demonstrated. Likewise, adsorption of cytosolic proteins to structural components during cell disruption and/or fractionation

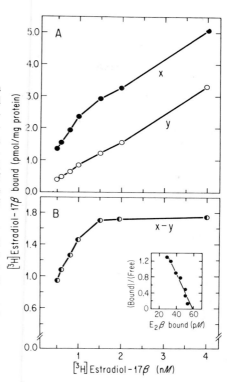

Fig. 8. Binding of [³H]estradiol-17β by a plasma membrane subfraction prepared from isolated uterine cells of the ovariectomized rat. A. Plasma membranes corresponding to F2 of Fig. 5 were incubated in Ca^{2+}-free medium with 0.25 M sucrose at approximately 60 μg of membrane protein/2 ml for 2 hours at 4° with concentrations of [³H]$E_2\beta$ given alone (● ; curve x) or in the presence of a 200-fold molar excess of unlabeled $E_2\beta$ plus [³H]$E_2\beta$ (○; curve y). The latter curve shows an essentially linear increment in $E_2\beta$ binding with increasing hormone concentration (r = .95). B. This curve shows the difference between the two curves in panel A and represents, according to the notation of Williams and Gorski (1973), the specific binding of hormone by plasma membranes. A Scatchard plot of these data is shown as an inset in panel B. Each point represents the mean of 2 independent determinations. (From Pietras and Szego, 1979c, reproduced by permission.)

must also be considered. However, when isolated membrane subfractions of uterine cells were subjected to extraction with hypotonic buffers, as well as with various media of high ionic strength, no more than 7% contamination of F2 from uterine cells with protein solubilized by such procedures was evident, while 95% of the binding sites for $E_2\beta$ remained integral to the membranes (Pietras and Szego, 1979c). Similarly in mixing experiments, only 6–9% of [³H]$E_2\beta$-labeled cytosolic components associated with plasma membranes at 4°, and the bulk of those that were so adsorbed were readily extractible with high-salt buffers. These data, paralleled by similar observations with plasmalemmal fractions from hepatocytes (Pietras and Szego, 1980a), are consonant with the mixing experiments of Jackson and Chalkley (1974b), who found that less than 10% of the input radioactivity associated with the [³H]$E_2\beta$: cytosol–receptor complex became bound to microsomal membranes of calf uterus at 4°. Additional data excluding more than minimal cross-contamination of isolated plasmalemmal fractions of hepatocytes and endometrial cells with material from microsomal, lysosomal, or mitochondrial sources, were also presented (Pietras and Szego, 1979c, 1980a).

These and related observations (Pietras *et al.*, 1978) give direct proof that limited numbers of macromolecules with characteristic high affinity for the binding of $E_2\beta$ are intrinsic to the plasmalemma of selective target cells and not the result of mere physical entrapment.

In contrast to these and other results (see Table II) for the positive identification of steroid binding sites in plasma membranes, several negative findings have been reported. Davidson *et al.* (1963) studied the interaction of aldosterone with crude plasma membranes and other cell fractions from kidney. The authors obtained kidneys from intact rats and then froze the tissues for 30 days. Thereafter, the thawed kidneys were disrupted in distilled water and various cell fractions were isolated. Using equilibrium dialysis, no specific binding of aldosterone to crude membranes was found. However, nuclei, microsomes, and cytosol proteins likewise showed no specific binding of hormone. Significant binding of aldosterone was detected only in mitochondrial fractions. Clearly, by virtue of hindsight, the overall negative findings of this study may be attributable to several experimental problems including contamination with endogenous hormone and loss of aldosterone binding activity during freeze-thaw, homogenization, or equilibrium dialysis steps.

In more recent work, Blyth *et al.* (1973) examined the sex steroid binding properties of a plasma membrane fraction from liver. Organs from intact rats were homogenized in *hypotonic* buffer, and plasma membranes with 12-fold enrichment of 5′-nucleotidase relative to the homogenate were prepared. However, less than 5% of total enzyme activity was recovered in the final membrane preparation. As might be predicted from the latter result (see Table VI), little to no saturable binding of total estradiol or testosterone to plasma membranes was found. Specific binding of hormones was not determined. It is noteworthy that Blyth *et al.* (1971) had earlier presented positive evidence for the occurrence of saturable high-affinity sex steroid binding sites in smooth microsomal fractions of liver prepared under *isotonic* conditions (Table I).

Müller *et al.* (1979) have attempted to provide more rigorous evaluation of occurrence of specific estradiol binding sites in plasma membranes from immature rat uterus. As in most previous studies, intact uterine organs, rather than isolated cells, were used as starting material. These were disrupted by Polytron homogenization under isotonic conditions. Following fractionation of the homogenate, activities of 5′-nucleotidase, glucose-6-phosphate dehydrogenase and $E_2\beta$ binding were determined. As recommended by de Duve (1967), a balance-sheet to account for the distribution of enzyme activities, but not hormone binding, was reported. Unfortunately, the total activities of enzymes recovered in the major cell fractions exceeded by as much as 20% the levels determined in the organ homogenate. These unusual findings are not consonant with other uterine cell fractionation studies (Kidwai *et al.*, 1971; Jackson and Chalkley, 1974a,b; Rufeger *et al.*, 1974; Vallieres *et al.*, 1978; Matlib *et al.*, 1979; Pietras and Szego, 1979c). The attempt by Müller *et al.* (1979) to estimate the purity of their final plasma membrane on the basis of such results is clearly invalid (cf. de Duve, 1967; DePierre and Karnovsky, 1973; Evans, 1978). Using similar Polytron homogenization and fractionation methods applied to whole uterus, Matlib *et al.* (1979) have reported purification of plasma membranes from rat uterus by 8- to 12-fold, but approximately 43% of total 5'-nucleotidase activity occurred in cytosol (cf. Table VI). Notwithstanding use of similar procedures, Müller *et al.* (1979) did find an estrogen-binding component in plasma membranes which exhibited tissue selectivity, steroid specificity, saturability, and high affinity. However, it represented only 2–3% of the estrogen-binding capacity identified in the cytosol extracts. On the basis of mixing experiments which suggested substantial association of added cytosol receptor–[^{3}H]E$_2\beta$ with membrane preparations, the authors concluded that the occurrence of hormone binding sites in uterine membranes was attributable to contamination with cytosol receptor. Others have also reported some association of E$_2\beta$-cytosol receptor complexes with uterine membranes in similar mixing experiments (Jackson and Chalkley, 1974b; Pietras and Szego, 1979c), but the extent of binding was five- to eightfold less than that observed by Müller *et al.* (1979). Moreover, such association appears to be due to nonspecific adsorption, which is readily reversible by washing membranes at the centrifuge with high-salt buffers (cf. Emmelot and Bos, 1966; Jackson and Chalkley, 1974b; Pietras and Szego, 1979c, 1980b). Unfortunately, therefore, the data of Müller *et al.* (1979) do not offer definitive proof or disproof of the occurrence of substantial numbers of E$_2\beta$ binding sites in plasmalemma of uterine cells.

e. Solubilization of E$_2\beta$-Binding Components from Isolated Plasma Membrane Subfractions and Their Properties. In contrast to the resistance of E$_2\beta$ recognition sites native to plasma membranes to extraction with buffers of various tonicities, the receptor-like macromolecules have yielded to solubilization by detergent treatment (Pietras and Szego, 1979c, 1980a; cf. also Ožegović *et al.*, 1977). It is instructive to compare preliminary findings on the characteristics of recognition sites so solubilized with the documented properties of cytosolic receptors. In turn, it is also well to determine what proportion of hormonal binding sites of intact cells is represented in such sites recovered in isolated membranes.

Plasma membrane subfractions of hepatocytes were purified 30-fold with respect to activities of marker-enzymes and 46-fold with respect to binding of the lectin, wheat germ agglutinin (ref. Table II). Saturable binding of $E_2\beta$ was equally enriched, with an apparent dissociation constant of 2.8×10^{-10} M at $4°$. This value is of the same order of magnitude as that of 0.7×10^{-10} M for binding of $E_2\beta$ to macromolecules in cytosol extracts of liver (Eisenfeld *et al.*, 1976; cf. also Smirnova *et al.*, 1974; Chamness *et al.*, 1975; Beers and Rosner, 1977). At saturation, specific $E_2\beta$ binding in highly purified membranes amounts to 526 fmol/mg of membrane protein (Pietras and Szego, 1980a). In contrast, the $E_2\beta$-binding capacity of the high-affinity system in relatively crude cytosol extracts of liver corresponds to 58 fmol/mg of protein (Eisenfeld *et al.*, 1976).

To characterize the hormone-binding component(s) of the plasma membrane further, membranes were partially solubilized with Triton X-100 (Pietras and Szego, 1980a). The resultant particle-free extracts were resolved on continuous sucrose-density gradients in the presence of either 10 mM (Fig. 9A) or 0.4 M (Fig. 9B) KCl. Macromolecule-bound

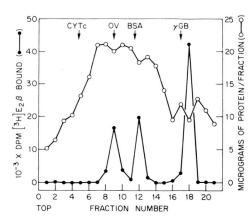

FIG. 9A. Sedimentation in low-salt sucrose density gradients of Triton-solubilized [³H]$E_2\beta$-binding macromolecules from highly purified plasma membrane fraction of hepatocytes from ovariectomized rats (corresponding to F2B of Pietras and Szego, 1980a). Samples or protein standards were layered onto a medium consisting of linear 5–20% (w/v) sucrose containing 10 mM KCl, 1.5 mM EDTA, 10 mM Tris-HCl, pH 7.4, and 0.01% (v/v) Triton X-100 and centrifuged at $4°$ for 18 hours at 50,000 rpm in a SW 50.1 rotor of a Beckman L5–75 ultracentrifuge. Aliquots of the fractionated gradients were analyzed for protein (Lowry *et al.*, 1951) and for specific [³H]$E_2\beta$ binding (see Fig. 8). Peaks for protein standards are indicated by arrows. In the representative gradient shown, peak positions for [³H]$E_2\beta$-binding macromolecules are at 3.6 S, 4.8 S, and 7.5 S. In 3 independent experiments, binding components sedimented at predominantly 3.6 ± 0.2 S (756 ± 111 dpm [³H]$E_2\beta$/μg of protein), 4.7 ± 0.3 S (955 ± 66 dpm/μg), and 7.4 ± 0.1 S (5344 ± 474 dpm/μg). (From Pietras and Szego, 1980a, reproduced by permission.)

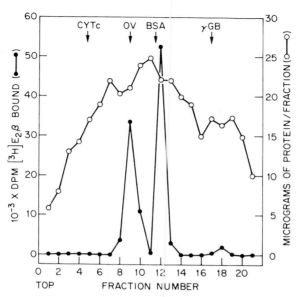

Fig. 9B. Sedimentation in high-salt sucrose density gradients of Triton-solubilized [³H]E₂β-binding macromolecules from highly purified plasma membrane fraction of hepatocytes from ovariectomized rats (corresponding to F2B of Pietras and Szego, 1980a). Sedimentation, fractionation, and analytical conditions corresponded to those in Fig. 9A, except that the gradients contained 0.4 M KC1. In the representative gradient shown, peak positions for [³H]E₂β-binding macromolecules are at 3.6 S and 4.8 S. In 3 independent experiments, binding components sedimented at 3.6 ± 0.0 S (1772 ± 197 dpm [³H]E₂β/μg of protein) and 4.9 ± 0.1 S (2381 ± 164 dpm/μg). (From Pietras and Szego, 1980a, reproduced by permission.)

E₂β, as determined by adsorption of the resultant gradient fractions to hydroxylapatite, sedimented at predominantly 7.4 S in the low-salt gradients. Specific hormone binding by this fraction was enriched approximately 1600 times over that of the homogenate. Under high-salt conditions, E₂β-binding macromolecules were resolved at both 3.6 S and 4.9 S (Fig. 9B). The occurrence of 4 S and 8 S binding components for estradiol in cytosol extracts of liver has been reported (Eisenfeld *et al.*, 1976). It is noteworthy that estrogen-binding macromolecules sedimenting at 3.5 S, 4.5 S, and in the 6–10 S region of sucrose-density gradients have previously been extracted from the microsomal fraction (i.e., microsomes together with plasma membrane vesicles) of pig uterus (Little *et al.*, 1972). Further consideration of these and related findings is presented elsewhere (Pietras and Szego, 1980a).

Oћegović *et al.* (1977) have also succeeded in solubilizing aldosterone-binding components from kidney plasma membranes. The membranes exhibited approximately sevenfold enrichment of Na^+/K^+-ATPase activity relative to that of the homogenate. Specific aldosterone binding to membrane was saturable, with a dissociation constant of $1.3 \times 10^{-8} M$ and a capacity of 1.7×10^{-13} mol/mg protein (compare with Edelman and Fimognari, 1967; Rousseau *et al.*, 1972a). Plasma membranes with bound aldosterone were solubilized with Lubrol-WX detergent and subjected to gel filtration on Sephadex G-200. The bulk of the hormone was found to be eluted in association with protein. Those proteins associated with aldosterone displayed low electrophoretic mobility and an apparently high molecular weight (Ožegović *et al.*, 1977).

Collectively, these properties, taken in further context with the literature summarized in Tables I–III, are in accord with the premise that multiple binding sites for steroid hormones occur in target cells. Intensified study on the nature of those sites in the plasma membrane compartment may ultimately define their relation to previously identified receptors in cytosol extracts. However, some have already concluded that the recognition sites for steroid hormones that have been identified in the membranes of their cellular targets represent a unique class of macromolecules distinct from the "traditional" intracellular ("cytosol") receptors (Ožegović *et al.*, 1977; Koch *et al.*, 1978; Baulieu, 1978; Carette *et al.*, 1979). This assumption is manifestly premature. There has been as yet no exhaustive inventory of the comparative properties of the membrane-oriented sites and those solubilized during conventional methods of cell disruption in course of preparation, in maximum yield, of macromolecules from the cell sap that bind the respective hormones. To the limited extent that comparisons have been established with appropriate methodology, similarities tend to predominate over differences (cf. Tables II and above). Nevertheless, even if significant differences between the presumptively unrelated molecular species were to be identified in further comparisons of both, as solubilized from respective cell fractions, it must be borne in mind that the microenvironment of macromolecules intrinsic to membrane would be expected to modify significantly their behavior *in situ* toward ligand—both during and subsequent to binding. This circumstance must be taken into account especially in relation to potential glycosylation of binding proteins by established pathways before, during, or after their association with the target cell membrane—a potential source of differences in molecular properties by physicochemical criteria. Possibly for these complex reasons, different investigators have encountered basic similarities in properties of membrane receptor for insulin *in situ* and as solubilized therefrom (Harrison *et al.*, 1978), while others have emphasized differences (Gorissen and Laduron, 1979).

Of even more significance, in the event of identification of clear-cut differences in structure and function of the "cytosolic" and membrane-oriented sites, is the powerful precedent for the existence of allosterically modifiable forms of hormonal recognition sites whose interconversion is regulated by ligand itself (as well as by ionic and other microenvironment). Plausible models for such properties are already indicated in the cases of membrane-localized receptor for acetylcholine (cf. Karlin, 1976), and for certain opiate-like compounds (Pert, 1974; cf. also Pert and Garland, 1978) and possibly for insulin (De Meyts, 1976; Krupp and Livingston, 1979). These limited examples may have their counterpart in the interaction of cardiac glycoside with the hydrophobic receptor site of ATPase (cf. Fortes, 1977) preferentially when the enzyme is in a given conformation (cf. Akera, 1977). More detailed analyses of stereochemical contributions to properties of specific digitalis genins are becoming available (Fullerton *et al.*, 1979).

These observations, taken together, suggest that *adaptive complementarity* on ligand binding may be a hormone-responsive modulatory phenomenon of broad applicability (cf. Ariëns and Rodrigues de Miranda, 1979). Additional instances of such induced-fit might well be sought with the appropriate probes among purified plasmalemmal subfractions of further target cells (cf. Aizono *et al.*, 1974).

f. Indications for Nonprotein Components of Receptor Macromolecules. Detailed analyses are not yet available for the chemical composition of steroid-binding plasmalemmal components. It is known only that these macromolecules are susceptible to heat denaturation and to proteolytic degradation (Pietras *et al.*, 1978; Pietras and Szego, 1979c). Indeed, although numerous studies have also shown that the steroid receptors in cytosol extracts are proteinaceous molecules, it is not known whether they are composed exclusively of amino acids. Since the role played by the receptor in the movement of steroid through the surface and nuclear membranes remains unknown, any evidence for lipid or carbohydrate moieties associated with the binding component could be of potential relevance. However, only limited data are currently available on the composition of purified receptor molecules (cf. Kuhn *et al.*, 1977; Sica and Bresciani, 1979; Coty *et al.*, 1979). The amino acid complement of the chromatin-binding subunit of the progesterone receptor has been determined, but no evidence for phosphorylated amino acids or carbohydrate substituents was obtained (Kuhn *et al.*, 1977). However, the absence of phosphate and carbohydrate from the receptor subunit may be attributable to unavoidable losses of these highly labile moieties during the extensive purification procedure. If such possible losses are substantiated, it appears plausible that they may account in part for the reduction in the anticipated steroid-binding capacity of highly purified receptor (cf. Coty *et al.*, 1979).

Direct insight into the native form of receptor macromolecules is presently limited to evaluating the sensitivity of the binding component to various chemical and enzymatic probes. The presence of a lipid moiety in cytosol receptor for $E_2\beta$ first seemed indicated in experiments by Erdos (1968), wherein dissociation of 8 S complex to a 4 S form occurred after addition of pancreatic lipase. Similar findings were obtained when soybean trypsin inhibitor was included in the incubation, indicating that the effect of the lipase could not be attributed to contamination of the enzyme preparation with a serine proteinase (Erdos, 1968). However, Erdos *et al.* (1971) later suggested that other proteolytic enzymes in the lipase preparation whose activity was not curtailed by the inhibitor may have elicited the observed results. Beato *et al.* (1971) have reported that about 50% of bound cortisol can be liberated from the 4 S glucocorticoid–receptor complex in liver cytosol after exposure to proteinase-free neuraminidase. Evidence that the estrogen receptor may contain phosphorus and carbohydrate moieties has also been presented. Reduced binding and retention of $E_2\beta$ by macromolecular components of uterus and breast carcinoma cytosols was observed in the presence of phospholipases A and C, and β-glucuronidase (Hähnel *et al.*, 1974). Other reports show that the uterine 8 S receptor for $E_2\beta$ readily incorporates ^{32}P from radioactive orthophosphate administered *in vivo* (Jensen and DeSombre, 1972).

Following work by Hackney and Pratt (1971) suggesting that the glucocorticoid receptor from the soluble fraction of fibroblasts behaves as a large lipoprotein, several investigators have examined the phospholipid requirements for specific binding of glucocorticoids to cytosol receptors. Schulte *et al.* (1976) have shown that the specific glucocorticoid-binding capacity extracted from fibroblasts and thymic lymphocytes is inactivated by incubation with phospholipases A_2. C. H. M. Westphal *et al.* (1978) have confirmed that phospholipase A_2 inactivates the glucocorticoid receptor of rat liver but find no significant effect of this enzymatic treatment on the binding activity of the uterine progesterone receptor. The latter authors further report that neither of the two binding systems is affected by phospholipase C. These workers suggest that phospholipase A_2 may be producing detergent products, which indirectly inactivate the receptor. However, Schulte *et al.* (1976) evaluated these potential artifacts in considerable detail, and their findings do not support an inactivation mechanism based solely on detergent effects. Since phospholipase C, which does not elicit detergent products, also blocks glucocorticoid binding, Schulte *et al.* (1976) proposed that the phospholipases may digest phospholipid which is a requisite component of the receptor molecule.

Several recent reports indicate that phosphorylation and dephosphorylation mechanisms may be involved in activation and in inactivation, respectively, of glucocorticoid receptors from cytosol. This proposal is derived from observations on the rapid inactivation of fibroblast receptors after addition of highly purified alkaline phosphatase (Nielsen *et al.*, 1977a) and on curtailment of this inactivation by known phosphatase inhibitors (Nielson *et al.*, 1977b). Additional work suggests that activation of receptors to the glucocorticoid-binding state requires an ATP-dependent phosphorylation mechanism (Sando *et al.*, 1979; cf. also Toft and Nishigori, 1979).

Effects of various hydrolytic enzymes on the uptake and/or accumulation of steroid hormones and analogs by intact cells have also been reported. Treatment of pituitary tumor cells with neuraminidase or phospholipase A_2 reduced the specific binding of glucocorticoids (Harrison *et al.*, 1974, 1977). In contrast, uptake of prednisolone by nontarget Novikoff hepatoma cells was not affected by treatment of the cells with neuraminidase or phospholipase C (Plagemann and Erbe, 1976). Uptake of sex steroids by isolated liver cells was reduced by 28–39% after prior exposure of the cells to either β-glucosidase, β-galactosidase, or phospholipase A (Rao *et al.*, 1977a).

The results of these studies indicate that phospholipid, phosphoprotein, or carbohydrate components may be associated with steroid hormone receptors in their native cellular environment. The potential chelating influence of such substituents is consistent with the occasional reports of metal complexes in receptor macromolecules for steroid hormones (Hechter, 1978). However, many of these observations must be considered tentative since enzyme preparations were often not rigorously controlled for trace contamination with other hydrolase activities. In such experiments, it is also conceivable that some potentially sensitive sites of the substrate may not be accessible to the enzyme or that removal of the reactive moiety may not significantly affect the steroid-binding properties of the receptor molecule as removed from its native orientation (cf. Schulte *et al.*, 1976). It is well known that steroid binding proteins in the extracellular compartment have a significant carbohydrate content (cf. Ryan and Westphal, 1972; Petrusz *et al.*, 1980), but removal of sialic acid from one such plasma protein is reported not to affect its affinity for binding steroid hormone (Ganguly and Westphal, 1968). In the case of cholesterol-binding high-density lipoproteins, it is also known that the phospholipid component of the serum carrier enhances, but is not essential to, binding of cholesterol by the apoprotein (Sodhi and Gould, 1967; Scanu and Wisdom, 1972). On the other hand, others have determined that both glycoprotein and phospholipid components of the thyrotropin receptor are required for cellular action of the hormone (cf. Aloj *et al.*, 1979).

Further characterization of receptor molecules is required in order to establish unequivocally the presence or absence of specific carbohydrate, lipid, or glycolipid constituents for which only fragmentary evidence is presently available. Such substituents at cell surfaces have deep significance in recognition properties of macromolecules for specific ligand (Steinman *et al.*, 1976; Cook, 1976; Morré and Ovtracht, 1977; Critchley and Vicker, 1977; Szego, 1978). Their possible occurrence in association with steroid hormone receptors must be established or excluded.

g. *Regulation of Steroid Binding Sites in Plasma Membranes under Various Physiological Conditions.* The prime criterion that must be satisfied in order to elevate a mere specific recognition site to the status of receptor is the demonstration that binding of a given ligand is an integral part of its mechanism of action. Among the known binding components for steroid hormones, this criterion is not often met (Mainwaring, 1975; Clark *et al.*, 1977). Experiments to assess the potential receptor functions of membranous steroid binding sites are under way. For example, treatment of intact hepatocytes with $1 \times 10^{-10} M$ $E_2\beta$, but not $E_2\alpha$, at $22°$ was found to promote a marked loss of hormone binding sites in plasma membrane subfractions which was coupled with a profound increase in $E_2\beta$ binding in partially purified nuclei (Pietras and Szego, 1980a). Whether such observations are the outcome of binding site unavailability through prior occupancy, internalization and recompartmentation, attrition, or other factors cannot presently be determined. Nevertheless, the findings are in keeping with the decline expected from independent data on "cytosolic" receptors under similar experimental conditions (cf. Clark *et al.*, 1977). It is noteworthy that the levels of cortisol binding sites in plasma membranes of ascites hepatoma cells are profoundly reduced, to 10–25% of that determined in membranes from normal liver cells (Terayama *et al.*, 1976). Other recent experiments indicate that a similar deficiency in the plasmalemmal concentration of $E_2\beta$ binding sites occurs in malignant vs. normal cells from human cervix (Pietras and Roberts, 1980).

Koch *et al.* (1978) have determined that the concentration of corticosterone binding sites in crude plasma membrane preparations from pituitary gland correlates well with adrenocortical activity. It was found that the number of binding sites was inversely related to the concentration of glucocorticoid in the circulation and was significantly increased by 15 days, as compared to 1 day after adrenalectomy.

h. Affinity Chromatography as a Means of Selection of Populations Especially Sensitive to Steroid Hormone and Properties of Binding and Nonbinding Cells

i. Preferential accumulation of the hormone. Evidence already presented identifies specific binding sites for a variety of steroid hormones and other low-molecular-weight lipophilic ligands as integral to the plasmalemma of the relevant target cells. This property of target cells for $E_2\beta$ has now been utilized in a novel fashion to select, from among a heterogeneous population of isolated hepatocytes and endometrial cells, respectively, those cells exhibiting extraordinary sensitivity to the hormone (Pietras and Szego, 1979a, 1980b). Thus, hepatic parenchymal cells that bind to fiber-immobilized estrogen may be dislodged from the fibers, washed extensively, and then plated in serum- and estrogen-free chemically-defined medium for 72 hours. Thereafter, such "fiber-binding" cells specifically accumulate 2.5-fold more free $E_2\beta$ during a subsequent 30-minute incubation with 1×10^{-9} M hormone than do the cells that had not bound the immobilized steroid (Fig. 10).

Similarly, in parallel experiments, the extent of binding of free $E_2\beta$ in endometrial cells that previously had become bound to the immobilized hormone surpasses that of their nonbinding counterparts (Fig. 11). Nevertheless, as presented in Fig. 11, both classes of cells exhibit saturability of binding over a range of $E_2\beta$ concentrations. Scatchard analysis of these data by the method of least squares reveals the total number of $E_2\beta$ binding sites per cell at saturation to be ~42,000 for the fiber-

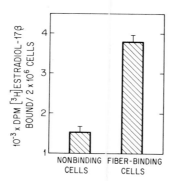

FIG. 10. Binding of [³H]estradiol-17β by liver cell fractions with diverse affinities for binding to immobilized estrogen. Isolated liver cells that bind (fiber-binding) and those that do not bind (nonbinding) to estrogen-derivatized fibers (see text and Figs. 2 and 3) were incubated in Ringer solution (1×10^6 cells/ml) for 30 minutes at 22° with 1×10^{-9} M [³H]E₂β. Only the specific accumulation of hormone by the cells is shown here (see Fig. 8). The extent of $E_2\beta$ binding is expressed relative to cell number as derived from measurements of DNA/cell. (From Pietras and Szego, 1979a, reproduced by permission.)

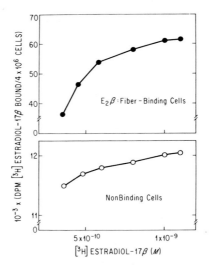

Fig. 11. Specific binding of free [³H]estradiol-17β by subpopulations of endometrial cells with diverse affinities for binding to immobilized estrogen. Isolated endometrial cells that bind (E₂β: fiber-binding cells) and those that do not bind (nonbinding cells) to estrogen-derivatized fibers were recovered under parallel conditions to those described previously (Pietras and Szego, 1977a, 1979a). After 72 hours in primary culture with steroid- and serum-free medium, the two groups of cells were suspended in 0.5 ml Ringer solution (8 × 10⁶ cells/ml) and exposed for 30 minutes at 22° to a series of [³H]E₂β (99 Ci/mmol) concentrations ranging from 3.5 × 10⁻¹⁰ to 2.0 × 10⁻⁹ M, as indicated on the abscissa (cf. Pietras and Szego, 1979b). Only specific binding is shown (cf. Williams and Gorski, 1973, and Fig. 8). Each point represents the mean of values obtained in two independent experiments. (From Pietras and Szego, 1980b, reproduced by permission.)

binding populations, while the corresponding value for nonbinding cells is ∼8300, approximately one-fifth the level of the binding population (Pietras and Szego, 1980b). In contrast, the relative affinities of the fractionated cells for the hormone are generally equivalent (*op. cit.*).

ii. Differential proliferative activities. What is even more provocative in these new findings follows from additional observations. For, it has now been demonstrated (Pietras and Szego, 1980b) that fiber-binding endometrial cells respond to mitogenic challenge of subsequently added E₂β with far greater intensity than do cells that fail to bind to immobilized E₂β during the initial selection process (Fig. 12; Pietras and Szego, 1980b). Analogous data have been obtained from hepatocytes (Pietras and Szego, 1979a).

The detailed mechanisms underlying these significant differences in behavior toward estrogen between target cells equipped with specific surface binding sites for the hormone and those cells not so endowed at a

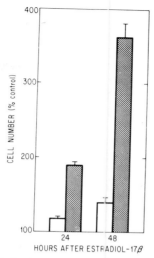

FIG. 12. Influence of estradiol-17β on proliferation of endometrial cells with diverse affinities for binding to immobilized estrogen. $E_2\beta$: fiber-binding cells (shaded bars) and non-binding cells (clear bars) were selected and then processed under parallel conditions (cf. Pietras and Szego, 1979a). After 72 hours in primary culture with $E_2\beta$- and serum-free medium (see text), proliferation of endometrial cells after 24- or 48-hour incubation with or without 2×10^{-9} M $E_2\beta$ was determined from cell numbers as described previously (Pietras and Szego, 1979b). Values in the figure are presented as mean ± SEM of results obtained in 3 independent experiments. (From Pietras and Szego, 1980b, reproduced by permission.)

given time are analyzed elsewhere (Pietras and Szego, 1979a, 1980a,b; Szego and Pietras, 1981). These new observations, which correlate acute events at the cell surface with eventual mitogenic responses, require intensive further investigation.

IV. THE CELL SURFACE: ALTERATIONS OF MEMBRANE ARCHITECTURE ON BINDING SITE OCCUPANCY

The exquisite specificity and selectivity of interaction of given ligands with their cell surfaces contrasts sharply with the generality of abrupt signals elicited by such recognition. For indeed, perturbation of membrane in a variety of cell types can be identified by changes in an array of indicators that are not necessarily peculiar to the given cell. For example, these signals may be electrical in neuronal or non-neuronal cells—in either case, predicated upon or concomitant with ionic fluxes. The triggering events may also be reflected in activation or inhibition of the activities of membrane-bound enzymes, such as nucleotide cyclases and certain ATPases, functional alterations of which are likewise critically associated with shifts in ionic environment. Although these suggestions have frequently been voiced in relation to events modulated by peptidal agonists, only rarely have allosteric modifications been invoked for agonists of lipid nature (see, however, Farnsworth, 1968; Johnson and Ramwell, 1973; Szego, 1972a, 1974, 1975). Nevertheless, there are now extensive examples of these apparently generalized consequences of insertion of steroid hormones into the molecular anatomy of their target cell membranes. Some of these indications of steroidal perturbation of target–cell membranes are summarized in this section.

A. Signals of Surface Deformation on Ligand Capture

1. Na^+/K^+-ATPase

The interaction of cardiac glycosides and aglycones with binding sites at surfaces of kidney and muscle cells at or near membrane-bound Na^+/K^+-ATPase, is by no means a novel concept (see recent summary by Akera, 1977). However well established, this phenomenon has been given "special-case" status by general consent, rather than being evaluated as a potential prototype, with parallels in membrane associations of other steroidal agonists (cf. Dransfeld and Greeff, 1964; Greeff *et al.*, 1964; Charney *et al.*, 1974; Tobin *et al.*, 1975). Nevertheless, an occasional minority view has been voiced, such as that of Farnsworth (1968), who identified in rat prostatic microsomes, known to cosediment with plasmalemmal vesicles, and in human prostatic tissue (1972), a ouabain-sensitive Na^+/K^+-ATPase that was stimulated within 15 minutes by $10^{-8}-10^{-12}\ M$ levels of physiologically relevant androgens. The activity, which was also sensitive to $E_2\beta$, was unaffected by a variety of C-19 metabolites, while a Mg^{2+}-dependent enzyme failed to respond to androgen. More recently, W. E. Farnsworth (personal communication, 1978) has studied isolated components and observes that the androgen-sensitive ATPase of human prostatic membranes has properties closely congruent with those of the "β receptor" extracted from prostatic microsomes with $0.4\ M$ KCl by Liao *et al.* (1976). Farnsworth has found that isolated membranes are enriched 20-fold over the crude microsomal fraction in DHT-stimulated K^+-dependent dephosphorylating function (*op. cit.*). Association of enzymatic activity with steroid binding was also demonstrated on a column of immobilized DHT.

These striking observations (cf. also Ritter *et al.*, 1969; Davis *et al.*,

1978) require prompt extension to additional systems and steroid hormones for, if independently confirmed, they deserve thoughtful evaluation and integration into the growing body of evidence for the interactions of these agonists with integral membrane proteins or elements closely coupled thereto. Indeed, it would be of profound significance if a substantial link were to be identified between specific binding of steroid hormones to the outer cell surface and fairly direct and intimate communication of this information to energy-yielding reactions powering the mechanisms that regulate selective permeability of the cell. Unfortunately, we seem to be little nearer to realization of the statement:

> A more complete understanding of the mode of action and interaction of the steroid hormones must await elicidation of the precise relationship between permeability and metabolic phenomena in the cell (Roberts and Szego, 1953),

than we were at the time it was written.

2. *Nucleotide Cyclase Activation: A Signal of Membrane Perturbation by Steroid Hormones*

> Facts are stubborn things; and whatever may be our wishes, our inclinations, or the dictates of our passions, they cannot alter the state of facts and evidence (Adams, 1770).

Because of the immense attractiveness of limiting the secondary messenger hypothesis for intracellular actions to the peptide hormones and to certain amino acid derived neurotransmitters, there has been notable reluctance to acknowledge the overlap between these agonists and the steroid hormones in eliciting acute alterations in activities of nucleotide cyclases, with resultant production by these enzymes of increased cyclic nucleotide levels in their target cells. This state of affairs has prevailed despite the manifest documentation in the literature that, like other low-molecular-weight lipophilic agonists, such as thyroid hormones (Levey and Epstein, 1969; cf., however, Caldwell and Fain, 1971) and prostaglandins (Samuelsson *et al.*, 1975), steroid hormones modulate levels of these nucleotides in target cells (Table VII A–D).[*]

This subject, which has been reviewed in part elsewhere (see Szego, 1972a,b, 1974, 1975), is riddled with misapprehensions. For example, the reservation by Higgins and Gehring in a recent review (1978), that "cyclic AMP does not always evoke the whole spectrum of steroid

---

[*] It is acknowledged that methods of isolation and assay for cyclic AMP content and determination of adenylate cyclase activity utilized in the representative papers summarized in Tables VII A–D are not uniformly sensitive and precise, nor are experimental conditions equally rigorous.

TABLE VII A

INFLUENCE OF STEROID HORMONES ON CYCLIC NUCLEOTIDES AND NUCLEOTIDE CYCLASES OF CELLULAR TARGETS:[a,b] ESTROGENS AND RAT UTERUS

Acute, positive effects of exogenous hormone on [cAMP]; augmentation of cyclase (ACase) in cyclic ♀ vs. ♂

Investigators	Parameter	Method[c]	Estrogen[c]	Dose	Route	Onset	Values (pmol/mg protein or [% of control])[a] ♀	♂	♀ + R[c]
1. Szego and Davis (1967)	cAMP	Modified Breckenridge (coupled-enzyme)	$E_2\beta$	0.1–0.5 µg/100 g	i.v.	15 sec	≈10	≈5	10–15
2. Szego (1971)	ACase	Modified Streeto and Reddy (double-isotope)	$E_2\beta$	1 µg/100 g	i.v.	30 sec	[412]		[183]
		Modified Krishna (double-isotope)	DES	1 µg/100 g	i.v.	2 min	[119]		[178]
3. Robison (1970); Robison et al. (1971)	cAMP	Activation of liver phosphorylase	$E_2\beta$		Details not given				"Confirmed ref. 1"
4. Rosenfeld and O'Malley (1970)	ACase	Modified Krishna	DES	5 µg/100 g	i.v.	ND[d]			[184]
5. Singhal (1973)	ACase	Modified Gilman radioligand[f]	$E_2\beta$	10µg/rat	i.p.	5 min	[228]		[257]
6. Dupont-Mairesse et al. (1974)*	cAMP	Gilman[f]	$E_2\beta$	10 µg/100 g	s.c.	ND[e]	6.9		14.4

Longer-term (above generally confirmed, but to a diminished degree and with unexplained time lag for exogenous estrogen)

7. Kuehl et al. (1974)*	cAMP	Gilman modified to pH 7.5 instead of pH 4; RIA	DES	100 µg/rat	s.c.	30 min[g]	≈10[h]	≈4	≈5.2[g]
			E₂β	1 µg/rat	i.p.			≈1	≈2−5.5
	cGMP		DES	100 µg/rat	s.c.	3−24 h			
8. Chew and Rinard (1974)	cAMP	Gilman[f]	E₂β	5 µg/rat		6 h		≈4	≈5
Lack of positive effects at any time									
9. Sanborn et al. (1973)	cAMP	Modified Gilman[f]	E₂β	1 µg/100 g	i.v.	0−30 min	7[i]	≈5	6−19[j]
10. Zor et al. (1973)	cAMP	Modified Gilman[f]	E₂β	5 µg/rat	i.p.	10 min	≈5	≈5	≈5

[a] In some cases, these values have been calculated from data presented within the several papers to facilitate comparison.

[b] Omitted from this compilation are cytochemical observations demonstrating enhanced ACase activities at surface membranes of neonatal mice (Àbro and Kvinnsland, 1974; Kvinnsland, 1976) and ovariectomized rats (Sananes and Psychoyos, 1974) after chronic and acute treatment, respectively, with E₂β.

[c] Abbreviations: DES, diethylstilbestrol; E₂β, estradiol-17β; RIA, radioimmunoassay; R, treatment.

[d,e] Not determined. Positive effects were noted at 20 minutes [d] and 5 minutes [e].

[f] See van de Werve et al. (1974) for a discussion of problems encountered by many investigators with this general method; cf. also Albano et al. (1974) and Kimura et al. (1974).

[g] Small increases at 30 minutes and 1 hour in rats ovariectomized 3 months before use and then treated with a massive dose of DES. The substantial effect, primarily on cGMP, after 3 hours may require reevaluation in view of the occasional identification of simultaneous elevation of both cAMP and cGMP in response to receptor occupancy by agonists (cf. Stoner et al., 1973; Matsuzawa and Nirenberg, 1975) and by indications of a degree of metabolic interconvertibility of the bases of the mononucleotides (Rubio, 1974; Simon, 1976).

[h] Estimated on the basis of 18% of fresh weight of tissue as protein.

[i] Divergence from ovariectomized controls occasionally downward by 100%. Range of variations seems excessive compared with data in refs. 1 and 6. Lack of effect of estradiol, despite marked effectiveness of isoproterenol, may reflect tachyphylaxis toward given agonist without loss of sensitivity toward another (cf. Franklin and Foster, 1973; Szego, 1974).

[j] Only 5−8 days after ovariectomy (note contrast to refs. 1, 4, 5, and 9); however, similar results were obtained at 21 days after gonadectomy. Also, *basal* values of ovariectomized group higher than intact, an observation at variance with refs. 1, 6, 7 and, by implication, with refs. 2 and 5; cf. also Sim and Chantharaksri (1973).

* cf. also, Flandroy and Galand (1973).

From Szego (1978) reproduced with permission.

TABLE VII B

Influence of Steroid Hormones on Cyclic Nucleotides and Nucleotide Cyclases of Cellular Targets: Androgens

Investigators	System	Hormone	Observations	Comment
Positive effects				
1. Singhal *et al.* (1971)	Male rat, 2 weeks after castration; single s.c. dose of androgen, 5 mg/100 g	Testosterone (propionate)	Increase in cAMP conc. in seminal vesicles and prostate to ~ 140% of controls at 8 hours; 145% and 210% at 24 hours (all, $P < .05$).	No earlier intervals appear to have been studied.
2. Mangan *et al.* (1973)	Male rat, 3 days after castration; 2.5 mg of androgen, s.c.; subcellular fractions of prostate prepared 1–3 hours later	Testosterone (phenylpropionate)	Adenylate cyclase activity in *"microsomal"*[a] fraction declined after ♂; restored by 2 hours of androgen **R**. *Nuclear* fraction, representing fairly small portion of separated activity, declined sharply after ♂; restored within 1 hour. *Mitochondrial fraction*, modest decline after ♂, no change with androgen.	Activity in total homogenate not given; no statistical analysis available. Despite manifest effects, esp. on nuclear fraction, influences of ♂ and of androgen **R** were dismissed as "small and even equivocal," . . . in "general agreement with the [negative]^b conclusion of Rosenfeld and O'Malley (1970)" [on dissimilar preparation]^b. Determinations of cAMP not carried out, since effects of hormonal treatment were "likely to be small."

3. Sutherland and Singhal (1974)	Male rat, 5 days after castration; single dose of androgen, 5 mg/100 g,i.v.	5α-DHT; testosterone	50% increase in adenylate cyclase activity of prostate in 1 hour; sustained to 4 hours; effect of i.v. testosterone antagonized by propranolol and by cyproterone. No effect of $E_2\beta$, progesterone, or prednisolone on prostatic cAMP at 4 hours.	No nontarget tissues analyzed; possible stripping of enzymatic activity from membrane sites by homogenization conditions (cf. Goldberg and Haddox, 1977).
4. Vesely (1979)	*In vitro* additions of steroids in DMSO to 37,000 g supernatant fractions of kidney, liver, skeletal muscle and ventral prostate of intact male rat	Testosterone and related steroids, both precursors and metabolites	Maximal increases in guanylate cyclase activities of all tissues tested with 1 μM testosterone, 19-nortestosterone, 17-methyltestosterone, and 5α-DHT; similar results with C-21 precursors and C-19 metabolites: some effect still evident at 1 nM; cholesterol inert.	
Lack of positive effects				
5. Rosenfeld and O'Malley (1970)	Male rat, hypophysectomized at 20 days; maintained 3 weeks; 2 mg of androgen s.c.	Testosterone (propionate)	No effect of androgen *in vivo* on adenylate cyclase activity of ventral prostate at 5, 30 minutes, nor at 4, 24 hours. No consistent effect of the androgen, added *in vitro* at 1 mM.	Note prolonged period after hypox; likely to have resulted in extreme involution and thus, androgen insensitivity.

(continued)

TABLE VII B (continued)

Investigators	System	Hormone	Observations	Comment
Lack of positive effects				
6, 7. Liao and Fang (1969), cited in Liao *et al.* (1971)	Intact male rat, 4–6 months	5α-DHT *in vitro* (1969)	Stimulation of adenylate cyclase of ventral prostate "not significant (10–20 % in 4 of the 12 experiments) at . . . 0.1–10 μM."	Lack of consistent effect of androgen on preparations from intact, adult rat should not have been unexpected.
		Testosterone ("1–3 days" to $\lozenge$ *in vivo*; 1971)	No change in adenylate cyclase activity of nuclear fraction of ventral prostate after either treatment.	
8. Craven *et al.* (1974)	Male rat, 1–7 days after castration; 400 μg/100 g of androgen, s.c., for 1–7 days thereafter	5α-DHT	Total cAMP declined with castration, restored with androgen, but only in proportion to tissue involution and recovery, respectively.	No significant change ($P > .05$) when values calculated on basis of DNA, protein content, or tissue weight.

[a] Known to be contaminated with plasmalemmal components (cf. DePierre and Karnovsky, 1973).
[b] Insertions, ours.

TABLE VII C

INFLUENCE OF STEROID HORMONES ON CYCLIC NUCLEOTIDES AND NUCLEOTIDE CYCLASES OF CELLULAR TARGETS: VITAMIN D METABOLITES

Investigators	System	Observations	Comment
Positive effects of near-physiological levels of hormone			
1. Neville and Holdsworth (1969)	Rachitic chicks	Elevation of adenylate cyclase activity in intestinal mucosal cells on administration of vitamin D_3.	
2. Corradino (1974, 1975, 1977)	Embryonic chick duodenum in serum-free organ culture	Elevation of endogenous cAMP concentrations by *in vitro* addition of D_3 and 1α, $25\text{-}(OH)_2D_3$.	
3. Corradino (1976)	As above $\pm$ diphenylhydantoin, in the mM range	The anticonvulsant drug inhibited, in a dose-dependent manner, the cAMP elevation as well as the $^{45}Ca^{2+}$ uptake and the synthesis of CaBP attributable to D_3.	The anticonvulsant effects of the drug are believed due to its membrane-stabilizing functions (Goodman and Gilman, 1975), a property shared by another anticonvulsant, propranolol (see text).

(continued)

TABLE VII C (*continued*)

Investigators	System	Observations	Comment
Positive effects of near-physiological levels of hormone			
4. Walling et al. (1976)	Duodenal mucosa of vitamin D-deficient rats	Elevation of endogenous cAMP levels and adenylate cyclase activity by 1α, 25-$(OH)_2D_3$.	
5. Wasserman et al. (1976)	Chicks maintained on high strontium diet (which inhibits 1α, 25-$(OH)_2D_3$ formation in kidney)	cAMP in intestine markedly reduced.	
	Addition to above diet of dried *Cestrum diurnum* leaf (containing a 1α, 25-$(OH)_2D_3$-like factor)	Reversed strontium-inhibition of Ca^{2+} adsorption and restored cAMP concentration.	
Absence of effect			
6. Wong et al. (1977)	Osteoclast-like and osteoblast-like bone cells isolated from mouse calvaria and maintained in culture	No rise in endogenous cAMP in presence of $1 \times 10^{-9} M$ 1α, 25-$(OH)_2D_3$.	Prior exposure to 10^{-9} M 1α, 25-$(OH)_2D_3$ first inhibited, then abolished, cAMP elevation due to parathyroid hormone (but not calcitonin).

TABLE VII D

INFLUENCE OF STEROID HORMONES ON CYCLIC NUCLEOTIDES AND NUCLEOTIDE CYCLASES OF CELLULAR TARGETS: MISCELLANEOUS STEROIDS

Investigators	System	Hormone	Observations	Comment
Positive effects				
1. Rosenfeld and O'Malley (1970)	Chick oviduct; hormone *in vivo*, 6.5 μg/100 g, s.c.	Progesterone	Delayed (3 hours) and progressive activation of adenylate cyclase to 340% of control at 24 hours; no effect on the enzyme in lung or liver.	
2. Kissel *et al.* (1970)	Chick oviduct; 5 mg/chick s.c.	Progesterone	Above essentially confirmed in DES-primed and unprimed animals; cAMP elevated at 6, 24 hours.	
3. Van den Berghe *et al.* (1970)	Liver of intact mice, pretreated with agonist, 1 mg/20 g, s.c. "at least 3 hours before death"	Prednisolone	Approx. 24% decline in cAMP concentration	
4. Pollard (1970)	Barley aleurone layers $\pm 2 \times 10^{-6}$ M hormone	Gibberellic acid	Incorporation of [8–^{14}C] adenine into labeled cAMP during 2.7 to 4 hours was essentially doubled over controls in 4 experiments.	See however ref. 21. These and additional experiments of similar design are also subject to the limitation that the observed effects may be secondary to hormonal influence on intracellular transfer of the precursor.
5. Logsdon *et al.* (1972)	Leucocytes from human peripheral blood $\pm 1 \mu M$ hormone	Cortisol	Stimulation of adenylate cyclase 24–35% in a 5-minute pulse in preps. from control or asthmatic subjects.	Isoproterenol, 1 μM, stimulated only 16–19% in leucocytes from control subjects.

(continued)

TABLE VII D (continued)

6. Stoff et al. (1972)	Toad quarter-bladders incubated for various times to deplete them of endogenous steroid, or incubated in presence of 0.2 μM hormone ± theophylline	Aldosterone	In presence of 30 mM theophylline, elevation of endogenous cAMP ($P < .05$); basal levels (in absence of phosphodiesterase inhibitor), unaffected.
7. Applebaum and Gilbert (1972)	Wing epidermis from chilled Hyalophora gloveri pupae, injected with hormone, 5 μg/g; or in presence of 1.33 μM hormone in vitro	β-Ecdysone	Approx. 140% increase in incorporation of label from [^{14}C]-adenine into cAMP by 1 hour after hormone in vivo; 10 minutes after hormone in vitro. In "preliminary experiments," these in vitro effects were not duplicated by the inactive α-isomer. In paired-wing experiments, β-ecdysone, 10 μg [in incubation volume of 0.6 ml][a] likewise increased incorporation of [^{14}C]guanine into cGMP 2-fold.
8. Manganiello and Vaughan (1972)	HTC hepatoma cells cultured ± 10 μM agonist 36, 72 hours	Dexamethasone	Slight increase in basal cAMP at 72 hours, 10-minute response to epinephrine vastly augmented. Effects attributed to 25–40% decline in cAMP-phosphodiesterase at 36 hours; no earlier observations made.
9. Steiner et al. (1972)	Skeletal muscle of male Sprague-Dawley rats ± adrenalectomy; ± steroid s.c., 0.2 mg × 2 daily for 3 days	Dexamethasone	cGMP concentration, which had declined significantly at 11 d after adrenalectomy, was restored toward normal by steroid treatment. No effects of adrenalectomy or dexamethasone on cAMP in skeletal muscle, liver, or renal cortex, nor on cGMP in the latter two.
10. Goldberg et al. (1973)	Kidney and lung of adrenalectomized rats ± theophylline (30 min before sacrifice); ± adrenal	Aldosterone; cortisol	Each steroid reduced by ~50% elevated levels of cGMP elicited by adrenalectomy ($P < .05$).

(continued)

	steroids: aldosterone (25 $\mu g/kg$), cortisol (10 mg/kg), 3 and 4 hours, respectively, before sacrifice		
11. Parker et al. (1973)	Leucocytes from peripheral blood of control and asthmatic humans treated i.v. with 200 mg cortisol; several glucocorticoids in vitro at 0.01–10 μM	Glucocorticoids, natural and synthetic; free and as H_2O-soluble derivatives	Glucocorticoids in vivo stimulated cAMP accumulation in leucocytes from both groups of subjects; in vitro effects, generally positive at 1–10 μM cortisol by 2 minutes, augmented by theophylline which also increased % positive responses in the submicromolar steroid range.
12. Castillón et al. (1973)	Homogenates of whole Ceratitis capita, during larval and pharate stages of development	Endogenous	Adenylate cyclase activity, low during early larval stages, gradually rose many-fold as development proceeded to emergence at 18 days.
13. Sapag-Hagar and Greenbaum (1974)	Membrane fractions of rat mammary gland during pregnancy and lactation	Progesterone; $E_2\beta$; cortisol	Coordinated changes in adenylate cyclase and phosphodiesterase activities during pregnancy, leading to peak in cAMP content of the tissue just before parturition. Addition of 20 μM progesterone or $E_2\beta$ led to substantial activation of the cyclase in vitro. Effect of $E_2\beta$ blocked by CI-628[b] which alone was ineffective. No effect of $E_2\alpha$,

TABLE VII D (*continued*)

			testosterone; E_1 and cortisol elicited modest activation.
14. Brostrom *et al.* (1974)	C-6 glial tumor cell cultures $\pm 1 \times 10^{-8}$ to 1×10^{-5} M steroid for various times	Corticosterone	Exposure of cells to 3 μM steroid for 8 days led to approx. 2-fold elevation of basal concentrations of cAMP and an augmented response to norepinephrine. The response was linear between 6 and 48 hours, with maximum at latter time. Half-maximal effect was achieved with ca. 5×10^{-6} M steroid. A 2-fold increase in adenylate cyclase was likewise observed, with no apparent change in phosphodiesterase activity.
15. Sibley *et al.* (1974)	S 49.1T.B4 mouse lymphoma cells cultivated in Dulbecco's MEM with 10% heat-denatured fetal calf serum in presence and absence of 1 μM agonist	Dexamethasone	With or without 10^{-4} M theophylline, levels of intracellular cAMP essentially doubled during 8-hour culture with agonist. Values of cAMP in medium not reported.
16. Guidotti *et al.* (1975)	Rat adrenal medulla 30 minutes after agonist, 12.7 μmol/kg, i.p.	Dexamethasone	Approx. 50% decline in cGMP ($P <$ .05).
17. Guillemant and Guillemant (1979)	Adrenal cortex of young ♂ rats, 7 d after hypophysectomy; 1 mg/kg agonist i.m.	Dexamethasone	Increase in endogenous cGMP concentration, detectable at 2 hours ($P <$ .05), 4 h ($P <$ .001);

Reference	Agonist	System	Result	Comments
18. Corradino (1979)	Cortisol (hemisuccinate)	Embryonic chick duodenum in serum-free organ culture ± 2.75 μM agonist	sustained to 8 hours ($P < .05$). No consistent change in cAMP levels was seen, except for a slight decline at 4 hours ($P < .02$). Statistically significant increase in cAMP conc. relative to DNA; effect of cortisol, essentially additive to that of Vitamin D_3, was also seen without supplementation with the vitamin.	

Absence of effects

Reference	Agonist	System	Result	Comments
19. Rinard et al. (1969)	Triamcinolone	Rat liver slices, incubated 2 hours with 10 μM agonist	No significant change in cAMP levels.	Lack of significant effect of 3 μM epinephrine casts some doubt on negative observations with the steroid drug under conditions tested. Note ~ 10-fold higher steroid concentration in this reference and no. 22 as compared to positive effect(s) in several refs. above.
20. Lang and Edelman (1972)	Aldosterone	Kidney homogenates from (2 to 7 days adrenalectomized), and intact rats; 2 μg of hormone/rat, 0.5 to 3 hours before nephrectomy	No statistically significant effect of adrx. on basal or NaF-stimulated activities of adenylate cyclase in renal cortex or medulla; 10^{-9} or 10^{-7} M aldosterone added *in vitro* to kidney homogenates.	Acknowledged that although the negative results obtained " . . . do not exclude the possibility that cAMP is involved in the action of aldosterone on Na^+ transport, the available evidence does not reinforce this possibility."

(continued)

377

TABLE VII D (continued)

21. Keates (1973)	Barley aleurone layers ± 10^{-6} M hormone	Gibberellic acid	No significant change in cAMP formed from U-^{14}C-adenosine during a 12-hour incubation, with G.A. added at 1–8 hours before termination of experiment. However, a 67% increase at 0.5 hour received no comment.	Note divergence from positive effects of aldosterone on cAMP in toad bladder (ref. 6). Divergence from positive effects in ref. 4 ascribed to less than adequately rigorous conditions of separation in latter.
22. Granner et al. (1977)	HTC hepatoma cells maintained 1 or 4 days in suspension culture ± 10μM agonist	Dexamethasone	No change in basal level of cAMP.	
23. Katz and Tenenhouse (1973)	Cell-free preparations of rat cerebral cortex ± 0.1 mM agonist	Ouabain	Modest increase in adenylate cyclase activity, but only with suboptimal concentrations of Mn^{2+} and in the absence of Ca^{2+}. No change in phosphodiesterase activity.	

^{a} Insertions, ours.
^{b} (1-[2-(p-[α-(p-methoxyphenyl)-β-nitrostyryl]phenoxy)ethyl]pyrrolidine (Parke-Davis); see Callantine et al. (1976).

action," seems unwarranted, in view of the corresponding situation, in which the *full* cellular effect(s) of peptidal hormones believed to act through cyclic AMP have not invariably been mimicked by the cyclic nucleotide (cf. Dumont, 1971). This judgment is especially unfortunate in light of the well-documented biphasic nature of the effects of exogenous cyclic nucleotides, with inversion at excessive levels and the unphysiologic concentrations that are generally employed (reviewed by Szego, 1975). For these reasons, and also because of the impossibility of equating the administered levels of cyclic nucleotide with the effective concentrations of relevant hormones, data obtained with exogenous cyclic AMP and derivatives were excluded from consideration (Table VII A–D).

Also readily refuted is the inference that the abrupt and unequivocal elevations of cyclic AMP elicited by physiologic levels of estrogen selectively in uterus of ovariectomized rats by thoroughly validated methods were attributable to "stress prior to sacrifice" (Higgins and Gehring, 1978). Adrenocortical hyperactivity, which invariably accompanies release of adrenal medullary catecholamines, has a powerful *depressant* effect upon the uterine cyclic AMP elevation evoked by estrogen (Szego and Davis, 1969b), while also suppressing other evidences of estrogen action (cf. Szego, 1952, 1972b; Pietras and Szego, 1975a,b). These data were unfortunately overlooked when that criticism was leveled.

Other workers have suggested that cyclic AMP elevations in uterus (Sanborn *et al.*, 1973; Krall *et al.*, 1978) as well as in the central nervous system after estrogen *in vivo* (Gunaga *et al.*, 1974) may be due to adrenergic mediation, and thus secondary to liberation of catecholamines. This inference which, on the one hand, summarily dismisses direct interaction of steroids at the plasma membrane level while, on the other hand, acknowledges the effect of the hormone in "spilling packets of enzymes" at the synaptosonal level, indeed appears to be strongly supported by the facts. Thus, cyclic AMP elevation due to estrogen in uterus, for example, is counteracted by β-blocking agents such as DL-propranolol (Szego and Davis, 1969a; Rosenfeld and O'Malley, 1970). However, what is not generally recognized is that the effective compound, propranolol, in addition to being a β-adrenergic antagonist, is also, like cortisol in appropriate concentrations, a membrane stabilizer (Howe and Shanks, 1966; cf. also Godin *et al.*, 1976). Although both epimers have equivalent anesthetic potency, the L-isomer is far more efficient as a β-blocker (Parmley and Braunwald, 1967; Barrett and Cullum, 1968). Cortisol (Szego and Davis, 1969b) and probably several other membrane-stabilizing agents (cf. Corradino, 1976; Ortmann and Perkins, 1977), are capable of interfering with elevation of cyclic AMP— the common event-marker of membrane perturbation. On the other hand, phentolamine, a powerful α-adrenergic antagonist, which lacks the membrane-stabilizing properties of propranolol, fails to block estrogen-induced cyclic AMP elevation. Nonetheless, it is entirely possible that in hypothalamus, as well as uterus, estrogen-induced cyclic AMP accumulation may be secondary to intervention by locally liberated catecholamines, perhaps as a reflection of estrogen influence in labilizing membrane-bounded vesicles (cf. Szego, 1971, 1974; Szego *et al.*, 1971). However, release of norepinephrine and other amines, as well as activation of the membrane-localized adenylate cyclase system may be concomitant but independent processes, reflecting the general influence of estrogen on membrane stability wherever receptors for the hormone occur (*v.i.*). Perhaps a very careful kinetic investigation may shed some light on the probable sequence of events. Unfortunately, this is likely to be difficult because of the extremely rapid and transitory (Szego and Davis, 1967) consequences of membrane binding of the steroid.

Exogenous cyclic AMP, alone, indeed has not been shown to supplant estrogen in eliciting the *full* range of cellular effects (cf. Dupont-Mairesse *et al.*, 1974). Nevertheless, the cyclic nucleotide has the function of reinforcing and amplifying the lysosome-labilizing influence of this hormone in its target cells. This topic has been reviewed elsewhere (Szego, 1972a,b, 1975), as has the effectiveness of DL-propranolol, but not phentolamine, in inhibiting the influence of the hormone on structural labilization and intracellular redistribution of the organelles. The existence of such a mechanism, recently confirmed in totally different contexts (Welman, 1979; Monder and Coufalik, 1979), may help to reconcile these apparently diverse views of one aspect of membrane-associated events in the action of steroid hormones.

Less helpful in permitting integration of data on cyclic AMP, together with *all* available observations on steroid hormone action, is the intuitive argument that, in contrast to peptide hormones, there is no "need" for a further intracellular mediator (Higgins and Gehring, 1978). By a similar line of reasoning, Vesely (1979), while focusing on the participation of a guanylate cyclase in the later phases of steroid hormone action, discounts the observations on the almost instantaneous stimulation of uterine adenylate cyclase by estrogen (Table VII,A), on the grounds of disparate distribution of these enzymic activities in cytosol and particulate fractions, respectively, during centrifugation of tissue homogenates. This seems especially naive in light of the data assembled in Tables I–III and VI of the present review.

It would be a far cry from the incomplete summation of data in Table VII (A–D) to implicate cyclic nucleotides in all of the direct actions of steroid hormones any more than has been established, with various degrees of adequacy, for peptidal agonists (cf. Szego, 1978). Nevertheless, the cyclic AMP gradient abruptly generated by estrogen in its target cells is capable of modifying the activities of specific kinases, resulting in functional alterations that mimic the action of the hormone. Thus, Berg (1978) has demonstrated that within 4 minutes of the intraperitoneal injection of $E_2\beta$ to mice, dephosphorylation (and thus, activation) of 12 of the 17 aminoacyl-tRNA synthetases occurred. Similar results were obtained with administration of dibutyryl cyclic AMP. These findings, which are of crucial significance in augmented initiation of translation under hormonal influence, were associated with cyclic AMP-dependent phosphorylation of the relevant phosphatase kinases. Moreover, the cyclic nucleotide also plays a supportive role in the redistribution of lysosomes and in augmentation of the graded release of their sequestered enzymes elicited on uptake of hormone by the organelles; membrane-stabilizing factors diminish or suppress these functions (Szego, 1972a,b, 1975, 1978). In the present context, the data on cyclic nucleotides have been marshalled primarily to document one further correlate of membrane function in relation to steroid hormone interaction with specific surface recognition sites at selective target cells. Thus, just as 5'-AMP is the universal signal of energy spent, so cyclic AMP seems to be the common indicator of a membrane-associated event.

As indicated by some of the citations in Table VII (A–D), such data have long been available without strong influence on the currents of thinking about steroid hormone action. They have either (a) been dismissed as irrelevant to *the* action of these hormones (presumably at the genome); (b) received alternative interpretations, or (c) been compartmentalized into "special-case" status. The inconsistencies so clearly evident in the present compilation of findings are probably attributable to uneven methodologies, with the burden of proof on the side of the negative. Clarification of interpretation will depend upon judicious and continual reassessment of the older data and a flexible outlook to accommodate the new. There are growing indications that such a renewed evaluation by additional criteria is already in progress (cf. McEwen *et al.*, 1978; Lieberburg and McEwen, 1979; Heinonen and Tuohimaa, 1979).

3. Influence of Steroid Hormones on Membrane-Associated Events in Neurons

There has long existed the tacit assumption that steroid hormone action in the brain proceeds along lines parallel to those delineated in other target organs. This would entail cytoplasmic accumulation, nuclear transfer, and, following the appropriate interval for operation of the transcriptional and translational machineries, induction of *de novo* synthesis of select proteins. Few, if any, data have indicated otherwise. However, there are now certain observations, sporadic and fragmentary as they may be, that suggest we have reached a turning-point. For they provide a fresh outlook upon neuronal interactions of the steroid hormones, indeed, specifically with some of the very cells that qualify as their targets (cf. Stumpf and Sar, 1977). Some of these exciting new data are presented in Table VIII.

It will be noted that among the representative observations summarized in Table VIII are indications for perturbations of target-cell membranes by steroid hormones, with particular emphasis on the estrogens (cf. also, Figs. 13 and 14), that meet many of the criteria for plasmalemmal interactions of nonsteroid agonists. For example, in light of the extremely rapid onset of detectable alterations elicited by steroid hormones in electrical properties of neurons and pituitary cells, these events are unlikely to be secondary to the transcriptional and translational mechanisms that have been postulated as the exclusive means of action of the steroid hormones (cf., nevertheless, Haug *et al.*, 1978). The demonstrable steroid specificities, sensitivities, and selective loci of the reactions are in accord with physiologic criteria (Kelly *et al.*, 1977a,b, 1979; Dufy *et al.*, 1979). Collectively, these observations constitute essential proof of direct membrane interaction of the relevant agonists, a conclusion similar to that voiced recently in a thoughtful essay by Lieberburg and McEwen (1979).

Along similar lines, a new and exciting relationship in terms of receptor interactions at the molecular level is now emerging between $E_2\beta$ and, more particularly, its catechol metabolite, 2-hydroxy estradiol-17β (cf. Fishman and Norton, 1975), and the central neurotransmitter, dopamine. The latter is postulated to be the endogenous prolactin inhibitory factor released by the hypothalamus (cf. Labrie *et al.*, 1979). Direct studies of specific binding to the dopamine receptor in a crude rat anterior pituitary membrane fraction have revealed that the 2-hydroxy steroid was capable of effective competition toward the interaction of [^{3}H]spiroperidol, a potent dopamine antagonist used as probe (Schaeffer and Hsueh, 1979). These observations are in keeping with physiological data from whole animals (Yanai and Nagasawa, 1979). Even more direct evidence is now available of modulation by $E_2\beta$ of dopamine-induced electrical activity of isolated pituitary cells (Dufy *et al.*, 1980). Likewise, in systematic analyses of specific binding as well as adenylate cyclase activation, the competitive effects of a series of structurally related drugs on postsynaptic dopamine receptors have identified certain compounds

TABLE VIII

PARTICIPATION OF STEROIDS IN MEMBRANE-ASSOCIATED EVENTS IN NEURONS AND PITUITARY CELLS AND/OR THEIR COMPONENTS *in Vitro*[a]

Observations	Interpretation/Comment	Reference
Modification of firing rates of a certain proportion of individual hypothalamic and mesencephalic neurons on microelectrophoretic application of dexamethasone. The predominant effect was inhibitory, with various latencies and durations; a small number was activated.	Direct effects on neurons in regions known to be sensitive to steroid.	Steiner *et al.* (1969)
Addition of cortisol (F; 6×10^{-8} to $6 \times 10^{-9} M$) to synaptosomes from sheep hypothalamus exerted a powerful inhibitory effect on the liberation of corticotrophin-releasing factor (CRF) elicited by electrical stimulation. Deoxycortisol (S) alone, ineffective, but seemed to block action of F by competition.	Concentrations of steroid which approximate the level of free cortisol in blood during stress elicit direct effects on nerve endings *in vitro* which correspond to actions *in vivo*.	Edwardson and Bennett (1974)
Gonadal steroids added at 10 nM concentrations *in vitro* to suspensions of hypothalamic synaptosomes modulated the liberation of luteinizing-hormone-releasing hormone (LHRH).	Nerve endings of peptidergic neurons in the hypothalamico-adenohypophysial system are target sites for direct feedback regulation by steroid hormones.	Bennett and Edwardson (1975)
A 5-minute incubation with cortisol (10^{-5} to $10^{-7} M$) or corticosterone ($10^{-5} M$) promoted uptake of L-[³H]tryptophan by synaptosomes of whole brain; no effect of $10^{-4} M$ 5α-DHT or 17α-hydroxy-progesterone.	Direct effect on membrane transport.	Neckers and Sze (1975)
Almost instantaneous inhibition of firing rate of single preoptic-septal neurons on microelectro-	Unequivocal conclusion from lack of appreciable latency was a direct membrane effect of $E_2\beta$.	Kelly *et al.* (1976, 1977a,b)

(continued)

TABLE VIII (*continued*)

Observations	Interpretation/Comment	Reference
phoretic application of $E_2\beta$, but not $E_2\alpha$. Some cells activated. Percentage of cells inhibited, stimulated, or unresponsive varied during estrous cycle.	Alternative possibilities carefully considered and excluded.	
Fast (and delayed) inhibitory effects on acetylcholine-induced liberation of CRF exhibited *in vitro* on hypothalamus of 1-day adrx. rats by corticosterone (B) and cortisol (~ 1 pg/ml; $P < .01$); basal secretion was unaffected; progesterone was inert. B inhibition unaffected by picrotoxin or phentolamine, but overcome by depolarization of the membrane with excess K^+.	Fast feedback action of corticosteroid not due to excitation of neuroinhibitory pathways, but to membrane stabilization toward the action of the neurotransmitter.	Jones *et al.* (1977)
Elevation of cAMP in hypothalamus due to DES or $E_2\beta$ (refs. 5, 6, 12, 13 in *op. cit.*), suppressed by preincubation with catechol derivatives of $E_2\beta$.	Implication for modulation of neurotransmitter release from membrane sequestration; observations consistent with membrane sites for interactions of the agonists (cf. also Table VII and text).	Paul and Skolnick (1977)
In ovariectomized rats, iontophoretic application of mixture of conjugated estrogens (presumably chosen for their water solubility) inhibited within 3–20 seconds single-unit firing responses to glutamate excitation in nuclei restricted to the anterior hypothalamus. Units in basomedial and posterior regions, as in thalamus and cortex, unresponsive.	Rapidity of onset supports direct membrane effect; regional localization has physiological implications.	Yamada and Nishida (1978)

Within 1 minute of application of 1 nM concentration to external surface, $E_2\beta$, but not $E_2\alpha$, excited clonal $GH_3/B6$ pituitary cells, causing, in $\sim 50\%$, a sustained train of action potentials comparable to those induced by TRH. The spiking activities were dependent upon Ca^{2+}. Effects were biphasic, with desensitization even more conspicuous after $E_2\beta$ than TRH.	Membrane-localized recognition sites with probable reflections in conformational changes in membrane components. Responses considered too rapid for genic model of estrogen action.	Dufy *et al.* (1979, 1980)
Iontophoretic application of the 7-α-butyric acid derivative of $E_2\beta$ (1 μM) elicited increased firing rate of approx. 20% of 91 neurons tested in the preoptic/septal region of guinea pig hypothalamus; glutamate-induced spiking activity suppressed by the modified steroid. Free $E_2\beta$ seems not to have been tested. The derivative, which may not have entered cells, failed to elicit the "conventional" intracellular effects of estrogen *in vivo* or *in vitro*.	Local membrane effects, without influence on intracellular parameters. The chemical stability of the ester believed to eliminate hydrolysis to the free steroid. Distinction drawn between surface and intracellular effects may be invalid in light of unphysiologic nature and conc. of synthetic steroid, and the positive effects of free $E_2\beta$ on neuronal membrane functions already established in independent investigations (*op. cit.*, this table).	Carette *et al.* (1979)
$E_2\beta$, 10^{-10} M, in the incubation medium elicited hyperpolarization (2 to 16 mV) in 6 out of 12 neurons from the arcuate-ventromedial nuclei or guinea pig hypothalamus.	Direct actions of $E_2\beta$ on the neuronal membrane, with implications for mediation by K^+ and/or Cl^-.	Kelly *et al.* (1979)

a Excluded from consideration for the immediate purposes of this table is a vast neuroendocrine literature on more delayed or long-term correlates at physiologic and behavioral levels of systematically administered and/or locally instilled steroid hormones.

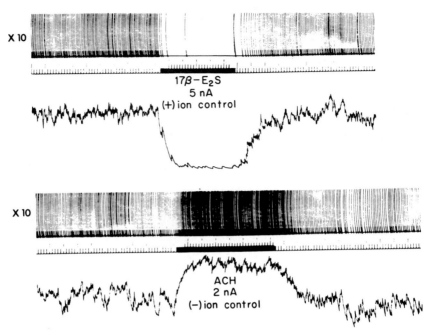

FIG. 13. The effects of microelectrophoretically applied 17β-estradiol hemisuccinate (17β-E$_2$S) and acetylcholine (ACH) on the firing rate of a preoptic-septal neuron. The baseline firing frequency of the cell was 22/sec. The lower trace for each compound is the integrated activity. The time scale divisions are in seconds. The steroid inhibited the cell while the transmitter excited. In a related study (Kelly et al., 1977a) the 17α-epimer was ineffective. (From Kelly et al., 1976, reproduced by permission, with approved minor modifications in notation.)

whose configuration corresponds to the extended conformation of dopamine in its β-rotamer form; an absolute requirement for hydroxyl groups in either the 3- or 4-positions of the benzene ring of phenylethylamine derivatives was indicated (cf. Woodruff et al., 1979). Although circumstantial, such findings lend support to available evidence for stereospecific interaction of estrogens, steroidal or other (cf. Hospital et al., 1972), at synaptic membrane loci (see also Inaba and Kamata, 1979).

4. [Ca²⁺] Flux

Alterations in electrical activities at cell surfaces are clearly predicated upon ionic translocations at the membrane level. Accordingly, the data compiled in Table VIII, taken together with the calcium dependence identified in the electrical activity of GH$_3$/B6 pituitary cells elicited either by TRH or E$_2$β (Dufy et al., 1979), permit retrospective correlation of the

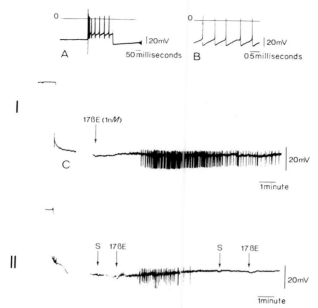

Fig. 14. Effect of 17β-E ($E_2\beta$; 1n*M*, 2n1) on the membrane potential of two excitable GH₃/B6 cells, I and II. (IA) Excitability of the cell is tested by ejecting a depolarizing current (0.16 nA); (IB) oscilloscope trace showing the actual size of the spike; (IC) injection of 17β-E (1 n*M*, 2 n1) directly onto the membrane of the cell induces a burst of action potentials. (II) Two ejection pipettes are positioned close to the membrane of a GH₃/B6 cell, enabling consecutive administrations of 17β-E (1 n*M*, 2 n1) and solvent (2 n1) to be made. Solvent alone does not elicit spiking activity. After a single administration of 17β-E, the cell is no longer excitable and subsequent injections are ineffective. (From Dufy *et al.*, 1979, reproduced by permission.)

possible role of ionic shifts in the implicit stimulus-secretion coupling in these or other estrogen-sensitive cells.

A degree of light may indeed be shed upon this phenomenon by data already available which reveal an abrupt redistribution of ions such as Ca^{2+} (Pietras and Szego, 1975c, 1980b) and Na^+ (Spaziani and Szego, 1959; Pietras and Szego, 1975a) on exposure of estrogen-responsive cells to this hormone. Some of the relevant findings obtained in isolated endometrial cells with the aid of the stop-flow chamber shown in Fig. 15, are depicted in Fig. 16 (A) and (B). These combined data reflect alterations in net distribution of Ca^{2+} as the resultant of oscillations in rates of both efflux and uptake on addition of $E_2\beta$ *in vitro*.

These observations are not without their parallels in the effects of glucocorticoids (Shlatz and Marinetti, 1972; Kimura and Rasmussen,

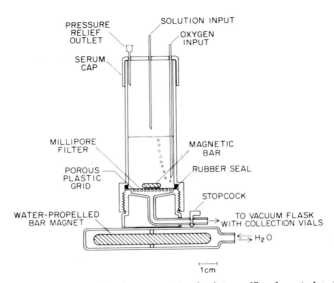

Fig. 15. Stop-flow chamber for determination of calcium efflux from isolated epithelial cell suspensions. The top of the polycarbonate chamber is sealed with a rubber serum cap through which O_2 and wash solutions can be introduced and chamber pressure relieved by means of syringe needles. The chamber screws onto the base of a modified Swinnex-25 (Millipore) filtration unit equipped with a stopcock. With the stopcock open, the chamber is connected to a thick-walled filter flask, the bottom of which is cut off and ground. This end rests on a matched ground-glass plate. A small negative pressure within the flask draws solution from the chamber and into collection vials positioned inside the flask during filtration intervals. Cells are retained in the chamber by a 0.45-μm Millipore filter which is supported by a large-pore plastic grid at the mouth of the funnel. The chamber is immersed in a 22° water bath and rests above a water-propelled bar magnet which drives a 1-cm magnetic bar inside the chamber. The operation of the chamber during efflux experiments is described in more detail in Pietras and Szego (1975c).

1977; Kaiser and Edelman, 1977) and progesterone (cf. Baulieu, 1978) on Ca^{2+}–membrane interactions. The linkage that now emerges between ionic fluxes and electrical events (cf. Table VIII; Figs. 16A,B) on steroid hormone capture constitutes a potential analogy to the phenomena associated with membrane perturbations by a variety of specific extracellular coordinating agents, for example, neurotransmitters (Changeaux, 1974), peptide hormones (cf. Rasmussen and Goodman, 1977) including those of the hypothalamus (Labrie *et al.*, 1979), lectin activators of lymphocytes (Quastel and Kaplan, 1970; Allwood *et al.*, 1971, and even toxins (Boquet and Pappenheimer, 1976; Cuatrecasas, 1977). The emergence of these parallels promotes confidence that a continuum of cellular events may prevail generally on ligand binding at cell surfaces, with labilization–stabilization of membrane functions serving as the primary

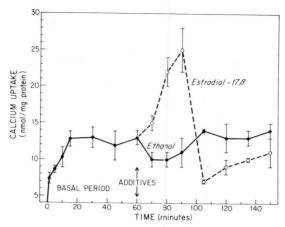

FIG. 16A. Calcium uptake of isolated endometrial cells is expressed as (dpm/mg of cell protein) ÷ (dpm/nmol medium calcium). After a 60-minute basal period, estradiol-17β (○), to a final concentration of 1×10^{-9} M, or its vehicle, ethanol (●), to a final concentration of 0.02%, were added *in vitro* to experimental and control suspensions, respectively. The incubations were then continued for 90 minutes. Each point (mean ± SEM) represents data from three to six independent experiments. (From Pietras and Szego, 1975c, wherein additional details may be found, reproduced by permission.)

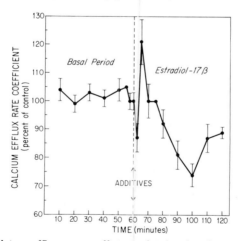

FIG. 16B. The calcium efflux rate coefficient of isolated endometrial cells. Efflux was calculated according to Isaacson and Sandow (1967). With the rate coefficient of the control group being taken as 100%, the changes in the estradiol-treated group at each point were expressed as percentage of control. After a 60-minute basal period, additives were introduced *in vitro*, at the concentrations indicated in Fig. 16A. Each point (mean ± SEM) represents data from three to seven independent experiments; points without SEM are taken from the results of two experiments. (From Pietras and Szego, 1975c, wherein additional details may be found, reproduced by permission.)

means of communication of intercepted ligand–signal to the cell interior. The array of new observations on electrophysiologic correlates of externally applied steroid add a new dimension to the existing literature on acute redistribution of ions under hormonal influence. The new data thus contribute to our continuing analysis of the mechanisms of hormone action. At the very least, they provide additional evidence of the blurring of the lines of demarcation between functions of regulatory agents that had been based merely upon chemical class of agonist (cf. Szego, 1975, 1978).

5. Membrane Reorganization

From the data immediately above (Tables VII and VIII; Figs. 13, 14, and 16), it is tempting to suggest that conformational changes on ligand interaction are the source of altered output of the several indicators of membrane perturbation cited. There are grounds, both theoretical and experimental, which favor such a conclusion, as will be developed below.

Because of powerful precedent for ligand-induced changes in membrane structure and function (cf. Changeaux *et al.*, 1967) that are, in turn, propagated to the interior of the cell (Ash and Singer, 1976), we undertook with the aid of lectin probes to explore hormone-induced modifications of the surface architecture of estrogen-sensitive cells. As is generally recognized, certain lectins, such as concanavalin A (Con A), become associated in highly discriminate fashion with specific carbohydrate substituents of glycoproteins or glycolipids at cell surfaces. Being multivalent, the lectin is capable of cross-linking such carbohydrate functions if they occur in sufficient concentration or are displayed in closely arranged clusters on the same or neighboring cells.

As a first requirement for this experimental approach, it was necessary to establish (1) that binding sites for Con A occurred at the surfaces of endometrial cells; (2) that these binding sites were saturable and specific for the lectin, as demonstrated in part by effective competition of α-methyl-D-mannoside; and (3) that treatment of the cells *in vitro* with physiologic concentrations of $E_2\beta$ did not lead to significant change in extent of binding of Con A per se. These criteria were met before the following series of experiments was conducted (Pietras and Szego, 1975b, 1979b).

Direct analysis was undertaken by means of fluorescence micrography to determine whether $E_2\beta$ was capable of provoking a redistribution of surface binding sites for the lectin at its target cells. Toward this end, endometrial cells that had been exposed briefly to $E_2\beta$ or to control vehicle were treated with Con A that had been covalently linked to fluorescein isothiocyanate (F–Con A) and freed of unconjugated fluorescein by column chromatography. The cells were washed exhaustively to remove unbound fluorescence, and photographed in the darkfield ultraviolet (Fig.

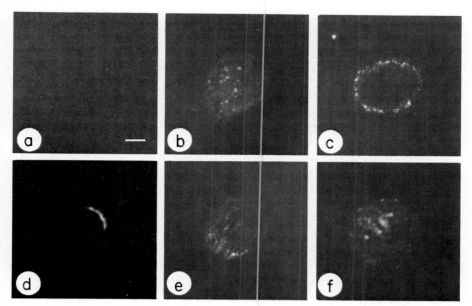

FIG. 17. Darkfield-ultraviolet fluorescence micrographs of F-Con A binding for 3 minutes at 22° to endometrial cells isolated from ovariectomized rats. Before exposure to F-Con A, cells were treated 5 minutes *in vitro* with hormone vehicle (b), or with $1 \times 10^{-9} M$ E$_2\alpha$ (c), or $1 \times 10^{-9} M$ E$_2\beta$ (d). Additional paired cells were incubated with $4.5 \times 10^{-7} M$ leupeptin for 30 minutes before exposure to hormone vehicle (e) or to $1 \times 10^{-9} M$ E$_2\beta$ (f). Binding of F-Con A at the cell surface could be blocked by the addition of a fivefold excess of unmodified Con A (a). No significant alteration in the basal level of Con A binding to cells was elicited by treatments described above (all at $P > .10$; t test). Preparations were photographed on Kodak Tri-X Panatomic film (ASA 400). Approximately 50 cells in each treatment group were observed in each of three independent experiments. Bar, 5 μm; $\times 1000$. (From Pietras and Szego, 1979b, reproduced by permission.)

17). In contrast to the apparent random distribution of fluorescence attributable to F–Con A in cells treated with hormone vehicle (Fig. 17b) or with the relatively inert epimer, E$_2\alpha$ (Fig. 17c), the "capping" pattern of fluorescence concentration, of which a representative example is shown in Fig. 17d, was elicited within 5 minutes of exposure *in vitro* to E$_2\beta$. Such polar clustering of recognition sites for the lectin was induced by the active hormone in approximately 25% of the cells observed, probably a submaximal value in light of the short period of hormone treatment. The latter was chosen in order to minimize cell–cell aggregation (see below) and permit photomicrographic observation of the topologic distribution of fluorescence on individual cells.

The polar clustering of recognition sites for Con A (Pietras and Szego,

1979c) and for labeled derivatives of $E_2\beta$ (Nenci et al., 1980) induced by this hormone in its target cells has numerous additional parallels. These have been identified with a variety of probes, both in hormone-modulated surface responses such as those elicited by vasopressin in epithelial cells from bullfrog bladder (Pietras, 1976), by insulin and epidermal growth factor on mouse fibroblasts (Schlessinger et al., 1978), and by hCG in rat granulosa cells (Amsterdam et al., 1979), as well as in the immunologic context (Taylor et al., 1971; de Petris and Raff, 1972; Yahara and Edelman, 1973). In turn, Con A itself, functioning as effector early in the triggering sequence leading to mitogenesis in normal and transformed lymphocytes, is capable of promoting polar redistribution of its own surface receptors (Sachs, 1974). Similarly, using another indirect measure of membrane dynamics, that of phospholipid methylation, Hirata et al. (1979) have shown that β-adrenergic agonists promote fluidity of rat reticulocyte ghosts. Likewise a "receptor–aggregation factor" from cholinergic neurons promotes the clustering of plasmalemmal receptors for acetylcholine in cultured embryonic muscle cells (Christian et al., 1978). Thus, there now appear to be common grounds for participation of cell surface membrane rearrangements at early stages in the actions of a variety of effectors, including a steroid hormone (cf. Szego, 1978).

The remainder of the fluorescence micrographs in Fig. 17 will be discussed in Section IV,B,2,i.

In an attempt to obtain a quantitative estimate of the influence of $E_2\beta$ in promoting redistribution of Con A receptors in target cell surfaces, we made use of a stop-flow chamber such as that depicted in Fig. 15. Modifications in membrane architecture elicited by the hormone may be recognized by observing the effect of 1×10^{-9} $E_2\beta$ on the lectin-mediated cross-linking of isolated endometrial cells to isologous erythrocytes coincubated with them, according to the scheme shown in Fig. 18. After thorough washing to remove nonadherent cells, the aggregates remaining on the filter were solubilized and the numbers of erythrocytes adsorbed to the surfaces of the endometrial cells determined by analysis for hemoglobin. Aliquots of the solubilized material were also taken for analysis of protein. Endometrial cell protein was corrected for concomitant erythrocyte protein by a standard curve of hemoglobin absorbance/mg erythrocyte protein prepared in each experiment.

In the presence or absence of hormone, Con A-mediated hemadsorption was, as anticipated, significantly greater at 22° than at 4° (Fig. 19). Hormone pretreatment failed to modify this membrane-related function at 4°, a temperature at which lateral mobility of proteins integral to the

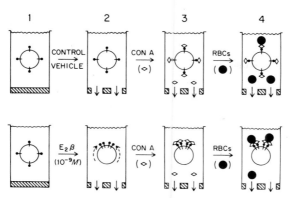

Fig. 18. Schematic representation of concanavalin A-mediated hemadsorption to isolated endometrial cells and the influence of estradiol-17β. Methods were described in detail previously (Pietras and Szego, 1975b, 1979b). In brief, isolated cells are suspended in a stop-flow chamber (Fig. 15) with an 8-μm filter mounted at its base. Endometrial cells (> 8 μm diam.) are retained in the chamber throughout the experiment. The cells initially exhibit a diffuse distribution of surface binding sites for Con A at 22° (cf. Pietras and Szego, 1979b). (2) This distribution appears to be uninfluenced by exposure of cells to control vehicle, ethanol, at a final concentration of 0.02% (*ibid.* and Fig. 17). In contrast, treatment with 1 × 10⁻⁹ M E₂β for 5–30 minutes elicits a clustering of Con A binding sites. (3) These lectin binding sites are then labeled with Con A for 3 minutes and unbound Con A is removed by filtration and washing. (4) Erythrocytes (rbc) with complementary binding-sites for the multivalent lectin are added and allowed to bind to the Con A—labeled endometrial cells. After 7 minutes, unbound erythrocytes (i.e., diam. ≤ 8 μm) are removed by filtration. Material retained by the 8-μm filter is then solubilized and analyzed for endometrial cell protein or DNA, and for rbc hemoglobin. The extent of rbc binding to lectin-labeled endometrial cells thus determined appears to be related to the degree of aggregation of surface binding-sites for Con A (see text and Fig. 17).

membrane is severely restricted by relative rigidity of the lipid bilayer. However, at 22°, exposure to 1 × 10⁻⁹ E₂β (Pietras and Szego, 1975b, 1979b) or DES (Pietras and Szego, 1976), profoundly increased Con A-mediated hemadsorption, while the equivalent concentration of E₂α was ineffective (Fig. 19).

Additional evidence of plasma membrane alterations early after E₂β treatment was found in studies of intercellular adhesion. The active hormone, but not E₂α, elicited marked aggregation of endometrial cells within 15–30 minutes (Table IX). Fractionation of endometrial cells by selection for adhesiveness due to E₂β exposure yielded a subpopulation of cells with preferential sensitivity to the mitogenic effect of the hormone (Pietras and Szego, 1979b). The latter cells also surpassed their less-adhesive counterparts in Con A-mediated hemadsorption elicited by

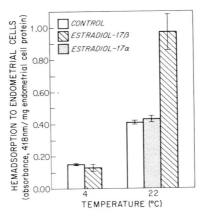

Fɪɢ. 19. The effects of temperature and estrogen treatment on Con A-mediated hemadsorption to endometrial cells. Experiments were conducted at 4° and 22° following treatment of cells with 1×10^{-9} M E$_2\beta$ or E$_2\alpha$ (latter not tested at 4°), or hormone vehicle during a 60-minute incubation period at the test temperature. The result was then expressed relative to mg of endometrial cell protein. Each bar represents the mean ± SEM of 3 to 10 independent experiments (From Pietras and Szego, 1975b, reproduced by permission.)

E$_2\beta$. Thus, only those endometrial cells which exhibited profound membrane alterations early after steroid treatment were capable of substantial proliferation at later times.

Collectively, such data are interpreted as evidence for reorientation of surface membrane components as a rapid consequence of hormone recognition. These observations are consistent with the Singer-Nicolson (1972) fluid mosaic model of the cell membrane, which stresses the fluidity of the discontinuous lipid bilayer at temperatures greater than ~15°, and the intercalation of protein and glycoprotein components into the lipid bilayer, maintained in their lowest free-energy state by various hydrophobic, hydrophilic, and hydrogen-bond interactions. As in the well-documented case of the lymphocyte response to mitogen (Edelman, 1976; Mandel and Santer, 1977), a powerful key to the understanding of the behavior of target cells to steroid hormones may lie in our gaining a greater depth of knowledge of the molecular mechanisms that operate at this critical site of interaction with specific regulatory factors: the surface membrane. Possible means of communication of information contingent upon steroidal ligand recognition at the cell surface will be considered briefly in Section IV,B, below, and, in greater detail, elsewhere (Szego and Pietras, 1981).

While thus far in this review we have been stressing interaction of

TABLE IX

EFFECT OF ESTROGENS ON THE AGGREGATION
OF ENDOMETRIAL CELLS AND THE INFLUENCE
OF PRIOR TREATMENT WITH LEUPEPTIN

Group	μg DNA cells retained/ μg DNA input cells[a]
Control (0.02% ethanol)	0.00 ± 0.00 (4)
$E_2\alpha$ ($1 \times 10^{-9} M$)	0.00 (2)
$E_2\beta$ ($1 \times 10^{-9} M$)	0.34 ± 0.02 (4)[b]
Leupeptin ($4.5 \times 10^{-7} M$) and vehicle control	0.00 (2)
Leupeptin and $E_2\beta$	0.03 ± 0.01 (3)

[a] Endometrial cells were suspended in divalent cation-free Ringer's with 0.1 mM EDTA and 1 mM sodium pyruvate, and filtered over 63-μm nylon mesh. Filtered cells were then incubated for 30 minutes at 22° with or without estrogens as indicated in the table. In experiments with leupeptin, cells were incubated with the peptide aldehyde for 30 minutes before the 30-minute treatment with $E_2\beta$ or hormone vehicle. At the end of the treatment period, cells were filtered again over 63-μm nylon and washed twice with 2 vol of medium. Cells retained by the filter and those passed through the 63-μm mesh were collected and analyzed for DNA. The extent of intercellular adhesion was then expressed as the ratio of μg DNA of cells retained by the filter to μg DNA of all cells in suspension at the start of the procedure (i.e., input cells).

[b] Value significantly different from that of paired control at $P < .001$.

From Pietras and Szego (1979b), reproduced with permission.

steroid ligand with protein(s) integral to the membrane, we do not intend to do so to the exclusion of more direct modifications by these ligands of regions of the lipid bilayer itself, with predictable consequences on state of intramembranous order that have been proposed in model systems (Munck, 1957; Willmer, 1961; Lucy, 1968; and below). Whether influenced directly or indirectly, the physical state of membrane lipids has profound effects upon surface events in immunologic (Esser *et al.*, 1979), toxicologic (van Heynigen, 1976; King, 1976), enzymatic (Zakim and Vessey, 1976; Sandhoff and Pallmann, 1978; Roberts *et al.*, 1979), developmental (Barber, 1979), and endocrine (Bhattacharya and Vonderhaar, 1979) contexts. Even more cogent for the present purpose is the available evidence that alterations of the cellular ectoenzyme complement is influenced not only by the lipid composition of the membrane itself (cf. Solyom and Trams, 1972; Levey and Lehotay, 1976; Madden *et al.*, 1979), but more immediately by the dynamic state of membrane lipids (cf. Coleman, 1973; Kimelberg, 1977). These considerations form the basis of the following section.

B. Coupling to Effector Systems

1. Membrane-Bound Enzymes and Their Flux
on Plasmalemmal Perturbation

It has been demonstrated that membrane fluidity has a direct influence on the conformation of the active site of some membrane-bound enzymes (cf. McMurchie and Raison, 1979). And, indeed, there is a substantial complement of enzymes associated with the plasmalemma of most cells in relatively immobilized state. Immobilization itself has the effect of stabilization of the relevant enzyme toward a variety of perturbing, and even degradative influences (cf. Klibanov, 1979). Since enzymes may occur in cryptic form at the outer cellular membrane (cf. Yagil *et al.*, 1978), "activation" by ligand-induced distortions of the immediate plasmalemmal environment, associated with increased fluidity of the lipid bilayer, is consistent with available data on state transitions (Lucy, 1968; Blanquet, 1978). Significantly, reversible partition of several enzymes between soluble and membrane-bound forms can be influenced by specific metabolites, usually substrates or allosteric effectors. This pattern of behavior has been reviewed in relation to metabolic regulation (Wilson, 1978; Masters, 1978), but has scarcely been considered in the present context of state of aggregation of integral membrane proteins, as influenced by hormonal ligand binding to membrane sites, whether or not these adjoin the enzymatic domain. For it is evident from the rapid achievement of steroid-induced modificatons of membrane fluidity, as inferred in part from the data summarized in the preceding section, that relatively long-range and widespread influences on membrane-bound enzyme may be achieved by this means, with substantial chemical gain on input of minimum mass.

An array of ectoenzymes, some intrinsic to the plasmalemma, with active sites generally accessible to its outer environment, and others present more or less regularly as adventitious elements of the glycocalyx, may be identified in a variety of cell types. Such activities cover a wide range, from protein kinases in cultured 3T3 cells (Mastro and Rozengurt, 1976) and rat adipocytes (Kang *et al.*, 1979) to electron transferring enzymes in Ehrlich ascites cells (Kilberg and Christensen, 1979), and certain glycosyltransferases, highly significant in manifestations of intracellular recognition and adhesion (cf. Verbert *et al.*, 1976). In addition, there occur at the surfaces of certain cells (cf. von Figura and Voss, 1979) a series of hydrolases, many of which are also highly concentrated in the lysosomal compartment. Because lysosomal enzymes are glycoproteins, it has been suggested (Hickman and Neufeld, 1972; Neufeld *et al.*, 1977) that transport of the newly secreted enzymes to the lysosomal compartment involves their specific recognition at the cell surface and receptor-mediated internalization (cf. also Kaplan *et al.*, 1977; Stahl *et al.*, 1976, 1978; Rome *et al.*, 1979; Ullrich *et al.*, 1979; Natowicz *et al.*, 1979). Alternatively, Lloyd (1977) has proposed that lysosomal enzymes associated with the cell surface are derived from secondary lysosomes that reach the plasmalemma during membrane recycling (cf. also Halley *et al.*, 1978; von Figura and Weber, 1978), thus minimizing their liberation into the extracellular medium. Regardless of the outcome of these divergent views on the route through which typical lysosomal hydrolases reach the cell membrane (cf. Sly, 1980), recent evidence from our laboratory provides a new outlook on the episodic delivery of selected lysosomal enzymes to the outer surface of specific target cells as an acute response to hormonal binding. These data, together with functions of the activities so delivered in remodeling of the surface architecture, form the subjects of the following sections.

2. Accentuated Delivery of Lysosomal Components to the Cell Surface Induced by Specific Hormone

a. Identified by Immunologic Probes. One strong indication that sites of redistribution of lysosomal contents include the cell surface may be noted from immunocytologic analyses of cryostat tissue sections with and without brief treatment *in vivo* with tropic hormone. Thus, direct and indirect staining with fluorescein-labeled immunoglobulin raised against a group of high-density lipoproteins that are known to bind $E_2\beta$ selectively, demonstrated intense immunofluorescence at the luminal surfaces of preputial gland sections from ovariectomized rats within 1–2 minutes after $E_2\beta$ i.v. (see Fig. 4f in Szego *et al.*, 1977).

b. Enhanced Levels of Lysosomal Hydrolases in the Extracellular Environment. There is now strong evidence that characteristic lysosomal components, including marker-enzymes, are delivered to the cell surface as an acute correlate of hormone action (Pietras and Szego, 1975b, 1979a,b, 1980b; Pietras *et al.*, 1975; Nemere and Szego, 1981). Some

TABLE X

EFFECT OF ESTROGEN TREATMENT FOR 30 MINUTES ON ACTIVITIES OF HYDROLYTIC ENZYMES IN THE
PARTICLE-FREE MEDIA FROM SUSPENSIONS OF ENDOMETRIAL CELLS

Group	Extracellular enzyme activity		
	Cathepsin B1	β-Glucuronidase (pmol/min/mg cell protein[a])	Alkaline phosphatase
Control (0.02% ethanol)	43 ± 3 (5)	2,227 ± 30 (5)	10 ± 1 (5)
E$_2\alpha$ (1 × 10^{-9} M)	45 ± 1 (3)	2,272 ± 42 (3)	11 ± 2 (3)
E$_2\beta$ (1 × 10^{-9} M)	88 ± 1 (5)[b]	2,606 ± 48 (5)[c]	11 ± 1 (5)
E$_3$ (1 × 10^{-9} M)	70 ± 2 (3)[d]	2,450 ± 102 (3)	10 ± 2 (3)

[a] After 30-minute incubation at 22° with or without estrogens, enzyme activities detected in particle-free supernatant fractions from cell suspensions were < 0.5% of total available cell hydrolase activities; no significant change in total enzyme contents was found after 30-minute E$_2\beta$ treatment ($P > .80$ vs. controls).

[b] Value significantly different from control at $P < .001$.

[c] Value significantly different from control at $P < .05$.

[d] Value significantly different from control at $P < .01$.

From Pietras and Szego (1979b), reproduced with permission.

typical data are presented in Table X. It may be seen that brief incubation with 1 × 10^{-9} M E$_2\beta$ elicits striking increases in extracellular cathepsin B (CB) and lesser increments in the activities of other typical lysosomal enzymes. Enhancement induced by estrogen in net extracellular release of these activities is not accompanied by augmented liberation of lactate dehydrogenase and thus is not to be construed as resulting from generalized cellular lysis (cf. also Pantalone and Page, 1975; Nemere and Szego, 1981). It is also of some significance in this context that cortisol suppresses the excess liberation of CB from endometrial cells due to E$_2\beta$ treatment (Pietras and Szego, 1975b), a finding in accord with other restraints imposed by membrane stabilization upon early correlates of E$_2\beta$ action (cf. Szego, 1972a; Briggs, 1973).

   c. Roles in Modification of Surface Architecture: Established and Potential.   As summarized elsewhere (Pietras and Szego, 1979b, 1980b), recent data indicate that reorganization of the cell surface may be an obligatory precedent or concomitant in the progression of cells to mitosis (cf. Noonan, 1978). The means by which such surface changes are elicited by mitogenic agents, including hormones, and the potential mechanisms by which the alterations are communicated to the cell interior are analyzed in depth elsewhere (Szego, 1975; Szego and Pietras, 1981).

   Although concerted actions of limited amounts of lysosomal hydrolases are likely to lead to remodeling of the cell surface, probably a tonic set of events in membrane attrition and renewal prevails during the life cycle of cells. However, for the present purposes, the potential roles of some representative enzymes will be singled out for particular emphasis: those of phosphatase, glycosidases, and the thiol proteinase, cathepsin B. It seems of special significance that the properties of the latter enzyme include that of calcium dependence (Szego *et al.*, 1976; Quinn and Judah, 1978), a circumstance relatively rare among proteinases.* It seems not unreasonable to predict that the accentuated activity of free CB, both at surfaces and within the affected cell under estrogen domination is likely to be closely modulated by the increased availability of Ca^{2+} (Pietras and Szego, 1975c, 1980b) in its microenvironment (see above).

    i. Limited proteolysis, activation of steroid-bound receptor and hormone action. Physiological roles for limited and highly specific proteolysis in the processing of receptor and its potential precursor forms have strong implications not only in the biology of steroid hormone recognition but in its consequences as well (cf. also Agarwal, 1979). Since the first suggestions that limited proteolysis may play a role in the process of receptor "activation" or "transformation" (Szego, 1969; Rochefort and Baulieu, 1971; Puca *et al.*, 1972; Notides *et al.*, 1973), there has arisen ample evidence in support of this hypothesis. Transformation by lytic functions of a series of steroid hormone receptors in cytosol of a variety of cells from their precursor, to altered forms that have affinity for chromatin acceptor sites, is now demonstrated for estrogens (Puca *et al.*, 1977), progesterone (Sherman *et al.*, 1974), and glucocorticoids (Wrange and Gustafsson, 1978; Sherman *et al.*, 1978; Carlstedt-Duke *et al.*, 1979). However, Wilson and French (1979) report that changes in the size of the androgen receptor do not occur during migration from cytoplasm to nucleus. Although receptor alterations by diisopropyl fluorophosphate-sensitive and -insensitive proteinases were observed *in vitro*, these workers suggest that this phenomenon does not occur *in vivo*.

    In related studies with proteinase inhibitors, the peptide aldehyde, leupeptin (acetyl- and propionyl-L-leucyl-L-leucyl-L-arginal), was found to be capable of eliciting a concentration-dependent reduction of specific $E_2\beta$ binding by intact endometrial cells (Fig. 20). In contrast, binding of hormone by macromolecules in cytosol extracts was not influenced by this inhibitor of cathepsin B and trypsin-like proteinases. Soybean trypsin inhibitor, which fails to curtail the activities of sulfhydryl-dependent proteinases (e.g., cathepsin B), was inert in both systems (Fig. 20). It is

---

* Excess Ca^{2+} is inhibitory; this property, coupled with Ca^{2+} dependence, renders CB particularly susceptible to stringent regulation.

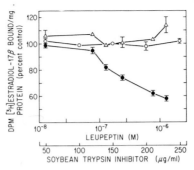

FIG. 20. Effects of proteinase inhibitors on [³H]E₂β binding to intact endometrial cells and to high-speed supernatant fractions obtained after cell homogenization. Intact cells were incubated in Ringer solution with leupeptin (●) or SBTI (○) at the concentrations indicated for 30 minutes before exposure to $1 \times 10^{-9} M$ [³H]E₂β for 30 minutes at 22°. *Cytosol* fractions in Tris-buffered solution were incubated with leupeptin (△) for 1 hour at 4° before incubation with hormone for 2 hours at 4°. Only specific binding (see Fig. 8) is shown. All values are given as percent of specific E₂β binding in paired cells incubated without the respective proteinase inhibitors (i.e., 24,597 ± 824 dpm [³H]E₂β bound/mg *cell* protein), or in paired supernatant fractions not exposed to leupeptin (i.e., 31,730 ± 1050 dpm [³H]E₂β bound /mg *cytosol* protein), in two to three independent experiments. Means of duplicate determinations are shown without the SEM that is given in the cases of triplicates. (From Pietras and Szego, 1979b, reproduced by permission.)

noteworthy that other investigators have also found that the sulfhydryl-blocking reagents and cathepsin B inhibitors, iodoacetamide and iodoacetate, exert a greater inhibition of estradiol accumulation in intact uterus than that observed for hormone binding in cytosol extracts (Milgrom *et al.*, 1973). Such observations are in harmony with other data demonstrating that estrogen binding by solubilized uterine receptors was unaffected by iodoacetate or iodoacetamide (Puca and Bresciani, 1970), whereas it was inhibited when intact organs were incubated with hormone (Jensen *et al.*, 1967; Terenius, 1967).

Baker and colleagues (1978) have reported a reduction in cell-free binding of adrenal and sex steroids in the presence of proteinase inhibitors. Phenylmethyl sulphonylfluoride (PMSF), tosyl-lysine chloromethyl ketone (TLCK) and tosylamide-phenylethyl-chloromethyl ketone (TPCK) all reduced binding of aldosterone, dexamethasone, dihydrotestosterone, progesterone (Baker *et al.*, 1978), and deoxycorticosterone (Baker and Fanestil, 1977) by cytosol extracts of their respective target cells. At 25 μM, TPCK was most effective in suppressing steroid binding, to approximately 50% of control levels. The synthetic proteinase substrates, *p*-toluenesulphonylarginine methylester (TAME) and tryptophan methylester (TME), were also effective, but only at millimolar concentrations. These several observations clearly require further pursuit.

The mode by which these various proteinase inhibitiors elicit a reduction in specific steroid binding remains largely unknown. However, recent equilibrium-binding experiments with intact cells reveal that, in the presence of an effective concentration of leupeptin ($4 \times 10^{-7}M$), the principal inhibitory function was exerted upon affinity of hormone binding (Fig. 21), without substantial effect upon apparent number of binding

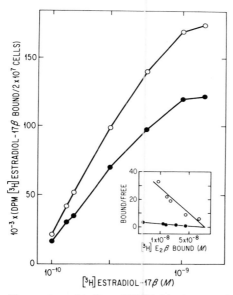

FIG. 21. Influence of leupeptin on binding of [³H]$E_2\beta$ by intact endometrial cells. After a 30-minute incubation with (●), or without (○), 4.5×10^{-7} M leupeptin, approx. 2×10^7 endometrial cells (i.e. ≅ 5 mg cell protein) per ml Ringer solution were expsoed for 30 minutes at 22° to a series of [³H]$E_2\beta$ concentrations ranging from 1×10^{-10} M to 2.5×10^{-9} M as indicated on the abscissa. Only specific binding of [³H]$E_2\beta$ (see Fig. 8) is shown. Each point represents the mean of values obtained in two independent experiments. A Scatchard plot of $E_2\beta$ binding in cells with (●) or without (○) prior exposure to leupeptin is shown as an inset. Calculation of these latter data is similar to that described by Alberga and Baulieu (1968) and Williams and Gorski (1973). The mass of bound estradiol is obtained from the specific radioactivity of the hormone associated with the cells. The concentration of $E_2\beta$ so bound is obtained by estimating a volume of 1×10^{-5} liter per 2×10^7 endometrial cells (i.e. 2×10^9 packed cells/ml). The estradiol remaining unbound at the end of the incubation is calculated from the difference between the total amount of $E_2\beta$ added initially to the incubation medium and the amount of bound hormone. (From Pietras and Szego, 1979b, reproduced by permission.)

sites per cell (Fig. 21 inset). Thus, analyses of specific binding of 1×10^{-9} M [^{3}H]E$_2\beta$ in control cells yielded an apparent molar dissociation constant of 1.9×10^{-9}, while the corresponding value in cells pretreated with the proteinase inhibitor was 2×10^{-8}.

It is important to determine whether these new findings are relevant to recent reports which indicate that a leupeptin-sensitive proteinase is involved in the expression of uterine functions elicited by exposure to E$_2\beta$. For example, the redistribution of Con A binding sites at the surfaces of endometrial cells under the influence of estradiol-17β (Fig. 17d) is curtailed by leupeptin (Fig. 17f); the proteinase inhibitor has no detectable influence in vehicle-control preparations (Fig. 17b). Other data also show that treatment of endometrial cells with leupeptin-loaded liposomes evokes a selective reduction in endogenous cathepsin B activity and marked suppression of the anticipated growth response after E$_2\beta$ exposure (Pietras and Szego, 1979b, 1980b). Likewise, subcutaneous administration of milligram amounts of leupeptin to intact cyclic mice elicits a dramatic decrease in uterine weight and DNA content (Katz *et al.*, 1977).

The further implications of the above and related data (Pietras and Szego, 1979b,c, 1980b) relate to the possibility that enhanced availability of a leupeptin-sensitive proteinase at the surface membranes of target cells after E$_2\beta$ treatment may promote cleavage of an estrogen-binding fragment with high nuclear affinity from a membrane-localized binding component. Ample precendent for this hypothesis is available. A growing list of such controlled cleavage includes conversion of cryptoenzymes (Neurath and Walsh, 1976), prohormones (Smith and Van Frank, 1975; Ansorge *et al.*, 1977), and other precursor proteins, such as proalbumin (Quinn and Judah, 1978), to their active forms; activation of complement (Porter and Reid, 1978); and promotion of infectious processes by bacterial agents during their surface recognition-related entry into mammalian (cf. Pappenheimer, 1978) and bacterial (Watson and Sherratt, 1979) cells. Indeed, in three of these cases (Smith and Van Frank, 1975; Ansorge *et al.*, 1977; Quinn and Judah, 1978), stringent substrate specificity, with cleavage at the C-terminal side of paired dibasic amino acid residues, dependence of the proteolytic activity in question upon sulfhydryl integrity and Ca^{2+}, its effectiveness at near-neutral pH (Aronson and Barrett, 1978) as well as its leupeptin sensitivity, suggest the endopeptidase, CB, as a prime candidate (cf. Szego *et al.*, 1976). It should be mentioned in passing that certain stimulatory (Parchman *et al.*, 1977), as well as inhibitory (Litwack, 1979) effects on steroid receptor activation and nuclear binding may be achieved by interactions involving basic amino acids, possibly as they become accessible at the C-terminal ends of lytic products generated by limited proteolysis. There are also strong indications of similar enzymatic properties in relation to proteolytic activation of adenylate (Lacombe *et al.*, 1977; Richert and Ryan, 1977; Schlegel *et al.*, 1979) and guanylate (Lacombe and Hanoune, 1979) cyclases, which occur in cell membranes in part in complexed or otherwise masked form. Such activation involves extremely rapid effects, of the order of seconds (cf. Lacombe *et al.*, 1977). Therefore, it is tempting to postulate, both by analogy and on the basis of the direct data already available, that similar conversions operate in proreceptor-receptor transformation.

The data presented for apparent proteolytic processing of membrane recognition sites specific for $E_2\beta$ in endometrial cells and hepatocytes by Pietras and Szego (1975b, 1979a,b, 1980b), and, more indirectly, for progesterone on perturbation of the outer membrane of amphibian oocytes (cf. Masui and Clarke, 1979, and Table II D, above), now permit a broadened view of the modulatory steps in this chain reaction: binding of specific ligand at the cell surface; reflection of this perturbation, via mechanisms incompletely understood, in rapid availability of lysosomal proteinase at that and at other strategic sites within the affected cell (cf. Szego *et al.*, 1976); and amplification of the immediate consequences of ligand recognition by a leupeptin-sensitive enzymatic process that renders available active receptor from a cryptic form. However, it is also conceivable that binding of supramaximal levels of ligand can lead to explosive liberation of lysosomal contents at the cell surface, and loss of receptor from this site through more extensive proteolysis, as had been documented in the case of receptors for certain peptide hormones, concomitantly with accentuated degradation of their tropic ligands (cf. Szego, 1975, 1978).

Without intentionally neglecting the parallel and possibly concerted roles of other lysosomal enzymes such as glycosidases and a variety of lipases, potential roles for which may also be induced from indirect data (cf. Hackney and Pratt, 1971; Hähnel *et al.*, 1974; Schulte *et al.*, 1976; H. M. Westphal *et al.*, 1978; cf. also Harrison *et al.*, 1974, 1977; Richards *et al.*, 1979), these considerations provide powerful impetus for further investigations in the critical area of the role of limited proteolysis in the processing of agonist/receptor, and in tonic remodeling of the cell membrane (cf. Sylvén *et al.*, 1974), under control of tropic hormone. For the implications of this mechanism are indeed profound in terms of generating from a poised system perturbed by ligand interaction an active fragment capable of participation in the cascade of reactions that lead to full expression of hormonal stimulation. This topic will be considered in detail elsewhere (Szego and Pietras, 1981).

ii. Membrane phosphorylation and dephosphorylation. The above considerations notwithstanding, it is also instructive to assess further means by which ligand-induced deformation of surface membrane may trigger additional pathways of information transfer in the propagation of initial signal. Such a train of events is implicit in the hormone-induced generation of cyclic nucleotide, leading in turn to activation of cyclic AMP-dependent protein kinases within the membrane or in its immediate environment. This general pathway has received much emphasis in the writings of Greengard (1978, 1979) who views net protein phosphorylation as the final common denominator in the actions of a host of effectors, including, by a somewhat circuitous route, the effects of steroid hormones. Recently, Bellé *et al.* (1978) have demonstrated that the burst of protein phosphorylation accompanying exogenous progesterone action in promoting meiotic maturation of *Xenopus laevis* oocytes involves both cytoplasmic (cf. also Berg, 1978) and membrane-bound proteins. But even more direct evidence for steroid hormone-enhanced phosphorylation of proteins present in prostatic plasmalemma is available in the work of Farnsworth (1977). Thus $10^{-8}M$ dihydrotestosterone intensified progressive, Na^+-dependent phosphorylation of membrane proteins, to 268% of control levels. The effect of DHT was evident by seconds, and highly pronounced within minutes.

Steroid hormones have also been reported to elicit dephosphorylation of membrane-bound proteins, e.g., nM aldosterone in toad bladder (Liu and Greengard, 1974) and 10^{-8} M DHT in human prostatic membranes (Farnsworth, 1977), the latter to 137% of control. The substantial concentration of acid phosphatase in lysosomal membranes as well as in the interior (cf. Dobrota *et al.*, 1979), raises the possibility, not often considered, that liberated enzyme or cyclic fusion and dissociation of the lysosome–plasmalemma continuum (cf. Szego *et al.*, 1971; Dean and Barrett, 1976) could offer a hormone-modulated mechanism for the controlled delivery of phosphatase, with the requisite activities toward given phosphoproteins (cf. Tappel, 1969; Barrett, 1969, 1972), to the cell surface (Szego, 1975). It should be reemphasized here that in addition to their complement of enzymes that operate optimally at acid pH values, lysosomes also sequester hydrolases that function at neutral and alkaline pH values (cf. Dean and Barrett, 1977), even including an alkaline phosphatase in mouse duodenal mucosa (Hugon and Borgers, 1967).

The metabolic short-circuit implicit in the concomitant activation by steroid hormone of *both* phosphorylations and dephosphorylations is more apparent than real. For this type of reciprocal and coordinate control has long been recognized as leading to more precise responsiveness of independent pathways of glycogen regulation to constituents in the microenvironment of the relevant hydrolytic and synthesizing enzymes. Similarly, parallel regulation of cyclic AMP-dependent protein kinase and phosphoprotein phosphatase in rat thyroid by TSH has now been demonstrated (Huprikar *et al.*, 1979; cf. also Walton, 1978). Accordingly, it is entirely feasible, on the basis of data presently available, to anticipate identification of coordinate and reciprocal controls of both classes, operating under steroid hormonal influence at the surfaces of responsive cells. If more extensive work verifies for additional steroid hormones early indications for such coordinate effects now at hand (Farnsworth, 1977), it should permit better integration of data on the proximate effects of steroid hormones on membrane parameters, such as abrupt alterations in cyclic nucleotide levels, ionic fluxes, especially that of Ca^{2+} (cf. Nishikori and Maeno, 1979), and enhanced permeation of nutrients into the affected cell. To what extent these functions may be interrelated is presently mere conjecture.

C. Multiple Membrane Signals Generated by Ligand Binding

From the foregoing, it appears likely that there are concerted, if not coordinated, changes induced by the steroid hormones when they occupy recognition sites at the surfaces of their target cells. These may be listed for convenience:

1. Alterations in Na^+/K^+-ATPase activity
2. Rapid shifts in availability of cyclic AMP
3. Fluxes in Ca^{2+} and other ions, with implications for modulation of neural activities and numerous enzymatic and mechanoeffector systems
4. Release of endogenous amines,* with implications for modulation of microcirculation in intact organs
5. Promotion of lectin-mediated hemagglutination
6. Enhanced aggregation of like cells
7. Accentuated delivery of enzymes and other components of lysosomes to the cell surface, with potential diffusion to adjoining cells

---

* Significance of this phenomenon, as an early clue to steroid-induced membrane labilization, is outlined in Szego (1971, 1974).

It is abundantly clear that the order of such listing is not intended to imply a consecutive time-sequence. Indeed, their very simultaneity may be the key to understanding of the triggering of multiple manifestations of membrane perturbation on receptor occupancy. A constellation of responses in surface-linked cell functions can be elicited by other effectors, such as lectins in thymocytes (Reilly and Ferber, 1976). Similarly, parallel unmasking of adenylate cyclase and ATPase activities occurs in cardiac sarcolemmal vesicles in the presence of the channel-forming ionophore, alamethicin (Besch *et al.*, 1977). Moreover, it is likely that many of the abrupt changes listed above may be closely integrated in the amplification and propagation of second-order and further responses to the hormone.

D. THE CELL SURFACE AS BARRIER: KINETIC ANALYSES OF STEROID HORMONE ENTRY

1. General Considerations

It has been widely assumed that the plasma membrane offers little to no resistance to diffusion of steroid hormones into cells (cf. Peck *et al.*, 1973; Gorski and Gannon, 1976). This view is based largely on the well-known thermodynamic tendency of lipophilic nonelectrolytes, which have more free energy in an aqueous than in a lipid environment, to pass readily from extracellular fluids into the hydrophobic phase of the cell membrane. Indeed, the movement of steroid hormones into nontarget cells and organs appears to occur by a process of simple diffusion across an infinite number of membrane sites, driven solely by the chemical activity of the hormone in the pericellular space (Bischoff and Bryson, 1960; Meli *et al.*, 1968; Scheuplein *et al.*, 1969; Couturier *et al.*, 1973; Plagemann and Erbe, 1976; Giorgi and Stein, 1980). However, the actual mechanism of steroid hormone entry into target cells is currently ill-defined and a subject of considerable controversy (see Table XI).

In many respects, questions on the movement of steroid hormones into target cells relate to the general problem of nonelectrolyte permeation through biological membranes. Most lipophilic molecules appear to enter cells either by a process of passive permeation or by binding to a finite number of sites in the cell membrane, followed, in defined circumstances, by uptake via an endocytotic process (cf. Dietschy, 1978). However, several investigators have found evidence for the coexistence of both transport systems (i.e., a passive transport component superimposed

TABLE XI

EVIDENCE FOR FACILITATED VS. PASSIVE ENTRY OF STEROID HORMONES AND RELATED
AGONISTS INTO TARGET CELLS

Agonists	Passive	Facilitated
Estrogens	Gurpide and Welch (1969) Scheuplein *et al.* (1969) De Hertogh *et al.* (1971) Tseng *et al.* (1972) Peck *et al.* (1973) Müller and Wotiz (1979)	Terenius (1967) Milgrom *et al.* (1973) Rao *et al.* (1977b)
Androgens		Giorgi (1976)
Glucocorticoids	Levinson *et al.* (1972) Mayer *et al.* (1976) Plagemann and Erbe (1976) Giorgi and Stein (1980)	Harrison *et al.* (1975) G. S. Rao *et al.* (1976) Rao *et al.* (1977b) Alléra *et al.* (1980) Fant *et al.* (1979) Harrison and Yeakley (1979) Harrison *et al.* (1979)

upon a facilitated transport system) under normal physiological conditions (cf. Holt, 1964; Schiff *et al.*, 1972; Thomson, 1978; Brown and Goldstein, 1979).

The process of passive transport involves partitioning of the solute into the membrane, diffusion or movement within the membrane and finally partitioning out of the membrane (cf. Diamond and Wright, 1969; Lieb and Stein, 1971). The passive permeability coefficient of a solute is a composite function of its partition coefficient between the cell membrane and the medium, the diffusion coefficient in the membrane and the reciprocal of membrane thickness (cf. Stein, 1967). As first suggested by Overton (1902) and later confirmed by others (cf. Collander and Bärlund, 1933; Diamond and Wright, 1969), permeation of lipophilic nonelectrolytes in cells varies in direct proportion to lipid solubility. Thus, the partition coefficient appears to be the most important factor in determining the passive movement of such solutes. In consideration of evidence that lipid/water partition coefficients for physiologically active steroid hormones range from approximately 10^{-1} to as high as 10^5 (Bischoff *et al.*, 1954; Scheuplein *et al.*, 1969; Sato *et al.*, 1979; Giorgi and Stein, 1980), it is reasonable to postulate that the cell membrane would pose little barrier to the uptake of these molecules (cf. however, Conrad and Singer, 1979). On the other hand, early studies of hexestrol and steroid hormone uptake, with *in vivo* or *in vitro* exposures of a few minutes to several hours, invariably suggested that saturable entry against a concentration gradient was characteristic of hormone uptake by target, but not by nontarget cells (cf. Glascock and Hoekstra, 1959; Jensen and Jacobson, 1962; Bellamy *et al.*, 1962; Sulya *et al.*, 1963; Stone, 1963; Eisenfeld and Axelrod, 1965; Terenius, 1967; Gorski *et al.*, 1968). Nevertheless, as pointed out by Sharp and Leaf (1966; cf. also Clark *et al.*, 1977), such studies may more accurately reflect the retention of hormone after its binding to intracellular receptors, rather than merely its rate of entry into target cells. If the hormone is rapidly bound to receptors in the interior, the chemical activity of the hormone would be maintained lower in the intracellular than in the extracellular compartments, and net movement of hormonal molecules into the cell could continue down a chemical gradient. Clearly, this argument is correct, but valid in the present context only if the finite number of target-cell receptors are localized *in situ* in cytosol rather than in cell membrane (see Section III,A). As outlined in Table XI numerous investigators have, over the years, attempted to define the characteristics of steroid hormone uptake by target cells, and the results of these studies are considered in the following sections.

2. Determination of Steroid Hormone Permeation with Steady-State Perfusion and Adsorption Techniques

Gurpide and Welch (1969) and later Tseng *et al.* (1972) estimated the permeability of human endometrial cells to estrogen. Endometrial curettings obtained at surgery from women at defined stages of their menstrual cycle were minced and placed in a superfusion chamber. Steady-state distribution of labeled hormones was achieved in about 2 hours. Due to extensive metabolic conversion of $E_2\beta$ to estrone during the course of these experiments, chromatography with organic solvents was required to determine the final concentrations of $[^3H]E_2\beta$. The fraction of superfused hormone that enters cells thus depends not only on permeability factors, as outlined above, but also on variables such as the activities of 17β-dehydrogenase and other steroid-metabolizing enzymes, the thickness of the tissue fragments, and the rate of flow of medium (cf. Gurpide and Tseng, 1976). The results show that $E_2\beta$ enters these target cells at a rate proportional to steroid concentration in the perfusate over a range of 0.2 to 5000 ng/ml. These and similar data purporting to demonstrate nonsaturable uptake of estrogen have been offered as evidence for its cellular entry by simple diffusion (Gurpide and Welch, 1969; Tseng *et al.*, 1972; Gurpide and Tseng, 1976; Clark *et al.*, 1977). However, the limited precision of such measurements confounds the interpretation of these experiments. Moreover, other investigators have emphasized the problem of proteolytic degradation of $E_2\beta$ receptors as a result of tissue damage inflicted when endometrium is obtained by curettage and have also drawn attention to the difficulty of demonstrating any specific binding of estradiol in endometrium obtained during those phases of the menstrual cycle when endogenous levels of $E_2\beta$ are high (Siiteri *et al.*, 1972).

In *in vivo* perfusion experiments, De Hertogh *et al.* (1971) found that rat uteri could be saturated with $E_2\beta$ by increasing rates of intravenous infusion of the labeled hormone. However, saturation occurred only at nonphysiological concentrations of $E_2\beta$. In further work by these investigators, a model for the equilibrium distribution of estrogen between plasma and uterus was tested in immature rats. The agreement between theoretical and experimental points was good at pharmacologic concentrations, but poor at lower, physiologic concentrations of estradiol. Therefore, these and related experiments provide no conclusive evidence on the mechanism whereby steroid hormones are taken up by target cells in the circumstances of the very low levels of hormone that prevail *in vivo* (cf. King and Mainwaring, 1974).

Other steady-state superfusion experiments with prostate slices *in vitro* indicate that entry of 5α-dihydrotestosterone may occur by facilitated diffusion (Giorgi, 1976). This investigator showed that the hormone was transported into the target tissue against a concentration gradient, and uptake was reduced by competitive inhibition with cyproterone or cyproterone acetate.

Percutaneous absorbtion of steroid hormones was studied by Scheuplein *et al.* (1969). The phenomenon of percutaneous absorption entails adsorption onto the stratum corneum, the principal permeability barrier of the epidermis, diffusion through the corneum and the underlying viable epidermis, and finally diffusion through the papillary dermis and into the microcirculation (Scheuplein *et al.*, 1969; Scheuplein and Blank, 1971). The permeability constants for 14 steroids from aqueous solutions through the hydrated stratum corneum were found to vary over 3 orders of magnitude from approximately 6×10^{-5} cm sec^{-1} for estrone to 5×10^{-8} cm sec^{-1} for cortisol. No significant correlation between permeability and partition coefficients (e.g., stratum corneum/water; hexadecane/water; amyl caproate/water) was found within this group of steroids. It is clear that the complex nature of skin as an organ precludes more definitive experiments.

3. *In Vitro Studies of Steroid Hormone Uptake by Intact Target Organs*

In *in vitro* studies on the initial rates of uptake of $E_2\beta$ by segments of uterus from immature rats, Peck *et al.* (1973) concluded that the entry of hormone occurs by *passive* diffusion, while Milgrom *et al.* (1973) obtained data suggesting that the movement of estrogen into uterine cells occurs by *facilitated* diffusion. Some explanation for these contradictory findings may be found in the different methods employed by the two groups. Peck *et al.* (1973) determined the initial rates of $E_2\beta$ uptake after 15- to 30-second incubations at 37° in the presence of serially increased extracellular concentrations of hormone. The uterine segments were then rinsed with buffer solution *without* $E_2\beta$ and processed for determination of tissue-associated radioactivity. The uptake of $E_2\beta$ was not saturable up to 40 nM hormone in the bulk medium, and uptake was unaffected by excess DES, by the sulfhydryl-blocking reagent, N-ethylmaleimide, or by the application of 2, 4-dinitrophenol to inhibit energy-yielding reactions. On the other hand, Williams and Gorski (1971), and later, Milgrom *et al.* (1973) argued that some free or nonspecifically-bound $[^3H]E_2\beta$ becomes trapped in the extracellular space of uterine tissues and cannot be washed out by buffer solution alone. When such preparations are later homogenized, significant amounts of the trapped hormone then became available for binding to receptor proteins (cf. Williams and Gorski, 1971). Therefore, Milgrom *et al.* (1973), unlike Peck *et al.* (1973), added excess unlabeled $E_2\beta$ to the uterine preparation at 4° following incubation and prior to homogenization. This dilution prevents spurious binding of $[^3H]E_2\beta$ during homogenization, whereas the $[^3H]E_2\beta$ initially bound during the primary incubation is essentially stable, due to the extremely slow rate of dissociation of the hormone–receptor complex at 4°. After homogenization, specific binding of $[^3H]E_2\beta$ in nuclear and cytosol extracts was determined and taken as an indication of the extent of $E_2\beta$ entry into cells at a given time-point, usually after 5 minutes of incubation (Milgrom *et al.*, 1973). Consequently, the latter procedure appears to provide a relatively accurate determination of the amount of $[^3H]E_2\beta$ that actually enters the target cell. Analyses of the uptake data by Eadie- and Scatchard-type plots indicated that entry of $E_2\beta$ into uterine cells after 5 minutes of incubation was dependent on a saturable process at low physiological concentrations of hormone, but a nonsaturable process was also evident at higher concentrations of $E_2\beta$ (Milgrom *et al.*, 1973). The dissociation constant for the saturable process of $E_2\beta$ entry in uterine segments was $3.2 \times 10^{-9} M$ as compared to K_d of $3.5 \times 10^{-10} M$ for binding of $E_2\beta$ in cytosol extracts from whole uteri. Baulieu (1973) has suggested that this difference of an order of magnitude in the equilibrium binding constants of whole organ uptake vs. cell-free (cytosolic) binding may be interpreted as evidence of a rate-limiting step at the level of steroid entry into the former. In the report of Milgrom *et al.* (1973), uptake of $E_2\beta$ was not inhibited by a 100-fold molar excess of cortisol, corticosterone, progesterone, or testosterone, but was reduced by a two- to 20-fold molar excess of estriol or DES.

The method used by Milgrom *et al.* (1973) to extract $E_2\beta$–receptor complexes from nuclei (i.e., a single extraction with 0.4 M KCl) has been criticized by Müller and Wotiz (1979) as being only semiquantitative (cf. also Traish *et al.*, 1977). These authors argue on the basis of cell fractionation experiments reported by Williams and Gorski (1972) that the total intracellular concentration of bound $E_2\beta$ may have been underestimated by Milgrom *et al.* (1973) by as much as 60%, since the bulk of $E_2\beta$ would be bound in cell nuclei after a 5-minute incubation of intact uterine horns (cf. Williams and Gorski, 1972). It appears that this factor is significant for uterine incubations at 37° for 30 minutes (cf. Müller and Wotiz, 1979), a time at which Milgrom *et al.* (1973) report that 80–90% of bound $E_2\beta$ is localized in the nucleus. Unfortunately, the latter authors did not report the ratio of nuclear to extranuclear binding in entry experiments which were terminated after 5 minutes of incubation. It is relevant to mention that Gurpide and Tseng (1976) have also criticized these experiments. They argue, on the basis of autoradiographic studies of $E_2\beta$ uptake by organ segments (cf. Tchernitchin *et al.*, 1973), that the 5-minute incubation period used by Milgrom *et al.* (1973) was insufficient for complete intracellular penetration of uterine horns by the hormone. The validity of these apparently contradictory criticisms remains to be determined.

4. Effects of Selected Sulfhydryl-Blocking Reagents on Steroid Entry into Target Organs in Vitro

As mentioned in an earlier section, Milgrom *et al.* (1973) found that certain sulfhydryl-blocking reagents (e.g., iodoacetamide, iodoacetate) elicited a significantly greater inhibition of $E_2\beta$ entry into intact cells than that observed for its binding in cytosol extracts. Certain organic mercurial compounds, which do not readily enter cells (cf. Vansteveninck *et al.*, 1965; Bloom *et al.*, 1972), have also been found to elicit differential effects on uptake of steroid hormones by segments of intact organs or isolated cells, as compared with their influence on binding of hormone by soluble extracts. Thus, at a concentration of $5 \times 10^{-4}\ M$, p-chloromercuriphenylsulfonate significantly reduced the entry of $E_2\beta$ into intact rat uterus but did not inhibit binding by the solubilized receptors (Milgrom *et al.*, 1973). Terenius (1967) had also reported that *p*-chloromercuribenzoate blocked the uptake of E₂β by mouse uterus. However, in experiments with cultured hepatoma cells incubated for 5–15 minutes, Levinson *et al.* (1972) found that *p*-chloromercuribenzene sulfonate and *p*-chlormercuribenzoate, at concentrations of 5×10^{-4} M, reduced binding of dexamethasone in intact cells by 4–45%, but binding in cytosol extracts showed a greater reduction (e.g., 78–100%). The latter authors concluded that intact cells are relatively insensitive to mercurial reagents that do not readily penetrate cells and that dexamethasone binding activity is restricted to the cell interior. However, in more recent studies, G. S. Rao *et al.*, (1976) have reexamined this question with glucocorticoids. These workers determined that exposure of isolated liver cells to 1 mM *p*-chlormercuribenzoate elicited a greater reduction in the *initial* rate of cortisol uptake than in the binding of the steroid to cytosol extracts incubated under similar conditions. In a more definitive study, Harrison and Yeakley (1979) demonstrated a 90–100% inhibition of glucocorticoid uptake into intact pituitary cells incubated with 1 mM *p*-chloromercuriphenylsulfonate for 15 minutes. The inhibition of glucocorticoid entry was shown to occur under conditions which did not affect binding by intracellular receptors. Such differences in steroid binding sensitivity to the relatively impermeant mercurial compounds in intact cells and in cell-free extracts could be explained either on the assumption that the physical state of the receptor is different in cytosol extracts from that in intact cells or that some portion of the steroid receptor is available for interaction at the surface membrane.

5. Determination of Steroid Hormone Uptake in Isolated Target Cells in Vitro

To circumvent some of the limitations associated with studies of steroid hormone uptake in intact organs, many recent investigators have chosen to analyze this process in preparations of target cell suspensions or monolayer cultures. Müller and Wotiz (1979) prepared suspensions of predominantly myometrial cells by collagenase digestion of immature uterine organs. Cells were suspended in complex tissue culture medium (i.e., Medium 199 containing 0.1% methylcellulose), and the initial rates of [³H]E₂β binding to cells were determined after incubations of 5–150 seconds at 27°, followed by washing in the presence of 1×10^{-6} M unlabeled E₂β for 30 minutes in the cold. The authors asserted that the micromolar concentrations of E₂β in the latter procedure were necessary to reduce nonspecific binding of hormone which exceeded the amount of specific intracellular binding. The requirement for such excessive levels of nonradioactive E₂β to overcome low-affinity binding seems unwarranted (cf. Chamness and McGuire, 1975), and it should be noted that several investigators have reported that concentrations of $E_2\beta$, as well as of other steroids, in excess of 2×10^{-7} M are toxic to both target and non-target cells (Lippman *et al.*, 1976; Breslow *et al.*, 1978, 1979). Unfortunately, Müller and Wotiz (1979) did not evaluate the integrity of their cell preparations after this treatment. Under these conditions, the uptake of $E_2\beta$ by the cell suspensions was extremely rapid and found to become saturable after the first 20 seconds of incubation. The authors attribute this saturability to the formation of intracellular estradiol–receptor complexes. Therefore, to ensure conditions of excess intracellular receptors uncomplexed with steroid, initial rates of $E_2\beta$ uptake were estimated by extrapolation to zero time or calculated from the linear portion of each curve and plotted as a function of the steroid concentration in the culture medium. The results indicated that the initial rate of $E_2\beta$ uptake was linear with steroid concentrations ranging from 8.7×10^{-10} M to 1.7×10^{-8} M. Uptake of $E_2\beta$ showed a marked temperature dependence, with a Q_{10} of 2.0. The energy of activation for uptake by intact cells was 16.2 kcal/mol, and thus closely comparable to the value of 19.0 kcal/mol for $E_2\beta$ binding to cytosolic extracts.

Müller and Wotiz (1979) also reported that the rates of $E_2\beta$ binding to intact cells were slightly inhibited by the addition of 6-carboxymethyl-oxime-17β-estradiol covalently bound to bovine serum albumin (i.e., ca. 33% inhibition at 5 minutes of incubation). They reasoned that partial or total occupancy of a membrane-associated binding component or carrier with estradiol bound to a macromolecule which does not penetrate the cell should inhibit the uptake of free $E_2\beta$. However, the authors failed to take into account the fact that the affinity of 6-carboxymethyl-oxime-17β-estradiol for binding to uterine receptors is approximately 54,000 times less than that of $E_2\beta$ (Sica *et al.*, 1976). On these grounds, therefore, no significant competition for specific binding sites between $E_2\beta$ and the estrogen-derivatized albumin should have been demonstrable. The competition reported by Müller and Wotiz (1979) in exhaustively dialyzed preparations thus raises further questions about the nature of specific $E_2\beta$ binding measured by their protocols.

Studies of $E_2\beta$ uptake by parenchymal target cells from liver provide contrasting results (Rao *et al.*, 1977a). Due to the rapid uptake of hormone at elevated temperatures, accurate measurements of the initial rate of uptake were possible only in experiments conducted at 15°. Under these conditions, uptake of $E_2\beta$ and estrone was linear with time only up to 10 seconds. The initial rate of $E_2\beta$ uptake was concentration-dependent and saturable at approximately 5×10^{-7} M (Rao *et al.*, 1977a). However, these experiments must be interpreted with great caution since no correction for nonspecific hormone binding was carried out.

The authors asserted that no detectable metabolism of $E_2\beta$ occurred during the course of the experiments.

Rao and colleagues have also studied the kinetics of the binding of cortisol (G. S. Rao *et al.*, 1976; M. L. Rao *et al.*, 1976) and corticosterone (Rao *et al.*, 1977b) by liver parenchymal cells. Binding of cortisol by liver cells was found to be saturable after 60 seconds of incubation at 27° (M. L. Rao *et al.*, 1976). The initial rate of cortisol uptake was more sensitive to temperature variation from 5°–37° than the binding of this steroid by cytosol extracts (G. S. Rao *et al.*, 1976). In agreement with earlier studies by Harrison *et al.* (1975), an Arrhenius plot of glucocorticoid uptake was characterized by a sharp change in the slope at 15°–20° (G. S. Rao *et al.*, 1976). The activation energy calculated for cellular uptake of cortisol at 5–20° was 18 kcal/mol and at 20–32°, 6 kcal/mol. In contrast, the Arrhenius plot for cortisol binding to corresponding cytosol extracts was linear from 5°–32°, with an activation energy of 1.2 kcal/mol (G. S. Rao *et al.*, 1976). This transition in the velocity of glucocorticoid uptake was interpreted by Harrison *et al.* (1975) and by G. S. Rao *et al.* (1976) as evidence for a temperature-induced change in the physical state of membrane lipids (cf. Linden *et al.*, 1973), which diminishes the activity of a membrane binding component at low temperatures. However, the permeation of lipophilic solutes is also known to be diffusion-limited at physiological temperatures (cf. Dietschy, 1978), and this factor may contribute to the observed temperature dependence of steroid uptake.

G. S. Rao *et al.* (1976) and M. L. Rao *et al.* (1976) have also studied the concentration dependence of the initial rates of total cortisol uptake by liver cells. Analyses of the uptake data by double-reciprocal and Scatchard plots indicated that the initial rate of cortisol uptake was characterized by both saturable and nonsaturable components. Treatment of cells with KCN or 2, 4-dinitrophenol appeared to inhibit the saturable uptake components, which were operative in the physiological range of glucocorticoid concentrations, but the nonsaturable process, which was evident only at cortisol concentrations above $6 \times 10^{-7} M$, was not blocked by the latter inhibitors (G. S. Rao *et al.*, 1976; M. L. Rao *et al.*, 1976). Kinetics of the nonsaturable component were indicative of simple diffusion. Thus, as suggested earlier by Milgrom *et al.* (1973), uptake of steroid hormones may occur by a saturable process at low physiological concentrations and a nonsaturable process at higher concentrations (cf. Rao *et al.*, 1977b). Unfortunately, the hormonal specificity of the uptake process at low physiological concentrations and a nonsaturable process at higher concentrations of the uptake process in the studies of Rao *et al.* (1977b) was evaluated in separately reported experiments only in the presence of micromolar concentrations of competing steroids. Under these conditions, the saturable uptake of cortisol was blocked by cortisone, corticosterone, and dexamethasone, and was partially reduced by estradiol and testosterone (G. S. Rao *et al.*, 1976; M. L. Rao *et al.*, 1976).

Harrison *et al.* (1974, 1975) have studied the specific binding of a synthetic glucocorticoid, triamcinolone acetonide, by pituitary adenocarcinoma cells. Initial rates of uptake were not reported, but several differences in the characteristics of binding by intact cells vs. cell-free extracts (i.e., sensitivity to temperature and enzymes) indicated that glucocorticoid binding by this target cell involves a membrane-associated component (cf. also, Gross *et al.*, 1970).

Mayer *et al.* (1976) have investigated the binding of dexamethasone by isolated rat thymocytes. Cells were incubated in complex tissue culture media but in the absence of serum for 5–90 minutes with $2.2 \times 10^{-8}\ M$ [³H]dexamethasone and then washed in the cold in the presence of $1 \times 10^{-5}\ M$ unlabeled dexamethasone for a total of 15 minutes. Under these conditions, the extent of glucocorticoid binding by intact cells was found to increase with increasing temperature from $0°$ to $30°$. In contrast, specific binding of dexamethasone in cytosol extracts declined progressively within the same temperature range. In additional experiments on the concentration dependence of dexamethasone binding, cells were incubated at $20°$ for 3 hours, and binding of the glucocorticoid was found to be a linear function of the external dexamethasone concentration (6–38 nM). Mayer *et al.* (1976) interpreted these data as evidence for uptake of dexamethasone into thymocytes by a simple solubility-diffusion mechanism. Clearly, this conclusion is not warranted by the data presented. Instead, the data would appear to suggest that thymocyte binding of dexamethasone at equilibrium is not saturable within the narrow range of concentrations tested.

The initial rate of uptake of prednisolone by glucocorticoid-responsive Reuber rat hepatoma cells at $18°$, as estimated from 1-minute observation times, was studied by Plagemann and Erbe (1976). Total, rather than specific, uptake of prednisolone was determined, although the authors reported that accumulation of prednisolone was not affected by competition with $1 \times 10^{-4}\ M$ dexamethasone or deoxycorticosterone in independent experiments. Their results showed that the initial rate of uptake of prednisolone so determined was directly proportional to hormone concentration in the medium from $1 \times 10^{-8}\ M$ to $8 \times 10^{-3}\ M$, indicating uptake by simple diffusion (Plagemann and Erbe, 1976). However, this conclusion is difficult to reconcile with data from additional experiments of these workers who found that binding of prednisolone by paired cells after 20 minutes of incubation was likewise directly proportional to hormone concentrations ranging from $1 \times 10^{-8}\ M$ to $8 \times 10^{-3}\ M$. The latter findings would seem to indicate that even intracellular binding of the glucocorticoid is not saturable. These unusual results may be attributable to treatment of the preparations with trypsin to disperse cells of confluent monolayers immediately before the start of the uptake experiments (cf. Plagemann and Erbe, 1976). Others have reported that specific binding of cortisol by whole target cells is markedly reduced by mild trypsinization (Melnykovych and Bishop, 1969).

Giorgi and Stein (1980) have undertaken extensive studies on the initial rates of uptake of natural and synthetic glucocorticoids, progesterone, free and conjugated estrogens, and androgens into monolayer cultures of hamster fibroblasts and rat hepatoma cells. Although the reponsiveness of the cell cultures to these various steroids was not tested, the authors have assumed on the basis of independent reports that the hepatoma cells are sensitive to glucocorticoids and relatively insensitive to the remaining steroids. The fibroblast cell line was considered to be insensitive to all of the indicated hormones. It is critical to note that these workers incubated their cell cultures in media containing 10% (v/v) newborn calf serum which was replaced by phosphate-buffered saline shortly before measurements of hormone uptake from 8 to 30 seconds. It is clear from other investigations (cf. Armelin et al., 1974; Esber et al., 1973; Bottenstein et al., 1979) that hormonal depletion of the serum component of the medium is required to demonstrate specific hormone binding and hormone-dependent responses of cells in culture. Appreciable concentrations of steroid hormones are present in serum-containing media commonly used to support cell growth (Esber et al., 1973). Therefore, serum must be depleted of endogenous steroids; for example, by treatment with dextran-coated charcoal at 50° (cf. Armelin et al., 1974). This expedient was not utilized by Giorgi and Stein (1980). The results of their study were interpreted as evidence that uptake rates of all steroids by both cell lines were linearly proportional to the external steroid concentration. However, inspection of their data on the concentration dependence of glucocorticoid uptake indicates that hormone entry may be characterized by both saturable and nonsaturable components, as recognized previously by other workers (Milgrom et al., 1973; Rao et al., 1977b). Specific binding of hormones was not determined, but uptake of labeled cortisol was found to *increase* in competition experiments with micromolar concentrations of unlabeled corticosterone, dexamethasone, and testosterone. In both lines of cells, the temperature coefficient, Q_{10}, calculated from initial rates of uptake was between 1.02 and 1.39 for $E_2\beta$ and progesterone over the entire range of temperatures tested, while the corresponding values for cortisol and dexamethasone lay between 1.40 to 3.60. Permeability coefficients for all free steroids showed little variation and were approximately 10^{-4} cm second^{-1}. Giorgi and Stein (1980) contend that these data proved that free steroids enter both target and non-target cells by simple diffusion. However, the potential contamination of their cell preparations with serum-derived steroid hormones leaves this conclusion open to serious reservations.

6. Problems Associated with Determination of Steroid Hormone Uptake: Limited Solubility and Diffusion Barriers

It is clear from the preceding analysis of currently available data that there is little rigorous evidence either to support or to refute facilitated, as opposed to passive, transport of steroid hormones into target cells. There are serious limitations in the interpretation of the publications, since these studies failed to account for (1) the actual chemical activity of the lipophilic steroid molecules in solution, as distinguished from the total concentration of the molecules in the bulk phase, and (2) the effect of diffusion barriers between the cell surface and the bulk medium (e.g., unstirred layers of water; cf. Dainty, 1963; Dietschy, 1978). The first factor is the more difficult to compensate for but it is especially relevant to these studies since steroid hormones were commonly added to cell and tissue preparations in amounts exceeding their true solubilities in buffer (cf. King and Mainwaring, 1974). Various proteins, solvents, or detergents were often added *in vitro* to enhance the solubility of the hormones in the bulk phase solution, but the actual amount of hormone in true solution and readily available for interaction with the plasma membrane may have been substantially less. Moreover, when rates of steroid uptake are determined from solutions containing other molecules with which the hormone can interact (e.g., complex tissue culture media), the experimental results may be determined by events in the bulk solution as much as by the kinetic characteristics of the cellular transport process (cf. Dietschy, 1978).

Dainty (1963) as well as several earlier workers (Nernst, 1904; Osterhout, 1933; Teorell, 1936) have drawn attention to possible errors in the determination of biological transport constants of solutes by virtue of unstirred layers of water at the boundary between the cell surface and the extracellular medium. Due to the limited water solubility and lipophilic nature of steroid hormones, the main barrier to cellular uptake of these hormones may well be the time required for diffusion within a thin layer of water that, because of very weak intermolecular (adhesive) forces between constituents of the plasma membrane and water, remains essentially unstirred (cf. Dainty, 1963; Davson, 1970; Dietschy, 1978). The thickness of this unstirred layer of water adjacent to the surfaces of epithelial membranes in both *in vivo* and *in vitro* studies has been found to vary from 75 to 5000 μm depending on the rate of mixing of the external bulk solution (cf. Davson, 1970; Dietschy, 1978). An example of the effect of unstirred layers of water on the cellular permeability of steroids can be given by assuming that there is no plasma membrane barrier, but instead, only an unstirred layer of water separating the cell interior from the external solution. Under these conditions, the permeation of the hormone will be equal to its diffusion coefficient in water and the reciprocal of the thickness of the unstirred layer (cf. Dainty, 1963; Davson, 1970). Thus, permeabilities of approximately 1×10^{-4} cm second^{-1} may be computed for estradiol and progesterone on the basis of diffusion coefficients of approximately 5×10^{-6} cm^2 second^{-1}[*] and an unstirred layer of 500 μm. A layer 1000-μm thick, on the other hand, would yield a permeability of approximately 6×10^{-5} cm second^{-1}. The latter calculated values are in accord with cellular permeability coefficients for steroid hormones reported in the literature (cf. Scheuplein *et al.*, 1969; Couturier *et al.*, 1973; Giorgi and Stein, 1980). Such calculations suggest that unstirred layers of water may have been wholly rate limiting to the cellular uptake of steroid hormones in studies hitherto, and emphasize the difficulty in interpreting membrane transport data without appropriate mathematical or experimental corrections for unstirred layer effects (cf. Dainty, 1963; Wright and Pietras, 1974; Dietschy, 1978). It is important to note that in the presence of a significant diffusion barrier, uptake of steroids as a linear and nonsaturable function of the extracellular concentration is entirely to be anticipated (cf. Dietschy, 1978). Consequently, such data cannot be interpreted as evidence against the possibility that uptake of steroid hormones proceeds by transport facilitated by a finite number of membrane binding sites.

7. Uptake of Steroid Hormones by Plasma Membrane Vesicles Derived from Target Cells

In very recent studies, several investigators have mounted a different approach, the use of plasma membrane vesicles, to determine the kinetics of steroid hormone uptake (Alléra *et al.*, 1980; Fant *et al.*, 1979; Harrison *et al.*, 1979). This approach offers several advantages over those methods described above: (1) The thickness of unstirred layers of water

---

[*] Diffusion coefficients for estradiol and progesterone were estimated by use of the Stokes-Einstein relation which applies to the diffusion of large particles of known radius in liquid medium (cf. Stein, 1967). Radii of the steroids were determined from their respective molecular volumes (cf. Hodgman *et al.*, 1960) which are directly related to molecular weight (estradiol, 272; progesterone, 314) and inversely related to density (estradiol, 1.25; progesterone, 1.17; cf. Hodgman *et al.*, 1960; D. Ellis, personal communication).

surrounding plasma membrane vesicles suspended in an incubation medium is probably considerably less than 10 μm (cf. Sha'afi *et al.*, 1967; Sherrill and Dietschy, 1975). (2) Plasma membrane vesicles prepared under appropriate conditions show minimal contamination with soluble cellular components (Jackson and Chalkley, 1974b; Alléra *et al.*, 1980; Fant *et al.*, 1979; Harrison *et al.*, 1979; Pietras and Szego, 1979c; see also Section III,A, above). Thus, the potential role of membrane components in mediating the process of steroid hormone uptake can be assessed in the absence of significant artifacts attributable to unstirred layers or intracellular binding.

Alléra *et al.* (1980) have examined the uptake of [^{3}H]corticosterone by liver plasma membrane vesicles with a 25-fold enrichment in the activities of appropriate marker-enzymes. Highly reproducible determinations of specific glucocorticoid binding within 5 seconds were made possible by use of the oil-centrifugation technique of Livingstone and Lockwood (1975). Under these conditions, specific binding of corticosterone to osmotically intact membrane vesicles was saturable within 8–11 seconds. In contrast, displaceable binding was linearly proportional to the external steroid concentration. The saturable binding component exhibited a dissociation constant of 7.2×10^{-9} *M*. Moreover, in competition experiments with excess molar concentrations of unlabeled steroids, specific binding of corticosterone was strongly inhibited by both natural and synthetic glucocorticoids, partially reduced by androstanolone and DES, and affected little or not at all by testosterone, estriol, or aldosterone.

Corticosterone uptake by plasma membrane vesicles prepared from pituitary tumor cells (Harrison *et al.*, 1979) and from human term placenta (Fant *et al.*, 1979) exhibited similar characteristics. However, in competition experiments with pituitary membrane vesicles, neither dexamethasone nor triamcinolone acetonide inhibited specific binding of corticosterone under conditions in which blockade of binding could be elicited by natural glucocorticoids (Harrison *et al.*, 1979). Likewise, Fant *et al.* (1979) also reported that triamcinolone acetonide was not an effective competitor for specific corticosterone binding sites in placental membrane vesicles, although dexamethasone and natural glucocorticoids were effective inhibitors. In both membrane-vesicle preparations, little to no reduction of specific corticosterone binding was observed in the presence of excess concentrations of several steroid hormones without glucocorticoid activity. Thus, Harrison *et al.* (1979) and Fant *et al.* (1979) suggest that specificity of membrane binding components for glucocorticoids is distinct from that of cytosol extracts, which appear to bind synthetic glucocorticoids preferentially (cf. Thompson and Lippman, 1974). This conclusion, however, must remain tenuous since, as acknowledged by

Harrison *et al.* (1974), several reports indicate that a class of proteins in cytosol extracts of target tissues bind corticosterone but not dexamethasone (Agarwal, 1976; DeKloet and McEwen, 1976; Koch *et al.*, 1976; Agarwal and Philippe, 1977; Barlow *et al.*, 1979).

Results of efforts to determine whether corticosterone binds to fixed sites on the plasma membrane vesicles or whether the glucocorticoid is free in the intravesicular space have been inconclusive. When placental membrane vesicles were reduced in size by incubation in hypertonic media, corticosterone content at equilibrium was reduced proportionately, indicating that the steroid existed as predominantly unbound solute in the intravesicular space (Fant *et al.*, 1979). However, intravesicular accumulation of steroid may be enhanced by extensive metabolic conversion of corticosterone to 11-dehydrocorticosterone (cf. Fant *et al.*, 1979). In contrast to these results, the bulk of corticosterone binding by plasma membrane vesicles from liver (Alléra *et al.*, 1980) and pituitary (Harrison *et al.*, 1979) was unaffected by a similar reduction in intravesicular space, indicating that the saturable uptake of steroid is attributable largely to binding by a fixed number of membrane sites.

Such conflicting data may well be attributable to differences in the purity [e.g., plasmalemmal marker-enzymes enriched by 25-fold in vesicles prepared by Alléra *et al.* (1980) vs. sevenfold and 20-fold in membranes prepared by Harrison *et al.* (1979) and Fant *et al.* (1979), respectively] and/or the effective concentration of steroid binding sites of these various plasma membrane preparations. However, it is apparent that refinement and extension of this approach (see Table II) offers promise of more definitive answers to still largely open questions of the mode of steroid hormone uptake by target cells.

8. Steroid Hormone Transport Complexes in Blood and Their Interactions with Target Cells

Steroid hormones occur in the blood in both free and protein-bound forms (cf. Brunelli, 1934; Roberts and Szego, 1946; Westphal, 1970). The relative proportion of steroid in each state has a profound influence on the quantity of hormone available for entry into target cells. Under normal physiological conditions it has been determined that 90–96% of endogenous steroids exist in the circulation in protein-bound form (cf. Westphal, 1970; King and Mainwaring, 1974; Ballard, 1979). With the possible exception of aldosterone (Zager *et al.*, 1976), which binds primarily to albumin and transcortin in plasma (i.e., 60–65% protein bound; Daughaday *et al.*, 1961; Meyer *et al.*, 1961), the bulk of the bound steroids associate with specific plasma binding proteins with relatively high affinity (e.g., $K_d \approx 10^{-8}\ M$) and low capacity, but significant binding of steroids to albumin also occurs. The latter binding is characterized by low affinity (e.g., $K_d = 10^{-4} - 10^{-6} M$) but high capacity due to the high plasma concentration of albumin, normally 4 g% (cf. King and Mainwaring, 1974; Ballard, 1979).

It was initially assumed that these proteins might be required to enhance the solubility of steroids in the vascular space, but considerable evidence shows that steroid hormones are relatively soluble in aqueous media at prevailing physiological concentrations (King and Mainwaring, 1974; Ballard, 1979). Abundant data also suggest that these proteins are not obligatory for steroid hormone action (cf. King and Mainwaring, 1974; Clark *et al.*, 1977; Ballard, 1979). Dissociation of plasma protein-bound hormone appears to be a prerequisite for entry into target cells (Giorgi and Moses, 1975; Rao *et al.*, 1977b). Consequently, the physiologic role of such carrier proteins has remained unclear.

Indications of a more significant role for plasma proteins in mediating the interaction of lipid ligands with target cells are available in the literature. It is well known that many regulatory molecules form complexes with plasma proteins, and it was first suggested by Bennhold (1938) that they might be carried into cells in protein-bound form (cf. also Troensegaard and Koudahl, 1926). In a narrow sense, cholesterol, an essential component of the plasma membrane of all mammalian cells, has limited functions as a steroid hormone. The relatively insoluble sterol is produced in liver, packaged into lipoprotein particles, and the soluble lipoprotein–cholesterol complexes are secreted into plasma and carried to cells such as fibroblasts (cf. Brown and Goldstein, 1979). Intracellular functions of the cholesterol are dependent upon receptor-mediated endocytosis of the cholesterol–lipoprotein complex, a sequence of events in which saturable receptor binding and internalization are coupled in specialized regions of the plasma membrane (cf. Brown and Goldstein, 1979).

Plasma carrier proteins also appear to facilitate the interaction of another lipid ligand, retinol, with target cells. Uptake of retinol by retinal pigment epithelial cells (Chen and Heller, 1977) and by intestinal epithelial cells (Rask and Peterson, 1976) appears to require prior association of the polyene lipid with retinol binding protein (RBP). Saturable binding sites specific for retinol–RBP complexes occur exclusively on the surface membrane facing the systemic circulation (Heller, 1975; Chen and Heller, 1977). Only retinol is accumulated by these target cells; RBP does not enter the cell (Rask and Peterson, 1976; Heller, 1975). As with steroid hormones, the mode of transport of retinol through the plasma membrane is not clear. Recent studies by Maraini *et al.* (1977) show that a retinol-binding macromolecule with an approximate molecular weight of 14,500 is present in plasma membranes isolated from eye pigment epithelium. The relation of this membrane binding component to other retinol binding proteins discovered in cytosol extracts of responsive cells (cf. Chytil and Ong, 1978) remains to be determined. It is noteworthy that the cytosolic binding protein is found to have a molecular weight of approximately 14,600 and, as in the case of steroid hormones, may serve to allow specific interaction of retinol with the nucleus (cf. Chytil and Ong, 1978; Takase et al., 1979).

Binding of vitamin D in vivo is recognized to involve a serum binding protein (DBP) specific for the sterol and its metabolites and two tissue binding proteins (cf. Haussler and Brumbaugh, 1976). DBP is a 3.5 S moiety and has a binding preference for 25-hydroxycholecalciferol (25-OH-D_3) over vitamin D_3 and 1, 25-dihydroxycholecalciferol (1, 25-$(OH)_2D_3$; Haddad and Walgate, 1976). A cytosolic 3.7 S tissue protein which preferentially binds 1, 25-$(OH)_2D_3$ but not 25-OH-D_3 has been demonstrated in several target tissues and appears to be a receptor analogous to those proposed for mediating steroid hormone action (cf. Brumbaugh and Haussler, 1973; Tsai and Norman, 1973). A 5–6 S binding protein also occurs in cytosol extracts of apparently all nucleated cells and preferentially binds 25-OH-D_3. Since the latter 6 S cytosol binder shares common antigenic sites with plasma DBP, it is generally considered to reflect plasma contamination of tissues during cytosol preparation (cf. Cloix et al., 1978; Kream et al., 1979; Cooke et al., 1979a). The absence of the 5–6 S component in cultured cells grown without serum (Van Baelen et al., 1977) and in isolated intestinal cells after extensive washing (Kream et al., 1979) appears to support the contention that this complex is not physiologically significant. However, Cooke et al. (1979b) find that the level of immunoreactive DBP in washed tissues is two to three times higher than that in serum. They also present new evidence which suggests that entry of serum DBP into cells and its intracellular binding with high affinity and specificity to a cytosol protein (i.e., yielding the 5–6 S complex), contribute to the intracellular transport of vitamin D sterols (Cooke et al., 1979a,b). These recent observations on the nature of the 5–6 S complex in cytosol extracts and on its capacity to transfer vitamin D metabolites to nuclei (Oku et al., 1974) clearly require further investigation.

The association of corticosteroid binding globulin (CBG) or CBG-like substances with target cells has been reported by many investigators (cf. Munck and Leung, 1977). Although the possibility of contamination due to extracellular sources was not rigorously excluded in many studies, a few investigations provide evidence that the presence of a CBG-like component in lymphocytes (Werthamer *et al.*, 1973), perfused muscle (Mayer *et al.*, 1975), and isolated pituitary cells (Koch *et al.*, 1976; DeKloet *et al.*, 1977; cf. also DeKloet and McEwen, 1976) cannot be attributed solely to plasma contamination. Koch *et al.* (1978) further show that the CBG-like material may be complexed with crude pituitary plasma membranes. In autoradiography studies, Peterson and Spaziani (1969, 1971) have also found that uterus, but not nontarget tissue, accumulates [^{131}I] albumin and α-globulin from the circulation at 1–6 hours after injection of E$_2\beta$. Evidence that another serum binder for estradiol, α-fetoprotein, may account entirely for the high E$_2\beta$-binding properties of uterine cytosols (cf. Uriel *et al.*, 1976) has not received independent confirmation (Radanyi *et al.*, 1977; Aussel and Masseyeff, 1978).

A cellular function for steroid hormone binding globulins is equally difficult to determine. Such plasma proteins appear to be unable to fulfill one major function characteristic of presently described receptor protein, namely the transfer of steroid hormones into nuclei in cell-free systems (Mainwaring and Peterken, 1971; Mainwaring and Irving, 1973; Koch *et al.*, 1976). Moreover, CBG, for example, also has little affinity for binding glucocorticoid analogs such as dexamethasone (Rousseau *et al.*, 1972b). Nevertheless, a role for steroid hormone carrier proteins at the blood–membrane interface can be postulated. Keller *et al.* (1969) have suggested that CBG may influence the tissue distribution of corticosteroids by directing hormones toward those organs with protein-permeable vascular beds. Bischoff *et al.* (1954) have also found that plasma proteins such as albumin can profoundly reduce the oil/water partitioning coefficients of steroid hormones (e.g., 6% albumin reduces the K_{oil} for E$_2\beta$ by 93-fold). Since the partition coefficient is the most important factor in determining the cellular permeability of such hormones (see above), it is apparent that passive movement of steroids through cell membranes will be markedly reduced in the presence of the levels of plasma proteins present *in vivo*. This factor may limit the *nonspecific* permeation of steroid hormones into nontarget cells and favor uptake by responsive cells if cellular binding components with higher affinity are available at the blood: target-cell–membrane boundary (cf. Roberts and Szego, 1946; Pietras and Szego, 1977a, 1979c). Finally, steroid carrier proteins and albumin may also serve to shuttle these hydrophobic hormones across complex diffusion barriers (i.e., unstirred layers of water) to more immediate sites of uptake at the aqueous–membrane interface. A similar role has been suggested for plasma proteins involved in the transport of fatty acids (cf. Dietschy, 1978), and the physiologic importance of this function has been emphasized in our analysis of unstirred layer effects on steroid hormone permeability in a preceding section. Clearly, a rigorous evaluation of these potential plasma protein functions in steroid hormone action is required in future studies.

E. POTENTIAL ROLE OF THE CYTOARCHITECTURE IN STEROID ENTRY: ENDOCYTOSIS

Willmer (1961) was among the first to elaborate a theory of steroid hormone action based on the physical interaction of steroids with cell membranes. On the basis of early studies on the orientation of cholesterol in various lipid monolayers, he proposed that insertion of steroid molecules into the phospholipid–cholesterol core of cell membranes occurred in a nonrandom specific manner, with the long axis of the hormone molecule parallel to the hydrocarbon chains of the membrane lipids. The action of a steroid on a given cell was considered to depend on the molecular shape of the hormone, on its affinity for membrane lipids, and on interactions with membrane-associated proteins. However, Munck (1957) found that most steroid hormone molecules, which have more hydrophilic sites than cholesterol, tend to orient horizontally, rather than vertically, at a heptane–water interface. More recent work confirms these experimental observations and indicates that steroid hormones may influence the properties of lipid monolayers by altering the aqueous environment at the lipid–water interface (cf. Pak and Gershfeld, 1967; Lucy, 1968). In studies with erythrocytes under hemolytic conditions, Hubbell et al. (1970) found that spin-labeled steroids can gain access to protein sites deeply embedded in the membrane (cf. also Table II D, and Klausner et al., 1979). The authors suggested that lower concentrations of steroids may act to increase the disorder of membrane lipids to a critical level to the point of interference with interactions between protein and lipid constituents of the membrane. However, these workers argued that such physical interactions can be relevant *in vivo* only if some selective mechanism exists to increase the local concentration of steroid in certain membranes. Such a concentrating mechanism in target cells may be embodied in the recently identified plasma membrane receptors for steroid hormones (see Table II). However, new studies on the behavior of $E_2\beta$ molecules at a lipid-water interface also show that the interface functions to concentrate, orient, and enhance the association of molecules of the hormone with each other (Khaïat et al., 1975). These several physical interactions, as well as specific hormone binding to membrane components as such, may lead to distortion of membrane structure sufficient to generate small infoldings of plasma membrane which rapidly bud off as vesicles into the cytoplasm. Such a transport process may be analogous to adsorptive pinocytosis or to micropinocytosis (cf. Palade, 1960; Roth and Porter, 1964; Allison and Davies, 1974; Sly *et al.*, 1978).

In contrast to pinocytosis by vesicles with diameters ranging from 0.1 to 5 μm, the formation of microvesicles (i.e., approximately 30–90 nm) and their dissociation from plasma membranes do not require direct input of metabolic energy (Casley-Smith, 1969). However, micropinocytosis is reduced at low temperature (Allison and Davies, 1974). The thermal energy needed for vesicular movements and coalescence to form larger vesicles appears to be supplied solely by Brownian motion (Casley-Smith, 1969; Green and Casley-Smith, 1972). Microvesicles, as well as other endocytotic vesicles, are also known to fuse with organelles of the lysosome system (cf. Allison, 1973; Allison and Davies, 1977; de Petris, 1977), and may gain access thereby to the nucleus (cf. Szego, 1975; Schneider *et al.*, 1978). The rate of the micropinocytotic uptake process is extremely rapid. Using several electron-microscopic tracers, Casley-Smith and Chin (1971) have found that steady-state uptake of tracer molecules was achieved by approximately 10 seconds.

Despite the fragmentary nature of evidence for such a process, some of the relevant criteria are found to be met in studies of steroid–target-cell interactions. For example, after treatment of ovariectomized rats with $E_2\beta$ for just 2 minutes, *vesicles visible only at the TEM level* occur in the cortical cytoplasm and deep within the interior of uterine cells (Fig. 22; see also Fig. 13a in Szego, 1975). In some sections, the microvesicles at the membrane surface appear to communicate with the external environment (Szego *et al.*, 1980). The prominent occurrence of minute vesicular elements in the cytoplasmic matrix of hepatocytes within 15 minutes after glucocorticoid administration to adrenalectomized rats, as noted by Rancourt and Litwack (1968), may have been another manifestation of this phenomenon. The *lack of indication for an endergonic process* in steroid uptake in the hands of most, but by no means all investigators (see preceding section) is also characteristic of entry by membrane microvesiculation, as noted above.

Redistribution of integral proteins into patches and clusters in the plasmalemma as a result of membrane perturbation is now recognized as one means of triggering regional internalization of the cell surface (i.e., adsorptive or ligand-induced pinocytosis). This function, represented schematically in Fig. 23 (Singer, 1975, 1976), is sharply accentuated, as much as 4000-fold, when specific binding to given ligand occurs (Cohn, 1975). The mechanism for such "provoked internalization" (Szego, 1978) is believed to be related to the stress of deformation of the membrane, with resultant local change in permeability to some critical

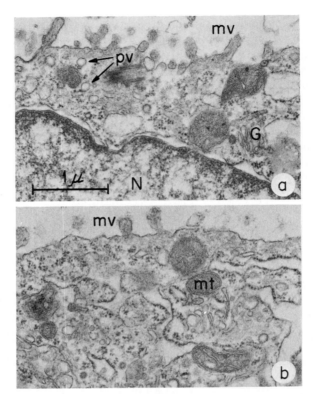

Fɪɢ. 22. Transmission electron micrographs of luminal endometrial cells. (a) Taken 2 minutes after i.v. administration of $E_2\beta(0.1\ \mu g/100$ g body wt.) to ovariectomized rat. (b) Control preparation that received equivalent volume of vehicle only (cf. Szego and Davis, 1967). To be noted are the frequency of occurence of micropinocytotic vesicles (pv) in the cortical cytoplasm of the estrogen-pretreated cell and the lack of such microvesiculation in the control. N, Nucleus; G. Golgi; mv, microvillus; mt, mitochondrion; $\times$ 20,400. (Electron micrographs were prepared by Ms. Monica Wong under the supervision of Dr. W. Jann Brown, who also advised on their detailed interpretation.)

factor which, in turn, activates contractile elements in the subplasmalemmal cytoskeleton, leading to regional internalization (Singer, 1975, 1976).* By means of dual fluorescence and immunofluorescence staining of the same cells, the coordinate movement of surface receptors for multivalent ligands in the plane of the membrane and intracellular mechanoproteins immediately below them has been demonstrated (Ash

---

* An alternative mechanism, "membrane flow," has been proposed to explain capping, but the two ideas are not mutually exclusive (Stern and Bretscher, 1979).

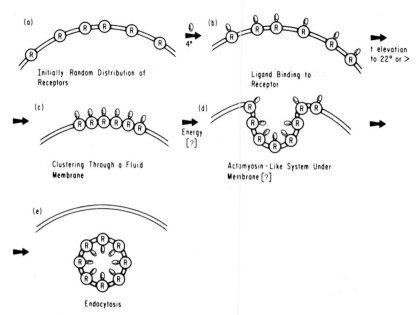

(a) Initially Random Distribution of Receptors

(b) Ligand Binding to Receptor

(c) Clustering Through a Fluid Membrane

(d) Actomyosin - Like System Under Membrane [?]

(e) Endocytosis

FIG. 23. Endocytotic uptake of given ligands on interaction with specific receptors at the cell surface. (From Singer, 1975, reproduced by permission, with approved minor modifications.)

and Singer, 1976; Bourguingnon and Singer, 1977; cf. also Albertini and Clark, 1975; Edelman, 1976). However, the specific molecular mechanisms controlling such closely linked behavior remain to be elucidated. It has been proposed that phosphorylation of given cell surface proteins, such as histocompatibility antigens (Pober *et al.*, 1978), promotes their interaction with cytoskeletal elements. This suggestion has recently been extended to events associated with internalization of recognition sites for β-adrenergic agonists concomitantly with depletion of such sites in the cell surface on receptor occupancy (Chuang and Costa, 1979). Several concomitants of ligand association with integral protein that could support and modulate membrane phosphorylation include nucleotide cyclase stimulation, protein kinase activation, and redistribution of Ca^{2+}. These closely coupled events could thus promote further transmission of information to the cytoskeletal elements in the submembrane cytoplasmic compartment, leading to internalization of ligand together with its membrane recognition site. All three concerted changes are evidently elicited by cell surface interactions of steroid hormone, as noted in preceding sections.

Microfilaments and perhaps other undefined mechanochemical elements are generally considered to play an active role in ligand-induced clustering of surface components (Rutishauser and Edelman, 1978; Singer *et al.*, 1978). Some investigators suggest that microtubules are also involved in this process (Albertini and Clark, 1975; Rutishauser and Edelman, 1978) but others dispute this contention (de Petris, 1974; Singer *et al.*, 1978). The possible role of microtubule–microfilament systems in mediating the accumulation of steroid hormones by target cells remains to be rigorously investigated. A preliminary communication by Gorski and Raker (1973) provided evidence that binding of $E_2\beta$ in uterus is not markedly reduced by treatment with cytochalasin B, a relatively specific inhibitor of microfilament function. However, vinblastine, an inhibitor of microtubule assembly, did reduce the accumulation of hormone after a 4-hour prior incubation with the drug. Similarly, after incubation of isolated endometrial cells for 4 hours with $2 \times 10^{-5} M$ colchicine, the drug effected a reduction of specific $E_2\beta$ uptake by 30–40%, as compared to control cells exposed to the inactive compound, lumicolchicine (Pietras and Szego, 1977b). Concomitantly, colchicine inhibited the surface change elicited by the hormone in corresponding cells, as analyzed by Con A-mediated hemagglutination and cathepsin B extrusion (all, $P < .001$). In contrast to these occasional observations, Kalimi and Fujimoto (1978) found no effect of colchicine administered either simultaneously with, or up to 1 hour prior to, $E_2\beta$ injection on nuclear accumulation of the hormone in uterus. However, under similar conditions, the microtubule inhibitor did restrict uptake of water induced by the hormone (Fujimoto and Morrill, 1978). It is clear from inspection of results presented by Gorski and Raker (1973) that even 1 hour of incubation with such microtubule inhibitors is not sufficient time for drug uptake and binding to tubulin subunits in the cell interior. Aubin *et al.* (1975) have shown that cellular permeability to colchicine is the major factor limiting the interaction of the drug with microtubule subunits. Thus, the effect of colchicine observed by Fujimoto and Morrill (1978) on $E_2\beta$-induced net water transport in uterus appears to be distinct from the capacity of the drug to promote depolymerization of cytoplasmic microtubules (cf. also Beebe *et al.*, 1979). Related studies on the accentuated endocytotic activity of uterine epithelium on days 5–6 of pregnancy indicate that colchicine, after 4 hours, elicits significant reduction in the coordinated intracellular movements of endocytotic vesicles and lysosomes (Parr *et al.*, 1978). It is clear that extension of these studies is critical to understanding the significance of microtubule and/or microfilament systems in the cellular distribution of steroid hormones.

Certain preceding examples of ligand uptake provoked by redistribution of surface receptors appear to be restricted to multivalent antibodies and lectins. If ligand-induced clustering is involved in steroid hormone uptake, this would probably represent a special case, since these compounds presumably do not act as cross-linking agents. However, Singer and Nicolson (1972) have proposed that a univalent agonist, after binding to its receptor, may induce cooperative binding interactions leading to aggregation of both bound and perhaps unbound specific receptors in the plane of the membrane. Evidence for positive cooperativity in the binding of estradiol to solubilized receptors (Ellis and Ringold, 1971; Erdos *et al.*, 1971; Puca *et al.*, 1971; Sanborn *et al.*, 1971) as well as to plasmalemmal binding sites of high affinity (Pietras and Szego, 1980a) is available. However, Gorski and colleagues were unable to demonstrate cooperative binding of hormone in cytosol extracts (Clark and Gorski, 1969; Giannopoulos and Gorski, 1971; Williams and Gorski, 1974).

A related mechanism by which mammalian cells endocytose ligand–receptor complexes may be better adapted to the function of "univalent" agonists. For example, surface receptors for cholesterol–lipoprotein complexes appear to be largely confined to structures termed *coated pits*, which constitute only a minute portion of the total surface area of the plasma membrane (Roth and Porter, 1964; Brown and Goldstein, 1976). Endocytosis resulting from these ligand–receptor interactions is presumably not triggered by ligand-induced clustering of membrane receptors, since the latter are already aggregated (cf. Singer *et al.*, 1978).*

A new set of observations by Nenci and co-workers (1980) has revealed a quite striking redistribution of plasmalemmal binding sites for a fluorescein-labeled estradiol–albumin complex in human breast cancer cells, but not in nontarget cells. When labeling was carried out at 4°, E-BSA-F was distributed homogeneously over the cell surface. However, on warming, the labeled steroid was first redistributed into patchy aggregates and then into polar caps. Similar results were obtained when polyestradiol phosphate complexed with rabbit IgG was used as probe and challenged with horseradish peroxidase-labeled secondary antibody. Clearly, these findings provide additional support for specific estradiol–

---

* The relegation of receptor-mediated cellular entry processes for protein ligands (Brown and Goldstein, 1979; Willingham *et al.*, 1979) to those regions of the cell surface equipped with coated pits (Roth and Porter, 1964; Pearse, 1975) has had a limiting influence upon extension of these concepts. Evidence now available for entry of β_2-microglobulin into fibroblasts indicates that regions of the cell surface associated with stress fibers, but independent of coated pits, may be involved in the uptake process (S. J. Singer, personal communication, September, 1979; cited by permission).

target-cell membrane interactions (cf. Pietras and Szego, 1977a, 1979a,c) and further indicate that these interactions may parallel the ligand-induced clustering model. However, the possible contribution of protein conjugated to estradiol, i.e., E-BSA-F, as well as second antibody in independent experiments, to the observed cross-linking of surface components, remains to be evaluated.

There is mounting evidence that the endocytotic process is also involved in the cellular uptake of peptide hormones (Szego, 1975, 1978). Indeed, as early as 30 seconds after addition, low concentrations of epidermal growth factor elicited pinocytotic vesiculation and internalization of plasma membrane in human epithelioid carcinoma cells (Haigler et al., 1979). A general pattern of endocytotic entry of protein hormones, independently proposed by Singer (1975) and Szego (1975) has rapidly become accepted for a very broad range of proteins, whether initially bound to specific surface recognition sites or not.

As summarized in Table II and Section IV,D, entry of steroid hormones into their respective target cells is equally rapid. The rate of this process has hampered adequate consideration of the endocytotic mechanism as a means of steroid access to the cell interior. Moreover, the intuitive assumption that the lipid bilayer poses no barrier to essentially instantaneous accessibility of steroid hormone to the cytoplasmic environment of all cells has had a similar restrictive influence upon consideration of alternative processes. However, we have seen that redistribution of integral proteins and capping are common not only to the effects of protein and steroid on specific surface recognition, but that these events are of truly rapid onset. But are they rapid enough to account for steroid entry? The answer to this is uncertain. One present limitation to our understanding, which might be remedied by appropriate instrumentation and attention to experimental design, is our inability to bring about essentially instantaneous arrest of the entry process at very brief intervals, of the order of milliseconds (cf. Hess et al., 1979). For, if gross alterations of membrane ultrastructure leading to unequivocal endocytotic microvesiculation can be identified within seconds to minutes, as noted above, we can be confident that the underlying molecular events have long been under way. We have not yet found means sufficiently rapid to arrest and observe them. The newer finding of Rao et al. (1977b) who note membrane-associated limitation of steroid entry into target cells within mere seconds at 15°, point the way toward more discriminatory experimental conditions. Some means of utilization of fluorescent (cf. Nenci et al., 1977) or other probes (cf. Hochberg, 1979) of extraordinary sensitivity will be needed, as will a procedure for near-instant fixation other than cryostatic, with its unfavorable effects on structural relations. Better yet, direct observation of unfixed living cells with video–image intensification (VIM) for fluorescent probes (cf. Schlessinger *et al.*, 1978) may become more generally feasible, especially with advances permitting finer discrimination between the fluorescence-defined membrane/cellular events and the fluorescent surround. For conventional fixation methods are far too slow to resolve this vital issue. Prefixation, followed by exposure to protein (Willingham *et al.*, 1979) or steroid (Pietras and Szego, 1979a) hormone, has other limitations.

Additional problems hamper ready demonstration of the endocytotic entry pathway for specific ligands. It is readily overwhelmed by membrane "noise" at temperatures much above 22°. Indeed, clustering of binding sites through increased membrane fluidity may be evoked by the very circumstances in which hormone binding is frequently tested (i.e., in cultivated cells, often of tumor lines; in the presence of high concentrations of metabolites, sometimes with inadequate buffering; and, most of all, at elevated temperatures, such as 37°). It has been pointed out elsewhere that such conditions may preclude ready identification of redistribution of recognition sites on binding of specific ligand because of high noise/signal ratio (Szego, 1974, 1978; Pietras and Szego, 1975b). Indeed, the magnitude and rapidity of induction, by isologous serum and a variety of other proteins, of changes in surface topography, including mobilization of labile microvilli and the formation of pre-endocytotic vesiculated pits in various cell types, are impressive. Thus, by 2 minutes, there is a threefold increase in surface changes in mesothelial cells of mouse omentum by both criteria (Madison *et al.*, 1979). The same order of onset may be identified in PC12 pheochromocytoma cells exposed to nerve growth factor (Connolly *et al.*, 1979) or in fibroblasts presented with lipoproteins (Anderson *et al.*, 1977).

Possibly additional data may reveal that internalization of steroid hormone is a compound function, occurring in part through utilization of specific recognition sites (adsorptive endocytosis) and also by means of nonspecific fluid-phase (bulk) entry. In the latter case, adventitious engulfment of neighboring regions further enhances and facilitates steroid (and other) entry. Conceivably, both specific endocytosis and bulk translocation may be contributory, by analogy to the internalization of other agonists (Steinman *et al.*, 1978). It is apparent that too little is currently known about the molecular mechanisms involved in the regulation of endocytosis to warrant further speculation. Additional work on the nature of these processes and their relation to steroid hormone entry is clearly required.

V. DYNAMICS OF CELL SURFACE RECOGNITION SITES: MOLECULAR AND CELLULAR ASPECTS

What are macromolecules with numerous attributes of receptors for steroid hormones doing in the surface membrane? Data that have now been reviewed with certain retrospective logic lead to the conclusion that, if they function efficiently, such molecules intercept and capture ("hit and hold") steroid ligands and, directly or indirectly, promote their cellular entry ("uptake") as well. But where do such molecules—regardless of their absolute identity with receptors in the intracellular environment—come from? How are they delivered to the cell surface? If, indeed, their internalization is triggered when ligand-loaded, what happens to that fraction of the (transformed?) complex that never reaches the nuclear compartment (cf. Giannopoulos and Gorski, 1971)? Is there a receptor graveyard?

Here we enter essentially uncharted territory.

Most plasmalemmal proteins appear to be associated with the cytoplasmic surface of the membrane (Bretscher, 1973). However, some extend across the lipid bilayer and generally have carbohydrate constituents on that portion of the molecule exposed at the cell surface. The substituents are believed to prevent diffusion of the membrane protein into the cytoplasm. Of the three to four structural classes of proteins presently considered as integral components of plasma membrane (Bretscher, 1973; Singer, 1977), two appear to exhibit properties corresponding to those identified for steroid binding sites in membranes. Proteins of type C as shown in Fig. 2 bear a hydrophilic domain protruding at the inner cytoplasmic surface of the plasmalemma and a hydrophobic domain embedded deep within the membrane. The proteins seem to be large enough to span the membrane but apparently do not (Singer, 1977). These proteins exhibit spontaneous binding to lipid bilayers and biological membranes, a property that seems to be shared, at elevated temperatures (e.g., 37°), with 4 S receptors for estradiol from uterine cytosol extracts (Jackson and Chalkley, 1974b). Integral proteins of type A (see Fig. 2) would seem to have properties similar to those of type C, but the existence of the former as distinct from that of loosely associated proteins at the cell surface remains to be demonstrated (Bretscher, 1973; Singer, 1977).

Integral membrane proteins of type D as shown in Fig. 2 are perhaps most interesting for the present discussion. It has been suggested that proteins of type C might spontaneously dimerize and thus form type-D components (Singer, 1977). The latter proteins are either homo- or heteroaggregates which span the plasma membrane. Singer (1977) notes that the dimeric structure of these membrane proteins is also very common among soluble proteins. Additional data indicate that, with appropriate modification of substituent groups, proteins integral to plasma membrane may occur in soluble states (cf. Bretscher, 1973; Thompson *et al.*, 1978). This point is especially relevant in view of the reported dimeric structures of steroid receptors purified from cytosol extracts (Vedeckis *et al.*, 1978; Sica and Bresciani, 1979) and of estrogen-binding components isolated from membranes (Little *et al.*, 1973; Pietras and Szego, 1980a). It is noteworthy that Na^+/K^+-ATPase, which binds cardiac glycosides (see Table II D) with high affinity, also has structural properties consistent with those of integral proteins of this class (cf. Kyte, 1975; Singer, 1977).

It is generally proposed that cytoplasmic ribosomes synthesize those proteins used intracellularly, whereas membrane-bound ribosomes of the endoplasmic reticulum (ER) synthesize proteins for secretion. Although it was initially postulated that plasmalemmal proteins as a special class of secretory proteins, are also synthesized on the RER (cf. Dauwalder *et al.*, 1972), others have proposed that synthesis occurs entirely (Bretscher, 1973), or in part (Lodish and Small, 1975) on ribosomes free in the cytoplasm. One source of the conflict in this area must be attributed to unavoidable redistribution artifacts that occur in the course of polysome isolation (Palade, 1975). Nevertheless, more recent investigations appear to favor the view that eukaryotic plasma membrane components are synthesized predominantly on polysomes bound to ER and to a lesser extent by free polysomes (cf. Parry, 1978). Thus, most mRNA species coding for $5'$-nucleotidase in mouse liver were found to be associated with ER, with a smaller portion in the free polysome fraction (Bergeron *et al.*, 1975). It will be interesting to examine additional systems to determine whether synthesis on a particular type of polysome is related to sidedness of protein distribution in the membrane (cf. Lodish and Small, 1975; Parry, 1978).

In pancreatic exocrine cells, products synthesized in ER pass through the Golgi apparatus for final processing and concentration in Golgi secretory granules (Palade, 1975). These granules ultimately fuse with plasma membrane where exocytosis occurs by a process which appears to require Ca^{2+}, contractile proteins and possibly a cyclic nucleotide generating system (Palade, 1975; cf. also Douglas, 1968; Smith and Winkler, 1972, in the neuronal and chromaffin cell contexts). In other cell types, components with receptor properties for agonists such as acetylcholine (Fambrough and Devroetes, 1978), insulin (Bergeron *et al.*, 1973, 1978; Posner *et al.*, 1978a), melanocyte-stimulating hormone (Varga *et al.*, 1976), and gonadotropins (Mitra and Rao, 1978b) have been identified in the Golgi apparatus. Moreover, parallel observations are available for agonists of lipid nature, e.g., prostaglandins (Mitra and Rao, 1978b), receptors for which are also concentrated in lysosomes (Mitra and Rao, 1978a). In cell fractionation experiments, the microsome fraction, which constitutes the *in vitro* equivalent of predominantly ER and Golgi components (as well as some plasmalemmal vesicles of low density), has also been found to have specific and selective binding components for given steroid hormones (see Table I and III). Indeed, Jungblut and colleagues (Little *et al.*, 1973; Jungblut *et al.*, 1976) have proposed that precursors of estrogen receptors in uterus are synthesized in microsomal fractions, and then modified and translocated to other cellular sites by mechanisms as yet undefined (cf. also Sato *et al.*, 1979).

In a number of cell types, the entire population of secretory granules for intracellular transport corresponds either to primary lysosomes or related vesicular structures with which acid hydrolases and secretory proteins are associated (Novikoff *et al.*, 1962; Cohn *et al.*, 1966; Smith and Farquhar, 1966; Palade, 1975; Holtzman *et al.*, 1977). The production of lysosomal enzymes is believed to involve ER and Golgi elements (Poste and Allison, 1973; Palade, 1975; Dean and Barrett, 1976). Novikoff *et al.* (1966) have suggested that formation of lysosomes may actually occur in a special compartment, the GERL (Golgi–ER–lysosomes), intercalated between the ER and trans-Golgi components. However, the alternative "secretion–recapture" hypothesis states that, as noted in a preceding section, lysosomal enzymes are first exocytosed as modified glycoproteins and then endocytosed as a consequence of interaction with surface membrane receptors (Neufeld *et al.*, 1977; Halley *et al.*, 1978; von Figura and Voss, 1979). In any event, it is clear that a wide variety of newly synthesized macromolecules may gain access to lysosomes or lysosome-like structures after vesicular segregation and brief sojourn in the Golgi apparatus (Novikoff *et al.*, 1964; Palade, 1975).

These interactions appear to have profound implications for studies on the origin and turnover of specific binding sites for steroid hormones in plasma membranes of their target cells. The localization, within lysosomes of target cells, of macromolecules with specific receptor properties for steroid agonists has been documented in Table III, and in greater detail elsewhere (Szego, 1974, 1975, 1976, 1978; Szego and Pietras, 1981). As has been pointed out above, such compartmentalized receptor may contribute artifactually to the "soluble" fraction of cell homogenates as a result of rupture and stripping of membrane-bounded vesicles by the customary vigorous homogenization procedures. However, under basal conditions, in the intact cell, this compartment is subject to far less stringent tests of structural integrity until hormonal challenge (Szego, 1974, 1975).

The end result of exocytosis of secretion granules or lysosome-like

vesicles is the extracellular discharge of secretory products and the reloca-
tion of some or all vesicle membrane in plasma membrane (Palade, 1975;
Bergelson and Barsukov, 1977; Parry, 1978). Such plasmalemma–vesicle
encounters may be transitory, leading to minimal release of vesicular
content, or prolonged, with the more extensive interaction permitting
"fission of the fused membranes" (Palade, 1975; Phillips, 1976). In turn,
plasma membrane renewal may also occur by the process of vesiculation
of ER and Golgi components and fusion of the resultant vesicles with existing plasmalemma (Singer, 1977). Moreover, there is a substantial
literature on the parallels in composition, presumably because of the traf-
fic between them, of the plasma membrane and the lysosomal structures
given cells (cf. Szego, 1975). The selective, quantal secretion of representative enzymes and additional lysosomal components from viable cells
elicited under conditions of heightened cellular activity by *steroid*
(Pietras and Szego, 1975b, 1979a; Szego *et al.*, 1977; Nemere and Szego,
1980) or *peptide* (Pietras *et al.*, 1975; Nemere and Szego, 1981) *hormone,*
prostaglandin F2α (Kaley and Weiner, 1975), or appropriate concentrations of *vitamin A* alcohol (Roels, 1969), without concomitant release of
lactate- or succinate-dehydrogenases (*op. cit.;* cf. also Brunk and
Ericsson, 1972), provide substantial precedent for the contribution of the
lysosomal compartment to such exchanges. Moreover, evidence is
available for accentuation of exocytosis, preceded by fusion of secretion
granules with the apical surface of endometrial glands, as early responses
(5 minutes) to the i.v. administration of progesterone to estrogen-primed
cats (Bareither and Verhage, 1980; cf. also, Abel *et al.*, 1975). Tsukada
and co-workers (1979) have also found that optimal concentrations (5 ×
10^{-7}–5 × 10^{-9} M) of dexamethasone stimulated secretion of α-fetoprotein
from cells of a hepatoma line cultured in serum-free medium, without
concomitant effect on albumin secretion, thus supporting more indirectly
the possibility of selective (vesicular?) delivery in steroid-responsive cells.

It has been pointed out by many workers that the steady state of cell
surfaces is a function of controlled attrition and renewal, with both processes subject to variation during the cell cycle and in accord with
metabolic activities of the given cell (see Cook, 1976; Doljanski and
Kapeller, 1976; Poste and Nicolson, 1977; Parry, 1978). There is evidence
that membrane recycling by coupled endocytosis–exocytosis may occur
under a variety of conditions (see Szego, 1978; Schneider *et al.*, 1978).
For example, the emptying of specific, apical vesicles into the thyroid
follicle lumen under the influence of thyroid-stimulating hormone, while
the hormone also accentuates endocytosis, is strongly suggestive of causal
and functional coupling between the two processes (Ekholm *et al.*, 1975).
Similar conclusions have been indicated from neurohypophyseal hormone treatment of amphibian urinary bladder (Masur *et al.*, 1972;

Pietras *et al.*, 1975). Thus, it has also been proposed recently that loss of polypeptide hormone receptors from plasma membrane, presumably by ligand-induced endocytosis, may provoke the synthesis and transport of new receptors from the ER–Golgi complex to the plasmalemma (Posner *et al.*, 1978b). These relationships are by no means unequivocally established. However, these examples do serve to demonstrate that surface membrane turnover under the influence of hormones is a closely coordinated composite of endo- and exocytotic events, in course of which partial or complete delivery of vesicular membrane as well as vesicular contents to the cell surface may be accomplished.

It is likely that the depletion of plasmalemmal steroid-binding sites after hormone treatment (Pietras and Szego, 1977a, 1980a), which may occur by some form of ligand-induced endocytosis, must also be balanced by a counterflow of either free or vesicle-bound material destined to replenish the plasma membrane. It is noteworthy that Bression *et al.* (1979) have found a striking periodicity in the specific uptake of the androgenic steroids, [³H]methyltrienolone and testosterone, in rat pituitary cells incubated *in vitro*. Likewise, rat liver cells showed cyclic accumulation of [³H]dexamethasone. There was corresponding periodicity in nuclear accumulation of the relevant steroids (cf. also Chamness and Bromley, 1979). This behavior was temperature dependent, with a full cycle requiring 18 hours at 0°, decreasing to 7 hours and 1.5 hours at 20° and 37°, respectively (Bression *et al.*, 1979). Altered numbers of glucocorticoid binding sites during the cell cycle in HeLa cells have also been noted (Cidlowski and Michaels, 1977). These data are strongly reminiscent of the coexistence in mixed cell populations from liver (Pietras and Szego, 1979a) and endometrium (Pietras and Szego, 1980b) of cells equipped with, or deficient in, surface receptor molecules *at a given time* (cf. also Dufy *et al.*, 1979). A similar periodicity of lysosomal behavior, both during the cell cycle (Quintart *et al.*, 1979a,b) and under conditions of hormonal stimulation and recovery therefrom (Szego, 1974, 1975), has also been documented. Clearly, such fragmentary indications of the intermittent availability of recognition sites for steroid hormone require the most intensive investigation, in part to determine whether this property is related to cellular percolation of receptor molecules during membrane recycling.* It will also be interesting to investigate the possibility that some portion of the early influences of steroid hormones

---

* Semiquantitative data on attrition of receptors for steroid and protein hormones by homologous as well as heterologous ligands constitutes a detailed chapter in itself and will not be pursued here. Similar considerations apply to rebound synthesis of specific receptor after ligand-mediated cellular entry and partial or complete degradation. Quantitative observations of such turnover are still in rudimentary stages.

on ribosomes (Liang and Liao, 1974) and on their attachment to ER (Sunshine *et al.*, 1971) may enhance synthesis of new receptor which might then become available to intercept additional hormone by the mechanisms outlined above.

We have seen evidence in the foregoing that limited numbers of macromolecules with specific and selective recognition properties for steroid (and nonsteroid) hormones occur in multiple cellular sites: the cell surface, the rough and smooth ER, the lysosomes, and even the mitochondria—to say nothing of the nucleus. How then can we reconcile the concept of compartmentation in the cellular economy, introduced early in this chapter (Section II), with candidates so avid for hormone capture in cellular sites so widespread? The available evidence indicates that these multiple sites are in closely regulated dynamic equilibrium with each other. The data suggest that it would be fruitful to investigate a potential mechanism for the orderly translocation of newly synthesized receptor molecules to and from the cell surface, with temporary sojourn, for various periods after their biosynthesis, in or on (cf. Tanabe *et al.*, 1979) membrane-bounded vesicles. Some fraction of such vesicles may correspond to components of the lysosomal apparatus. These organelles are notable for accumulation of a wide variety of substances, swift mobility, and a capacity for reversible fusion with other cellular membranes. Moreover, they are subject to controlled release of sequestered acid-, neutral-, and alkaline-hydrolases, nonhydrolytic enzymes (e.g., Griffiths and Lloyd, 1979; Dousset *et al.*, 1979), and other components (cf. Szego *et al.*, 1977) after binding of moderate concentrations of specific agonists (see de Duve and Wattiaux, 1966; Davies and Allison, 1976; Dean and Barrett, 1976; Szego, 1974, 1975, 1976, 1978; Petrusz, 1978). The implications of these properties for the regulated propagation of initial stimulus (i.e., surface membrane perturbation by ligand capture) to the numerous secondary responses of the target cell, including those involved in gene expression, form the subject of a separate review (Szego and Pietras, 1981).

VI. EVALUATION OF CURRENT MODELS OF STEROID HORMONE ACCUMULATION AND DISTRIBUTION IN TARGET CELLS

The generally prevailing concepts of the early stages of estrogen interaction with a target cell are presented schematically in Model A (Fig. 24). The hypothetical model is based upon voluminous experimental data reviewed by others (Bresciani *et al.*, 1974; Gorski and Gannon, 1976). In

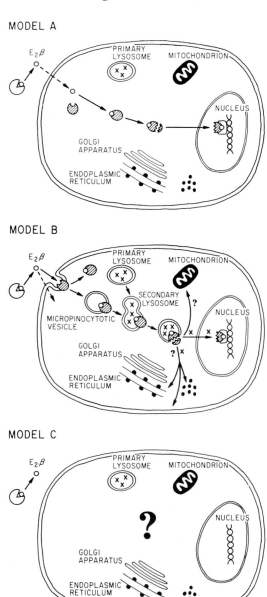

MODEL A

MODEL B

MODEL C

Fig. 24A–C. Schematic representations of models proposed to explain the accumulation and retention of estradiol-17β by target cells. Hormone in blood is predominantly bound to plasma proteins. Upon dissociation, free hormone is available for entry into the cell by the brief, free hormone, after dissociation from carrier proteins in blood, is considered to diffuse passively into the cell interior. The incoming steroid then binds to a specific receptor protein which is believed to be confined to the cytoplasmic matrix. Thereafter, activation of a "receptor-trans-forming factor" results in the production of a more mobile estrogen-receptor fragment which enters the nucleus and specifically interacts with an "acceptor" protein in chromatin (Thrall *et al.*, 1978). As noted in a preceding section, the nature of this activation step remains controversial (Gorski and Gannon, 1976; Puca *et al.*, 1977; Thrall *et al.*, 1978; Wilson and French, 1979; Pietras and Szego, 1980b). With minor exceptions, the general framework of Model A has been proposed to account for the target-cell interactions of all hormones with a steroid structure.

The recent observations of Sica and Bresciani (1979) indicate that the estrogen receptor in cytosol extracts of calf uterus consists of a single subunit endowed with one hormone binding site. Under physiological conditions, several subunits are considered to associate, forming a homo-aggregate. On the other hand, the progesterone receptor in cytosol extracts of chick oviduct is reported to be a hetero-aggregate composed of two distinct polypeptide subunits (cf. Vedeckis *et al.*, 1978). It is clear that experiments to evaluate the functional properties of these various structural forms of steroid hormone receptors are of paramount importance in determining the general applicability of Model A.

It is important to note that potential functions of plasmalemmal and cytoplasmic structures are seldom incorporated into the traditional view (i.e., Model A) of steroid hormone accumulation and retention by target cells. Indeed, it is widely believed that all actions of steroid hormones, including early alterations in the functions of the latter cellular structures, are a consequence of hormonal interactions with the genetic material of the target cell.

Based upon the experimental data summarized in the present review, a modified model for the cellular uptake and distribution of estrogen, and perhaps other steroid hormones, may be proposed (Fig. 24 B). Model B attempts to integrate presently available information on the several molecular forms of steroid hormone receptors (Erdos *et al.*, 1977), and

---

Fig. 24A–C *(continued)*.

several mechanisms discussed in the text. The plasma membrane and intracellular structures, including lysosomes with sequestered hydrolases or other components (X), mitochondria, Golgi apparatus, endoplasmic reticulum with bound ribosomes, free ribosomes, and the nucleus are shown in each model. Model A is adapted from previous schemes (Bresciani *et al.*, 1974; Gorski and Gannon, 1976). Model B is presently postulated; however, similar versions were proposed earlier by these (Szego, 1971, 1972a) and other (Jungblut *et al.*, 1970) laboratories. Model C remains as the alternative to all current hypotheses. See text for details.

the multiple cellular sites of their interactions with hormone. $E_2\beta$, which is initially bound to carrier proteins in the blood, probably enters the target cell by several different routes. At physiological concentrations of hormone, specific binding to high-affinity sites in plasma membrane is proposed as the major pathway (ligand-induced (*micro*)*pinocytosis*). Uptake of supraphysiological concentrations of hormone by passive diffusion, as well as by nonspecific entry of steroid still associated with carrier protein, may be superimposed on the primary pathway. Specific binding to plasma membrane components may provoke internalization of (micro) vesicles bearing the hormone–receptor complex, (see Section IV,E). These vesicles have potential for fusion with lysosomes, wherein transformation of receptor may be achieved. Subsequent delivery of hormone–receptor complex, together with certain lysosomal components to the cell nucleus is then envisaged (Szego, 1975).

This section cannot be left without comment on the many long years during which data have been accumulated on steroid-protein binding by methods that were often seriously flawed (reviewed in Szego, 1976). This has led to the development of a concept of hormone action which has emphasized nuclear events essentially to the exclusion of a large array of metabolic activities in the cytoplasm and at the cell surface (Szego, 1971, 1974, 1975). Model B permits us to confront the alarming information-gaps as they exist. For example, potential "extragenomic" effects of steroid hormones (cf. Spaziani, 1975; Lieberburg and McEwen, 1979) on surface membranes (Baulieu *et al.*, 1978; Pietras and Szego, 1979b, 1980b) as well as cytoplasmic structures (Blecher and White, 1960; Blyth *et al.*, 1971; Szego *et al.*, 1971; Hirsch and Szego, 1974) may be mediated either by the direct participation of steroid–receptor complex (Kanazir *et al.*, 1979) or by increased availability of certain lysosomal hydrolases or other effectors (Szego, 1975; Pietras and Szego, 1980b). Thus, Model B seeks to point up, for steroid (and other) hormones, the need to trace the origins, cellular distribution, and metabolic turnover of recognition molecules, both under basal conditions and in the hormone-activated cell. Model B also aims to remind us of the depth of our ignorance on the nature of coupling between the proximate events, which appear to be related to surface membrane binding of a hormone, and those culminating in the secondary responses of growth and differentiation.

In the case of cardiac glycosides and aglycones, it is obvious that *neither* Model A nor Model B describes the prevailing view that cardiotonic steroid action occurs exclusively at the target–cell surface (cf. Akera, 1977). It is quite clear that digitalis glycosides bind to and inhibit the Na^+/K^+-ATPase triphosphatase in plasma membrane (see Table IID). However, the basic site(s) and mechanism of action subserving the positive inotropic effect of these steroids in the heart remain unresolved (Dutta *et al.*, 1968; Park and Vincenzi, 1975). Other *in vitro* effects of ouabain on DNA synthesis and mitosis in lymphocytes and neuronal cells likewise have no adequate explanation (cf. Kaplan, 1978). However, accumulating evidence indicates that cardiac glycosides may undergo *facilitated* uptake by heart cells (Park and Vincenzi, 1975). Specific binding of these steroids in various heart cell fractions, including nuclei and other organelles, has also been documented (see Table I). Stumpf *et al.* (1977) have recently cited the estrogenic effects of cardiac glycosides and suggest that these substances may well act at atrial muscle cells through genomic stimulation. Thus, it appears the Model B or some variation thereof may provide a good working hypothesis to investigate the intracellular effects of cardiotonic steroids as well as steroid hormones.

A logical alternative to simplistic Models A and B is Model C (Fig. 24). It may well be a more productive hypothesis than either of the others, especially in light of the several observations already available (see Table XII, and Mainwaring, 1975), which, at present, appear to fit no currently postulated model (however, see Section IV,E; Szego, 1975; Szego and Pietras, 1981).

Apart from the inconsistencies noted briefly above, it appears that we have all been feeling different parts of the same elephant. No fundamental disparity appears to exist between the "traditional" views (Model A) of steroid hormone recognition, including propagation of their proximate effects, and those presented here (Model B). When methods and experimental approaches are taken into fullest account, and when the archaic view of the lysosome as an organelle engaged exclusively in cell destruction is finally dispelled, it is seen that these purportedly alternative views may be resolved into one continuum in which cellular structure and function play complementary and inseparable roles. Discord, in the present case more apparent than real, is but a transitional state from which synthesis must follow. For, to paraphrase Pavlov, one must sit down before truth without preconception, like a little child, and follow where the facts lead—or one will learn nothing.

VII. CLOSING COMMENTS

In the present work we have provided comprehensive documentation for a process of cell-surface recognition for the steroid hormones that has had a long hiatus, but is now receiving renewed attention. In so doing, we have tried to fulfill a further aim, lest the data thus assembled serve as a mere catalog. For we have made an effort to analyze the proximate re-

TABLE XII

SELECTED EXAMPLES OF FINDINGS NOT CONSISTENT WITH CURRENTLY POSTULATED MODELS OF STEROID HORMONE ACCUMULATION BY TARGET CELLS: NUCLEAR LOCALIZATION OF UNBOUND RECEPTORS OR DIRECT NUCLEAR INTERACTIONS OF STEROID HORMONES

Reference	Observation	Comments
Zava and McGuire (1977)	Unoccupied $E_2\beta$ receptors, representing 75% of total cell binding sites for $E_2\beta$, occur in Triton-treated nuclei[a] of human breast cancer cells grown in $E_2\beta$-free media (cf. Brooks et al., 1973). Confirmed by autoradiography (Sheridan et al., 1979).	Findings indicate that nuclear translocation and possibly function of $E_2\beta$ receptor can occur in absence of hormone in malignant cells.
Sheridan et al. (1979)	Autoradiographic studies show a portion of [^{3}H]$E_2\beta$ over nuclei of immature rat uterus after 5 minutes of incubation at 0°–4° (cf. Alberga et al., 1971; Jackson and Chalkley, 1974a; Kopp et al., 1979).	Conflicts with earlier studies showing only extranuclear distribution of [^{3}H]$E_2\beta$ in uterus at 0°–4° (Jensen et al., 1968); however, recent data show that nuclear translocation of $E_2\beta$–receptor complex does occur at 0°–4°, but at a reduced rate as compared to incubation of uterine cells at 37° (Traish et al., 1979).
Tsibris and McGuire (1977); Rüdiger et al. (1979)	Metabolism of estrogens by liver microsomes generates arene oxides and other species capable of (a) direct binding to DNA and (b) induction, at 10^{-9} M, of sister chromatid exchange, as in certain related carcinogenic processes (cf. Nelson et al., 1976; Glusker, 1979).	In some, but not in all, target organs, metabolism of testosterone to 5α-dihydrotestosterone by a microsomal enzyme also occurs under normal conditions (King and Mainwaring, 1974; King, 1976); however, microsomal conversion of estrogens may be more relevant to carcinogenesis.

[a] Crude nuclear fractions prepared from target organs at 0°–4° commonly contain 10–40% of total cell hormone binding sites (cf. Table I; Siiteri et al., 1972; Zava and McGuire, 1977). Much of this binding in nonmalignant tissue appears to be attributable to contamination with other particulate or soluble material during homogenization and may be reduced by further purification of nuclei (e.g., treatment with Triton X-100 and/or density-gradient centrifugation).

percussions of such interactions at membrane loci that may serve to couple surface recognition with secondary responses of the affected cells. We have also tried to integrate available evidence, old and new, of the means by which steroid hormones gain selective access to the cells they regulate. Beyond even these aims, we have endeavored to identify some common features of steroid and peptide hormone behavior toward surface recognition which seem to support the view that there exist certain qualitative similarities in their associations with relatively hydrophobic domains of the surface membranes of specific cellular targets. Numerous parallels have become evident in the rapid secondary transfer of both steroid and peptidal agonists to the Golgi–lysosomal compartment. Because we have been slow to grasp one lesson of natural history—*that development of responsive mechanisms is limited not by chemical nature of agonist but by the means available for signal transduction*—we are doomed to undertake the arduous and repetitive tasks of identifying the individual cases. At this stage in the evolution of this concept, available indications seem to favor only a limited qualitative understanding. However, while differences appear to be more of degree than kind, formidable problems exist in describing the potential parallels in quantitative terms.

In course of presenting this summary we have encountered some data seemingly, and some, in actual, conflict. We trust that the present analysis has made some contribution toward resolution of the former. We hope that our identification of some areas that require especially intensive investigation will promote resolution of the latter.

ACKNOWLEDGMENTS

The literature survey leading to the preparation of Tables II and III was conducted with the active collaboration of Ms. Sandra St. Dennis who also contributed efforts in additional ways. We thank Ms. Barbara J. Seeler for expert assistance in all laboratory phases of this work not previously acknowledged. Thanks are due to Mr. James Previdi and Mr. Kazmer Simon for meticulous maintenance of the low steroid environment in the animal quarters which permitted investigations to be carried out at submicrogram levels of hormone. Mr. George F. McGregor, Biomedical Reference Librarian, assisted in locating several elusive literature citations. We thank Ms. Jeanne-Marie Kuerschner and Ms. Margaret Kowalczyk for the graphic illustrations and Mr. Herman Kabe for the photographic reproductions. The skilled technical contribution of Ms. Monica M. Wong, who executed the electron micrographs shown in Figs. 7 and 22 under the supervision of Dr. W. Jann Brown, is gratefully acknowledged.

We are grateful to the following colleagues for helpful comments and/or provision of preprints of papers that were in press at the time the literature survey for this contribution (concluded on November 15, 1979), was in progress: Drs. M. L. Barber, California State University, Northridge, CA; M. L. Bareither and H. G. Verhage, University of Illinois School of

Medicine, Chicago, IL; E.-E. Baulieu, INSERM, Lab. Hormones, Bicêtre, France; R. A. Corradino, Cornell University, Ithaca, NY; B. Dufy, Institut National de la Santé et de la Recherche Médicale, Bordeaux-Cedex, France; D. Ellis, Syntex Research Center, Stanford, CA; T. Erdös, Centre National de la Recherche Scientifique, Gif Sûr Yvette, France; W. Farnsworth, VA Hospital, Buffalo, NY; E. Giorgi, National Institute of Biological Standards and Control, Hampstead, England; R. A. Gorski, University of California, Los Angeles; R. W. Harrison, Vanderbilt University, Nashville, TN; O. Hechter, Northwestern University, School of Medicine, Chicago, IL; K. Ishikawa, Shizuoka University, Japan; B. S. and J. A. Katzenellenbogen, University of Illinois, Urbana, IL; B. S. McEwen, Rockefeller University, NY; R. L. Moss, M. J. Kelly and C. A. Dudley, University of Texas, Dallas, TX; R. E. Müller, Boston University, MA; I. Nenci, Instituto di Anatomia e Istologia Patologia, Università di Ferrara, Italy; V. D. Ramirez, University of Illinois, Urbana, IL; G. S. Rao, Reinischen Friedrich-Wilhelms-Universität, Bonn, GFR; K. B. Ruf, McGill University, Montreal; P. J. Sheridan, University of Texas, San Antonio, S. J. Singer, University of California, San Diego; L. Sternberger, University of Rochester Medical Center, Rochester, NY; W. E. Stumpf, University of North Carolina, Chapel Hill; H. Terayama and T. Suyemitsu, University of Tokyo, Japan.

Portions of this work were aided by a USPHS postdoctoral fellowship CA 5176 (to R. J. Pietras) and by research grants PCM 78–22489 (NSF), HD 4354 and FR 7009 (USPHS), and by General Research Funds of the University of California.

Note added in proof: E. P. Giorgi has recently contributed a thoughtful review on the transport of steroid hormones into animal cells (*Int. Rev. Cytol.* **65**, 49–115, 1980).

REFERENCES

Abel, J. H., Jr., McClellan, M. C., Verhage, H. G., and Niswender, G. N. (1975). *Cell Tissue Res.* **158**, 461–480.

Åbro, A., and Kvinnsland, S. (1974). *Histochemistry* **42**, 333–344.

Adams, J. (1770). *In* "Legal Papers of John Adams" (L. K. Wroth and H. B. Zobel, eds.), Vol. 3, p. 269. Belknap Press, Cambridge, Massachusetts, 1965.

Agarwal, M. K. (1976). *Biochem. Biophys. Res. Commun.* **73**, 767–772.

Agarwal, M. K. (1979). *FEBS Lett.* **106**, 1–4.

Agarwal, M. K., and Philippe, M. (1977). *Biochem. Biophys. Acta* **500**, 42–48.

Aizono, Y., Roberts, J. E., Sonenberg, M., and Swislocki, N. I. (1974). *Arch. Biochem. Biophys.* **163**, 634–643.

Akera, T. (1977). *Science* **198**, 569–574.

Albano, J. D. M., Barnes, G. D., Maudsley, D. V., Brown, B. L., and Etkins, R. P. (1974). *Anal. Biochem.* **60**, 130–141.

Alberga, A., and Baulieu, E.-E. (1968). *Mol. Pharmacol.* **4**, 311–323.

Alberga, A., Massol, N., Raynaud, J.-P., and Baulieu, E.-E. (1971). *Biochemistry* **10**, 3835–3843.

Albertini, D. F., and Clark, J. I. (1975). *Proc. Natl. Acad. Sci. U.S.A.* **72**, 4976–4980.

Alléra, A., Rao, G. S., and Breuer, H. (1980). *J. Steroid Biochem.* **12**, 259–266.

Allison, A. C. (1973). *In* "Locomotion of Tissue Cells" (R. Porter and D. W. FitzSimons, eds.), pp. 109–148. Associated Scientific Publishers, Amsterdam.

Allison, A. C., and Davies, P. (1974) *In* "Advances in Cytopharmacology" (B. Ceccarelli, F. Clementi, and J. Meldolesi, eds.), Vol. 2, pp. 237–248. Raven, New York.

Allison, A. C., and Davies, P. (1977). *Symp. Soc. Exp. Biol.* **28**, 419–446.

Allwood, G., Asherson, G. L., Davey, M. J., and Goodford, P. J. (1971). *Immunology* **21**, 509–516.

Aloj, S. M., Lee, G., Grollman, E. F., Beguinot, F., Consiglio, E., and Kohn, L. D. (1979). *J. Biol. Chem.* **254**, 9040–9049.

Amsterdam, A., Berkowitz, A., and Kohen, F. (1979). *Endocrinology* **104**, Suppl., 200.

Anderson, R. G. W., Brown, M. S., and Goldstein, J. L. (1977). *Cell* **10**, 351–364.

Ansorge, S., Kirschke, H., and Friedrich, K. (1977). *Acta Biol. Med. Ger.* **36**, 1723–1727.

Appel, W. C., and Vincenzi, F. F. (1973). *J. Pharmacol. Exp. Ther.* **187**, 112–120.

Applebaum, S. W., and Gilbert, L. I. (1972). *Dev. Biol.* **27**, 165–175.

Ariëns, E. J., and Rodrigues de Miranda, J. F. (1979). *In* "Recent Advances in Receptor Chemistry" (F. Gualtieri, M. Giannella, and C. Melchiorre, eds.), pp. 1–36. Elsevier/North-Holland Biomedical Press, Amsterdam.

Armelin, H. A., Wishikawa, K., and Sato, G. H. (1974). *In* "Control of Proliferation in Animal Cells" (B. Clarkson and R. Baserga, eds.), pp. 97–104. Cold Spring Harbor Lab., Cold Spring Harbor, New York.

Aronson, N. N., Jr., and Barrett, A. J. (1978). *Biochem. J.* **171**, 759–765.

Ash, J. F., and Singer, S. J. (1976). *Proc. Natl. Acad. Sci. U.S.A.* **73**, 4575–4579.

Aubin, J. E., Carlsen, S. A., and Ling, V. (1975). *Proc. Natl. Acad. Sci. U.S.A.* **72**, 4516–4520.

Aussel, C., and Masseyeff, R. (1978). *J. Steroid Biochem.* **9**, 547–551.

Baker, M. E., and Fanestil, D. D. (1977). *Nature (London)* **269**, 810–812.

Baker, M. E., Vaughn, D. A., and Fanestil, D. D. (1978). *J. Supramol. Struct.* **9**, 421–426.

Ballard, P. L. (1979). *In* "Glucocorticoid Hormone Action" (J. D. Baxter and G. G. Rousseau, eds.), pp. 25–48. Springer-Verlag, Berlin and New York.

Barber, M. L. (1979). *Am. Zool.* **19**, 821–837.

Bareither, M. L., and Verhage, H. G. (1980). *Biol. Reprod.* **22**, 635–643.

Barlow, J. W., Kraft, N., Stockigt, J. R., and Funder, J. W. (1979). *Endocrinology* **105**, 827–834.

Barrack, E. R., Hawkins, E. F., Allen, S. L., Hicks, L. L., and Coffey, D.S. (1977). *Biochem. Biophys. Res. Commun.* **79**, 829–836.

Barrett, A. J. (1969). *In* "Lysosomes in Biology and Pathology" (J. T. Dingle and H. B. Fell, eds.), Vol. 2, pp. 245–312. North-Holland Publ. Co., Amsterdam.

Barrett, A. J. (1972). *In* "Lysosomes. A Laboratory Handbook" (J. T. Dingle, ed.), pp. 46–135. Elsevier, Amsterdam.

Barrett, A. M., and Cullum, V. (1968). *Brit. J. Pharmacol.* **34**, 43–55.

Baulieu, E.-E. (1973). *Adv. Exp. Biol. Med.* **36**, 80–84.

Baulieu, E.-E. (1978). *Mol. Cell. Endocrinol.* **12**, 247–254.

Baulieu, E.-E., Jung, I., Blondeau, J. P., and Robel, P. (1971). *Adv. Biosci.* **7**, 179–191.

Baulieu, E.-E., Godeau, F., Schorderet, M., and Schorderet-Slatkine, S. (1978). *Nature (London)* **275**, 593–598.

Beato, M., Schmid, W., Braendle, W., Biesewig, D., and Sekeris, C. E. (1971). *Adv. Biosci.* **7**, 349–367.

Beebe, D. C., Feagans, D. E., Blanchette-Mackie, E. J., and Nau, M. E. (1979). *Science* **206**, 836–838.

Beers, P. C., and Rosner, W. (1977). *J. Steroid Biochem.* **8**, 251–258.

Bellamy, D. (1963). *Biochem. J.* **87**, 334–340.

Bellamy, D., Phillips, J. G., Jones, I. C., and Leonard, R. A. (1962). *Biochem. J.* **85**, 537–545.

Bellé, R., Boyer, J., and Ozon, R. (1978). *Biol. Cell.* **32**, 97–102.

Bennett, G. W., and Edwardson, J. A. (1975). *J. Endocrinol.* **65**, 33–44.

Bennhold, H. (1938). *In* "Die Eiweisskörper des Blutplasmas" (H. Bennhold, E. Kylin, and St. Rusnyak, eds.), 220 pp. Steinkopff, Dresden.

Berezney, R., and Coffey, D. S. (1976). *Adv. Enzyme Regul.* **14**, 63–100.

Berezney, R., and Coffey, D. S. (1977). *J. Cell Biol.* **73**, 616–637.

Berg, B. H. (1978). *Biochim. Biophys. Acta* **521**, 274–287.

Bergelson, L. D., and Barsukov, L. I. (1977). *Science* **197**, 224–230.

Bergeron, J. J. M., Evans, W. H., and Geschwind, I. I. (1973). *J. Cell Biol.* **59**, 771–776.

Bergeron, J. J. M., Berridge, M. V., and Evans, W. H. (1975). *Biochim. Biophys. Acta* **407**, 325–337.

Bergeron, J. J. M., Posner, B. I., Josefsberg, Z., and Sikstrom, R. (1978). *J. Biol. Chem.* **253**, 4058–4066.

Berman, H. M., Gram, W., and Spirtes, M. A. (1969). *Biochim. Biophys. Acta* **183**, 10–18.

Besch, H. R., Jr., Jones, L. R., Fleming, J. W., and Watanabe, A. M. (1977). *J. Biol. Chem.* **252**, 7905–7908.

Bhattacharya, A., and Vonderhaar, B. K. (1979). *Biochem. Biophys. Res. Commun.* **88**, 1405–1411.

Birnbaumer, L., and O'Malley, B. W., eds. (1978). "Receptors and Hormone Action," Vol. 3. Academic Press, New York.

Bischoff, F., and Bryson, G. (1960). *J. Appl. Physiol.* **15**, 515–519.

Bischoff, F., Stauffer, R. D., and Gray, C. L. (1954). *Am. J. Physiol.* **177**, 65–68.

Blanquet, P. R. (1978). *J. Theor. Biol.* **70**, 345–399.

Blecher, M., and White, A. (1960). *J. Biol. Chem.* **235**, 3404–3412.

Bloom, G. D., Hellman, B., Idahl, L.-Å., Lernmark, Å, Sehlin, J., and Täljedal, I.-B. (1972). *Biochem. J.* **129**, 241–254.

Blyth, C. A., Freedman, R. B., and Rabin, B. R. (1971). *Nature (London), New Biol.* **230**, 137–139.

Blyth, C. A., Clark, R. P., Freedman, R. B., Hammond, J., James, D. W., Rabin, B. R., Ridge, D., Vintner, J., and Williams, D. (1973). *Eur. J. Biochem.* **32**, 57–62.

Boquet, P., and Pappenheimer, A. M., Jr. (1976). *J. Biol. Chem.* **251**, 5770–5778.

Bottenstein, J., Hayashi, I., Hutchings, S., Masui, H., Mather, J., McClure, D. B., Ohasa, S., Rizzino, A., Sato, G., Serrero, G., Wolfe, R., and Wu, R. (1979). *In* "Methods in Enzymology" (W. B. Jakoby and I. H. Pastan, eds.), Vol. 58, pp. 94–109. Academic Press, New York.

Bottoms, G., and Goetsch, D. D. (1967). *Proc. Soc. Exp. Biol. Med.* **124**, 662–665.

Bourguignon, L. Y. W., and Singer, S. J. (1977). *Proc. Natl. Acad. Sci. U.S.A.* **74**, 5031–5035.

Bresciani, F., Puca, G. A., Nola, E., and Sica, V. (1974). *In* "Control of Proliferation in Animal Cells" (B. Clarkson and R. Baserga, eds.), Vol. 1, pp. 67–83. Cold Spring Harbor Lab., Cold Spring Harbor, New York.

Breslow, J. L., Epstein, J., and Fontaine, J. H. (1978). *Cell* **13**, 663–669.

Breslow, J. L., Epstein, J., Forbes, G. B., and Fontaine, J. H. (1979). *J. Cell. Physiol.* **99**, 343–348.

Bression, D., Snochowski, M., Bélanger, A., Pousette, Å., Ekman, P., Högberg, B., and Gustafsson, J.-Å. (1979). *FEBS Lett.* **103**, 355–361.

Bretscher, M. S. (1973). *Science* **181**, 622–629.

Briggs, M. (1973). *J. Steroid Biochem.* **4**, 341–347.

Brooks, S. C., Locke, E. R., and Soule, H. D. (1973). *J. Biol. Chem.* **248**, 6251–6253.

Brostrom, M. A., Kon, C., Olson, D. R., and Breckenridge, B. M. (1974). *Mol. Pharmacol.* **10**, 711–720.

Brown, M. S., and Goldstein, J. L. (1976). *Science* **191**, 150–154.

Brown, M. S., and Goldstein, J. L. (1979). *Proc. Natl. Acad. Sci. U.S.A.* **76**, 3330–3337.

Browning, G., and Saunders, P. F. (1977). *Nature (London)* **265**, 375–377.

Brumbaugh, P. F., and Haussler, M. R. (1973). *Biochem. Biophys. Res. Commun.* **51**, 74–80.

Brunelli, B. (1934). *Arch. Int. Pharmacodyn. Ther.* **49**, 295–301.

Brunk, U. T., and Ericsson, J. L. E. (1972). *Histochem. J.* **4**, 479–491.

Brunkhorst, W. K., and Hess, E. L. (1964). *Biochim. Biophys. Acta* **82**, 385–393.

Buller, R. E., and O'Malley, B. W. (1976). *Biochem. Pharmacol.* **25**, 1–12.

Calandra, R. S., Naess, O., Purvis, K., Attramadal, A., Djoseland, O., and Hansson, V. (1978). *J. Steroid Biochem.* **9**, 957–962.

Caldwell, A., and Fain, J. N. (1971). *Endocrinology* **89**, 1195–1204.

Caldwell, P. C., and Keynes, R. D. (1959). *J. Physiol. (London)* **148**, 8P–9P.

Callantine, M. R., Humphrey, R. R., Lee, S. L., Windsor, B. L., Schottin, N. H., and O'Brien, O. P. (1976). *Endocrinology* **79**, 153–167.

Cantarow, A., Rakoff, A. E., Paschkis, K. E., Hansen, L. P., and Walking, A. A. (1942). *Endocrinology* **31**, 515–519.

Carette, B., Barry, J., Linkie, D., Férin, M., Mester, J., and Baulieu, E.-E. (1979). *C. R. Hebd. Séances Acad. Sci., Sér. D.* **288**, 631–634.

Carlstedt-Duke, J., Wrange, Ö., Dahlberg, E., Gustafsson, J.-Å., and Högberg, B. (1979). *J. Biol. Chem.* **254**, 1537–1539.

Casley-Smith, J. R. (1969). *J. Microsc. (Oxford)* **90**, 15–30.

Casley-Smith, J. R., and Chin, J. C. (1971). *J. Microsc. (Oxford)* **93**, 167–189.

Castillón, M. P., Catalán, R. E., and Municio, A. M. (1973). *FEBS Lett.* **32**, 113–115.

Catt, K. J., and Dufau, M. L. (1977). *Annu. Rev. Physiol.* **39**, 529–557.

Catt, K. J., Harwood, J. P., Aguilera, G., and Dufau, M. L. (1979). *Nature (London)* **280**, 109–116.

Chamness, G. C., and Bromley, J. M. (1979). *Endocrinology* **104**, Suppl., 275.

Chamness, G. C., and McGuire, W. L. (1975). *Steroids* **26**, 538–542.

Chamness, G. C., Costlow, M. E., and McGuire, W. L. (1975). *Steroids* **26**, 363–371.

Changeaux, J.-P. (1974). *In* "The Cell Surface in Development" (A. A. Moscona, ed.), pp. 207–220. Wiley, New York.

Changeaux, J.-P., Thiéry, J., Tung, Y., and Kittel, C. (1967). *Proc. Natl. Acad. Sci. U.S.A.* **57**, 335–341.

Charney, A. N., Silva, P., Besarab, A., and Epstein, F. H. (1974). *Am. J. Physiol.* **227**, 345–350.

Chen, C. C., and Heller, J. (1977). *J. Biol. Chem.* **252**, 5216–5221.

Chew, C. S., and Rinard, G. A. (1974). *Biochim. Biophys. Acta* **362**, 493–500.

Christian, C. N., Daniels, M. P., Sugiyama, H., Vogel, Z., Jacques, L., and Nelson, P. G. (1978). *Proc. Natl. Acad. Sci. U.S.A.* **75**, 4011–4015.

Chuang, D.-M., and Costa, E. (1979). *Proc. Natl. Acad. Sci. U.S.A.* **76**, 3024–3028.

Chytil, F., and Ong, D. E. (1978). *Vitam. Horm. (N.Y.)* **36**, 1–32.

Cidlowski, J. A., and Michaels, G. A. (1977). *Nature (London)* **266**, 643–645.

Clark, J. H., and Gorski, J. (1969). *Biochim. Biophys. Acta* **192**, 508–515.

Clark, J. H., Peck, E. J., Jr., and Glasser, S. R. (1977). *In* "Reproduction in Domestic Animals" (H. H. Cole and P. T. Cupps, eds.), pp. 143–173. Academic Press, New York.

Cloix, J. F., Bachelet, M., Ulmann, A., and Funck-Brentano, J. L. (1978). *Biochem. Biophys. Res. Commun.* **83**, 1456–1461.

Cohn, Z. A. (1975). *In* "Proteases and Biological Control" (E. Reich, D. B. Rifkin, and E. Shaw, eds.), pp. 483–493. Cold Spring Harbor Lab., Cold Spring Harbor, New York.

Cohn, Z. A., Fedorko, M. E., and Hirsch, J. G. (1966). *J. Exp. Med.* **123**, 757–766.

Colburn, P., and Buonassisi, V. (1978). *Science* **201**, 817–819.

Coleman, R. (1973). *Biochim. Biophys. Acta* **300**, 1–30.

Collander, R., and Bärlund, H. (1933). *Acta Bot. Fenn.* **11**, 1–114.

Connolly, J. L., Greene, L. A., Viscarello, R. R., and Riley, W. D. (1979). *J. Cell Biol.* **82**, 820–827.

Conrad, M. J., and Singer, S. J. (1979). *Proc. Natl. Acad. Sci. U.S.A.* **76**, 5202–5206.

Cook, J. S., ed. (1976). "Biogenesis and Turnover of Membrane Macromolecules." Raven, New York.

Cooke, N. E., Walgate, J., and Haddad, J. G., Jr. (1979a). *J. Biol. Chem.* **254**, 5958–5964.

Cooke, N. E., Walgate, J., and Haddad, J. G., Jr. (1979b). *J. Biol. Chem.* **254**, 5965–5971.

Corradino, R. A. (1974). *Endocrinology* **94**, 1607–1614.

Corradino, R. A. (1975). *In* "Calcium-regulating Hormones" (R. V. Talmage, M. Owen, and J. A. Parsons, eds.), pp. 346–361. Am. Elsevier, New York.

Corradino, R. A. (1976). *Biochem. Pharmacol.* **25**, 863–864.

Corradino, R. A. (1977). *In* "Vitamin D; Biochemical, Chemical and Clinical Aspects Related to Calcium Metabolism" (A. W. Norman, K. Schaefer, J. W. Coburn, H. F. DeLuca, D. Fraser, H. G. Grigoleit, and D. V. Herrath, eds.), pp. 231–240. de Gruyter, New York.

Corradino, R. A. (1979). *Arch. Biochem. Biophys.* **192**, 302–310.

Coty, W. A., Schrader, W. T., and O'Malley, B. W. (1979). *J. Steroid Biochem.* **10**, 1–12.

Couturier, E., Bruno, O. D., Metzger, P., Leclercq, R., and Copinschi, G. (1973). *J. Membr. Biol.* **13**, 89–96.

Craven, S., Lesser, B., and Bruchovsky, N. (1974). *Endocrinology* **95**, 1177–1180.

Critchley, D. R., and Vicker, M. G. (1977). *Cell Surf. Rev.* **3**, 307–370.

Cuatrecasas, P. (1969). *Proc. Natl. Acad. Sci. U.S.A.* **63**, 450–455.

Cuatrecasas, P., ed. (1977). "Receptors and Recognition, Series B," Vol. 1. Chapman & Hall, London.

Dainty, J. (1963). *Adv. Bot. Res.* **1**, 270–326.

Das, P. K., and Arora, R. B. (1957). *J. Pharmacol. Exp. Ther.* **121**, 149–159.

Daughaday, W. H., Holloszy, J., and Mariz, I. K. (1961). *J. Clin. Endocrinol. Metab.* **21**, 53–61.

Dauwalder, M., Whaley, W. G., and Kephart, J. E. (1972). *Sub-Cell. Biochem.* **1**, 225–275.

Davidson, E. T., De Venuto, F., and Westphal, U. (1963). *Proc. Soc. Exp. Biol. Med.* **113**, 387–391.

Davies, P., and Allison, A. C. (1976). *In* "Lysomes in Biology and Pathology" (J. T. Dingle and R. T. Dean, eds.), Vol. 5, pp. 61–98. North-Holland Publ. Co., Amsterdam.

Davis, R. A., Kern, F., Jr., Showalter, R., Sutherland, E., Sinensky, M., and Simon, F. R. (1978). *Proc. Natl. Acad. Sci. U.S.A.* **75**, 4130–4134.

Davson, H. (1970). "A Textbook of General Physiology." Little, Brown, Boston, Massachusetts.

Dean, R. T., and Barrett, A. J. (1976). *Essays Biochem.* **12**, 1–40.

de Duve, C. (1967). *In* "Enzyme Cytology" (D. B. Roodyn, ed.), pp. 1–26. Academic Press, New York.

de Duve, C., and Wattiaux, R. (1966). *Annu. Rev. Physiol.* **28**, 435–492.

De Hertogh, R., Ekka, E., Vanderheyden, I., and Hoet, J. J. (1971). *Endocrinology* **88**, 165–174.

DeKloet, E. R., and McEwen, B. S. (1976). *Biochim. Biophys. Acta* **421**, 115–123.

DeKloet, E. R., Burbach, P., and Mulder, G. H. (1977). *Mol. Cell. Endocrinol.* **7**, 261–273.

De Meyts, P. (1976). *In* "Cell Membrane Receptors for Viruses, Antigens and Antibodies, Polypeptide Hormones, and Small Molecules" (R. F. Beers, Jr. and E. G. Bassett, eds.), pp. 17–32. Raven, New York.

de Petris, S. (1974). *Nature (London)* **250**, 54–55.

de Petris, S. (1977). *Cell Surf. Rev.* **3**, 643–728.

de Petris, S. and Raff, M. C. (1972). *Eur. J. Immunol.* **2**, 523–535.

DePierre, J. W., and Karnovsky, M. L. (1973). *J. Cell Biol.* **56**, 275–303.

De Venuto, F., and Chader, G. (1966). *Biochim. Biophys. Acta* **121**, 151–158.

De Venuto, F., Kelleher, P. C., and Westphal, U. (1962). *Biochim. Biophys. Acta* **63**, 434–452.

Diamond, J. M., and Wright, E. M. (1969). *Annu. Rev. Physiol.* **31**, 581–646.

Dietschy, J. M. (1978). *In* "Disturbances in Lipid and Lipoprotein Metabolism" (J. M. Dietschy, A. M. Gotto, Jr., and J. A. Ontko, eds.), pp. 1–28. Am. Physiol. Soc., Bethesda, Maryland.

Dingman, C. W., and Sporn, M. B. (1965). *Science* **149**, 1251–1254.

Dionne, F. T., Lesage, R. L., Dubé, J. Y., and Tremblay, R. R. (1979). *J. Steroid Biochem.* **11**, 1073–1080.

Dobrota, M., Burge, M. L. E., and Hinton, R. H. (1979). *Eur. J. Cell Biol.* **19**, 139–144.

Doljanski, F., and Kapeller, M. (1976). *J. Theor. Biol.* **62**, 253–270.

Douglas, W. W. (1968). *Br. J. Pharmacol.* **34**, 451–474.

Dousset, J. C., Dousset, N., El Baba, A. M., Soula, G., and Douste-Blazy, L. (1979). *Artery* **5**, 432–447.

Dransfeld, H., and Greeff, K. (1964). *Naunyn-Schmiedebergs Arch. Exp. Pathol. Pharmakol.* **249**, 425–431.

Drury, K., and Schorderet-Slatkine, S. (1975). *C. R. Hebd. Séances Acad. Sci., Sér. D* **280**, 1273–1275.

Dufy, B., Vincent, J.-D., Fleury, H., Du Pasquier, P., Gourdji, D., and Tixier-Vidal, A. (1979). *Science* **204**, 509–511.

Dufy, B., Fleury, H., Gourdji, D., Tixier-Vidal, A., Du Pasquier, P., and Vincent, J. D. (1980). *In* "Synthesis and Release of Adenohyopophyseal Hormones" (M. Jutisz and K. W. McKerns, eds.). pp. 765–773 Plenum, New York.

Dumont, J. E. (1971). *Vitam. Horm. (N.Y.)* **29**, 288–412.

Dupont-Mairesse, N., Van Sande, J., Rooryck, J., Fastrez-Boute, A., and Galand, P. (1974). *J. Steroid Biochem.* **5**, 173–177.

Dutta, S., and Marks, B. H. (1969). *J. Pharmacol. Exp. Ther.* **170**, 318–325.

Dutta, S., Goswami, S., Datta, D. K., Lindower, J. O., and Marks, B. H. (1968). *J. Pharmacol. Exp. Ther.* **164**, 10–21.

Dutta, S., Rhee, H. M., and Marks, B. H. (1972). *J. Pharmacol. Exp. Ther.* **180**, 351–358.

Edelman, G. M. (1976). *Science* **192**, 218–226.

Edelman, G. M., Rutishauser, U., and Millette, C. F. (1971). *Proc. Natl. Acad. Sci. U.S.A.* **68**, 2153–2157.

Edelman, I. S., and Fimognari, G. M. (1967). *Recent Prog. Horm. Res.* **24**, 1–44.

Edwardson, J. A., and Bennett, G. W. (1974). *Nature (London)* **251**, 425–427.

Egert, D., Wolf, H., Maass, H., and Trams, G. (1977). *Steroids* **29**, 749–759.

Ehrlich, P. (1900). Croonian Lecture: "On Immunity with Special Reference to Cell Life." *In* "The Collected Papers of Paul Ehrlich" (F. Himmelweit, ed.), Vol. II, pp. 178–195. Pergamon, Oxford, 1957.

Eisenfeld, A. J., and Axelrod, J. (1965). *J. Pharmacol. Exp. Ther.* **150**, 469–475.

Eisenfeld, A. J., Aten, R., Weinberger, M., Haselbacher, G., Halpern, K., and Krakoff, L. (1976). *Science* **191**, 862–865.

Ekholm, R., Engström, G., Ericson, L. E., and Melander, A. (1975). *Endocrinology* **97**, 337–346.

Ellis, D. J., and Ringold, H. J. (1971). *In* "The Sex Steroids" (K. W. McKerns, ed.), pp. 73–106. Appleton, New York.

Emmelot, P., and Bos, C. J. (1966). *Biochim. Biophys. Acta* **121**, 434–436.

Erdos, T. (1968). *Biochem. Biophys. Res. Commun.* **32**, 338–343.

Erdos, T., Bessada, R., and Friès, J. (1969). *FEBS Lett.* **5**, 161–164.

Erdos, T., Bessada, R., Best-Belpomme, M., Friès, J., Gospodarowicz, D., Menahem, M., Reti, E., and Veron, A. (1971). *Adv. Biosci.* **7**, 119–135.

Erdos, T., Bessada, R., and Friès, J. (1977). *In* "Multiple Molecular Forms of Steroid Hormone Receptors" (M. K. Agarwal, ed.), pp. 113–128. Elsevier/North-Holland Biomedical Press, Amsterdam.

Eriksson, H., Upchurch, S., Hardin, J. W., Peck, E. J., Jr., and Clark, J. H. (1978). *Biochem. Biophys. Res. Commun.* **81**, 1–7.

Esber, H., Payne, I., and Bogden, A. (1973). *J. Natl. Cancer Inst.* **50**, 559–562.

Esser, A. F., Bartholomew, R. M., Parce, J. W., and McConnell, H. M. (1979). *J. Biol. Chem.* **254**, 1768–1770.

Evans, W. H. (1978). "Preparation and Characterization of Mammalian Plasma Membranes." North-Holland Publ., Amsterdam.

Eveloff, J., Karnaky, K. J., Jr., Silva, P., Epstein, F. H., and Kinter, W. B. (1979). *J. Cell Biol.* **83**, 16–32.

Fambrough, D. M., and Devreotes, P. N. (1978). *J. Cell Biol.* **76**, 237–244.

Fanestil, D. D. (1968). *Biochem. Pharmacol.* **17**, 2240–2242.

Fanestil, D. D., and Edelman, I. S. (1966). *Proc. Natl. Acad. Sci. U.S.A.* **56**, 872–879.

Fant, M. E., Harbison, R. D., and Harrison, R. W. (1979). *J. Biol. Chem.* **254**, 6218–6221.

Farnsworth, W. E. (1968). *Biochim. Biophys. Acta* **150**, 446–451.

Farnsworth, W. E. (1972). *J. Endocrinol.* **54**, 375–385.

Farnsworth, W. E. (1977). *Invest. Urol.* **15**, 75–77.

Feldman, D. (1978). *Biochem. Pharmacol.* **27**, 1187–1191.

Feldman, D., and Couropmitree, C. (1976). *J. Clin. Invest.* **57**, 1–7.

Fishman, J., and Norton, B. (1975). *Endocrinology* **96**, 1054–1059.

Flandroy, L., and Galand, P. (1978). *J. Cyclic Nucleotide Res.* **4**, 145–158.

Forte, L. R. (1972). *Life Sci.* **11**, Part I, 461–473.

Fortes, P. A. G. (1977). *Biochemistry* **16**, 531–540.

Franklin, T. J., and Foster, S. J. (1973). *Nature (London), New Biol.* **246**, 146–148.

Friedberg, F. (1977). *Horiz. Biochem. Biophys.* **4**, 63–90.

Fujimoto, G. I., and Morrill, G. A. (1978). *Biochim. Biophys. Acta* **538**, 226–230.

Fullerton, D. S., Yoshioka, K., Rohrer, D. C., From, A. H. L., and Ahmed, K. (1979). *Science* **205**, 917–919.

Ganguly, M., and Westphal, U. (1968). *J. Biol. Chem.* **243**, 6130–6139.

Giannopoulos, G., and Gorski, J. (1971). *J. Biol. Chem.* **246**, 2530–2536.

Giorgi, E. P. (1976). *J. Endocrinol.* **68**, 109–119.

Giorgi, E. P., and Moses, T. F. (1975). *Endocrinology* **65**, 279–280.

Giorgi, E. P., and Stein, W. D. (1980). *Endocrinology* (in press).

Glascock, R. F., and Hoekstra, W. G. (1959). *Biochem. J.* **72**, 673–682.

Glusker, J. P. (1979). *In* "Biochemical Actions of Hormones" (G. Litwack, ed.), Vol. 6, pp. 121–204. Academic Press, New York.

Godeau, J. F., Schorderet-Slatkine, S., Hubert, P., and Baulieu, E.-E. (1978). *Proc. Natl. Acad. Sci. U.S.A.* **75**, 2353–2357.

Godin, D. V., Ng, T. W., and Tuchek, J. M. (1976). *Biochim. Biophys. Acta* **436**, 757–773.

Goldberg, N. D., and Haddox, M. K. (1977). *Annu. Rev. Biochem.* **46**, 823–896.

Goldberg, N. D., Haddox, M. K., Hartle, D. K., and Hadden, J. W. (1973). *Proc. Int. Congr. Pharmacol. 5th, 1972* Vol. 5, pp. 146–169.

Goodman, L. S., and Gilman, A., eds. (1975). "The Pharmacological Basis of Therapeutics," 5th ed. Macmillan, New York.

Gorden, P., Carpentier, J.-L., Freychet, P., Le Cam, A., and Orci, L. (1978). *Science* **200**, 782–785.

Gorissen, H., and Laduron, P. (1979). *Nature (London)* **279**, 72–74.

Gorski, J., and Gannon, F. (1976). *Annu. Rev. Physiol.* **38**, 425–450.

Gorski, J., and Raker, B. (1973). *Endocrinology* **93**, 1212–1216.

Gorski, J., Toft, D., Shyamala, G., Smith, D., and Notides, A. (1968). *Recent Prog. Horm. Res.* **24**, 45–80.

Granner, D. K., Lee, A., and Thompson, E. B. (1977). *J. Biol. Chem.* **252**, 3891–3897.

Greeff, K., Meng, K., and Schwarzmann, D. (1964). *Naunyn-Schmiedebergs Arch. Exp. Pathol. Pharmakol.* **249**, 416–424.

Green, H. S., and Casley-Smith, J. R. (1972). *J. Theor. Biol.* **35**, 103–111.

Greene, G. L., Closs, L. E., Fleming, H., DeSombre, E. R., and Jensen, E. V. (1977). *Proc. Natl. Acad. Sci. U.S.A.* **74**, 3681–3685.

Greengard, P. (1978). *Science* **199**, 146–152.

Greengard, P. (1979). *Fed. Proc., Fed. Am. Soc. Exp. Biol.* **38**, 2208–2217.

Griffiths, P. A., and Lloyd, J. B. (1979). *Biochem. Biophys. Res. Commun.* **89**, 428–434.

Gross, S. R., Aronow, L., and Pratt, W. B. (1970). *J. Cell. Biol.* **44**, 103–114.

Guidotti, A., Hanbauer, I., and Costa, E. (1975). *Adv. Cyclic Nucleotide Res.* **5**, 619–639.

Guillemant, J., and Guillemant, S. (1979). *Biochem. Biophys. Res. Commun.* **88**, 163–169.

Gunaga, K. P., Kawano, A., and Menon, K. M. J. (1974). *Neuroendocrinology* **16**, 273–281.

Gurpide, E., and Tseng, L. (1976). *Mod. Pharmacol.-Toxicol.* **8**, Part I, 109–158.

Gurpide, E., and Welch, M. (1969). *J. Biol. Chem.* **244**, 5159–5169.

Hackney, J. F., and Pratt, W. B. (1971). *Biochemistry* **10**, 3002–3008.

Haddad, J. G., Jr., and Walgate, J. (1976). *J. Biol. Chem.* **251**, 4803–4809.

Hähnel, R., Twaddle, E., and Brindle, L. (1974). *Steroids* **24**, 489–506.

Haigler, H. T., McKanna, J. A., and Cohen, S. (1979). *J. Cell Biol.* **83**, 82–90.

Halley, D. J. J., de Wit-Verbeek, H. A., Reuser, A. J. J., and Galjaard, H. (1978). *Biochem. Biophys. Res. Commun.* **82**, 1176–1182.

Hamilton, T. (1968). *Science* **161**, 649–661.

Harding, B. W., and Samuels, L. T. (1962). *Endocrinology* **70**, 109–118.

Harrison, L. C., Billington, T., East, I. J., Nichols, R. J., and Clark, S. (1978). *Endocrinology* **102**, 1485–1495.

Harrison, R. W., and Yeakley, J. (1979). *Mol. Cell. Endocrinol.* **15**, 13–18.

Harrison, R. W., Fairfield, S., and Orth, D. N. (1974). *Biochem. Biophys. Res. Commun.* **61**, 1262–1267.

Harrison, R. W., Fairfield, S., and Orth, D. N. (1975). *Biochemistry* **14**, 1304–1307.

Harrison, R. W., Fairfield, S., and Orth, D. N. (1977). *Biochim. Biophys. Acta* **466**, 357–365.

Harrison, R. W., Balasubramanian, K., Yeakley, J., Fant, M., Svec, F., and Fairfield, S. (1979). *In* "Steroid Hormone Receptor Systems", (W. W. Leavitt and J. H. Clark, eds.), pp. 423–440. Plenum, New York.

Haug, E., Naess, O., and Gautvik, K. M. (1978). *Mol. Cell. Endocrinol.* **12**, 81–95.

Haukkamaa, M., and Luukkainen, T. (1974). *J. Steroid Biochem.* **5**, 330–331.

Haussler, M. R., and Brumbaugh, P. F. (1976). *In* "Hormone-receptor Interaction: Molecular Aspects" (G. S. Levey, ed.), pp. 301–332. Dekker, New York.

Hechter, O. M. (1978). *In* "Hormone Receptors" (D. M. Klachko, L. R. Forte, and J. M. Franz, eds.), pp. 1–43. Plenum, New York.

Heinonen, P. K., and Tuohimaa, P. (1979). *J. Steroid Biochem.* **10**, 629–631.

Heller, J. (1975). *J. Biol. Chem.* **250**, 3613–3619.

Hernández-Pérez, O., Ballesteros, L. M., and Rosado, A. (1979). *Arch. Androl.* **3**, 23–29.

Hess, G. P., Cash, D. J., and Aoshima, H. (1979). *Nature (London)* **282**, 329–331.

Hickman, S., and Neufeld, E. F. (1972). *Biochem. Biophys. Res. Commun.* **49**, 992–999.

Higgins, S. J., and Gehring, U. (1978). *Adv. Cancer Res.* **28**, 313–397.

Hill, A. V. (1928). *Proc. R. Soc. London, Ser. B* **103**, 138–162.
Hirata, F., Strittmatter, W. J., and Axelrod, J. (1979). *Proc. Natl. Acad. Sci. U.S.A.* **76**, 368–372.
Hirsch, P. C., and Szego, C. M. (1974). *J. Steroid Biochem.* **5**, 533–542.
Hochberg, R. B. (1979). *Science* **205**, 1138–1140.
Hodgman, C. D., Weast, R. C., and Selby, S. M. eds. (1960). "Handbook of Chemistry and Physics." Chem. Rubber Publ. Co., Cleveland, Ohio.
Hoffman, J. F. (1966). *Am. J. Med.* **41**, 666–680.
Holt, P. R. (1964). *Am. J. Physiol.* **207**, 1–7.
Holtzman, E., Schacher, S., Evans, J., and Teichberg, S. (1977). *Cell Surf. Rev.* **4**, 165–246.
Hospital, M., Busetta, B., Bucourt, R., Weintraub, H., and Baulieu, E.-E. (1972). *Mol. Pharmacol.* **8**, 438–445.
Howe, R., and Shanks, R. G. (1966). *Nature (London)* **210**, 1336–1338.
Hubbell, W. L., Metcalfe, J. C., Metcalfe, S. M., and McConnell, H. M. (1970). *Biochim. Biophys. Acta* **219**, 415–427.
Hugon, J., and Borgers, M. (1967). *J. Cell Biol.* **33**, 212–218.
Huprikar, S., Lang, M., Friedman, Y., and Burke, G. (1979). *FEBS Lett.* **99**, 167–171.
Inaba, M., and Kamata, K. (1979). *J. Steroid Biochem.* **11**, 1491–1497.
Inman, D. J., and Hornby, W. E. (1972). *Biochem. J.* **129**, 255–262.
Inman, D. R., Banfield, R. E. W., and King, R. J. B. (1965). *J. Endocrinol.* **32**, 17–22.
Isaacson, A., and Sandow, A. (1967). *J. Gen. Physiol.* **50**, 2109–2128.
Ishikawa, K., Hanaoka, Y., Kondo, Y., and Imai, K. (1977). *Mol. Cell. Endocrinol.* **9**, 91–100.
Jackson, V., and Chalkley, R. (1974a). *J. Biol. Chem.* **249**, 1615–1626.
Jackson, V., and Chalkley, R. (1974b). *J. Biol. Chem.* **249**, 1627–1636.
Jacobelli, S., Hanocq, J., Baltus, E., and Brachet, J. (1974). *Differentiation* **2**, 129–135.
Jensen, E. V., and DeSombre, E. R. (1972). *In* "Biochemical Actions of Hormones" (G. Litwack, ed.), Vol. 2, pp. 215–255. Academic Press, New York.
Jensen, E. V., and DeSombre, E. R. (1973). *Science* **182**, 126–134.
Jensen, E. V., and Jacobson, H. I. (1962). *Recent Prog. Horm. Res.* **18**, 387–414.
Jensen, E. V., Hurst, D. J., DeSombre, E. R., and Jungblut, P. W. (1967). *Science* **158**, 385–387.
Jensen, E. V., Suzuki, T., Kawashima, T., Stumpf, W. E., Jungblut, P. W., and DeSombre, E. R. (1968). *Proc. Natl. Acad. Sci. U.S.A.* **59**, 632–638.
Johnson, M., and Ramwell, P. W. (1973). *Prostaglandins* **3**, 703–719.
Jones, M. T., Hillhouse, E. W., and Burden, J. L. (1977). *J. Endocrinol.* **73**, 405–417.
Jungblut, D. W., McCann, S., Görlich, L., Rosenfeld, G. C., and Wagner, R. K. (1970). *Res. Steroids* **4**, 213–232.
Jungblut, P. W., Gaues, J., Hughes, A., Kallweit, E., Sierralta, W., Szendro, P., and Wagner, R. K. (1976). *J. Steroid Biochem.* **7**, 1109–1116.
Kahn, C. R. (1976). *J. Cell Biol.* **70**, 261–286.
Kaiser, N., and Edelman, I. S. (1977). *Proc. Natl. Acad. Sci. U.S.A.* **74**, 638–642.
Kaley, G., and Weiner, R. (1975). *Prostaglandins* **10**, 685–688.
Kalimi, M., and Fujimoto, G. I. (1978). *Biochim. Biophys. Acta* **538**, 231–235.
Kanazir, D., Ribarac-Stepić, N., Trajković, D., Blečić, G., Radojčić, M., Metlaš, R., Stefanović, D., Katan, M., Perišić, O., Popić, S., and Djordjević-Marković, R. (1979). *J. Steroid Biochem.* **11**, 389–400.
Kang, E. S., Gates, R. E., Chiang, T. M., and Kang, A. H. (1979). *Biochem. Biophys. Res. Commun.* **86**, 769–778.
Kaplan, A., Achord, D. T., and Sly, W. S. (1977). *Proc. Natl. Acad. Sci. U.S.A.* **74**, 2026–2030.

Kaplan, J. G. (1978). *Annu. Rev. Physiol.* **40**, 19–41.

Karlin, A. (1976). *Enzymes Biol. Membr.* **4**, 311–330.

Katz, J., Troll, W., Adler, S. W., and Levitz, M. (1977). *Proc. Natl. Acad. Sci. U.S.A.* **74**, 3754.

Katz, S., and Tenenhouse, A. (1973). *Br. J. Pharmacol.* **48**, 516–526.

Katzenellenbogen, B. S., and Gorski, J. (1975). *In* "Biochemical Actions of Hormones" (G. Litwack, ed.), Vol. 3, pp. 187–243, Academic Press, New York.

Katzenellenbogen, B. S., Bhakoo, H. S., Ferguson, E. R., Lan, N. C., Tatee, T., Tsai, T. -L. S., and Katzenellenbogen, J. A. (1979). *Recent Prog. Horm. Res.* **35**, 259–300.

Keates, R. A. B. (1973). *Nature (London)* **244**, 355–357.

Keller, N., Richardson, U. I., and Yates, F. E. (1969). *Endocrinology* **84**, 49–62.

Kelly, M. J., Moss, R. L., and Dudley, C. A. (1976). *Brain Res.* **114**, 152–157.

Kelly, M. J., Moss, R. L., Dudley, C. A., and Fawcett, C. P. (1977a). *Exp. Brain Res.* **30**, 43–52.

Kelly, M. J., Moss, R. L., and Dudley, C. A. (1977b). *Exp. Brain Res.* **30**, 53–64.

Kelly, M. J., Kuhnt, U., and Wuttke, W. (1979). *Endocrinology* **104**, Suppl., 282.

Khaïat, A., Ketevi, P., Ter-Minassian-Saraga, L., Cittanova, N., and Jayle, M. F. (1975). *Biochim. Biophys. Acta* **401**, 1–5.

Kidwai, A. M., Radcliffe, M. A., and Daniel, E. E. (1971). *Biochim. Biophys. Acta* **233**, 538–549.

Kilberg, M. S., and Christensen, H. N. (1979). *Biochemistry* **18**, 1525–1530.

Kim, R. S., Chow, E., Queen, G., and LaBella, F. S. (1978). *Proc. Can. Fed. Biol. Soc.* **21**, 156.

Kimelberg, H. K. (1977). *Cell Surf. Rev.* **3**, 205–293.

Kimura, H., Thomas, E., and Murad, F. (1974). *Biochim. Biophys. Acta* **343**, 519–534.

Kimura, S., and Rasmussen, H. (1977). *J. Biol. Chem.* **252**, 1217–1225.

King, R. J. B. (1976). *Essays Biochem.* **12**, 41–76.

King, R. J. B., and Gordon, J. (1966). *J. Endocrinol.* **34**, 431–437.

King, R. J. B., and Mainwaring, W. I. P. (1974). "Steroid-Cell Interactions". University Park Press, Baltimore, Maryland.

King, R. J. B., Gordon, J., and Inman, D. R. (1965). *J. Endocrinol.* **32**, 9–15.

Kissel, J. H., Rosenfeld, M. G., Chase, L. R., and O'Malley, B. W. (1970). *Endocrinology* **86**, 1019–1023.

Klausner, R. D., Fishman, M. C., and Karnovsky, M. J. (1979). *Nature (London)* **281**, 82–83.

Klibanov, A. M. (1979). *Anal. Biochem.* **93**, 1–25.

Koch, B., Lutz, B., Briaud, B., and Mialhe, C. (1976). *Biochim. Biophys. Acta* **444**, 497–507.

Koch, B., Lutz-Bucher, B., Briaud, B., and Mialhe, C. (1977). *J. Endocrinol.* **73**, 399–400.

Koch, B., Lutz-Bucher, B., Briaud, B., and Mialhe, C. (1978). *J. Endocrinol.* **79**, 215–222.

Kopp, F., Martin, P. M., Rolland, P. H., and Bertrand, M.-F. (1979). *J. Steroid Biochem.* **11**, 1081–1090.

Kowarski, A., Shalf, J., and Migeon, C. J. (1969). *J. Biol. Chem.* **244**, 5269–5272.

Krall, J. F., Mori, H., Tuck, M. L., LeShon, S. L., and Korenman, S. G. (1978). *Life Sci.* **23**, 1073–1082.

Kream, B. E., DeLuca, H. F., Moriarty, D. M., Kendrick, N. C., and Ghazarian, J. G. (1979). *Arch. Biochem. Biophys.* **192**, 318–323.

Krupp, M. N., and Livingston, J. N. (1979). *Nature (London)* **278**, 61–62.

Kuehl, F. A., Jr., Ham, E. A., Zanetti, M. E., Sanford, C. H., Nicol, S. E., and Goldberg, N. D. (1974). *Proc. Natl. Acad. Sci. U.S.A.* **71**, 1866–1870.

Kuhn, R. W., Schrader, W. T., Coty, W. A., Conn, P. M., and O'Malley, B. W. (1977). *J. Biol. Chem.* **252**, 308–317.

Kvinnsland, S. (1976). *Cell Tissue Res.* **173**, 325–334.

Kyte, J. (1975). *J. Biol. Chem.* **250**, 7443–7449.

LaBella, F. S., Bihler, I., and Kim, R. S. (1979). *Nature (London)* **278**, 571–573.

Labrie, F., Borgeat, P., Drouin, J., Beaulieu, M., Lagacé, L., Ferland, L., and Raymond, V. (1979). *Annu. Rev. Physiol.* **41**, 555–569.

Lacombe, M.-L., and Hanoune, J. (1979). *J. Biol. Chem.* **254**, 3697–3699.

Lacombe, M.-L., Stengel, D., and Hanoune, J. (1977). *FEBS Lett.* **77**, 159–163.

Lang, M. A., and Edelman, I. S. (1972). *Am. J. Physiol.* **222**, 21–24.

Laumas, K. R., Uniyal, J. P., Krishnan, A. R., Murugesan, K., and Koshti, G. S. (1970). *Res. Steroids* **4**, 145–152.

Lee, S. H. (1978). *Am. J. Clin. Pathol.* **70**, 197–203.

Lefebvre, Y., Po, L., and Watanabe, M. (1976). *J. Steroid Biochem.* **7**, 535–538.

Levey, G. S., and Epstein, S. E. (1969). *J. Clin. Invest.* **48**, 1663–1669.

Levey, G. S., and Lehotay, D. C. (1976). *Enzymes Biol. Membr.* **4**, 259–282.

Levinson, B. B., Baxter, J. D., Rousseau, G. G., and Tomkins, G. M. (1972). *Science* **175**, 189–190.

Liang, T., and Liao, S. (1974). *J. Biol. Chem.* **249**, 4671–4678.

Liao, S., and Fang, S. (1969). *Vitam. Horm. (N.Y.)* **27**, 17–90.

Liao, S., Lin, A. H., and Tymoczko, J. L. (1971). *Biochim. Biophys. Acta* **230**, 535–538.

Liao, S., Howell, D. K., and Chang, T.-M. (1974). *Endocrinology* **94**, 1205–1209.

Liao, S., Tymoczko, J. L., Castañeda, E., and Liang, T. (1975). *Vitam. Horm. (N.Y.)* **33**, 297–317.

Lieb, W. R., and Stein, W. D. (1971). *Curr. Top. Membr. Transp.* **2**, 1–39.

Lieberburg, I., and McEwen, B. S. (1979). *In* "Biochemical Actions of Hormones" (G. Litwack, ed.), Vol. 6, pp. 415–459. Academic Press, New York.

Linden, C. D., Wright, K. L., McConnell, H. M., and Fox, C. F. (1973). *Proc. Natl. Acad. Sci. U.S.A.* **70**, 2271–2275.

Lippman, M., Bolan, G., and Huff, K. (1976). *Cancer Res.* **36**, 4595–4601.

Little, M., Rosenfeld, G. C., and Jungblut, P. W. (1972). *Hoppe-Seyler's Z. Physiol. Chem.* **353**, 231–242.

Little, M., Szendro, P. I., and Jungblut, P. W. (1973). *Hoppe-Seyler's Z. Physiol. Chem.* **354**, 1599–1610.

Litwack, G. (1979). *T.I.B.S.* **4**, 217–220.

Litwack, G., Sears, M. L., and Diamondstone, T. L. (1963). *J. Biol. Chem.* **238**, 302–305.

Liu, A. Y.-C., and Greengard, P. (1974). *Proc. Natl. Acad. Sci. U.S.A.* **71**, 3869–3873.

Livingstone, J. N., and Lockwood, D. H. (1975). *J. Biol. Chem.* **250**, 8353–8360.

Lloyd, J. B. (1977). *Biochem. J.* **164**, 281–282.

Lodish, H. F., and Small, B. (1975). *J. Cell Biol.* **65**, 51–64.

Logsdon, P. J., Middleton, E., Jr., and Coffey, R. G. (1972). *J. Allergy Clin. Immunol.* **50**, 45–56.

Lowry, O. H., Rosebrough, N. J., Farr, A. L., and Randall, R. J. (1951). *J. Biol. Chem.* **193**, 265–275.

Lucy, J. A. (1968). *In* "Biological Membranes" (D. Chapman, ed.), Vol. 1, pp. 233–288. Academic Press, London.

McEwen, B. S., Drey, L. C., and Luine, V. N. (1978). *In* "The Hypothalamus" (S. Reichlin, R. J. Baldessarini, and J. B. Martin, eds.), pp. 255–268. Raven, New York.

McMurchie, E. J., and Raison, J. K. (1979). *Biochim. Biophys. Acta* **554**, 364–374.

Madden, T. D., Chapman, D., and Quinn, P. J. (1979). *Nature (London)* **279**, 538–541.

Madison, L. D., Bergstrom-Porter, B., Torres, A. R., and Shelton, E. (1979). *J. Cell Biol.* **82**, 783–797.

Mainwaring, W. I. P. (1975). *Vitam. Horm. (N.Y.)* **33**, 223–245.

Mainwaring, W. I. P., and Irving, R. A. (1973). *Biochem. J.* **134**, 113–127.

Mainwaring, W. I. P., and Peterken, B. M. (1971). *Biochem. J.* **125**, 285–295.

Mandel, T. E., and Santer, V. B. (1977). *In* "The Lymphocyte, Structure and Function" (J. J. Marchalonis, ed.), Vol. 5, Part II, pp. 511–539. Dekker, New York.

Mangan, F. R., Pegg, A. E., and Mainwaring, W. I. P. (1973). *Biochem. J.* **134**, 129–142.

Manganiello, V., and Vaughan, M. (1972). *J. Clin. Invest.* **51**, 2763–2767.

Maraini, G., Ottonello, S., Gozzoli, F., and Merli, A. (1977). *Nature (London)* **265**, 68–69.

Masters, C. J. (1978). *T.I.B.S.* **3**, 206–208.

Mastro, A. M., and Rozengurt, E. (1976). *J. Biol. Chem.* **25**, 7899–7906.

Masui, Y., and Clarke, H. J. (1979). *Int. Rev. Cytol.* **57**, 185–282.

Masui, Y., and Markert, C. L. (1971). *J. Exp. Zool.* **177**, 129–146.

Masur, S. K., Holtzman, E., and Walter, R. (1972). *J. Cell Biol.* **52**, 211–219.

Matlib, M. A., Crankshaw, J., Garfield, R. E., Crankshaw, D. J., Kwan, C.-Y., Branda, L. A., and Daniel, E. E. (1979). *J. Biol. Chem.* **254**, 1834–1840.

Matsuzawa, H., and Nirenberg, M. (1975). *Proc. Natl. Acad. Sci. U.S.A.* **72**, 3472–3476.

Mayer, M., Kaiser, N., Milholland, R. J., and Rosen, F. (1975). *J. Biol. Chem.* **250**, 1207–1211.

Mayer, M., Nir, S., Milholland, R. J., and Rosen, F. (1976). *Arch. Biochem. Biophys.* **176**, 28–36.

Mayewski, R. J., and Litwack, G. (1969). *Biochem. Biophys. Res. Commun.* **37**, 729–735.

Meli, A., Cargill, D. I., Giannina, T., and Steinetz, B. G. (1968). *Proc. Soc. Exp. Biol. Med.* **129**, 937–944.

Melnykovych, G., and Bishop, C. F. (1969). *Biochim. Biophys. Acta* **177**, 579–585.

Meyer, C. J., Layne, D. S., Tait, J. F., and Pincus, G. (1961). *J. Clin. Invest.* **40**, 1663–1671.

Milgrom, E., Atger, M., and Baulieu, E.-E. (1973). *Biochim. Biophys. Acta* **320**, 267–283.

Mills, J. W., Ernst, S. A., and Wisner, J. R., Jr. (1974). *J. Cell. Biol.* **63**, 227a.

Mitra, S., and Rao, C. V. (1978a). *Arch. Biochem. Biophys.* **185**, 126–133.

Mitra, S., and Rao, C. V. (1978b). *Arch. Biochem. Biophys.* **191**, 331–340.

Mollenhauer, H. H., and Morré, D. J. (1978). *Sub-Cell. Biochem.* **5**, 327–359.

Monder, C., and Coufalik, A. H. (1979). *FEBS Lett.* **102**, 169–172.

Morishige, W. K., and Uetake, C.-A. (1978). *Endocrinology* **102**, 1827–1837.

Morré, D. J., and Ovtracht, L. (1977). *Int. Rev. Cytol., Suppl.* **5**, 61–188.

Morris, D. J., and Barnes, F. W., Jr. (1967). *Biochim. Biophys. Acta* **136**, 67–78.

Müller, R. E., and Wotiz, H. H. (1979). *Endocrinology* **105**, 1107–1114.

Müller, R. E., Johnston, T. C., and Wotiz, H. H. (1979). *J. Biol. Chem.* **254**, 7895–7900.

Munck, A. (1957). *Biochim. Biophys. Acta* **24**, 507–514.

Munck, A., and Leung, K. (1977). *Mod. Pharmacol.-Toxicol.* **8**, Part 2, 311–397.

Murono, E. P., Kirdani, R. Y., and Sandberg, A. A. (1979). *J. Steroid Biochem.* **11**, 1347–1351.

Natowicz, M. R., Chi, M. M.-Y., Lowry, O. H., and Sly, W. S. (1979). *Proc. Natl. Acad. Sci. U.S.A.* **76**, 4322–4326.

Neckers, L., and Sze, P. Y. (1975). *Brain Res.* **93**, 123–132.

Nelson, S. D., Mitchell, J. R., Dybing, E., and Sasame, H. A. (1976). *Biochem. Biophys. Res. Commun.* **70**, 1157–1165.

Nemere, I., and Szego, C. M. (1981). In press.

Nenci, I., Beccati, M. D., Piffanelli, A., and Lanza, G. (1977). *Res. Steroids* **7**, 137–147.

Nenci, I., Fabris, G., Marchetti, E., and Marzola, A. (1980). *In* "Perspectives in Steroid Receptor Research" (F. Bresciani, ed.), pp. 61–72. Raven, New York.

Nernst, W. (1904). *Hoppe-Seyler's Z. Physiol. Chem.* 47, 52–55.

Neufeld, E. F., Sando, G. N., Garvin, A. J., and Rome, L. H. (1977). *J. Supramol. Struct.* 6, 95–101.

Neurath, H., and Walsh, K. A. (1976). *Proc. Natl. Acad. Sci. U.S.A.* 73, 3825–3832.

Neville, D. M., Jr., and Chang, T.-M. (1978). *Curr. Top. Membr. Transp.* 10, 65–150.

Neville, E., and Holdsworth, E. S. (1969). *FEBS Lett.* 2, 313–316.

Nielsen, C. J., Sando, J. J., and Pratt, W. B. (1977a). *Proc. Natl. Acad. Sci. U.S.A.* 74, 1398–1402.

Nielsen, C. J., Sando, J. J., Vogel, W. M., and Pratt, W. B. (1977b). *J. Biol. Chem.* 252, 7568–7578.

Nishikori, K., and Maeno, H. (1979). *J. Biol. Chem.* 254, 6099–6106.

Noonan, K. D. (1978). *Curr. Top. Membr. Transp.* 11, 397–461.

Noteboom, W. D., and Gorski, J. (1965). *Arch. Biochem. Biophys.* 111, 559–568.

Notides, A. C., Hamilton, D. E., and Rudolph, J. H. (1973). *Endocrinology* 93, 210–216.

Novikoff, A. B., Essner, E., and Goldfischer, S. (1962). *In* "The Interpretation of Ultrastructure" (R. J. C. Harris, ed.), pp. 149–192. Academic Press, New York.

Novikoff, A. B., Essner, E., and Quintana, N. (1964). *Fed. Proc., Fed. Am. Soc. Exp. Biol.* 23, 1010–1022.

Novikoff, A. B., Roheim, P. S., and Quintana, N. (1966). *Lab. Invest.* 15, 27–49.

Oku, T., Ooizumi, K., and Hosoya, N. (1974). *J. Nutr. Sci. Vitaminol.* 20, 9–21.

O'Malley, B. W., and Hardman, J. G., eds. (1975). "Methods in Enzymology," Vol. 36. Part A. Academic Press, New York.

Ortmann, R., and Perkins, J. P. (1977). *J. Biol. Chem.* 252, 6018–6025.

Osterhout, W. J. V. (1933). *Ergeb. Physiol., Exp. Pharmakol.* 35, 967–1021.

Overton, E. (1902). *Arch. Gestamte Physiol. Menschen Tiere* 92, 115–280.

Ožegović, B., Schön, E., and Milković, S. (1977). *J. Steroid Biochem.* 8, 815–819.

Ozon, R., and Bellé, R. (1973). *Biochim. Biophys. Acta* 320, 588–593.

Pak, C. Y. C., and Gershfeld, N. L. (1967). *Nature (London)* 214, 888–889.

Palade, G. E. (1960). *Anat. Rec.* 136, 254.

Palade, G. (1975). *Science* 189, 347–358.

Palmiter, R. D., and Mulvihill, E. R. (1978). *Science* 201, 356–358.

Pantalone, R. M., and Page, R. C. (1975). *Proc. Natl. Acad. Sci. U.S.A.* 72, 2091–2094.

Pappenheimer, A. M., Jr. (1978). *T.I.B.S.* 3, N220–224.

Parchman, L. G., Goidl, J., and Litwack, G. (1977). *FEBS Lett.* 79, 25–28.

Park, M. K., and Vincenzi, F. F. (1975). *J. Pharmacol. Exp. Ther.* 195, 140–150.

Parker, C. W., Huber, M. G., and Baumann, M. L. (1973). *J. Clin. Invest.* 52, 1342–1348.

Parmley, W. W., and Braunwald, E. (1967). *J. Pharmacol. Exp. Ther.* 158, 11–21.

Parr, M. B., Kay, M. G., and Parr, E. L. (1978). *Cytobiologie* 18, 374–378.

Parry, G. (1978). *Sub-Cell. Biochem.* 5, 261–326.

Paul, S. M., and Skolnick, P. (1977). *Nature (London)* 266, 559–561.

Pearse, B. M. F. (1975). *J. Mol. Biol.* 97, 93–98.

Peck, E. J., Jr., Burgner, J., and Clark, J. H. (1973). *Biochemistry* 12, 4596–4603.

Pert, C. B. (1974). Doctoral Dissertation, Johns Hopkins University, Baltimore, Maryland.

Pert, C. B., and Garland, B. L. (1978). *Recept. Horm. Action* 3, 535–549.

Peters, R. A. (1956). *Nature (London)* 177, 426.

Peterson, R P., and Spaziani, E. (1969). *Endocrinology* 85, 932–940.

Peterson, R. P., and Spaziani, E. (1971). *Endocrinology* 89, 1280–1286.

Petrusz, P. (1978). *In* "Structure and Function of the Gonadotropins" (K. W. McKerns, ed.), pp. 577–589. Plenum, New York.

Petrusz, P., Lea, O., and French, F. F. (1980). *In* "Reproductive Process and Contraception" (K. W. McKerns, ed.). Plenum, New York (in press).

Phillips, J. H. (1976). *Biochem. Soc. Trans.* 4, 1003–1007.

Pietras, R. J. (1976). *Nature (London)* 264, 774–776.

Pietras, R. J., and Roberts, J. A. (1980). Submitted for publication.

Pietras, R. J., and Szego, C. M. (1975a). *Endocrinology* 96, 946–954.

Pietras, R. J., and Szego, C. M. (1975b). *Endocrinology* 97, 1445–1454.

Pietras, R. J., and Szego, C. M. (1975c). *Nature (London)* 253, 357–359.

Pietras, R. J., and Szego, C. M. (1976). *Cancer Lett.* 1, 237–242.

Pietras, R. J., and Szego, C. M. (1977a). *Nature (London)* 265, 69–72.

Pietras, R. J., and Szego, C. M. (1977b). *Endocrinology* 100, Suppl., 79.

Pietras, R. J., and Szego, C. M. (1979a). *J. Cell. Physiol.* 98, 145–160.

Pietras, R. J., and Szego, C. M. (1979b). *J. Cell Biol.* 81, 649–663.

Pietras, R. J., and Szego, C. M. (1979c). *J. Steroid Biochem.* 11, 1471–1483.

Pietras, R. J., and Szego, C. M. (1980a). *Biochem. J.* 191, 743–760.

Pietras, R. J., and Szego, C. M. (1980b). *In* "Reproductive Processes and Contraception" (K. W. McKerns, ed.). Plenum, New York. (in press).

Pietras, R. J., Seeler, B. J., and Szego, C. M. (1975). *Nature (London)* 257, 493–495.

Pietras, R. J., Hutchens, T. W., and Szego, C. M. (1978). *Endocrinology* 102, Suppl., 76.

Plagemann, P. G. W. (1969). *Biochim. Biophys. Acta* 182, 46–56.

Plagemann, P. G. W., and Erbe, J. (1976). *Biochem. Pharmacol.* 25, 1489–1494.

Pliam, N. B., and Goldfine, I. D. (1977). *Biochem. Biophys. Res. Commun.* 79, 166–172.

Pober, J. S., Guild, B. C., and Strominger, J. L. (1978). *Proc. Natl. Acad. Sci. U.S.A.* 75, 6002–6006.

Pollard, C. J. (1970). *Biochim. Biophys. Acta* 201, 511–512.

Porter, R. R., and Reid, K. B. M. (1978). *Nature (London)* 275, 699–704.

Posner, B. I., Josefsberg, Z., and Bergeron, J. J. M. (1978a). *J. Biol. Chem.* 253, 4067–4073.

Posner, B. I., Raquidan, D., Josefsberg, Z., and Bergeron, J. J. M. (1978b). *Proc. Natl. Acad. Sci. U.S.A.* 75, 3302–3306.

Poste, G., and Allison, A. C. (1973). *Biochim. Biophys. Acta* 300, 421–465.

Poste, G., and Nicolson, G. L., eds. (1977). "Cell Surface Reviews," Vol. 3. North-Holland Publ., Amsterdam.

Puca, G. A., and Bresciani, F. (1970). *Res. Steroids* 4, 247–255.

Puca, G. A., Nola, E., Sica, V., and Bresciani, F. (1971). *Biochemistry* 10, 3769–3780.

Puca, G. A., Nola, E., Sica, V., and Bresciani, F. (1972). *Biochemistry* 11, 4157–4165.

Puca, G. A., Nola, E., Sica, V., and Bresciani, F. (1977). *J. Biol. Chem.* 252, 1358–1366.

Quastel, M. R., and Kaplan, J. G. (1970). *Exp. Cell Res.* 63, 230–233.

Quinn, P. S., and Judah, J. D. (1978). *Biochem. J.* 172, 301–309.

Quintart, J., Bartholeyns, J., and Baudhuin, P. (1979a). *Biochem. J.* 184, 133–141.

Quintart, J., Leroy-Houyet, M.-A., Trouet, A., and Baudhuin, P. (1979b). *J. Cell Biol.* 82, 644–653.

Radanyi, C., Mercier-Bodard, C., Secco-Millet, C., Baulieu, E.-E., and Richard-Foy, H. (1977). *Proc. Natl. Acad. Sci. U.S.A.* 74, 2269–2272.

Rancourt, M. W., and Litwack, G. (1968). *Exp. Cell Res.* 51, 413–422.

Rao, C. V. (1974). *J. Biol. Chem.* 249, 7203–7209.

Rao, C. V., and Mitra, S. (1979). *Biochem. Biophys. Acta* 584, 454–466.

Rao, G. S., Schulze-Hagen, K., Rao, M. L., and Breuer, H. (1976). *J. Steroid Biochem.* 7, 1123–1129.

Rao, M. L., Rao, G. S., Höller, M., Breuer, H., Schattenberg, P. J., and Stein, W. D. (1976). *Hoppe-Seyler's Z. Physiol. Chem.* 357, 573–584.

Rao, M. L., Rao, G. S., and Breuer, H. (1977a). *Biochem. Biophys. Res. Commun.* **77**, 566–573.

Rao, M. L., Rao, G. S., Eckel, J., and Breuer, H. (1977b). *Biochim. Biophys. Acta* **500**, 322–332.

Rask, L., and Peterson, P. A. (1976). *J. Biol. Chem.* **251**, 6360–6366.

Rasmussen, H, and Goodman, D. B. P. (1977). *Physiol. Rev.* **57**, 421–509.

Raspé, G., ed. (1971). "Advances in the Biosciences," Vol. 7. Pergamon, Oxford.

Reichman, M. E., and Villee, C. A. (1978). *J. Steroid Biochem.* **9**, 637–641.

Reilly, C. E., and Ferber, E. (1976). *In* "Surface Membrane Receptors, Interface Between Cells and Their Environment" (R. A. Bradshaw, W. A. Frazier, R. C. Merrell, D. I. Gottlieb, and R. A. Hogue-Angeletti, eds.), pp. 199–213. Plenum, New York.

Richards, D. E., Irvine, R. F., and Dawson, R. M. C. (1979). *Biochem. J.* **182**, 599–606.

Richert, N. D., and Ryan, R. J. (1977). *Proc. Natl. Acad. Sci. U.S.A.* **74**, 4857–4861.

Rinard, G. A., Okuno, G., and Haynes, R. C., Jr. (1969). *Endocrinology* **84**, 622–631.

Ritter, C., Linnetz, L., Enk, J., and Gardner, W. (1969). *Fed. Proc., Fed. Am. Soc. Exp. Biol.* **28**, 703.

Roberts, M. F., Adamich, M., Robson, R. J., and Dennis, E. A. (1979). *Biochemistry* **18**, 3301–3308.

Roberts, S., and Szego, C. M. (1946). *Endocrinology* **39**, 183–187.

Roberts, S., and Szego, C. M. (1953). *Physiol. Rev.* **33**, 593–629.

Robison, G. A. (1970). *J. Reprod. Fertil., Suppl.* **10**, 55–74.

Robison, G. A., Butcher, R. W., and Sutherland, E. W. (1971). "Cyclic AMP," pp. 338–399. Academic Press, New York.

Rochefort, H., and Baulieu, E.-E. (1971). *Biochimie* **53**, 893–907.

Roels, O. A. (1969). *In* "Lysosomes in Biology and Pathology" (J. T. Dingle and H. B. Fell, eds.), Vol. 1, pp. 254–275. North-Holland Publ. Co., Amsterdam.

Rogers, T. B., and Lazdunski, M. (1979). *Biochemistry* **18**, 135–140.

Rome, L. H., Weissmann, B., and Neufeld, E. F. (1979). *Proc. Natl. Acad. Sci. U.S.A.* **76**, 2331–2334.

Rosenfeld, M. G., and O'Malley, B. W. (1970). *Science* **168**, 253–255.

Rosenthal, H. E., and Sandberg, A. A. (1978). *J. Steroid Biochem.* **9**, 1133–1139.

Roth, T. F., and Porter, K. R. (1964). *J. Cell. Biol.* **20**, 313–332.

Rousseau, G., Baxter, J. D., Funder, J. W., Edelman, I. S., and Tomkins, G. M. (1972a). *J. Steroid Biochem.* **3**, 219–227.

Rousseau, G. G., Baxter, J. D., and Tomkins, G. M. (1972b). *J. Mol. Biol.* **67**, 99–115.

Rubio, R. (1974). *In* "Electron Microscopy of Enzymes" (M. A. Hayat, ed.), Vol. 3, pp. 54–67. Van Nostrand-Reinhold, Princeton, New Jersey.

Rüdiger, H. W., Haenisch, F., Metzler, M., Oesch, F., and Glatt, H. R. (1979). *Nature (London)* **281**, 392–394.

Rufeger, U., Tellhelm, B., and Kroker, R. (1974). *Comp. Biochem. Physiol. B.* **47**, 255–262.

Ruoho, A., and Kyte, J. (1974). *Proc. Natl. Acad. Sci. U.S.A.* **71**, 2352–2356.

Rutishauser, U., and Edelman, G. M. (1978). *In* "Differentiation and Development" (F. Ahmad, T. R. Russell, and J. Schultz, eds.), pp. 211–233. Academic Press, New York.

Ryan, M. F., and Westphal, U. (1972). *J. Biol. Chem.* **247**, 4050–4056.

Ryser, H. J.-P. (1968). *Science* **159**, 390–396.

Sachs, L. (1974). *In* "The Cell Surface in Development" (A. A. Moscona, ed.), pp. 127–139. Wiley, New York.

Samuelsson, B., Granström, E., Green, K., Hamberg, M., and Hammerström, S. (1975). *Annu. Rev. Biochem.* **44**, 669–695.

Sananes, N., and Psychoyos, A. (1974). *J. Reprod. Fertil.* **38**, 181–183.

Sanborn, B. M., Rao, B. R., and Korenman, S. G. (1971). *Biochemistry* **10**, 4955–4962.

Sandborn, B. M., Bhalla, R. C., and Korenman, S. G. (1973). *Endocrinology* **92**, 494–499.

Sandhoff, K., and Pallmann, B. (1978). *Proc. Natl. Acad. Sci. U.S.A.* **75**, 122–126.

Sando, J. J., La Forest, A. C., and Pratt, W. B. (1979). *J. Biol. Chem.* **254**, 4772–4778.

Sapag-Hagar, M., and Greenbaum, A. L. (1974). *Eur. J. Biochem.* **47**, 303–312.

Sato, B., Huseby, R. A., Matsumoto, K., and Samuels, L. T. (1979). *J. Steroid Biochem.* **11**, 1353–1359.

Scanu, A., and Wisdom, C. (1972). *Annu. Rev. Biochem.* **41**, 703–730.

Schaeffer, J. M., and Hsueh, A. J. W. (1979). *J. Biol. Chem.* **254**, 5506–5608.

Scheuplein, R. J., and Blank, I. H. (1971). *Physiol. Rev.* **51**, 702–747.

Scheuplein, R J., Blank, I. H., Brauner, G. J., and MacFarlane, D. J. (1969). *J. Invest. Dermatol.* **52**, 63–70.

Schiff, E. R., Small, N. C., and Dietschy, J. M. (1972). *J. Clin. Invest.* **51**, 1351–1362.

Schlegel, W., Kempner, E. S., and Rodbell, M. (1979). *J. Biol. Chem.* **254**, 5168–5176.

Schlessinger, J., Shechter, Y., Willingham, M. C., and Pastan, I. (1978). *Proc. Natl. Acad. Sci. U.S.A.* **75**, 2659–2663.

Schneider, Y.-J., Tulkens, P., and Trouet, A. (1978). *In* "Transport of Macromolecules in Cellular Systems" (S. C. Silverstein, ed.), pp. 181–196. Dahlem Konferenzen, Berlin.

Schorderet-Slatkine, S. (1972). *Cell Differ.* **1**, 179–189.

Schorderet-Slatkine, S., and Drury, K. C. (1973). *Cell Differ.* **2**, 247–254.

Schulte, H. F., Nielsen, C. J., Sando, J. J., and Pratt, W. B. (1976). *J. Biol. Chem.* **251**, 2279–2289.

Selye, H. (1941). *Proc. Soc. Exp. Biol. Med.* **46**, 116–121.

Sen, K. K., Gupta, P. D., and Talwar, G. P. (1975). *J. Steroid Biochem.* **6**, 1223–1227.

Sha'afi, R. I., Rich, G. T., Sidel, Y. W., Bossert, W., and Solomon, A. K. (1967). *J. Gen. Physiol.* **50**, 1377–1399.

Sharp, G. W. G., and Leaf, A. (1966). *Physiol. Rev.* **46**, 593–633.

Sheridan, P. J., Buchanan, J. M., and Anselmo, V. C. (1979). *Nature (London)* **282**, 579–582.

Sherman, M. R., Atienza, S. B. P., Shansky, J. R., and Hoffman, L. M. (1974). *J. Biol. Chem.* **249**, 5351–5363.

Sherman, M. R., Pickering, L. A., Rollwagen, F. M., and Miller, L. K. (1978). *Fed. Proc., Fed. Am. Soc. Exp. Biol.* **37**, 167–173.

Sherrill, B. C., and Dietschy, J. M. (1975). *J. Membr. Biol.* **23**, 367–383.

Shlatz, L., and Marinetti, G. V. (1972). *Science* **176**, 175–177.

Sibley, C., Gehring, U., Bourne, H., and Tomkins, G. M. (1974). *In* "Control of Proliferation in Animal Cells" (B. Clarkson and R. Baserga, eds.), Vol. 1, pp. 115–124. Cold Spring Harbor Lab., Cold Spring Harbor, New York.

Sica, V., and Bresciani, F. (1979). *Biochemistry* **18**, 2369–2378.

Sica, V., Nola, E., Puca, G. A., Cuatrecasas, P., and Parikh, I. (1976). *Mol. Pharmacol.-Toxicol.* **8**, Part 1, 85–108.

Siiteri, P. K., Ashby, R., Schwartz, B., and MacDonald, P. C. (1972). *J. Steroid Biochem.* **3**, 459–470.

Sim, M. K., and Chantharaksri, U. (1973). *Biochem. Pharmacol.* **22**, 1417–1422.

Simon, M. (1976). *Biochem. Biophys. Res. Commun.* **68**, 1219–1225.

Singer, S. J. (1975). *In* "Control Mechanisms in Development. Activation, Differentiation and Modulation in Biological Systems" (R. H. Meints and E. Davies, eds.), pp. 181–192. Plenum, New York.

Singer, S. J. (1976). *In* "Surface Membrane Receptors: Interface Between Cells and Their

Environment" (R. A. Bradshaw, W. A. Frazier, R. C. Merrell, D. I. Gottlieb, and R. A. Hogue-Angeletti, eds.), pp. 1–24. Plenum, New York.

Singer, S. J. (1977). *J. Supramol. Struct.* **6**, 313–323.

Singer, S. J., and Nicolson, G. L. (1972). *Science* **175**, 720–731.

Singer, S. J., Ash, J. F., Bourguignon, L. Y. W., Heggeness, M. H., and Louvard, D. (1978). *J. Supramol. Struct.* **9**, 373–389.

Singhal, R. L. (1973). *Adv. Pharmacol. Chemother.* **11**, 99–150.

Singhal, R. L., Parulekar, M. R. Vijayvargiya, R., and Robison, G. A. (1971). *Biochem. J.* **125**, 329–342.

Sly, W. S. (1980). *In* "Structure and Function of the Gangliosides" (L. Svennerholm, P. Mandel, H. Dreyfus, and P. F. Urban, eds.), pp. 433–451. Plenum, New York.

Sly, W. S., Bretscher, M. S., Brown, M. S., Cohn, Z. A., de Duve, C., Franke, W. W., Farquhar, M. G., Goldstein, J. L., Henning, R., Herzog, V., Heuser, J. E., Palade, G. E., Pearse, B., Pollard, T. D., Schneider, Y.-J., Silverstein, S. C., and Steinman, R. M. (1978). *In* "Transport of Macromolecules in Cellular Systems" (S. C. Silverstein, ed.), pp. 265–270. Dahlem Konferenzen, Berlin.

Smigel, M., and Fleischer, S. (1977). *J. Biol. Chem.* **252**, 3689–3696.

Smirnova, O. V., Smirnov, A. N., and Rozen, V. B. (1974). *Biokhimiya* **39**, 648–655.

Smith, A. D., and Winkler, H. (1972). *Handb. Exp. Pharmakol.* **33**, 538–617.

Smith, L. D., and Ecker, R. E. (1971). *Dev. Biol.* **25**, 232–247.

Smith, R. E., and Farquhar, M. G. (1966). *J. Cell Biol.* **31**, 319–347.

Smith, R. E., and Van Frank, R. M. (1975). *In* "Lysosomes in Biology and Pathology" (J. T. Dingle and R. T. Dean, eds.), Vol. 4, pp. 193–249. North-Holland Publ. Co., Amsterdam.

Smith, R. G., Clarke, S. G., Zalta, E., and Taylor, R. N. (1979). *J. Steroid Biochem.* **10**, 31–35.

Smith, T. W., Wagner, H., Jr., Markis, J. E., and Young, M. (1972). *J. Clin. Invest.* **51**, 1777–1789.

Sodhi, H. S., and Gould, R. G. (1967). *J. Biol. Chem.* **242**, 1205–1210.

Soloff, M. S. (1976). *In* "Hormone-Receptor Interaction: Molecular Aspects" (G. S. Levey, ed.), pp. 129–151. Dekker, New York.

Solyom, A., and Trams, E. G. (1972). *Enzyme* **13**, 329–372.

Spaziani, E. (1975). *Pharmacol. Rev.* **27**, 207–286.

Spaziani, E., and Szego, C. M. (1959). *Am. J. Physiol.* **197**, 355–359.

Stahl, P., Six, H., Rodman, J. S., Schlesinger, P., Tulsiani, D. R. P., and Touster, O. (1976). *Proc. Natl. Acad. Sci. U.S.A.* **73**, 4045–4049.

Stahl, P. D., Rodman, J. S., Miller, M. J., and Schlesinger, P. H. (1978). *Proc. Natl. Acad. Sci. U.S.A.* **75**, 1399–1403.

Stein, W. D. (1967). "The Movement of Molecules Across Cell Membranes." Academic Press, New York.

Steiner, A. L., Pagliara, A. S., Chase, L. R., and Kipnis, D. M. (1972). *J. Biol. Chem.* **247**, 1114–1120.

Steiner, F. A., Ruf, K., and Akert, K. (1969). *Brain Res.* **12**, 74–85.

Steinman, R. M., Brodie, S. E., and Cohn, Z. A. (1976). *J. Cell Biol.* **68**, 665–687.

Steinman, R. M., Silver, J. M., and Cohn, Z. A. (1978). *In* "Transport of Macromolecules in Cellular Systems" (S. C. Silverstein, ed.), pp. 167–180. Dahlem Konferenzen, Berlin.

Sterling, K. (1979). *N. Engl. J. Med.* **300**, 117–123.

Stern, P. L., and Bretscher, M. S. (1979). *J. Cell Biol.* **82**, 829–833.

Stoff, J. S., Handler, J. S., and Orloff, J. (1972). *Proc. Natl. Acad. Sci. U.S.A.* **69**, 805–808.

Stone, G. M. (1963). *J. Endocrinol.* **27**, 281–288.

Stoner, J., Manganiello, V. C., and Vaughan, M. (1973). *Proc. Natl. Acad. Sci. U.S.A.* **70**, 3830–3833.

Stumpf, W. E., and Sar, M. (1977). *Fed. Proc., Fed. Am. Soc. Exp. Biol.* **36**, 1973–1977.

Stumpf, W. E., Sar, M., and Aumüller, G. (1977). *Science* **196**, 319–321.

Sulya, L. L., McCaa, C. S., Read, V. H., and Bomer, D. (1963). *Nature (London)* **200**, 788–789.

Sunshine, G. H., Williams, D. J., and Rabin, B. R. (1971). *Nature (London) New Biol.* **230**, 133–135.

Sutherland, D. J. B., and Singhal, R. L. (1974). *Biochim. Biophys. Acta* **343**, 238–249.

Sutherland, E. W. (1972). *Science* **177**, 401–408.

Suyemitsu, T., and Terayama, H. (1975). *Endocrinology* **96**, 1499–1508.

Sylvén, B., Snellman, O., and Sträuli, P. (1974). *Virchows Arch. B* **17**, 97–112.

Szego, C. M. (1952). *Endocrinology* **50**, 429–441.

Szego, C. M. (1957). *In* "Physiological Triggers" (T. H. Bullock, ed.), pp. 152–163. Am. Physiol. Soc./Natl. Res. Counc., Washington, D.C.

Szego, C. M. (1969). *In* Discussion, pp. 141–142 of Katzman, P. A., Larson, D. L., and Podratz, K. C., *in* "The Sex Steroids, Molecular Mechanisms", (K. W. McKerns, ed.). Appleton, New York, 1971.

Szego, C. M. (1971). *In* "The Sex Steroids: Molecular Mechanisms" (K. W. McKerns, ed.), pp. 1–51. Appleton, New York.

Szego, C. M. (1972a). *Adv. Cyclic Nucleotide Res.* **1**, 541–564.

Szego, C. M. (1972b). *Gynecol. Invest.* **3**, 63–95.

Szego, C. M. (1974). *Recent Prog. Horm. Res.* **30**, 171–233.

Szego, C. M. (1975). *In* "Lysosomes in Biology and Pathology" (J. T. Dingle and R. Dean, eds.), Vol. 4, pp. 385–477. North-Holland Publ. Co., Amsterdam.

Szego, C. M. (1976). *Gynecol. Invest.* **7**, 251–279.

Szego, C. M. (1978). *In* "Structure and Function of the Gonadotropins" (K. W. McKerns, ed.), pp. 431–472. Plenum, New York.

Szego, C. M., and Davis, J. S. (1967). *Proc. Natl. Acad. Sci. U.S.A.* **58**, 1711–1718.

Szego, C. M., and Davis, J. S. (1969a). *Mol. Pharmacol.* **5**, 470–480.

Szego, C. M., and Davis, J. S. (1969b). *Life Sci.* **8**, Part I, 1109–1116.

Szego, C. M., and Pietras, R. J. (1981). *Int. Rev. Cytol.* (in preparation).

Szego, C. M., and Roberts, S. (1953). *Recent Prog. Horm. Res.* **8**, 419–469.

Szego, C. M., and Seeler, B. J. (1973). *J. Endocrinol.* **56**, 347–360.

Szego, C. M., Seeler, B. J., Steadman, R. A., Hill, D. F., Kimura, A. K., and Roberts, J. A. (1971). *Biochem. J.* **123**, 523–538.

Szego, C. M., Steadman, R. A., and Seeler, B. J. (1974). *Eur. J. Biochem.* **46**, 377–386.

Szego, C. M., Seeler, B. J., and Smith, R. E. (1976). *Eur. J. Biochem.* **69**, 463–474.

Szego, C. M., Nazareno, M. B., and Porter, D. D. (1977). *J. Cell Biol.* **73**, 354–365.

Szego, C. M., Brown, W. J., and Pietras, R. J. (1980). In preparation.

Takase, S., Ong, D. E., and Chytil, F. (1979). *Proc. Natl. Acad. Sci. U.S.A.* **76**, 2204–2208.

Talwar, G. P., Segal, S. J., Evans, A., and Davidson, O. W. (1964). *Proc. Natl. Acad. Sci. U.S.A.* **52**, 1059–1066.

Tanabe, T., Pricer, W. E., Jr., and Ashwell, G. (1979). *J. Biol. Chem.* **254**, 1038–1043.

Tappel, A. L. (1969). *In* "Lysosomes in Biology and Pathology" (J. T. Dingle and H. B. Fell, eds.), Vol. 2, pp. 207–244. North-Holland Publ. Co., Amsterdam.

Taylor, R. B., Duffus, W. P. H., Raff, M. C., and de Petris, S. (1971). *Nature (London) New Biol.* **233**, 225–229.

Tchernitchin, A., Tseng, L., Stumpf, W. E., and Gurpide, E. (1973). *J. Steroid Biochem.* **4**, 451–455.

Teorell, T. (1936). *J. Biol. Chem.* **113**, 735–748.

Terayama, H., Okamura, N., and Suyemitsu, T. (1976). *In* "Control Mechanisms in Cancer" (W. E. Criss, T. Ono, and J. R. Sabine, eds.), pp. 83–97. Raven, New York.

Terenius, L. (1967). *Mol. Pharmacol.* **3**, 423–428.

Thompson, E. B., and Lippman, M. E. (1974). *Metab., Clin. Exp.* **23**, 159–202.

Thompson, J. E., Chambers, J. A., and Semple, N. L. (1978). *Exp. Cell Res.* **113**, 127–137.

Thompson, A. B. R. (1978). *In* "Disturbances in Lipid and Lipoprotein Metabolism" (J. M. Dietschy, A. M. Gotto, Jr., and J. A. Ontko, eds.), pp. 29–55. Am. Physiol. Soc., Bethesda, Maryland.

Thrall, C. L., Webster, R. A., and Spelsberg, T. C. (1978). *Cell Nucleus* **6**, Part C, 461–529.

Tobin, T., Akera, T., Brody, S. L., Ku, D., and Brody, T. M. (1975). *Eur. J. Pharmacol.* **32**, 133–145.

Toft, D., and Gorski, J. (1966). *Proc. Natl. Acad. Sci. U.S.A.* **55**, 1574–1581.

Toft, D., and Nishigori, H. (1979). *J. Steroid Biochem.* **11**, 413–416.

Traish, A. M., Müller, R. E., and Wotiz, H. H. (1977). *J. Biol. Chem.* **252**, 6823–6830.

Traish, A. M., Müller, R. E., and Wotiz, H. H. (1979). *J. Biol. Chem.* **254**, 6560–6563.

Troensegaard, N., and Koudahl, B. (1926). *Hoppe-Seyler's Z. Physiol. Chem.* **153**, 111–118.

Tsai, H. C., and Norman, A. W. (1973). *J. Biol. Chem.* **248**, 5967–5975.

Tseng, L., Stolee, A., and Gurpide, E. (1972). *Endocrinology* **90**, 390–404.

Tsibris, J. C. M., and McGuire, P. M. (1977). *Biochem. Biophys. Res. Commun.* **78**, 411–417.

Tsukada, Y., Richards, W. L., Becker, J. E., Potter, V. R., and Hirai, H. (1979). *Biochem. Biophys. Res. Commun.* **90**, 439–446.

Tveter, K. J. (1969). *Endocrinology* **85**, 597–600.

Ullrich, K., Gieselmann, V., Mersmann, G., and von Figura, K. (1979). *Biochem. J.* **182**, 329–335.

Ulrich, F. (1959). *Am. J. Physiol.* **196**, 572–578.

Uriel, J., Bouillon, D., Aussel, C., and Dupiers, M. (1976). *Proc. Natl. Acad. Sci. U.S.A.* **73**, 1452–1456.

Uzuka, M., Nakajima, K., and Mori, Y. (1978). *Biochim. Biophys. Acta* **544**, 329–337.

Vallieres, J., Fortier, M., Somlyo, A. V., and Somlyo, A. P. (1978). *Int. J. Biochem.* **9**, 487–498.

Van Baelen, H., Bouillon, R., and De Moor, P. (1977). *J. Biol. Chem.* **252**, 2515–2518.

van Beurden-Lamers, W. M. O., Brinkmann, A. O., Mulder, E., and van der Molen, H. J. (1974). *Biochem. J.* **140**, 495–502.

Van den Berghe, G., De Wulf, H., and Hers, H.-G. (1970). *Eur. J. Biochem.* **16**, 358–362.

van de Werve, G., Van den Berghe, G., and Hers, H. G. (1974). *Eur. J. Biochem.* **41**, 97–102.

van Heyningen, W. E. (1976). *In* "Surface Membrane Receptors, Interface Between Cell and Their Environment" (R. A. Bradshaw, W. A. Frazier, R. C. Merrell, D. I. Gottlieb, and R. A. Hogue-Angeletti, eds.), pp. 147–167. Plenum, New York.

Vansteveninck, J., Weed, R. I., and Rothstein, A. (1965). *J. Gen. Physiol.* **48**, 617–632.

Varga, J. M., Moellmann, G., Fritsch, P., Godawska, E., and Lerner, A. B. (1976). *Proc. Natl. Acad. Sci. U.S.A.* **73**, 559–562.

Vedeckis, W. V., Schrader, W. T., and O'Malley, B. W. (1978). *In* "Biochemical Actions of Hormones" (G. Litwack, ed.), Vol. 5, pp. 321–372. Academic Press, New York.

Verbert, A., Cacan, R., and Montreuil, J. (1976). *Eur. J. Biochem.* **70**, 49–53.

Vesely, D. L. (1979). *Proc. Natl. Acad. Sci. U.S.A.* **76**, 3491–3494.

Voigt, J., Wieland, T., and Sekeris, C. E. (1978). *Arch. Biochem. Biophys.* **191**, 101–109.

von Figura, K., and Voss, B. (1979). *Exp. Cell Res.* **121**, 267–276.

von Figura, K., and Weber, E. (1978). *Biochem. J.* **176**, 943–950.

Walling, M. W., Brasitus, T. A., and Kimberg, D. V. (1976). *Endocrinol. Res. Commun.* **3**, 83–91.

Walton, K. G. (1978). *Recept. Horm. Action* **3**, 579–614.

Wasserman, R. H., Corradino, R. A., Krook, L., Hughes, M. R., and Haussler, M. R. (1976). *J. Nutr.* **106**, 457–465.

Watanabe, M., and Po, L. (1974). *Biochim. Biophys. Acta* **345**, 419–429.

Watanabe, M., Phillips, K., and Chen, T. (1973). *J. Steroid Biochem.* **4**, 613–621.

Watson, D. H., and Sherratt, D. J. (1979). *Nature (London)* **278**, 362–364.

Welman, E. (1979). *Br. J. Pharmacol.* **65**, 479–482.

Werthamer, S., Samuels, A. J., and Amaral, L. (1973). *J. Biol. Chem.* **248**, 6398–6407.

Westphal, H. M., Fleischmann, G., Climent, F., and Beato, M. (1978). *Hoppe-Seyler's Z. Physiol. Chem.* **359**, 1297–1305.

Westphal, U. (1970). *Res. Steroids* **4**, 1–19.

Westphal, U., Stroupe, S. D., Cheng, S.-L., and Harding, G. B. (1978). *J. Toxicol. Environ. Health* **4**, 229–247.

Williams, D., and Gorski, J. (1971). *Biochem. Biophys. Res. Commun.* **45**, 258–264.

Williams, D., and Gorski, J. (1972). *Proc. Natl. Acad. Sci. U.S.A.* **69**, 3464–3468.

Williams, D., and Gorski, J. (1973). *Biochemistry* **12**, 297–306.

Williams, D., and Gorski, J. (1974). *Biochemistry* **13**, 5537–5542.

Williams, M. A., and Baba, W. I. (1967). *J. Endocrinol.* **39**, 543–554.

Willingham, M. C., Maxfield, F. R., and Pastan, I. H. (1979). *J. Cell Biol.* **82**, 614–625.

Willmer, E. N. (1961). *Biol. Rev. Cambridge Philos. Soc.* **36**, 368–398.

Wilson, E. M., and French, F. S. (1979). *J. Biol. Chem.* **254**, 6310–6319.

Wilson, J. E. (1978). *T.I.B.S.* **3**, 124–125.

Wong, G. L., Luben, R. A., Cohn, D. V. (1977). *Science* **197**, 663–665.

Woodruff, G. N., Davis, A., Andrews, C. D., and Poat, J. A. (1979). *In* "Recent Advances in Receptor Chemistry" (F. Gualtieri, M. Giannella, and C. Melchiorre, eds.), pp. 165–188. Elsevier/North-Holland Biomedical Press, Amsterdam.

Wrange, Ö., and Gustafsson, J.-Å. (1978). *J. Biol. Chem.* **253**, 856–865.

Wright, E. M., and Pietras, R. J. (1974). *J. Membr. Biol.* **17**, 293–312.

Wright, K., Luborsky-Moore, J. L., and Behrman, H. R. (1979). *Mol. Cell. Endocrinol.* **13**, 25–34.

Wu, C. (1979). *Biochem. Biophys. Res. Commun.* **89**, 769–776.

Yagil, E., Beacham, I. R., Nissim, A., and Price, G. (1978). *FEBS Lett.* **85**, 133–136.

Yahara, I., and Edelman, G. M. (1973). *Exp. Cell Res.* **81**, 143–155.

Yamada, Y., and Nishida, E. (1978). *Brain Res.* **142**, 187–190.

Yamamoto, K. R., and Alberts, B. M. (1976). *Annu. Rev. Biochem.* **45**, 721–746.

Yanai, R., and Nagasawa, H. (1979). *J. Endocrinol.* **82**, 131–133.

Zager, P. G., Burtis, W. J., Leutscher, J. A., Dowdy, A. J., and Sood, S. (1976). *J. Clin. Endocrinol. Med.* **42**, 207–214.

Zakim, D., and Vessey, D. A. (1976). *Enzymes Biol. Membr.* **2**, 443–461.

Zava, D. T., and McGuire, W. L. (1977). *J. Biol. Chem.* **252**, 3703–3708.

Zava, D. T., and McGuire, W. L. (1978). *Science* **199**, 787–788.

Zor, U., Koch, Y., Lamprecht, S. A., Ausher, J., and Lindner, H. R. (1973). *J. Endocrinol.* **58**, 525–533.

CHAPTER 7

Activation of Steroid–Receptor Complexes

E. Milgrom

I. INTRODUCTION

There is considerable confusion in the literature relating to activation of steroid receptors. Many of the problems arise from the use of poorly controlled acellular systems or from the fact that data were obtained in experiments where activation was observed only indirectly. The first aim of this review is thus, to discuss the experimental and theoretical conditions required to study activation effectively. Some of the reasons for published discrepancies will then appear. Tentative explanations for the mechanism and possible regulation of activation will also be discussed but no attempt will be made to review the literature on this subject in its totality.

Steroid hormones act on target cells through the intervention of specific receptors. Under the influence of the hormone the properties of the receptor are markedly modified. For example, in adrenalectomized rats (deprived of endogenous glucocorticoids), over 95% of the receptor is found in the soluble fraction of cell homogenate (Milgrom *et al.*, 1973). If, however, these animals are injected with a glucocorticoid hormone, or liver slices are incubated with this hormone, about 90% of the glucocorticoid–receptor complexes become bound to nuclei (Atger and Milgrom, 1978). This translocation of receptor from cytosol to nucleus under the influence of the hormone is a general property of steroid hormone receptors, found for nearly all target cells and all hormones (reviews in Jensen and DeSombre, 1973; Chan and O'Malley, 1976; Gorski and Gannon, 1976). The great biological importance of the translocation stems from the fact that the interaction of the steroid–receptor complex with chromatin is thought to modify gene transcription and to lead ultimately to the synthesis of hormonally controlled proteins. Thus, upon binding the steroid, the properties of the receptor change so that it acquires an affinity for the nucleus. This change has been called activation.

The binding of hormone to receptor, and receptor activation are not simultaneous but, rather, successive events. This can be demonstrated by the finding that if target cells are exposed to steroid at low temperature, steroid–receptor complexes are formed in the cytosol and remain there for a relatively long time before binding to nuclei. This phenomenon can be reproduced under acellular conditions (Baxter *et al.*, 1973; Brecher *et al.*, 1967; Buller *et al.*, 1975; DeSombre *et al.*, 1972; Gschwendt and Hamilton, 1972; Higgins *et al.*, 1973; Kalimi *et al.*, 1975; Milgrom *et al.*, 1973). It is therefore, possible, under acellular conditions, to observe steroid–receptor complexes in either nonactivated or activated form, and to follow the transformation of the former into the latter.

II. METHODS OF STUDYING ACTIVATION

A. Study of Receptor Activtion in Reconstituted Acellular Systems

In such studies, cytosolic steroid–receptor complexes are incubated with nuclei and their translocation is examined. To be valid such a system must fulfill the following criteria:

1. There should be no endogenous steroid–receptor complexes in the nuclei. Their presence is often due either to an incomplete purification of nuclei or to the presence of endogenous hormone which has provoked the translocation of the receptor *in vivo*. For instance, incomplete adrenalectomy or regrowth of adrenals, documented by plasma corticosterone increase, is often responsible for the presence of glucocorticoid receptors in nuclei from livers of apparently adrenalectomized animals.

2. Absence of nonspecific binding of receptor to the nuclear fraction must be verified. Such an attachment is not hormone dependent and, again, is often due to impure nuclei, since receptors attach readily to membranes.

3. Steroid–receptor complexes should be recovered quantitatively (or nearly quantitatively) in cytosol and nuclei at the end of incubation with the nuclei. Dissociation of the hormone may be due either to intrinsic properties of the steroid–receptor complex (in this case it is also observed with isolated cytosol under the same conditions) or to the presence of proteases in the nuclear preparation.

4. Steroid–receptor complexes should be measured precisely. Thus, they must not be obscured by nonspecific binding of hormone to the nuclei (or, less often, to nonreceptor proteins in the cytosol). Nonspecific binding is often increased by adsorption of steroids to the tubes used for incubation.

We have shown that these conditions were met in our studies of glucocorticoid receptor interaction with rat liver nuclei (Table I) (Milgrom *et al.*, 1973). On the other hand, when using guinea pig progesterone receptor and uterine nuclei, we have been unable to establish a satisfactory system, due to dissociation of progesterone–receptor complexes when they are exposed to uterine nuclei (possibly due to proteolytic activity) and very high nonspecific binding of progesterone to nuclei (due to the hydrophobicity of this hormone) (Atger and Milgrom unpublished observations). Data obtained under such conditions must be regarded as uncertain.

TABLE I

VALIDATION OF THE GLUCOCORTICOID RECEPTOR RAT LIVER NUCLEI SYSTEM FOR THE STUDY
OF ACTIVATION[a]

A. Dependence on hormone and receptor Incubation of nuclei	Concentration of [³H]dexamethasone– receptor complexes or unoccupied recep- tor bound to nuclei ($\times$ 10^{13})
Nuclei incubated with cytosol + hormone	4.31
Nuclei incubated with buffer + hormone	0.11
Nuclei incubated with cytosol alone	0.15

B. Nonspecific binding and recovery of steroid–receptor complexes
  Nonspecific binding of hormone to nuclei = ~ 2–5% of total binding
  Total (cytosol + nuclei) complexes recovered = ~ 90–97% of input

[a] For experimental details see (Milgrom et al., 1973).

B. QUANTITATION OF ACTIVATED COMPLEXES

1. Titration with Pure Nuclei

For precise studies it is necessary to measure accurately the concentration of activated complexes. With the glucocorticoid receptor from rat liver this measurement is achieved by titrating the activated receptor with high concentrations of nuclei (Fig. 1) (Atger and Milgrom, 1976a). At low ionic strength and in the absence of divalent cations, nuclei at concentrations above 0.7 mg DNA/ml of incubation bind all the activated complexes. This is demonstrated by the fact that any further increase in the concentration of nuclei does not change the concentration of bound complexes. Also, further incubation of the soluble phase with a new suspension of nuclei does not result in a significant proportion of complexes becoming bound to the fresh nuclei. It has been verified that nonreceptor constituents of the cytosol do not interfere with the assay. This may at first appear in contradiction to the fact that cytosol contains proteins which inhibit binding of activated complexes to nuclei (Milgrom and Atger, 1975). However, this inhibition is only observed in incubations containing markedly lower concentrations of nuclei. The very high concentrations of nuclei which are used in these activation assays totally overcome the effect of the inhibitors.

Finally, it has also been shown that incubation of cytosol with nuclei at low temperature, low ionic strength and neutral pH does not lead to a

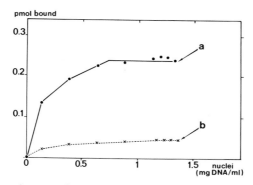

FIG. 1. Titration of activated complexes by increasing concentrations of nuclei. (From Atger and Milgrom, 1976a) (a) Activated complexes (liver cytosol was incubated with [^{3}H]triamcinolone acetonide and heated at 25° for 15 minutes). (b) Nonactivated complexes (cytosol was incubated with [^{3}H]triamcinolone acetonide at 0°, it contained a small proportion of activated complexes). Incubation with nuclei was 30 minutes at 0°, the nuclei were isolated, washed and counted for radioactivity.

shift in equilibrium between activated and nonactivated complexes. Under conditions where the rate of activation is markedly enhanced (increased temperature or pH) this is not true; activated complexes are removed by the contact with nuclei and the equilibrium is shifted, resulting in the appearance of newly activated complexes during the contact with nuclei (Atger and Milgrom, 1976a).

2. Use of Other Acceptors

The preparation of pure nuclei is tedious; in many tissues it is very difficult or even impossible. It is, therefore, desirable to replace homologous nuclei by some easily available acceptor. This would apparently seem feasible since activation results in the enhancement of the affinity of the receptor towards all types of polyanions (Milgrom *et al.*, 1973). We have systematically compared the titration of activated glucocorticoid complexes using phosphocellulose (Fig. 2), DNA-cellulose, or homologous nuclei. In the case of phosphocellulose (Atger and Milgrom, 1976b) it was observed that exposure to the resin of nonactivated complexes resulted in their progressive activation (Fig. 3). This seems to be due to the effect of the large concentration of ionic charges carried by the resin. It was also observed that the rate of binding of activated complexes to the resin was rather slow. Thus it is possible to perform either a rapid chromatography which underestimates the concentration of activated complexes, or to increase the time of contact with the resin and transform a portion of the nonactivated complexes into activated complexes. Therefore, phospho-

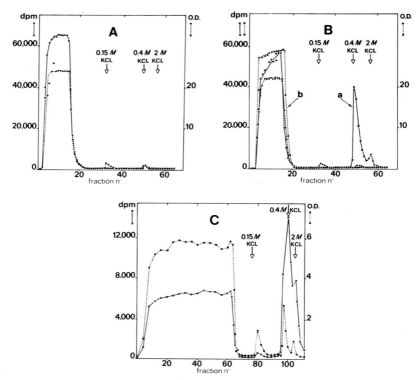

FIG. 2. Binding to phosphocellulose of [³H]triamcinolone acetonide–receptor complexes. (From Atger and Milgrom, 1976b.) (A) Nonactivated complexes. (B) Complexes activated by heating. (C) Complexes activated by increase in ionic strength.

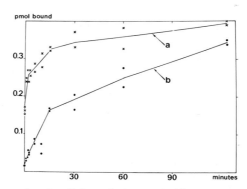

FIG. 3. Binding to phosphocellulose of glucocorticoid–receptor complexes during prolonged exposure to the resin at 0°. (From Atger and Milgrom, 1976b.) (a) Initially activated complexes (heated 30 minutes at 25°). (b) Initially nonactivated complexes (kept at 0°).

cellulose may only be used for comparative experiments but will not yield precise measurements of the proportion of complexes which are activated. The same limitation holds true for DNA-cellulose, but for different reasons (Lefèvre *et al.*, 1979). Here also, overly long incubations resulted in a progressive activation of initially nonactivated complexes. However, since the rate of association of activated complexes was faster than for phosphocellulose, it was possible to choose conditions (about 30 minutes of incubation) such that there is a maximal concentration of activated complexes bound with minimal activation of nonactivated complexes. Even so, the concentration of activated complexes bound under optimal conditions to DNA-cellulose was lower than that bound to nuclei (Fig. 4). This was probably due to the release of DNA during incubation with the cytosol. Since free DNA has a five-fold higher affinity for steroid–receptor complexes than does DNA attached to cellulose (Simons, 1977) a 5% release was sufficient to compete markedly with binding to the DNA-cellulose pellet. Thus again, DNA-cellulose, at least in batch conditions, may be used for comparative purposes, but not for precise measurements. However, the search for an alternative to using nuclei

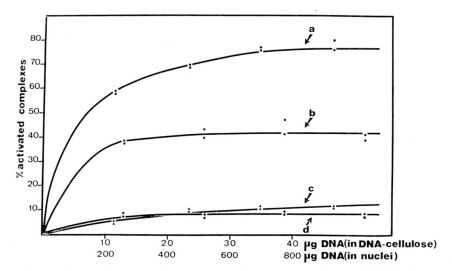

Fig. 4. Compared titration of activated steroid–receptor complexes with DNA-cellulose and nuclei. (From Lefèvre *et al.*, 1979.) (a) Cytosol containing activated complexes, binding to nuclei (liver cytosol incubated with [³H]triamcinolone acetonide, heated 15 minutes at 25° and incubated 30 minutes at 0° with nuclei). (b) Cytosol containing activated complexes, binding to DNA-cellulose. (c) Cytosol containing nonactivated complexes (kept at 0°), binding to nuclei. (d) Cytosol containing nonactivated complexes, binding to DNA-cellulose.

should be pursued, and there is no reason why an acceptor having the desired properties could not be designed.

When receptors are activated a region of positive charges appears on their surface. This enhances their affinity toward polyanions, but decreases their affinity toward polycations. DEAE-cellulose or DEAE-Sephadex retain nonactivated complexes better than activated complexes (Sakaue and Thompson, 1977; Parchman and Litwack, 1977). However, it has not been determined if the separation is quantitative nor if the resin modifies the equilibrium between activated and nonactivated complexes.

C. How to Devise Experiments on Activation

1. It is Necessary to Distinguish Activation from Binding of Previously Activated Complexes to the Acceptor

The endpoint in all these experiments is the measurement of binding of steroid–receptor complexes to nuclei (or other acceptors). This involves two steps: the activation reaction, followed by the binding of activated complexes to the acceptor. It is thus necessary to devise experiments which clearly distinguish effects related to each of these separate processes. For instance, we have observed a compound of low molecular weight which, when present in the cytosol, decreases the proportion of complexes which are bound to nuclei (Bailly *et al.*, 1977). To determine its site of action two series of incubations were performed. In the first, the inhibitor was added during the period of activation of the complexes (heating of the complexes in the absence of nuclei) and then nuclei were added. The inhibitor was thus present during both activation and binding steps. In the second set of incubations, the activation (heating of steroid–receptor complexes) was performed in the absence of the inhibitor, and then the latter rapidly added, followed shortly by the nuclei. In this case, activation was carried out in the absence of the inhibitor, whereas the molecule was present during the time of incubation with nuclei. Since inhibition was observed only in the first set of incubations, it could clearly be ascribed to an effect on the activation step and not on the binding of previously activated complexes to the acceptor. When devising such experiments it is always necessary to complement the incubations in such a way that all incubations are identical during the contact with acceptor.

2. The Problem of "Dysactivated" Steroid–Receptor Complexes

When glucocorticoid–receptor complexes are maintained for relatively long periods of time at temperatures above 15°, a form of receptor is observed which has retained its property of binding the hormone but has, apparently irreversibly, lost its capacity to become activated and/or bound to nuclei (Fig. 5) (Atger and Milgrom, 1976a). This state may also be achieved by increasing the ionic strength or pH (Bailly *et al.*, 1978). We propose to call this form "dysactivated steroid–receptor complex." Thus, the domain of the receptor protein which is necessary for its activation or binding to acceptors (it is impossible to distinguish which) is markedly more labile than the steroid binding domain. We do not know if this is an artifact of the acellular system or if similar reactions may occur *in vivo*. The conditions under which dysactivation occurs vary from receptor to receptor. This may be the reason for some misinterpretation of activation experiments. For example, incubation for 30 minutes at 25° will promote an important activation (increase in affinity towards nuclei) of the rat liver glucocorticoid receptor. In contrast, with the rabbit progesterone receptor maximal activation is already passed after 30 minutes at 25° and an important fraction of the complexes are dysactivated, showing only a very small increase in affinity toward nuclei when compared to nonheated cytosol (A. Bailly and E. Milgrom, unpublished observations). For these reasons it is necessary to examine the effect of an activating agent, e.g., heating, at different times, different temperatures, and different ionic and pH conditions before drawing any conclusions. In any case, this dysactivation of the complexes makes the inter-

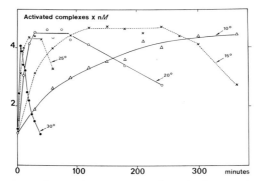

Fig. 5. Dysactivation of steroid–receptor complexes by heating (Atger and Milgrom, 1976a). Liver cytosol incubated with [^{3}H]triamcinolone acetonide at 0° was heated for various lengths of time at the indicated temperatures. Activated complexes were then measured by titration with nuclei at 0°. After optimal activation has been attained the concentration of activated complexes started to decline. This did not correspond to dissociation of steroid–receptor complexes since the latter followed first order kinetics and was only of 0% per hour at 10°, 1.5% per hour at 15°, 4.7% per hour at 20°, 15.2% per hour at 25°, and 30.1% per hour at 30°.

pretation of experiments more difficult since it requires consideration of a third form of the complex (nonactivated, activated, and dysactivated).

It is therefore more convenient to devise experiments in which this reaction is minimized, by avoiding high temperatures, ionic strengths, or pH for overly long periods of time. In a later section of this discussion relating to deactivation (the reversible change from the activated to non-activated state), it will be emphasized that it is especially important to distinguish deactivation from this irreversible "dysactivation" reaction.

III. THE MECHANISM OF ACTIVATION

In the study of hormonal mechanisms of activation it is, of course, of foremost importance to understand the functional and structural modifications displayed by the receptor upon binding the hormone.

To address this problem unequivocally it would be necessary to purify the receptor in both the nonactivated and activated state and to compare its chemical composition, size and physical properties in the two forms. Such an experiment is presently impossible for at least two reasons. One reason is the fact that these procedures require great quantities of pure protein, which are impossible to obtain. The second reason is that in all methods presently used, steroid–receptor complexes, and not free receptors, are purified. It has been shown that under these conditions one obtains most of the receptor as the activated complex (Atger and Milgrom, 1976b). The latter problem may be resolved once activation is better understood and if conditions can be defined to reverse activation of receptors to the nonactivated state.

Indirect methods may, however, be used to try to approach the problem of the mechanism of activation. For example, kinetic studies may yield some information.

A. KINETIC STUDIES OF ACTIVATION

Two types of mechanisms have been proposed to explain the activation reaction. The first is the dimerization of the receptor or its interaction with an unidentified molecule X (Yamamoto and Alberts, 1972; Notides and Nielsen, 1974; Notides et al., 1975; Notides, 1978; Weichman and Notides, 1979). The second is a simple change in conformation of the steroid–receptor complexes, without any interaction with another molecule (Atger and Milgrom, 1976a). It is theoretically possible to distinguish between these hypotheses by examining the kinetics of the reaction. For the dimerization mechanism the reaction should be of second order, while for the change-of-conformation hypothesis it should be of first order. Glucocorticoid–receptor complexes at various concentrations, were heat-activated at 25°. For a short interval, the concentration of activated complexes increased linearly with time. It was thus possible to define an initial velocity (v_i) of the activation reaction. A plot of log v_i versus log concentration of complexes yields a line, the slope of which corresponds to the order of the reaction (Fig. 6). The concentration of complexes was varied in one of two ways: either by diluting the cytosol after incubation with hormone, or by varying hormone concentration for a constant cytosol concentration. The results should be different if there is receptor dimerization or interaction with another molecule. However, in both cases the order of the reaction was found to be 1 (Atger and Milgrom, 1976a) (These experiments must not however be performed at cytosol concentrations above 12–15 mg protein/ml since the effect of the low molecular weight inhibitor is then observed.) This method gives very clearcut experimental results. For instance, a fourfold dilution will give a fourfold decrease in the rate for a first order reaction but a 16-fold decrease for a second order reaction.

Identical experiments were recently performed with the estrogen receptor from rat uterus, and, again, the order of the reaction was found to be 1 (Bailly *et al.*, 1980).

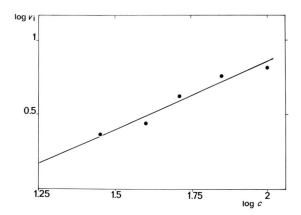

Fɪɢ. 6. Apparent order of the reaction of thermal activation of glucocorticoid–receptor complexes. (From Atger and Milgrom, 1976a.) Liver cytosol was diluted to various extents, incubated at 0° with [³H]triamcinolone acetonide and heated at 25° for short periods of time (0, 1, 2, 3, 4, 5 minutes). Activated complexes were titrated. The rate of activation (v_i) was found to be linear during this period of time in all experiments. Log $(v_i \times 10^{10}\ M/\text{minute})$ was plotted versus log c (concentration steroid–receptor complexes $\times 10^9\ M$).

B. Activation and Changes in the Size of the Receptor

Another method of distinguishing among various mechanisms proposed to explain receptor activation is to study the molecular weight of the receptor before and after activation. Dimerization or addition of supplementary subunits should, of course, result in modifications of receptor size. Such studies were actually the basis for the concept of receptor activation. Jensen and co-workers (Jensen and DeSombre, 1973), who were the first to introduce this concept, found that nonheated rat or calf uterine steroid–receptor complexes sedimented at 4 S in 0.4 M KCl gradients. The same complexes, when previously heated, sedimented at 5 S under the same conditions. Since the phenomenon was hormone dependent and paralleled changes in affinity toward nuclei, it was thought to be the expression of activation. Notides (1978) studied the kinetics of this reaction, and found it to be of second order. He concluded that the mechanism was probably a dimerization of the receptor or, less likely, the addition of receptor to another subunit of similar molecular weight and similar concentration in the cytosol. Yamamoto and Alberts (1972) arrived at essentially similar conclusions. However, these results were difficult to reconcile with the data obtained using glucocorticoid receptor. In the case of the glucocorticoid receptor, increased ionic strength (0.4 M KCl) by itself provoked steroid–receptor complex activation. Thus, complexes exposed to 0.4 M KCl during the 16–18 h of centrifugation must have been activated whether previously heated or not. The second discrepancy lay in the fact that when activation, defined as the appearance of an affinity toward nuclei, was examined for the glucocorticoid receptor from rat liver, the reaction was of first order. Thus it was obvious that either glucocorticoid and estrogen systems were completely different, which seemed unlikely when all the other similarities in the properties of the receptors were considered, or that activation (defined as an acquisition of the affinity toward nuclei) and the 4 S to 5 S transformation were different reactions.

To examine this question we systematically compared the 4 S to 5 S change, and activation, in the case of estrogen receptors. To study activation we used DNA-cellulose and not nuclei as an acceptor. This is acceptable for comparative purposes as has previously been shown (Lefèvre *et al.*, 1979). This choice was dictated by technical reasons, i.e., difficulties in obtaining the very high amounts of pure uterine nuclei necessary for the titration of activated receptors. With this tool, the problem of the effect of high ionic strength on estrogen receptor activation and 4 S to 5 S transformation was studied.

It was first confirmed that exposure to 0.4 M KCl provoked activation of estradiol–receptor complexes (Bailly *et al.*, 1980). The reaction was maximal in about 1–3 h; at this time only a minute number of 5 S complexes have been formed. Since it is necessary to dilute the high-salt activated complexes to lower ionic strength for their assay, it was carefully verified by various means that it was exposure to 0.4 *M* KCl, and not dilution which provoked activation. Thus, the kinetics of activation, and of the 4 S to 5 S transformation by salt, were different.

To confirm this point, estradiol–receptor complexes in either 4 S form (nonheated) or 5 S form (heated) were recovered from gradients run in 0.4 *M* KCl. They were shown to contain equivalent proportions of activated complexes (Fig. 7) (Bailly *et al.*, 1980).

Activation and sedimentation coefficients were also compared for rat liver glucocorticoid and rat uterine progesterone receptors. In both cases heating at 25° increased the proportion of complexes binding to DNA, but did not change the sedimentation properties of the steroid–receptor complex (Bailly *et al.*, 1980). This was of particular interest in the case of the progesterone receptor, since the same cytosol was used as for estradiol receptor studies.

Finally, the apparent order of the reaction for activation of estradiol–receptor complexes was examined. Initial velocities (v_i) of activation by exposure to 25° were measured for various concentrations of complexes (c). By plotting log v_i versus log c, a line is obtained the slope of which

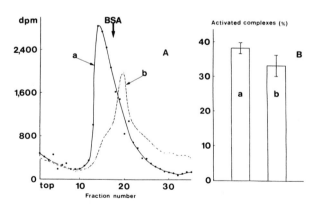

FIG. 7. The proportion of activated complexes in the 4 S and 5 S forms of estradiol–receptor complexes is identical. (From Bailly *et al.*, 1980.) (A) Sedimentation profiles. (B) Binding to DNA-cellulose, (a) nonheated cytosol, (b) cytosol heated 30 minutes at 25°. Uterine cytosol, incubated with [³H]estradiol was either kept at 0° (a) or heated 30 minutes at 25° (b). Aliquots were centrifuged through sucrose gradients containing 0.4 *M* KCl (A). This yielded either 4 S complexes (a) or 5 S complexes (b) which were recovered from the gradients and tested for activation by binding to DNA-cellulose (B).

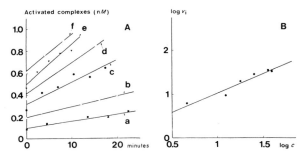

FIG. 8. Apparent order of the reaction of thermal activation of estrogen–receptor complexes (Bailly *et al.*, 1980). The experiment was performed as described in Fig. 6 except that rat uterine cytosol and [³H]estradiol were used. (A) Activation at different time periods and for steroid–receptor concentration varying between 0.46 nM (a) and 3.88 nM (f). (B) Log of initial velocity of activation ($v_i \times 10^{12}$ M/minute) was plotted versus total concentration of complexes (c $\times 10^{10}$ M).

corresponds to the apparent order of the reaction. The result was clearly that of a first order reaction (Fig. 8).

All of these experiments show the difference between activation and 4 S to 5 S transformation. However, although both activated and nonactivated 4 S complexes are observed, 5 S complexes are only seen after activation. Thus it is probable that the estradiol–receptor complex undergoes two successive reactions:

$$4SE_2R \rightarrow 4SE_2R^* \rightarrow 5SE_2R^*$$
$$\quad\quad (1)\quad\quad\quad (2)$$

The first reaction (1), activation, leads to a 4 S activated complex, is of apparent first order and is accelerated by increased ionic strength. The second reaction (2), is that of the activated 4 S complex with another molecule (or itself). This reaction is of apparent second order and is markedly decelerated by increased ionic strength. It yields a 5 S activated complex. It is not known if it is the 4 S or the 5 S activated complex which elicits the biological response thought to be a modification of gene transcription. However the fact that the 4 S to 5 S transformation is not observed for other steroid receptors whose function seems to be similar to that of the estrogen receptor, and the fact that cytosolic and nuclear estrogen receptors extracted by enzymatic methods appear to have the same size (André *et al.*, 1978) favor the hypothesis that the 4 S to 5 S transformation is not necessary for the biological activity of the steroid–receptor complex. Previously observed differences in the size of cytosolic and nuclear receptors might have been due to extraction conditions. Extraction of nuclei using high ionic strength provokes solubilization of nucleic acids and chromatin proteins, which could have interacted with estrogen–receptor complexes. The evidence is, however, indirect and it remains possible that the 5 S complex exists for other receptors and other biological systems but is unstable. To test such hypotheses it is necessary to await purification of the receptors. In any case it appears from the experiments described above, that no 4 S to 5 S transformation is necessary for the complex to acquire the ability to bind to nuclei.*

C. Equilibrium between Activated and Nonactivated Complexes

When glucocorticoid–receptor complexes are heated, the proportion of activated complexes increases with time up to a point where a plateau value is attained. At this point only a fraction of complexes are activated. For instance, at low ionic strength, pH 7.4, in liver cytosol containing about 8 mg protein/ml, about 60% of the complexes are activated. We questioned whether this was due to the existence of an equilibrium between activated and nonactivated complexes, or to the presence of a population of complexes unable to undergo activation.

Three types of experiments were undertaken to answer this question. In the first experiment (Atger and Milgrom, 1976a) glucocorticoid–receptor complexes were heated to the point where they were maximally activated. The activated complexes were then removed, and heating was resumed. It was observed that a fraction of the complexes which had not initially been activated now became activated (Fig. 9). This result could be explained easily by the existence of an equilibrium between activated and nonactivated complexes. In the second experiment, activation was performed either in the absence or in the presence of acceptor (Atger and Milgrom, 1976a). In the former case 60% of the complexes become activated, in the latter, over 80%. This experiment can be explained in terms of an equilibrium, which was displaced by the presence of the acceptor in favor of activated complexes. The third piece of evidence showing that there was an equilibrium between activated and nonactivated complexes comes from experiments in which this equilibrium could be shifted forward and backward by different factors (Bailly *et al.*, 1978).

---

* It must also be emphasized that the 4 to 5 S transformation of the estrogen receptor is only a first step in the aggregation procedure and that for longer times of activation bigger aggregates are formed (Bailly *et al.*, 1980).

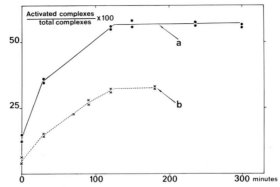

FIG. 9. Evidence in favor of an equilibrium between activated and nonactivated steroid–receptor complexes. (From Atger and Milgrom, 1976a.) Liver cytosol previously incubated at 0° with [³H]triamcinolone acetonide was heated for various time periods at 15°. The proportion of activated complexes was measured (a). After 150 minutes of heating (the plateau being attained) cytosol was exposed twice to saturating amounts of nuclei in order to remove all activated complexes. Heating at 15° of the cytosol was then resumed (b) showing that previously nonactivated complexes now started to activate. The lower proportion of complexes becoming activated in (b) was probably due to the fact that some complexes become "dysactivated" during the first heating period.

D. PRODUCT OF THE ACTIVATION REACTION

Kinetic studies may be used to determine the number of molecules that are produced by the activation reaction. The equilibrium is studied at different concentrations of steroid–receptor complexes. The plot of log (concentration of nonactivated complexes at equilibrium) versus log (concentration of activated complexes at equilibrium) yields the number of molecules resulting from the activation reaction. This plot was linear (at least when overly high cytosol concentrations were avoided, since at high concentration the effect of the low molecular weight inhibitor is apparent). Its slope was 1.08, which implies that the product of the reaction was a single molecule (Atger and Milgrom, 1976a).

E. THERMODYNAMICS OF HEAT ACTIVATION

At 25° under conditions previously described (Atger and Milgrom, 1976a), the rate constant of activation (in the thermodynamic sense) of the reaction was $k = 1.37 \times 10^{-3}\text{s}^{-1}$. This corresponds to a change in free energy of $\Delta G^{\ddagger} = 21,250$ cal. Studying the rate at different temperatures by an Arrhenius plot allowed calculation of the change in enthalpy,

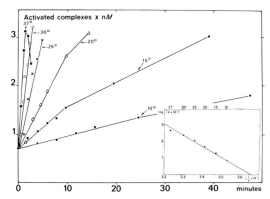

Fig. 10. Arrhenius plot of the activation reaction (Atger and Milgrom, 1976a). Liver cytosol previously incubated with [³H]triamcinolone acetonide at 0° was heated for various time periods at temperatures ranging between 10° and 37° (T = absolute temperature). The initial linear rates of activation were measured. First order rate constants k were calculated and log k was plotted versus $1/T$. $\Delta H^{\ddagger}$ = 31.38 kcal.

$\Delta H^{\ddagger}$ = 31,380 cal. (Fig. 10), and entropy $\Delta S^{\ddagger}$ = 34 cal./degree. These high, positive values of enthalpy and entropy resemble those which are observed for protein denaturation. This may indicate that activation necessitates breakage of several noncovalent bonds for the change in conformation of the receptor protein to take place.

If one examines the energy changes which accompany first the binding of hormone to receptor and then the activation of the complex at 25°, some remarkable points emerge (Fig. 11). The binding of hormone to receptor necessitates a moderate thermodynamic activation energy ($\Delta G^{\ddagger}$ = + 10.6 kcal.), but the complex corresponds to a markedly lower level of free energy (ΔG = − 11.3 kcal.). Passage to the activated state of the complex necessitates a very high energy of thermodynamic activation ($\Delta G^{\ddagger}$ = + 21.3 kcal.), but the activated complex is at a level of free energy very similar to that of nonactivated complex (ΔG = − 0.24 kcal.). It is thus obvious that the overall reaction is driven mainly by binding of hormone to receptor.

F. Conclusions Regarding the Mechanism of Activation

From these experiments it may be concluded that activation consists of a simple change in conformation of the receptor molecule induced by the hormone. There is no association with any other molecule or subunit, nor any splitting of the receptor molecule.

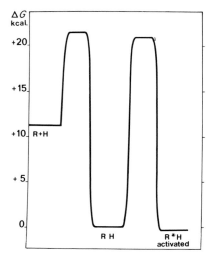

FIG. 11. Variations of energy during binding of [³H]triamcinolone acetonide (H) to receptor (R) and complex activation. (From Atger and Milgrom, 1976a.) RH = nonactivated steroid–receptor complex. R*H = activated steroid–receptor complex.

Genetic experiments dealing with glucocorticoid hormone-resistant mouse lymphoid cell lines also support this conclusion. The absence of positive or negative complementation in various hybrid cells (Pfahl, 1979) suggests that there is no necessity for association of several polypeptidic subunits in order for the biological activity of the receptor to be exerted.

IV. FACTORS EFFECTING THE ACTIVATION REACTION

A. FACTORS EFFECTING ACTIVATION

1. Heating or Increase in Ionic Strength

Heating or increase in ionic strength are now well-established methods to promote steroid–receptor complex activation.

2. pH

When steroid–receptor complexes were exposed for 6 hours at low temperature to pH values varying between 6 and 8, and then incubated with nuclei, a linear increase in the proportion of complexes taken up by

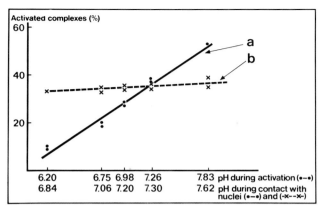

Fig. 12. Effect of pH on the activation and binding to nuclei of steroid–receptor complexes. (From Bailly *et al.*, 1978.) Liver cytosol was previously incubated with [³H]triamcinolone acetonide at 0°. (a) pH in cytosol was brought to 6.20–7.83 (abscissa 1st line) and activation allowed to proceed at 0° during 6 hours. Activated complexes were measured by adding nuclei in pH 7.4 buffer. During binding to nuclei the actual pH varied between 6.84 and 7.62 (abscissa 2nd line). (b) pH was constant (7.26) during the activation phase (6 hours at 0°). During binding to nuclei the same values in pH as in (a) were produced (6.84–7.62) (abscissa 2nd line).

the nuclei was observed with increasing pH (Fig. 12). This effect must have been due to an increase in activation, since if pH was varied only during the time of contact with nuclei, no such difference was observed (Bailly *et al.*, 1978).

3. Low Molecular Weight Inhibitor

The characterization of this molecule (Bailly *et al.*, 1977; Goidl *et al.*, 1977) stems from the observation that activation of various receptors is more efficient in diluted than in undiluted cytosol. That this is due to an inhibitor can be demonstrated by adding cytosol in which the receptor has been inactivated to diluted cytosol containing steroid–receptor complexes. An inhibition of activation is then observed. That the inhibitor is of low molecular weight has been shown by using ultrafiltrated, dialyzed or chromatographed cytosol in these experiments (Fig. 13). Proteins precipitated from cytosol by ammonium sulfate were also shown to be ineffective. Some properties of this inhibitor have been established: it is thermostable (resists 30 minutes at 100°); it is not a steroid; it cannot be complexed by EDTA; and it seems to be positively charged.

It has been suggested that this inhibitor might be pyridoxal phosphate. However, pyridoxal phosphate acts by preventing binding to DNA or

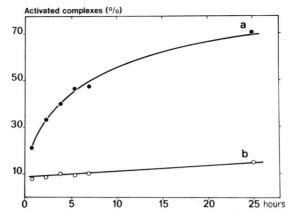

FIG. 13. Spontaneous activation of [³H]triamcinolone acetonide–receptor complexes after removal of the low-molecular-weight inhibitor by Sephadex G-25 chromatography. (From Bailly *et al.*, 1977.) (a) Chromatographed cytosol. (b) Nonchromatographed cytosol. Protein concentration (25 mg/ml) and total concentration of complexes (10.95 pmol/ml) were identical. Activation took place at 0°.

nuclei of previously activated complexes (Cake *et al.*, 1978), and thus is not an inhibitor of activation per se.*

B. DIFFERENCES IN THE ACTION OF VARIOUS EFFECTORS OF ACTIVATION

Known effectors of the activation reaction act via different mechanisms: some of them modify only the rate of the reaction, whereas others also modify the equilibrium between activated and nonactivated species (Bailly *et al.*, 1978).

Temperature effects are in the first category. Increased temperature enhances the rate of the reaction, but since both on (k_1) and off (k_2) rate constants are increased, the same equilibrium is attained at all temperatures (10°–30°) (see Fig. 5).

In contrast, ionic strength not only speeds up the reaction but also increases the proportion of activated complexes at equilibrium (both k_1 and k_2 are increased, but the former to a greater extent than the latter) (Fig. 14). The low molecular weight inhibitor has a similar effect, in the opposite sense: it reduces both the rate of the reaction and the proportion of

* Recently *mobybdate* has been shown to inhibit receptor activation (Nishigori and Toft, 1980).

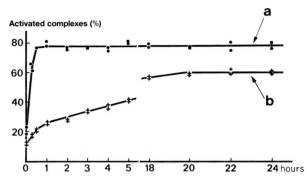

Fig. 14. Effect of ionic strength on the equilibrium between activated and nonactivated forms of steroid–receptor complexes. (From Bailly *et al.*, 1978.) Liver cytosol was incubated at 0° with [^{3}H]triamcinolone acetonide. KCl was added at final concentrations of 0.4 M (a) or 0.15 M (b). Activation was allowed to proceed at 0° for various times. Dilution was performed in order to bring all incubations to the same KCl concentration during contact with nuclei (0.025 M). Activation in the total absence of KCl was difficult to observe at 0° since it was exceedingly slow. Thus 0.15 M KCl was used for the comparison with 0.4 M KCl to study salt effect on activation.

activated complexes. (Both k_1 and k_2 are decreased but the former to a greater extent than the latter.)

Increase in pH is the only known factor which acts in opposite directions on k_1 and k_2; k_1 is increased and k_2 decreased. A marked effect on the equilibrium is, of course, observed (Table II).

C. Effect of the Hormone

The binding of steroid is necessary to promote activation.

1. The question may be raised, if there is any *relationship between the equilibrium of the reaction* (proportion of activated complexes at equilibrium) and *the affinity of the steroid for the receptor.* In regard to this problem, we have examined the effects of dexamethasone and triamicinolone acetonide, which differ by a factor of three in their affinities for the receptor. No difference was observed in the proportion of activated complexes at equilibrium (Bailly *et al.*, 1978). However, in terms of energy, a three-fold difference in affinity may be too small to give a clear answer. It is difficult to test steroids having a lower affinity for the receptor, since they dissociate readily from steroid–receptor complexes and measurements are, therefore, difficult. Recently, Svec and Harrison (1979) have presented evidence that there might be a difference in the effects of cor-

TABLE II
RATE CONSTANTS OF ACTIVATION AND REVERSAL OF ACTIVATION IN VARIOUS EXPERIMENTAL
CONDITIONS

pH	[KCl] (M)	Dilution of the cytosol (-fold)	Temperature (°C)	$10^4 \times k_1$ (second^{-1})	$10^4 \times k_2$ (second^{-1})
7.4	0	4	10	0.85	0.56
7.4	0	4	15	2.68	1.79
7.4	0	4	20	9.66	6.44
7.4	0	4	25	15.60	10.40
7.4	0	1	15	2.34,2.44	1.49,2.16
				2.58	2.02
7.4	0	20	15	5.06,5.54	3.37,3.40
7.4	0.15	5/4	15	3.21	2.41
7.4	0.15	4	0	0.33	0.22
7.4	0.4	5/4	0	1.83	0.79
7.4	0.4	4	0	8,86,11.8	1.44,3.30
8	0	20	0	0.29	0.10
8	0	5/4	0	0.07	0.06
8	0.4	5/4	0	3.83	0.43
6.5	0	20	0	0.13	0.46
6.5	0	20	15	2.52	4.12
6.5	0.4	5/4	0	2.75	1.47

Assuming that both the reactions of activation and reversal of activation are of apparent first order it is possible to calculate the rate constants k_1 (activation) and k_2 (reversal of activation) from:

$$\frac{(k_1 + k_2)\, t}{2.3} = \log \frac{(a_0 - a_e)}{(a - a_e)} \quad \text{and} \quad \frac{k_1}{k_2} = K$$

where t is the time, and a, a_0, and a_e are the concentrations of nonactivated complexes at time t, time 0 and equilibrium, respectively. K is the equilibrium constant. In all cases, when the actual experimental data were plotted according to the first equation, a linear relationship was observed. In some situations several separate experiments using different cytosol preparations were performed, the individual results are given in these cases.

tisol and potent synthetic glucocorticoids on the activation of glucocorticoid receptor in pituitary cells.

2. *Another unresolved question is whether there exist steroids which bind to receptor but do not promote activation.* Initially it was thought that antihormones might act in this way. It has, however, been demonstrated that antiestrogens do promote the transfer of the receptor into the nuclei. Unfortunately, the picture is complicated by the fact that these compounds are not only antagonists, but also partial agonists. It is unknown to which class of activity activation of the receptor is to be ascribed. The problem is thus open experimentally. However, if a com-

pound having pure antagonist activity could be shown to provoke receptor activation, this would mean that activated complexes can exist in two different conformations. One of these conformations would lead to the biological effect, whereas the other would not.

V. REVERSAL FROM THE ACTIVATED TO THE NONACTIVATED STATE (DEACTIVATION)

It must be emphasized again that the reversible deactivation reaction is to be distinguished from the dysactivation described above. The latter involves the irreversible loss of receptor's capacity to be activated while retaining the property of binding the hormone is retained.

The fact that the activation reaction does not go to completion but, rather exists in equilibrium, means that the reverse reaction must, of course, occur. More direct evidence for the deactivation reaction can be obtained by following shifts in equilibrium provoked by various methods (changes in pH or ionic strength). Rapid shift in pH is convenient, since this does not necessitate any dilution or dialysis of the cytosol (Fig. 15) (Bailly *et al.*, 1978).

Cytosol containing complexes of receptor with [³H]triamcinolone acetonide was activated at pH 8 at 15°. After 60 minutes, a plateau was reached at which the maximal proportion, 75%, of complexes were ac-

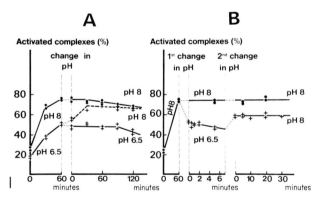

Fig. 15. Reversal from activated to the nonactivated state. (From Bailly *et al.*, 1978.) Liver cytosol incubated with [³H]triamcinolone acetonide was activated at 15° and pH 8. Once maximal activation was achieved (60 minutes), pH was adjusted to 6.5. A decrease in the proportion of activated complexes was observed. After 7 minutes the pH was again changed, so that the value was again 8. The proportion of activated complexes increased once more.

tivated. Maintaining the complexes at this pH and temperature for longer times did not modify the proportion of the activated species. When the pH was shifted to 6.5 a rapid decrease in the proportion of activated complexes was observed (46% after 7 minutes). When the pH was again increased to 8 a new equilibrium was established (59% activated complexes). This experiment thus shows that the decrease in proportion of activated complexes caused by lowering the pH is, at least in part, reversible. The observation that the final equilibrium at pH 8 is established with a smaller proportion of activated complexes than is the equilibrium obtained if the complexes were left throughout at pH 8, can probably be explained by damage to some complexes in the course of manipulation.

Reversal experiments were also performed using shifts in ionic strength and similar results obtained.

Thus, although we have some tentative ideas about the existence of the deactivation reaction, no direct studies have been performed to date. This reaction is of great importance in understanding the unknown events that accompany the exit of the steroid from the target cell.

VI. USE OF ACTIVATION TO PURIFY THE RECEPTOR

Activation must be taken into account when purifying receptor using methods that involve ionic interaction. Nonactivated receptor will have a low affinity for polyanions, a high one for polycations. The reverse will be observed for the activated steroid–receptor complex. Thus the chromatographic behavior of steroid–receptor complexes will differ if they are tested at the beginning of a purification procedure (nonactivated complexes) or at the end (activated complexes).

One may take advantage of this change in the properties of the receptor to devise very effective techniques of receptor purification. For instance, nonactivated steroid–receptor complexes are chromatographed on phosphocellulose. The nonactivated complexes do not bind, whereas proteins having an affinity for the resin are retained. The complexes are then activated and again chromatographed on phosphocellulose. The receptor complex is one of the few proteins that is not bound during the first passage through the column, but is retained during the second (Atger and Milgrom, 1976b; Colman and Feigelson, 1976). Still, only partial purification may be achieved. However once the process of deactivation is better understood cycles of activation–deactivation should be possible which will allow the complete purification of the receptor utilizing several such steps.

VII. CONCLUSION

A. ACTIVATION AND BINDING TO NUCLEI

To transmit hormonal information in the cell any receptor must have at least two conformations: one nonactive and one active. The binding of hormone must induce the change from the former to the latter conformation, thus provoking what has been referred to here as activation. In the case of steroid hormones, activation is characterized by a very large change in affinity of the receptor toward chromatin. This simplifies experimental studies, but from a functional point of view does not seem obligatory. The active and nonactive forms of receptor might differ by less obvious changes in interaction with the genome. This is probably the case for the thyroid hormones. Their receptors have characteristics very similar to those of steroid receptors and probably work via similar mechanisms; however, even in the absence of the hormone, the receptor is already attached to the chromatin (Oppenheimer *et al.*, 1972). Binding of the hormone certainly provokes a functional (and thus conformational) activation, but more sophisticated methods of study than those which have been used for steroids will have to be devised. By analogy to thyroid hormones it should not be unexpected that similar situations may exist, in some systems, for steroid receptors. Experimental results along this line have recently been reported (Zava *et al.*, 1976) but their general applicability and biological significance remain uncertain.* Finally, it is unknown if steroid receptors are, in fact, localized in the cellular cytoplasm in the absence of the hormone. They could very well exist intranuclearly and only be extracted during cell fractionation. The effect of the hormone might then not be to cause the translocation of the hormone from cytosol to nucleus, but rather to provoke a tighter binding of receptor to chromatin. Such a possibility does not greatly modify the terms of the present discussion.

B. MECHANISM OF ACTIVATION

An hypothesis which explains some features of activation may be formulated on the basis of the thermodynamic studies described above.

Activated steroid-receptor complexes acquire an affinity for chroma-

---

* These authors have recently reported that their previous results were due to incomplete purification of the nuclei (Edwards, D. P., Martin, P. M., Horwitz, K. B., Chamness, G. C. and McGuire, W. L., (1980), *Exp. Cell Res.* **127**, 197–213).

tin, DNA, phosphocellulose, i.e., toward various polyanions. It is thus probable that the change in conformation, which is responsible for activation, exposes a positively charged region on the surface of the protein which is inaccessible in the nonactivated receptor.

At low ionic strength and physiological pH, activation is extremely slow if the complexes are not heated. This demonstrates that there is a high energy barrier (activation energy in the thermodynamic sense). Large positive enthalpy and entropy of activation values suggest that some noncovalent bonds are broken. A measurement of $\Delta H^* = \sim 31$ kcal. allows calculation of the number of these bonds. If only hydrogen and ionic bonds are involved, there must be approximately 6–7 such bonds (~ 5 kcal. per bond). If hydrophobic bonds of lower energy are also involved, the total number of bonds broken may be higher. The observation that at increased ionic strength the reaction proceeds readily at low temperature, shows that ΔH^* is then lower (ΔH^* at 0.4 M KCl is 15.5 kcal.) (Bailly and Milgrom, 1980). This implies that some of the bonds which must be broken in order to allow the change in conformation to occur must be ionic bonds, which are weakened at increased ionic strength. The decrease in ΔH^* between low ionic strength and 0.4 M KCl suggests that about three ionic bonds are involved in this conformational change.

The fact that when pH is increased to 8 the reaction will also proceed at $0°$ suggests that one (or several) positively charged group(s) with a pK in the region of 6–8 is (or are) involved in the ionic bridges stabilizing the nonactivated complex. The most straightforward interpretation, although not the only one, is that the same positively charged groups which take part in stabilization of the nonactivated complex are the groups exposed on its surface after activation (Fig. 16).

To conclude, it must be emphasized that the concept of activation does not necessarily entail heating. The necessity for heating is only related to the high energy, the number of bonds, which must be broken to change the conformation of the receptor molecule. It is not unlikely that in some systems the energy needed to be furnished (the number of bonds to be broken) may be lower, and activation can then readily proceed at low temperature.

C. Biological Regulation at the Activation Step

One of the important factors in determining the magnitude of the biological response to a steroid hormone is the concentration of steroid–receptor complexes present in the nucleus. This seems to be dependent on

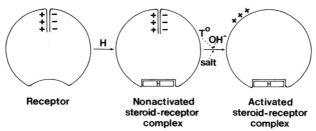

Receptor   Nonactivated   Activated
steroid-receptor   steroid-receptor
complex   complex

FIG. 16. Mechanisms involved in the activation of steroid–receptor complexes. The change in conformation induced by the binding of hormone (activation) necessitates breaking several noncovalent bonds, among them ionic bonds. After the change of conformation has taken place new positive charges appear on the surface of the activated complex. This model is based on thermodynamic data, effect of ionic strength and pH, and changes in affinity of receptors towards polyanions and polycations after activation (see text).

two parameters: the available concentration of hormone and the cellular concentration of receptor. However, we have seen that for a given concentration of steroid–receptor complexes, the proportion of these complexes that will bind to nuclei depends also on the equilibrium of activation (ratio of activated/nonactivated complexes). While this equilibrium may be modified *in vitro* by various agents (pH, salt, low molecular weight inhibitor, etc.), it is not known if any of these exerts an effect *in vivo*. The biological meaning of the low molecular weight inhibitor is not understood and it is not known if it is modulated according to the physiological state of the animal. Other, as-yet-unknown factors, may also regulate this equilibrium and thus play an important role in the biological activity of steroid hormones.

ACKNOWLEDGMENTS

I thank my colleagues M. Atger, A. Bailly, B. Lefèvre, N. Sallas, and J. F. Savouret who have participated to the studies described in this review. N. Malpoint has typed the manuscript.

This work has been supported by the INSERM, the CNRS, the DGRST, the U.E.R. Kremlin-Bicêtre and the Fondation pour la Recherche Médicale Française.

REFERENCES

André, J., Raynaud, A., and Rochefort, H. (1978). *Biochemistry* 17, 3619–3626.
Atger, M., and Milgrom, E. (1976a). *J. Biol. Chem.* 251, 4758–4762.
Atger, M., and Milgrom, E. (1976b). *Biochemistry* 15, 4298–4305.

Atger, M., and Milgrom, E. (1978). *Biochem. Biophys. Acta* **539**, 41–53.

Bailly, A., and Milgrom, E. (1980). In preparation.

Bailly, A., Sallas, N., and Milgrom, E. (1977). *J. Biol. Chem.* **252**, 858–863.

Bailly, A., Savouret, J. F., Sallas, N., and Milgrom, E. (1978). *Eur. J. Biochem.* **88**, 623–632.

Bailly, A., Lefèvre, B., Savouret, J. F., and Milgrom, E. (1980). *J. Biol. Chem.* **255**, 2729–2734.

Baxter, J. D., Rousseau, G. G., Benson, M. L., Garcea, R. L., Ito, J., and Tomkins, G. M. (1973). *Proc. Natl. Acad. Sci. U.S.A.* **69**, 1892–1896.

Brecher, P. I., Vigersky, R., Wotiz, H. S., and Wotiz, H. H. (1967). *Steroids* **10**, 635–651.

Buller, R. E., Toft, D. O., Schrader, W. T., and O'Malley, B. W. (1975). *J. Biol. Chem.* **250**, 801–808.

Cake, M. H., Di Sorbo, M. M., and Litwack, G. (1978). *J. Biol. Chem.* **253**, 4886–4891.

Chan, L., and O'Malley, B. W. (1976). *N. Engl. J. Med.* **294**, 1322–1328.

Colman, P. D., and Feigelson, P. (1976). *Mol. Cell. Endocrinol.* **5**, 33–40.

DeSombre, E. R., Mohla, S., and Jensen, E. V. (1972). *Biochem. Biophys. Res. Commun.* **48**, 1601–1608.

Edwards, D. P., Martin, P. M., Horwitz, K. B., Chamness, G. C., and McGuire, W. L. (1980). *Exp. Cell Res.* **127**, 197–213.

Goidl, J. A., Cake, M. H., Dolan, K. P., Parchman, L. G., and Litwack, G. (1977). *Biochemistry* **16**, 2125–2130.

Gorski, J., and Gannon, N. F. (1976). *Annu. Rev. Physiol.* **38**, 425–450.

Gschwendt, M., and Hamilton, T. H. (1972). *Biochem. J.* **361**, 84–96.

Higgins, S. J., Rousseau, G. G., Baxter, J. D., and Tomkins, G. M. (1973). *J. Biol. Chem.* **248**, 5866–5872.

Jensen, E., and DeSombre, E. R. (1973). *Science* **182**, 126–134.

Kalimi, M., Colman, P., and Feigelson, P. (1975). *J. Biol. Chem.* **250**, 1080–1086.

Lefèvre, B., Bailly, A., Sallas, N., and Milgrom, E. (1979). *Biochim. Biophys. Acta* **585**, 266–272.

Milgrom, E., and Atger, M. (1975). *J. Steroid Biochem.* **6**, 487–492.

Milgrom, E., Atger, M., and Baulieu, E. E. (1973). *Biochemistry* **12**, 5198–5205.

Nishigori, H., and Toft, D. (1980). *Biochemistry* **19**, 77–83.

Notides, A. C. (1978). *Recept. Horm. Action* **2**, 33–61.

Notides, A. C., and Nielsen, S. (1974). *J. Biol. Chem.* **249**, 1866–1873.

Notides, A. C., Hamilton, D. E., and Auer, H. E. (1975). *J. Biol. Chem.* **250**, 3945–3950.

Oppenheimer, J. H., Koerner, D., Schwartz, H. L., and Surks, M. I. (1972). *J. Clin. Endocrinol. Metab.* **35**, 330–333.

Parchman, L. G., and Litwack, G. (1977). *Arch. Biochem. Biophys.* **183**, 374–382.

Pfahl, M. (1979). *Cancer Treat. Rep.* **63**, 1171.

Sakaue, Y., and Thompson, E. B. (1977). *Biochem. Biophys. Res. Commun.* **77**. 533–541.

Simons, S. S. (1977). *Biochim. Biophys. Acta* **496**, 349–358.

Svec, R., and Harrison, R. W. (1979). *Endocrinology* **104**, 1563–1568.

Weichman, B. M., and Notides, A. C. (1979). *Biochemistry* **18**, 220–235.

Yamamoto, K. R., and Alberts, B. M. (1972). *Proc. Natl. Acad. Sci. U.S.A.* **69**, 2105–2109.

Zava, D. T., Chamness, G. C., Horwitz, K. B., and McGuire, W. L. (1976). *Science* **196**, 663–664.

CHAPTER 8

Estradiol and Progesterone Receptors in Human Endometrium

Paul Robel, Rodrigue Mortel, and Etienne-Emile Baulieu

I. INTRODUCTION

In the past two decades, the development of saturation analysis methods has permitted specific and accurate measurements of circulating sex steroid hormones and their cyclic changes during the menstrual cycle are well documented. For the past ten years, a large body of evidence has been accumulated indicating that hormones interact with a receptor system before triggering cellular responses. Hormone receptors were first identified and physicochemically studied for steroids, particularly estradiol in the rat uterus. Once reliable measurements of hormone receptors became available in animal models, correlations were attempted between receptor concentrations and circulating level of various hormones. It was discovered that concentration of receptor molecules is not fixed but varies with the physiological state of the animals. Particularly, variations of the concentrations and subcellular distributions of receptors were observed during the estrus cycle and mimicked by injecting estradiol and progesterone to hormone deprived animals (Baulieu *et al.*, 1975).

In the immature rat uterus, estradiol receptor is found almost exclusively in the soluble fraction of the cytoplasm, which is commonly called cytosol. After injection of estradiol *in vivo*, estradiol–receptor complexes are translocated into the nuclear compartment of the cell. A considerable amount of efforts has been devoted to the search for nuclear "acceptors," which may be the sites where characteristic changes of gene expression occur. However, it should be stressed that the location of receptor in the nucleus does not necessarily mean triggering of hormone action. For example, antiestrogens are capable of transferring the receptor into the nucleus, nevertheless no response may occur (Sutherland *et al.*, 1977). Another example is the finding in some target tissues, including human endometrium, of readily available (apparently unoccupied) nuclear receptor sites, which estradiol can reach directly. Therefore, it appears that on occasion, the formation of hormone–receptor complexes in the cytoplasm is not a mandatory step for hormone action. In practical terms, the cytosol/nuclear receptors ratio is worth considering but should be interpreted with caution.

In addition, the presence of free and occupied receptor sites both in cytosol and nuclei must be kept in mind. Because of the slow dissociation rate of estradiol from receptor sites, technics have been designed to measure separately available sites at low temperature or both available and occupied sites by "exchange" at higher temperature. Actually, the latter measurements are fraught with difficulties because of the easy inactivation of receptors. Available receptor sites may be either unoccupied, or occupied by low affinity natural or synthetic ligands. Finally, it should be emphasized that technics worked out for the measurement of receptor sites occupied by natural hormones (estradiol or progesterone) may have to be adjusted in certain physiological or pharmacological conditions when receptor sites are occupied by other ligands. For example, estradiol receptor sites may be occupied by (1) natural estrogens other than estradiol (estrone, estriol, catechol-estrogens); (2) synthetic steroidal estrogens (ethinyl-estradiol); (3) non-steroidal estrogen (diethylstilbestrol); (4) antiestrogen; (5) androgen with significant affinity for estrogen receptor (androst-5-ene-3β,17β-diol,5α-androstane-3β,17β-diol); and (6) synthetic progestagens of the 19-nor-testosterone series. Likewise, progesterone receptor sites may be occupied by synthetic progestagens derived from either progesterone or 19-nor-testosterone.

For pathophysiological purposes, we have considered as absolutely necessary the measurement of both cytoplasmic and nuclear receptor concentrations, whether occupied or unoccupied by any ligand.

The presence of estradiol receptor in human female reproductive tract was suggested by selective retention of radioactive estradiol in the normal human uterus (Davis *et al.*, 1963) and endometrium (Brush *et al.*, 1967; Evans and Hähnel, 1971). The first quantitative approach to total receptor concentration in human endometrium was that of Tseng and Gurpide (1972a) who applied the technic of endometrium slice superfusion. Wiest and Rao (1971) should be credited for the first unambiguous demonstration of progesterone receptor in human endometrium. A systematic study of estradiol and progesterone receptor in both cytoplasmic and nuclear fraction was conducted by our group in normal women (Bayard *et al.*, 1978).

II. METHODOLOGICAL PROBLEMS

A. GENERAL

It is generally impossible to obtain endometrial tissue from women deprived of estrogens. However, when the endometrium is exposed to endogenous hormones, part or all receptor sites may be occupied by hormones and a large fraction of the hormone receptor complexes are found in the nuclear compartment. Therefore, interpretation of published results must take into account which among the following fractions has been measured (1) free cytoplasmic receptor sites; (2) free and occupied cyto-

plasmic receptor sites; (3) free nuclear receptor sites; (4) free and occupied nuclear receptor sites; and (5) total cellular receptor sites. Indeed,
the physiological significance of the results will be different according to
the category of receptor site assayed. Unfortunately, the many published
reports are difficult to interpret because the assay conditions used were
mostly empirical. For instance, the assay will measure part of available
sites when less than saturating concentrations of hormones are used.
Similarly, it will determine part of occupied sites when exchange reactions are incomplete. In cases where receptor concentrations is determined following incubation of tissue slices with radioactive hormones, it
is clear that such technic does not measure endogenous nuclear receptor
but translocated cytosolic hormone–receptor complexes. Such improper
terminology associated or not with improper methodology explains most
discrepancies found in the literature.

The labeling of receptor sites, particularly the occupied ones, with
tritiated hormones of high specific activity is based on the knowledge of
equilibrium and kinetic association and dissociation rate constants. They
provide ground for the so-called exchange techniques, in which nonradioactive hormone filling the receptor sites is replaced by radioactive hormone. Besides the receptor, crude endometrial extracts contain other hormone binding components which may be divided into low affinity
nonsaturable binding and high affinity saturable binding components.
The latter are similar to plasma proteins which bind specifically natural
steroid hormones. Consequently, the binding of hormone to the receptor
must be differentiated from its binding to both kinds of nonreceptor
binding components. A rational approach to such discrimination is
presently based on the knowledge of the physicochemical properties of
estradiol and progesterone receptors, namely affinity and specificity of
the binding, heat stability, and other characteristics related to size, electrophoretic mobility and sensitivity to various reagents.

B. PHYSICOCHEMICAL PROPERTIES OF ESTRADIOL RECEPTOR

1. Estradiol Binding Parameters

Most data related to estradiol binding constants in human endometrium have been obtained with dextran-coated charcoal adsorption technique. The reported K_{deq} varied from 0.1 nM to 0.3 nM at 0° (Krishnan et
al., 1973; Crocker et al., 1974; Makler and Eisenfeld, 1974; Tsibris et al.,
1978) and from 0.3 nM to 0.6 nM at 30° (Robertson et al., 1971; Bayard

et al., 1978). These values are in keeping with those reported by Baulieu *et al.* (1975) in other mammalian species. At 4°, the association rate constant is $1 \times 10^{-7} M^{-1} min^{-1}$ and the dissociation rate constant is very small in the order of $1 \times 10^{-3} min^{-1}$ (Makler and Eisenfeld, 1974).

2. Binding Specificity

The affinity displayed by estradiol for the receptor is about 2 to 10 times greater than that of its metabolites, estrone and estriol. Other compounds like 17α-ethinyl-estradiol and 11β-methoxy-17α-ethinyl-estradiol (moxestrol) bind also well to the receptor. Among non-steroidal compounds, there are conflicting reports concerning the relative affinity of diethylstilbestrol as compared to estradiol. If the important binding to nonspecific components is taken into consideration, it seems established that diethylstilbestrol has higher affinity for the receptor than estradiol. Antiestrogens of the non-steroidal series, such as *cis*-clomifen, C1-628, or U 11, 100 A (nafoxidin) have weak affinity for the receptor (Notides *et al.*, 1972; Krishnan *et al.*, 1973). Androgens have very low affinity for the receptor, although androst-5-ene-3β,17β-diol and 5α-androstane-3β, 17β-diol are better competitors for estradiol binding ($K_i \sim 10^{-7} M$) than testosterone or dihydrotestosterone. Corticosteroids, progesterone, and C_{21} progestagens used in oral contraceptives do not bind the receptor, although chlormadinone acetate has been reported to compete for estradiol binding (Notides *et al.*, 1972; Krishnan *et al.*, 1973; Makler and Eisenfeld, 1974; Pollow *et al.*, 1975a; Raynaud *et al.*, 1978).

Interestingly non–steroidal compounds such as diethylstilbestrol and tamoxifen or steroidal derivative (moxestrol) while binding well to the receptor, do not bind significantly to the sex hormone binding plasma protein (SBP).

3. Gradient Ultracentrifugation

The use of gradient sedimentation analysis in a medium of low ionic strength has shown a predominantly 8 S variety (Notides *et al.*, 1972; Krishnan *et al.*, 1973; Pollow *et al.*, 1975a; Raynaud *et al.*, 1978) whereas Bayard *et al.* (1978) reported a 4–5 S form. The reason for such discrepancy has not been established but differences due to the various physiological states or unstability of the receptor cannot be ruled out. For instance diisopropylfluorophosphate, a proteolytic enzyme inhibitor, favors the appearance of a 8 S component (Notides *et al.*, 1972). Because of these considerations, it appears that gradient ultracentrifugation is not a reliable procedure to distinguish the estradiol–receptor complex from other specific proteins sedimenting in the 4–5 S region.

C. Physicochemical Properties of Progesterone Receptor

1. Progesterone Binding Parameters

The K_{deq} has been measured generally between $0°$ and $4°$ and most authors report values of 1–4 nM for endometrial receptor (Haukkamaa and Luukkainen, 1974; Bayard *et al.*, 1978). However, Rao *et al.* (1974) indicated a slightly higher affinity (0.3–0.4 nM). In any case, the affinity of progesterone for the endometrial receptor is not very different from that of progesterone for corticosteroid binding globulin (CBG) (3 nM at $0°$–$4°$, Seal and Doe, 1966). The dissociation rate of progesterone–receptor complexes is very rapid but is reduced by the addition of glycerol to assay buffer (Feil *et al.*, 1972; Bayard *et al.*, 1978). Thus, exchange of occupied receptor sites with radioactive hormone is possible at $0°$–$4°$ but the measurement must take into account the rapid dissociation of progesterone–receptor complexes even at low temperature. This is accomplished either by adding glycerol to assay buffer, or by the use of synthetic ligands with slower dissociation rates (R 5020: Philibert and Raynaud, 1974; ORG 2058: Jänne *et al.*, 1976).

2. Binding Specificity

Extensive reports of structural requirements of progesterone receptors have been published (Smith *et al.*, 1974; Kontula *et al.*, 1975). The results demonstrated a good correlation of relative binding affinity with progestational activity as measured by subcutaneous Clauberg assay. Removal of the 19-methyl group is the only modification of ring A, which does not decrease or eliminate receptor binding. The α,β unsaturated carbonyl system is essential. The C_{20} carbonyl group of the 17β side chain is also essential although this CH_3CO 17β side chain can be replaced by 17α-ethinyl 17β-hydroxyl group. Removal of the angular methyl group at C-10 increases binding of progesterone and two radioactive derivatives of 19 norprogesterone, R 5020 and ORG 2058 have been proposed for the assay of progesterone receptor. They are characterized by slow dissociation rate from the receptor and minimal binding to CBG.

Other steroid hormones, i.e., androgens, estrogens and glucocorticosteroids have negligible affinity for the progesterone receptor in human endometrium (Wiest and Rao, 1971; Haukkamaa and Luukkainen, 1974).

The binding affinities of synthetic progestagens used as contraceptive steroids appear to fall roughly into three groups. Compounds that bind strongly are *d*-norgestrel, norethisterone, medroxyprogesterone acetate, and megestrol acetate. Moderately strong binding is shown by *d*-norgestrel, and chlormadinone acetate, but a large number of estrane progestagens show only insignificant binding affinity (norethisterone acetate, norethynodrel, ethynodiol diacetate, lynestrenol). There is however good evidence that the latter compounds are metabolized to norethisterone (Briggs, 1975).

3. *Gradient Ultracentrifugation*

Gradient sedimentation analysis in a medium of low ionic strength has shown a predominant 4 S variety, even in the presence of proteolytic enzymes inhibitors (Wiest and Rao, 1971; Bayard *et al.*, 1978). However, when patients had been pretreated with estrogens prior to hysterectomy, a predominant 7.5 S variety was observed (Philibert and Raynaud, 1974). In addition, Pollow *et al.* (1975a) reported a 8 S receptor variety in normal premenopausal endometrium. Such discrepancies might be related to the influence of receptor concentration on its sedimentation rate, already observed in guinea pig uterus (Milgrom *et al.*, 1973).

D. Properties of Estradiol and Progesterone Receptors

Estradiol and progesterone receptors are of proteinaceous nature, as shown by sensitivity to proteolytic enzymes, particularly pronase and papain (Makler and Eisenfeld, 1974; Jänne *et al.*, 1975). They are very unstable at $\geq 37°$ temperature (Hähnel *et al.*, 1974) and the binding of steroids is inhibited by sulfhydryl reagents (Rao *et al.*, 1974; Makler and Eisenfeld, 1974; Jänne *et al.*, 1975). Furthermore, progesterone binding to the progesterone receptor is inhibited by metal ions (Hg^{2+}, Cu^{2+}, Ag^+, and Zn^{2+}) (Kontula *et al.*, 1974) probably by interference with the SH groups. Consequently, addition of EDTA and of SH reducing agents is commonly used to protect the receptor sites. Conversely, heat or sulfhydryl reagents have been proposed to inactivate receptor binding in order to measure residual binding of hormone to nonspecific components. However, such treatments often result in a significant increase of nonsaturable binding, and consequently an underestimation of receptor concentration.

A pH optimum for binding close to 8 has been reported for both receptors (Hähnel, 1971; Rao *et al.*, 1974; Jänne *et al.*, 1975), with a greater sensitivity to acidic environment. The isoelectric point of estradiol receptor is close to 5 (Pollow *et al.*, 1975a), that of progesterone receptor is 4.8 (Jänne *et al.*, 1975), and both can be selectively precipitated by basic proteins such as protamine (Steggles and King, 1970). This last property is yet to be used for measurement of endometrial receptors. Precipitation of receptors can equally be achieved by ammonium sulfate to a fractional saturation of 35% (Kontula *et al.*, 1975). This procedure results in a purification of about 10-fold, eliminating most nonsaturable binding proteins, and allowing a more accurate appraisal of binding specificity and affinity.

Few attempts have been made to obtain highly purified receptors from human uterus. One report, where both endometrium and myometrium were included, claims a 40,000-fold purification of progesterone receptor by ammonium sulfate fractionation, affinity chromatography, and ion-exchange chromatography (Smith *et al.*, 1975). The purified receptor sedimented at 3.7 S on sucrose gradient ultracentrifugation. Recently a 20,000-fold purification of uterine estradiol receptor has been described (Coffer *et al.*, 1977).

E. Endogenous Hormones in Human Endometrium

Proliferative endometrium contains about 1 ng and secretory endometrium 0.5 ng of estradiol/g of tissue. Such amount (Guerrero *et al.*, 1975; Batra *et al.*, 1977) produces concentrations of endogenous estradiol in cytosol of 0.5 nM or less which can be neglected in most utilized receptor assay procedures.

Concentration of progesterone in the endometrium has been determined by several authors (Bayard *et al.*, 1975; Kreitmann *et al.*, 1978; Batra *et al.*, 1977; Guerrero *et al.*, 1975; Haukkamaa and Luukkainen, 1974). When recalculated in ng/g of tissue, rather widespread values were obtained. In the follicular phase, progesterone levels ranged between 2 and 9 ng/g of tissue, and values for mean secretory phase varied between 8.5 and 27 ng/g. Therefore, at least in secretory endometrium, the concentration of endogenous progesterone will bring about a very significant isotopic dilution of added tracer. In fact the concentration of progesterone receptors sites doubled when cytosol was stripped of endogenous progesterone using the dextran-coated charcoal procedure (Haukkamaa, 1974).

F. Plasma Proteins in Endometrial Cytosol

As initially demonstrated in the rat uterus (Milgrom and Baulieu, 1970) a major difficulty encountered in developing an assay to measure progesterone receptor is the presence of CBG-like component in uterine cytosol in spite of thorough washing of tissues before homogenization. In Verma and Laumas (1973) report, the only observed binding component showed the physicochemical properties and binding specificity of CBG. In others, a combination of physical methods such as gradient ultracentrifugation, polyacrylamide gel electrophoresis, and appropriate binding competition experiments (Young and Cleary, 1974; Philibert and Raynaud, 1974; Bayard *et al.*, 1978; Kreitmann *et al.*, 1978) indicated the simultaneous presence of progesterone receptor and CBG. An absolute requirement in setting up the assay is the demonstration that progesterone can be displaced from binding sites by only progestagens and not by cortisol. A convenient approach is to determine the binding of [³H]progesterone in presence of competitors and of 100- to 1000-fold excess of nonradioactive cortisol. This technique prevents the binding of progesterone to CBG (Bayard *et al.*, 1978) by saturation of CBG binding sites with the nonradioactive cortisol. Kreitmann *et al.* (1978) have measured the concentration of CBG in human endometrium and observed wide variations from sample to sample which were apparently unrelated to the phase of the menstrual cycle. The reported values averaged 25 pmol/g which represent approximately 5% of the plasma values (about 500 nM). In endometrial cytosol, the concentration of CBG is generally severalfold greater than that of progesterone receptor (Kreitmann *et al.*, 1978). Since, as previously indicated the affinity of progesterone is similar for CBG and receptor, it is quite conceivable that most saturable binding site in endometrial samples with low receptor content may be due to contamination by plasma CBG. No enrichment of endometrial cytosol in CBG versus other plasma proteins has been observed (Kreitmann *et al.*, 1978). The SBP is one of the plasma proteins that contaminate human endometrium. However, its concentration in nonpregnant female plasma is 10 times lower than that of CBG, approximately 60 nM (Heyns and De Moor, 1971). Likewise, its affinity for estradiol (K_{deq} 1.3 nM at 4°) (Mercier-Bodard *et al.*, 1970), is much lower than that of estradiol for the receptor. Consequently, the binding of estradiol to SBP in cytosol preparations can be generally considered negligible (Bayard *et al.*, 1978).

G. METABOLISM OF LIGANDS

Following the work of Tseng and Gurpide (1972a,b), estradiol dehydrogenase activity has been well demonstrated in human endometrium and its changes correlated with hormonal status. This enzyme converts estradiol into estrone and is mainly located in the glandular epithelium of secretory endometrium (Scublinsky *et al.*, 1976), particularly in the endoplasmic reticulum and mitochondrial subcellular fractions (Pollow *et al.*,

1975b). NAD is the preferred cofactor and the K_m for estradiol is 3.3 μM at 40° and pH 9.5. The oxidation of estradiol to estrone by estradiol dehydrogenase is greatly enhanced in secretory endometrium as shown by Tseng and Gurpide (1972b, 1974) as well as Pollow *et al.* (1975b). In addition, the activity of this enzyme can be increased by progestagens either *in vivo* or *in vitro* (Tseng and Gurpide, 1975a).

Progesterone is also metabolized by human endometrium as reported by Sweat and Bryson (1970). According to these authors, the major metabolites were 5α-pregnane-3, 20-dione (pregnanedione), an undefined dihydroxy compound, and 6β-hydroxyprogesterone. However, when NADPH was added, the major products were pregnanedione and 20α-OH-pregn-4-ene-3-one (20α-OH progesterone) (Collins and Jewkes, 1974). Pollow *et al.* (1975c) demonstrated 5α-reductase, 5β-reductase, and 20α-hydroxysteroid dehydrogenase activity. The latter has been reported to be more active during the secretory phase of the menstrual cycle. However, these enzyme activities do not preclude the use of the corresponding natural hormones in receptor measurements because no significant metabolism of ligand was observed under the assay conditions (Hähnel, 1971; Bayard *et al.*, 1978). This lack of ligand metabolism is mainly due to the localization of most enzyme activities in the particulate fractions of the cytoplasm and to the relatively large K_m values of enzyme compared to the hormone concentrations needed for receptor assays. However, the *in vivo* metabolism of estradiol and progesterone in human endometrium explains partly the dissimilarities observed between plasma and tissue concentration of both hormones.

H. Main Characteristics of Reliable Assays for Estradiol and Progesterone Receptors in Human Endometrium

1. General

Pathophysiological changes in receptor concentration cannot be evaluated without a thorough validation of the specificity of the technique adopted. It is imperative that the binding assay is specific for estradiol and/or progesterone receptor and that it gives an accurate evaluation of binding constants. It must be realized that no evidence exists for significant affinity changes of receptors with physiological states and therefore the only parameter that is subjected to variations is the concentration of receptor sites. It is equally important to be mindful that human endometrium is generally exposed to endogenous ovarian hormones, and that receptor sites can be expected to be either filled or unfilled with hormones and located both in the cytoplasm and in the nuclear fractions. It should also be recalled that, since estradiol dissociates very slowly from receptor sites at low temperature, only unfilled sites will be measured in these conditions, whereas the sum of filled and unfilled sites will be determined when an exchange technique is used (Anderson *et al.*, 1972). Conversely, the dissociation of progesterone–receptor complexes being very rapid, some exchange will necessarily occur regardless of the assay conditions. Therefore, in the case of progesterone receptors, only the sum of unfilled and occupied receptor sites can be rigorously measured.

2. *Choice of Ligand*

The criteria for selection of the best radioactive ligand are: high affinity, slow dissociation rate, strict binding specificity, and absence of metabolism. In the case of estrogen receptors, [³H]estradiol has been generally utilized, since it fulfills roughly all of these conditions. Assay conditions have been described where no metabolism occurs and where binding to SBP and to androgen receptor (present in very minute amounts, J. Ch. Mercier and P. Robel, unpublished), has been prevented by adding 20 n*M* dihydrotestosterone to the incubation buffers (Bayard *et al.*, 1978). Recently, the use of [³H]moxestrol has been proposed by Raynaud *et al.* (1978), because it binds minimally to SBP, androgen receptor, and nonsaturable low affinity proteins.

In the case of progesterone receptors, the use of [³H]progesterone is acceptable providing the rapid dissociation of progesterone–receptor complexes is alleviated by the addition of glycerol and that binding of the hormone to CBG is prevented by an excess of nonradioactive cortisol added to the incubation buffers (Feil *et al.*, 1972; Milgrom *et al.*, 1972; Bayard *et al.*, 1978). As an alternative, a synthetic progestagen, such as ³H-R 5020, which does not bind to CBG can be used (Raynaud, 1977), but this compound binds rather strongly to nonsaturable components (Seematter *et al.*, 1978), and displays in addition relatively high affinity for glucocorticosteroid receptor. The latter difficulty can be circumvented by the addition of cortisol to assay buffers. Another synthetic progestin ³H-ORG 2058 seems to have properties similar to those of R 5020 (Jänne *et al.*, 1976).

3. *Choice of the Binding Assay*

Few systematic efforts have been made to define the most efficient and accurate techniques for measuring receptors. In general, low ionic strength buffers containing EDTA, SH-reducing agents and eventually glycerol are used at a slightly alkaline pH (7.8–8), because they are thought to protect cytosol receptors. The dextran-coated charcoal adsorption technique has been utilized in most reports for binding assay (Wiest and Rao, 1971; Krishnan *et al.*, 1973; Crocker *et al.*, 1974; Evans *et al.*, 1974; Rao *et al.*, 1974; Young and Cleary, 1974; MacLaughlin and Richardson, 1976; Bayard *et al.*, 1978), and likewise gel filtration (Makler and Eisenfeld, 1974; Trams *et al.*, 1973), has been employed. Several authors (Verma and Laumas, 1973; Philibert and Raynaud, 1974) have reported on the use of equilibrium dialysis which apparently results in large losses of binding sites. More selective procedures such as ammonium sulfate or protamine sulfate precipitation have not been currently adopted.

The measurement of binding sites concentration can be performed either by constructing a Scatchard plot or in performing a single point analysis at a saturating concentration of ligand. The former approach allows in addition the K_{deq} determination thus confirming the specificity of the measured binding. However, in presence of endogenous hormone, once isotopic equilibrium has been reached, the plot provides only acceptable estimate of receptor sites concentration, with an underestimation of the affinity constant. The single point analysis is obtained by labeling the sites with a saturating concentration of radioactive hormone. It requires smaller amounts of material and under carefully controlled conditions, gives results similar to the multipoint analysis necessary for constructing a Scatchard plot (Haukkamaa and Luukkainen, 1974).

Regardless of the method employed, binding to nonsaturable proteins must be subtracted by parallel incubation(s) with the same concentration(s) of radioactive hormone plus a large excess of nonradioactive hormone. On occasions, nonsaturable binding has been evaluated following inactivation of the receptor by heat or SH reagents. The binding to specific plasma proteins or possibly to other receptors must be prevented, as previously indicated by the use of appropriate radioactive ligand and/or by the addition of appropriate nonradioactive competitors.

In the case of progesterone receptor, endogenous progesterone, depending on its concentration, may interfere with the binding assay. Such difficulty has been avoided by exposing the cytosol to dextran-coated charcoal at 4° for ≤ 30 min, procedure which removes most endogenous progesterone prior to incubation (Young and Cleary, 1974). Likewise, the concentration of endogenous progesterone can be measured by radioimmunoassay and the result used to correct the specific activity of the added tracer (Bayard *et al.*, 1978). If such correction is neglected, the concentration of progesterone receptor sites can be underestimated to as much as ½ or ⅓ of the actual values. This is particularly true for progesterone receptor measurement in gestational endometrium.

4. Practical Constraints

For clinical investigation purpose, measurements of receptors concentration are most often performed on endometrial samples obtained by biopsy. The weight of such samples rarely exceeds 200 mg, part of which must be kept for histological examination. Therefore, it becomes advantageous to use assay techniques that allow measurement of both estradiol and progesterone receptors concentration in cytosol prepared from samples equal or greater than 50 mg. Recently Levy *et al.* (1980c) has introduced and proposed a glass fiber filter exchange assay, which permits the measurement of nuclear receptors on the same amount of tissue.

a. Distribution of Estrogen and Progesterone Receptors in Human Endometrium. The location of the biopsy inside the uterine cavity is often unknown, and therefore the interpretation of receptor assay would be greatly facilitated if receptors were evenly distributed throughout the endometrial lining. Conflicting results have been published on this matter. For Robertson *et al.* (1971) and Tsibris *et al.* (1978), the concentration of receptor in endometrium showed a progressive decrease throughout the length of the organ from the fundus to the cervix, whereas Lunan and Green (1975) reported more receptors in the body than in the fundus. Brush *et al.* (1967) indicated that in some cases the uptake of estradiol by different regions of the endometrium varies considerably. Bayard *et al.* (1978) also reported large differences in receptor concentration between biopsies of the fundus or of the body of the uterus, but they concluded that no systematic trend was observed, and the ratio of progesterone to estradiol receptors remained practically constant. In any case, a compromise can be reached by taking biopsies systematically from the midregion of the endometrium.

b. Preservation of Endometrium Samples. Endometrial samples, kept in isotonic saline or homogenization buffer at 0°–4° must be processed relatively rapidly (within 1 h) to prevent inactivation of receptor sites. Receptors are also inactivated when endometrial curettings are kept in liquid nitrogen. However, cytosol and nuclear estrogen and progesterone receptors remained stable when endometrial samples were immersed in a preservation medium and then frozen in liquid nitrogen (Bayard *et al.*, 1978). Likewise, Koenders *et al.* (1978) reported no loss of cytosol receptor sites when samples were frozen in liquid nitrogen, lyophylized in glass vials stoppered under vacuum and stored at 4°. Both techniques allow the shipment of endometrial biopsies from clinical departments to remote biochemical laboratories and permit convenient and simultaneous receptors measurement in small series of samples.

III. ESTRADIOL AND PROGESTERONE RECEPTORS IN THE NORMAL MENSTRUAL CYCLE

The dating of normal endometrium is usually based on a combination of several criteria, namely: day of cycle (when the regularity of cycles is known), basal body temperature, histological evaluation and serial measurements of plasma LH, estradiol, and progesterone. At best, the dating of the biopsy can be made with ± 1 day precision. In most reports dealing with receptor measurement, only broad terms are used such as *proliferative* and/or *secretory* endometrium. In the few publications where receptors had been measured on a daily basis, the criteria for dating were usually not well defined. In our opinion, valuable information can be obtained by separate investigations of the four following periods of the menstrual cycle (1) the early proliferative phase; (2) the late proliferative phase, when the preovulatory plasma estradiol surge occurs; (3) the early secretory phase extending from the day of ovulation to the day of implantation; and (4) the late secretory phase.

A. ESTRADIOL RECEPTOR

1. Retention of [³H]Estradiol in Whole Tissue

The first indication of variable retention of [³H]estradiol throughout the menstrual cycle came from *in vivo* experiments. Two hours following intravenous injection of radioactive hormone, concentration of retained radioactivity was higher in proliferative than in secretory endometrium (Brush *et al.*, 1967). This was confirmed by *in vitro* incubation of tissue slices (Evans and Hähnel, 1971; Trams *et al.*, 1973). Tseng and Gurpide (1972a) measured the amount of estradiol tightly bound to nuclei after *in vitro* superfusion or incubation of endometrial slices. Under carefully controlled conditions, the amount of nuclear estradiol–receptor complexes was found to be 3.1 pmol/mg DNA in proliferative, 1.6 in early secretory, 0.6 in mid-secretory, and 0.5 in late secretory endometrium (Gurpide *et al.*, 1976; Tseng *et al.*, 1977). A similar approach was utilized by Crocker *et al.* (1974) who observed that the nuclear uptake of estradiol reached a peak in the late proliferative phase.

2. Cytosol Receptor

In most reports, the adopted methodology has allowed the measurement of unfilled receptor sites, and failed to account for the portion occupied by hormone. Under these conditions, receptors concentration was found to be higher in proliferative than in secretory endometrium (Trams *et al.*, 1973; Crocker *et al.*, 1974; Evans *et al.*, 1974; Pollow *et al.*, 1975a; Schmidt-Gollwitzer *et al.*, 1978). In one published article, a maximum of 2.3 pmol/mg cytosol protein was measured in the late proliferative phase (Crocker *et al.*, 1974). All other publications indicate a continuous decrease of mainly unfilled receptor sites from early proliferative until late secretory phase. This trend is undoubtedly due to a progressive increase of occupied receptor sites, because, when the incubation temperature was raised to 25°, the concentration of receptors increased more than twice (Evans *et al.*, 1974). In addition, an inverse relationship was observed between the apparent K_d and the apparent concentration of receptor, a situation typical of measurements performed in the presence of endogenous hormone and nonsteady-state conditions (Pollow *et al.*, 1976).

Several authors have determined the sum of unfilled and occupied receptor sites after exchange (Robertson *et al.*, 1971; Bayard *et al.*, 1978; Sanborn *et al.*, 1978; Levy *et al.*, 1980a). All of them agree that an increased amount of estradiol receptor appears at mid cycle with mean values reported between 1.2–3.5 pmol/mg DNA.

3. Nuclear Receptor

Several investigators have measured specific nuclear binding following incubation of tissue slices with estradiol. However it should be recognized that such technique does not measure endogenous nuclear receptors but rather nuclearly translocated hormone–receptor complexes. An exchange assay of nuclear receptors in human endometrium has been reported (Bayard *et al.*, 1978). The concentration of nuclear receptor site was found to be doubled between early and late proliferative phase, becoming almost equal to cytosolic sites. Then, during the secretory phase, the nuclear receptor level decreased but at slower rate than cytoplasmic receptor. Recently, it has been shown that endometrial nuclei may contain a significant proportion of receptor sites which can be labeled with [³H]estradiol at 0°, and presumably are unoccupied by endogenous hormones (Levy *et al.*, 1980b).

B. Progesterone Receptor

1. Cytosol Receptor

Due to the rapid dissociation of endogenous progesterone–receptor complexes in the assay conditions used, both unfilled and occupied receptor sites have been measured by most authors, but often without consideration of isotopic dilution brought in by endogenous progesterone. Binding to CBG has been eliminated either by the addition of cortisol to incubations with progesterone or by the use of synthetic progestagens. In some early publications, very large values were reported (Rao *et al.*, 1974; Haukkamaa and Luukkainen, 1974), without significant changes throughout the cycle. In general, however, there is consensus that a remarkable increase of receptor concentration occurs in the late proliferative, or mid cycle period (MacLaughlin and Richardson, 1976; Syrjälä *et al.*, 1978; Sanborn *et al.*, 1978; Bayard *et al.*, 1978; Levy *et al.*, 1980a). Although early papers published by Pollow's group (Pollow *et al.*, 1975a, 1976) reported very low amounts of progesterone receptor in proliferative phase, their recent reports showed agreement that a mid cycle rise does occur (Schmidt-Gollwitzer *et al.*, 1978).

There is some divergence of opinion concerning the absolute concentration of progesterone receptor. In the late proliferative phase, the mean value reported and expressed in pmol/mg DNA were: 0.7 (MacLaughlin and Richardson, 1976), 2.8 (Levy *et al.*, 1980a), 12 (Syrjälä *et al.*, 1978), 23 (Sanborn *et al.*, 1978), and 30 (Schmidt-Gollwitzer *et al.*, 1978). However the levels of progesterone receptor recorded are always several-fold higher than those of estradiol receptor at the same phase of the menstrual cycle. The highest values were obtained with the use of synthetic progestins. The reasons for this discrepancy are not quite clear. However, it has been shown that, in addition to binding to progesterone receptor, R 5020 (the most used synthetic progestagen), has considerable affinity for glucocorticoid receptors, and appears to bind to serum and tissue proteins with greater avidity than does progesterone (Lippman *et al.*, 1977; Seematter *et al.*, 1978; Powell *et al.*, 1979).

2. Nuclear Receptor

Only our group has published results concerning nuclear receptor (Bayard *et al.*, 1978; Levy *et al.*, 1980a), the values reported were consistently lower than those observed for the cytosol receptor. A definite increase occurred in the early secretory phase, reaching 0.6 pmol/mg DNA (2500 sites/cell).

C. HORMONAL CORRELATIONS OF ESTRADIOL AND PROGESTERONE RECEPTORS

The simultaneous increases of estradiol and progesterone receptors at mid cycle follow the plasma estradiol surge in the late proliferative phase and strongly suggest a positive relationship between estradiol and endometrial receptors. Indeed, during the proliferative phase, estradiol blood levels are positively correlated with total progesterone and estradiol receptor sites (Levy *et al.*, 1980a) and with cytoplasmic progesterone receptor sites as well (Schmidt-Gollwitzer *et al.*, 1978).

A similar correlation was also reported between progesterone receptor and cytosol estradiol in human myometrium (Kontula, 1975). However, the concentration of unoccupied estradiol receptor sites correlated inversely with the concentration of estradiol in the blood (Trams *et al.*, 1973; Schmidt-Gollwitzer *et al.*, 1978). The inductive action of estradiol was confirmed in estrogen treated postmenopausal women by the appearance of progesterone receptors in endometrial cytosol (Jänne *et al.*, 1975), and the elevation of myometrial progesterone receptor to values reaching those reported for the proliferative phase (Illingworth *et al.*, 1975).

The large decrease of both estradiol and progesterone receptors in the secretory phase occurs when plasma and endometrial progesterone concentrations are increased. Indeed, a negative correlation has been reported between plasma progesterone and cytosol estradiol and progesterone receptors (Schmidt-Gollwitzer *et al.*, 1978; Jänne *et al.*, 1975). However, in one report where statistical evaluation was performed, this inverse relationship was found not to be significant (Levy *et al.*, 1980a). Tseng and Gurpide (1975b) have demonstrated that progesterone and synthetic progestins reduce the level of estradiol receptor in human endometrium.

Another important feature of progesterone action is the large increase of microsomal 17β-hydroxysteroid dehydrogenase activity reported in secretory endometrium by Tseng and Gurpide (1974) as well as Pollow *et al.* (1975b). This effect explains the relatively low concentration of estradiol in endometrium during the secretory phase (Schmidt-Gollwitzer *et al.*, 1978) and may account partly for the antiestrogenic characteristics of progestins (Gurpide *et al.*, 1977). Human endometrial estradiol dehydrogenase showed a severalfold increase under the influence of progestins, either *in vivo* or following *in vitro* incubation (Tseng and Gurpide, 1975a; Pollow *et al.*, 1978). Since progesterone increases estradiol dehydrogenase activity and decreases progesterone receptor level, an inverse relationship between both parameters could be predicted and was indeed recently reported by Levy *et al.* (1980a) contrary to a preceeding article by Schmidt-Gollwitzer *et al.* (1978).

IV. GENERAL CONCLUSIONS

The changes of estradiol and progesterone receptors in human endometrium throughout normal menstrual cycle are in keeping with the findings previously described in experimental animals. The increase of estradiol receptor in the preovulatory period is related to the plasma estradiol surge, leading to synthesis of more receptor in the cytoplasm and to nuclear translocation of the hormone–receptor complexes. At the same time, cytoplasmic progesterone receptor equally increases as a result of the inductive effect of estradiol (Milgrom *et al.*, 1972, 1973; Brenner *et al.*, 1974; Vuttai *et al.*, 1978).

The postovulatory decrease of the estradiol receptor is possibly related to both progesterone effects on the conversion of estradiol to estrone and on the level of the estradiol receptor (Mester *et al.*, 1974; Hsueh *et al.*, 1975). Consequently there is a decrease of the estrogen-dependent synthesis of progesterone receptor. In addition, progesterone has been observed to directly "inactivate" its own receptor (Milgrom *et al.*, 1973; Brenner *et al.*, 1974; Tseng and Gurpide, 1975b). However, only cytoplasmic receptor sites decrease immediately following ovulation, whereas the nuclear receptor sites of both receptors do not. Rather, the nuclear progesterone receptor concentration increases probably as a consequence of sustained nuclear transfer of hormone-receptor complexes (Bayard *et al.*, 1978; Levy *et al.*, 1980a). This observation stresses the critical importance of measuring both filled and unfilled, cytosolic and nuclear receptor sites whenever receptor physiology is being investigated.

During the menstrual cycle, the concentration of nuclear progesterone and estradiol receptors does not exceed that of cytoplasmic receptors because the levels of both hormones in the endometrium are far below the values needed to saturate the receptor sites. Consequently, a large proportion of receptor sites remains unoccupied and located in the cytoplasm.

However, this is not the case for gestational endometrium in which very little cytosol (MacLaughlin and Richardson, 1976; Kreitmann *et al.*, 1978; Levy *et al.*, 1980a) and large amounts of nuclear progesterone receptor concentrations were reported (Kreitmann *et al.*, 1978; Levy *et al.*, 1980a). The concentration of endogenous progesterone in gestational endometrium is markedly elevated and might explain the predominantly nuclear location of the progesterone receptors in the decidua of 8–12 weeks of pregnancy.

The interest of sex steroid hormone receptor measurement for clinical investigation of gynecological disorders is illustrated by the results obtained in cases of endometrial hyperplasia (Haukkamaa and Luukkainen, 1974; Gurpide *et al.*, 1976; Syrjälä *et al.*, 1978), anovulatory cycles, and luteal insufficiency (Levy *et al.*, 1980a). The high risk of endometrial hyperplasia and adenocarcinoma in patients with anovulatory cycles (Gusberg, 1976) may prove to be related to unopposed prolonged estradiol secretion. It creates sustained high concentrations of nuclear estradiol–receptor complexes and a state of estrogen hyper-receptivity.

Recent reviews have appeared dealing with the application of progesterone and estradiol receptor measurements in human endometrial adenocarcinoma (McGuire *et al.*, 1977; Brush *et al.*, 1978; Richardson and MacLaughlin, 1978). The knowledge acquired in the hormonal control of these receptors has permitted us to evaluate biochemical changes in endometrial adenocarcinoma samples following *in vivo* challenge with progestagen, estrogen, or antiestrogen (Robel *et al.*, 1978). Preliminary results are encouraging and if confirmed, a more rational program could be designed for the treatment of patients with advanced or metastatic endometrial cancer.

REFERENCES

Anderson, J., Clark, J. H., and Peck, E. J. (1972). *Biochem. J.* **126**, 561–567.

Batra, S., Grundsell, H., and Sjöberg, N. O. (1977). *Contraception* **16**, 217–224.

Baulieu, E. E., Atger, M., Best-Belpomme, M., Corvol, P., Courvalin, J. C., Mester, J., Milgrom, E., Robel, P., Rochefort, H., and De Catalogne, D. (1975). *Vitam. Horm. (N.Y.)* **33**, 649–736.

Bayard, F., Louvet, J. P., Monrozies, M., Boulard, A., and Pontonnier, G. (1975). *J. Clin. Endocrinol. Metab.* **41**, 412–414.

Bayard, F., Damilano, S., Robel, P., and Baulieu, E. E. (1978). *J. Clin. Endocrinol. Metab.* **46**, 635–648.

Brenner, R. M., Resko, J. A., and West, N. B. (1974). *Endocrinology* **95**, 1094–1104.

Briggs, M. H. (1975). *Curr. Med. Res. Opin.* **3**, 95–98.

Brush, M. G., Taylor, R. W., and King, R. J. B. (1967). *J. Endocrinol.* **39**, 599–607.

Brush, M. G., King, R. J. B., and Taylor, R. W. (1978). "Endometrial Cancer," Baillière, London.

Coffer, A. I., Milton, P. J. D., Pryse-Davies, J., and King, R. J. B. (1977). *Mol. Cell. Endocrinol.* **6**, 231–246.

Collins, J. A., and Jewkes, D. M. (1974). *Am. J. Obstet. Gynecol.* **118**, 179–185.

Crocker, S. G., Milton, P. J. D., and King, R. J. B (1974). *J. Endocrinol.* **62**, 145–152.

Davis, M. E., Wiener, M., Jacobson, H. I., and Jensen, E. V. (1963). *Am. J. Obstet. Gynecol.* **87**, 979–990.

Evans, L. H., and Hähnel, R. (1971). *J. Endocrinol.* **50**, 209–229.

Evans, L. H., Martin, J. D., and Hähnel, R. (1974). *J. Clin. Endocrinol. Metab.* **38**, 23–32.

Feil, P. D., Glasser, S. R., Toft, D. O., and O'Malley, B. W. (1972). *Endocrinology* **91**, 738–746.

Guerrero, R., Landgren, B. M., Monteil, R., Cekan, Z., and Diczfalusy, E. (1975). *Contraception* **11**, 169–177.

Gurpide, E., Gusberg, S., and Tseng, L. (1976). *J. Steroid Biochem.* **7**, 891–896.

Gurpide, E., Tseng, L., and Gusberg, S. (1977). *Am. J. Obstet. Gynecol.* **129**, 809–816.

Gusberg, S. (1976). *Am. J. Obstet. Gynecol.* **126**, 535–542.

Hähnel, R. (1971). *Steroids* **17**, 105–132.

Hähnel, R., Twaddle, E., and Brindle, L. (1974). *Steroids* **24**, 489–506.

Haukkamaa, M. (1974). *J. Steroid Biochem.* **5**, 73–79.

Haukkamaa, M., and Luukkainen, T. (1974). *J. Steroid Biochem.* **5**, 447–452.

Heyns, W., and De Moor, P. (1971). *Steroids* **18**, 709–730.

Hsueh, A. J., Peck, E. J., and Clark, J. H. (1975). *Nature (London)* **254**, 337–339.

Illingworth, D. V., Wood, G. P., Flickinger, G. L., and Mikhail, G. (1975). *J. Clin. Endocrinol. Metab.* **40**, 1001–1008.

Jänne, O., Kontula, K., Luukkainen, T., and Vihko, R. (1975). *J. Steroid Biochem.* **6**, 501–509.

Jänne, O., Kontula, K., and Vihko, R. (1976). *J. Steroid Biochem.* **7**, 1061–1068.

Koenders, A. J., Geurts-Moespot, J., Kho, K. H., and Benraad, T. J. (1978). *J. Steroid Biochem.* **9**, 947–950.

Kontula, K. (1975). *J. Steroid Biochem.* **6**, 1555–1561.

Kontula, K., Jänne, O., Luukkainen, T., and Vihko, R. (1974). *J. Clin. Endocrinol. Metab.* **38**, 500–503.

Kontula, K., Jänne, O., Vihko, R., de Jager, E., de Visser, J., and Zeelen, F. (1975). *Acta Endocrinol. (Copenhagen)* **78**, 574–592.

Kreitmann, B., Derache, B., and Bayard, F. (1978). *J. Clin. Endocrinol. Metab.* **47**, 350–353.

Krishnan, A. R., Hingorani, V., and Laumas, K. R. (1973). *Acta Endocrinol. (Copenhagen)* **74**, 756–758.

Levy, C., Robel, P., Gautray, J. P., de Brux, J., Verma, U., Descomps, B., and Baulieu, E. E. (1980a). *Am. J. Obstet. Gynecol.* **136**, 646–651.

Levy, C., Mortel, R., Eychenne, B., Robel, P., and Baulieu, E. E. (1980b). *Biochem. J.* **185**, 733–738.

Levy, C., Eychennê, B., and Robel, P. (1980c). *Biochem. Biophys. Acta* **630**, 301–305.

Lippman, M., Huff, K., Bolman, G., and Neifeld, J. P. (1977). *In* "Progesterone Receptors in Normal and Neoplastic Tissues" (W. L. MacGuire, J. P. Raynaud, and E. E. Baulieu, eds.), pp. 193–210. Raven, New York.

Lunan, C. B., and Green, B. (1975). *Acta Endocrinol. (Copenhagen)* **78**, 353–363.

McGuire, W. L., Raynaud, J. P., and Baulieu, E. E., eds. (1977). "Progesterone Receptors in Normal and Neoplastic Tissues." Raven, New York.

MacLaughlin, D. T., and Richardson, G. S. (1976). *J. Clin. Endocrinol. Metab.* **42**, 667–678.

Makler, A., and Eisenfeld, A. J. (1974). *J. Clin. Endocrinol. Metab.* **38**, 628–633.

Mercier-Bodard, C., Alfsen, A., and Baulieu, E. E. (1970). *Acta Endocrinol. (Copenhagen)* **147**, 204–224.

Mester, J., Martel, D., Psychoyos, A., and Baulieu, E. E. (1974). *Nature (London)* **250**, 776–777.

Milgrom, E., and Baulieu, E. E. (1970). *Endocrinology* **87**, 276–287.

Milgrom, E., Atger, M., Perrot, M., and Baulieu, E. E. (1972). *Endocrinology* **90**, 1071–1078.

Milgrom, E., Luu Thi, M., Atger, M., and Baulieu, E. E. (1973). *J. Biol. Chem.* **248**, 6366–6374.

Notides, A. C., Hamilton, D. E., and Rudolph, J. H. (1972). *Biochim. Biophys. Acta* **271**, 214–224.

Philibert, D., and Raynaud, J. P. (1974). *Contraception* **10**, 457–466.

Pollow, K., Lübbert, H., Boquoi, E., Kreuzer, G., and Pollow, B. (1975a). *Endocrinology* **96**, 319–328.

Pollow, K., Lübbert, H., Boquoi, E., Kreuzer, G., Jeske, R., and Pollow, B. (1975b). *Acta Endocrinol. (Copenhagen)* **79**, 134–145.

Pollow, K., Lübbert, H., Boquoi, E., and Pollow, B. (1975c). *J. Clin. Endocrinol. Metab.* **41**, 729–737.

Pollow, K., Boquoi, E., Schmidt-Golliwitzer, M., and Pollow, B. (1976). *J. Mol. Med.* **1**, 325–342.

Pollow, K., Schmidt-Gollwitzer, M., Boquoi, E., and Pollow, B. (1978). *J. Mol. Med.* **3**, 81–89.

Powell, B., Garola, R. E., Chamness, G. C., and McGuire, W. L. (1979). *Cancer Res.* **39**, 1678–1682.

Rao, B. R., Wiest, W. G., and Allen, W. M. (1974). *Endocrinology* **95**, 1275–1281.

Raynaud, J. P. (1977). *In* "Progesterone Receptors in Normal and Neoplastic Tissues" (W. L. McGuire, J. P. Raynaud, and E. E. Baulieu, eds.), pp. 9–21. Raven, New York.

Raynaud, J. P., Martin, P. M., Bouton, M. M., and Ojasoo, T. (1978). *Cancer Res.* **38**, 3044–3050.

Richardson, G. S., and MacLaughlin, D. T., eds. (1978). "Hormonal Biology of Endometrial Cancer," UICC Tech. Rep. Ser., Vol. 42. UICC, Geneva.

Robel, P., Levy, C., Wolff, J. P., Nicolas, J. C., and Baulieu, E. E. (1978). *C. R. Hebd. Seances Acad. Sci.* **287**, 1353–1356.

Robertson, D. M., Mester, J., Beilby, J., Steele, S. J., and Kellie, A. E. (1971). *Acta Endocrinol. (Copenhagen)* **68**, 534–542.

Sanborn, B. M., Kuo, H. S., and Held, B. (1978). *J. Steroid Biochem.* **9**, 951–955.

Schmidt-Gollwitzer, M., Genz, T., Schmidt-Gollwitzer, K., Pollow, B., and Pollow, K. (1978). *In* "Endometrial Cancer" (M. G. Brush, R. J. B. King, and R. W. Taylor, eds.), pp. 227–241. Baillière, London.

Scublinsky, A., Marin, C., and Gurpide, E. (1976). *J. Steroid Biochem.* **7**, 745–747.

Seal, U. S., and Doe, R. P. (1966). *In* "Steroid Dynamics" (G. Pincus, T. Nakao, and J. F. Tait, eds.), pp. 63–90. Academic Press, New York.

Seematter, R. J., Hoffman, P. G., Kuhn, R. W., Lockwood, L. C., and Siiteri, P. K. (1978). *Cancer Res.* **38**, 2800–2806.

Smith, H. E., Smith, R. G., Toft, D. O., Neergaard, J. R., Burrows, E. P., and O'Malley, B. W. (1974). *J. Biol. Chem.* **249**, 5924–5932.

Smith, R. G., Iramain, C. A., Buttram, V. J., Jr., and O'Malley, B. W. (1975). *Nature (London)* **253**, 271–272.

Steggles, A. W., and King, R. J. B. (1970). *Biochem. J.* **118**, 695–701.

Sutherland, R., Mester, J., and Baulieu, E. E. (1977). *Nature (London)* **267**, 434–435.

Sweat, M. L., and Bryson, M. J. (1970). *Am. J. Obstet. Gynecol.* **106**, 193–201.

Syrjälä, P., Kontula, K., Jänne, O., Kauppila, A., and Vihko, R. (1978). *In* "Endometrial Cancer" (M. G. Brush, R. J. B. King, and R. W. Taylor, eds.), pp. 242–251. Baillière, London.

Trams, G., Engel, B., Lehmann, F., and Maass, H. (1973). *Acta Endocrinol. (Copenhagen)* **72**, 351–360.

Tseng, L., and Gurpide, E. (1972a). *Am. J. Obstet. Gynecol.* **114**, 995–1001.

Tseng, L., and Gurpide, E. (1972b). *Am. J. Obstet. Gynecol.* **114**, 1002–1008.

Tseng, L., and Gurpide, E. (1974). *Endocrinology* **94**, 419–423.

Tseng, L., and Gurpide, E. (1975a). *Endocrinology* **97**, 825–833.
Tseng, L., and Gurpide, E. (1975b). *J. Clin. Endocrinol. Metab.* **41**, 402–404.
Tseng, L., Gusberg, S., and Gurpide, E. (1977). *Ann. N.Y. Acad. Sci.* **286**, 190–198.
Tsibris, J. C. M., Cazenave, C. R., Cantor, B., Notelovitz, M., Kalra, P. S., and Spellacy, W. N. (1978). *Am. J. Obstet. Gynecol.* **132**, 449–454.
Verma, U., and Laumas, K. R. (1973). *Biochim. Biophys. Acta* **317**, 403–419.
Vu Hai, M. T., Logeat, F., and Milgrom, E. (1978). *J. Endocrinol.* **76**, 43–49.
Wiest, W. G., and Rao, B. R. (1971). *Adv. Biosci.* **7**, 251–264.
Young, P. C. M., and Cleary, R. E. (1974). *J. Clin. Endocrinol. Metab.* **39**, 425–439.

D

Contents of Previous Volumes